AS-Level
Mathematics

AS Maths is seriously tricky — no question about that.
To do well, you're going to need to revise properly and practise hard.

This book has thorough notes on everything in modules C1, C2, S1, M1 and D1.
It'll help you learn the stuff you need and take you step-by-step through loads of examples.

It's got practice questions... lots of them. For every topic there are warm-up and exam-style
questions. Plus there are two full practice exams at the end of each module.

And of course, we've done our best to make the whole thing vaguely entertaining for you.

Complete Revision and Practice
Exam Board: OCR MEI

Contents

Contents

Mechanics M1

Decision Mathematics D1

Editors:
Josephine Gibbons, Paul Jordin, Sharon Keeley-Holden, Simon Little, Sam Norman, Ali Palin,
Andy Park, David Ryan, Lyn Setchell, Caley Simpson, Jane Towle, Jonathan Wray, Dawn Wright

Contributors:
Andy Ballard, Charley Darbishire, Claire Jackson, Tim Major, Mark Moody,
Garry Rowlands, Mike Smith, Claire Thompson, Julie Wakeling, Chris Worth

Proofreaders:
Vicky Daniel, Alastair Duncombe, Allan Graham, Glenn Rogers

Published by CGP

ISBN: 978 1 84762 583 0

Printed by Elanders Ltd, Newcastle upon Tyne.

Based on the classic CGP style created by Richard Parsons.

A Few Definitions and Things

Yep, this is a pretty dull way to start a book. A list of definitions. But at least it gets it out of the way right at the beginning — it would be a bit mean of me to try and sneak it in halfway through and hope you wouldn't notice.

Polynomials

POLYNOMIALS are expressions of the form $a + bx + cx^2 + dx^3 + ...$

$5y^3 + 2y + 23$ — Polynomial in the variable y.

$1 + x^2$

$z^4 + 3z - z^2 - 1$ — Polynomial in the variable z.

An expression is made up of <u>terms</u>.

E.g: z^4, $3z$, $-z^2$ and -1

x, y and z are always VARIABLES
They're usually what you solve equations to find. They often have more than one possible value.

Letters like a, b, c are always CONSTANTS
Constants never change. They're fixed numbers — but can be represented by letters. π is a good example. You use the symbol π, but it's just a number = 3.1415... If a constant is in front of a variable, then it's called a COEFFICIENT So c is the coefficient of x^2 in the term cx^2.

Functions

FUNCTIONS take a value, do something to it, and output another value.

$f(x) = x^2 + 1$ — function f takes a value, squares it and adds 1.

$g(x) = 2 - \sin 2x$ — function g takes a value (in degrees), doubles it, takes the sine of it, then takes the value away from 2.

You can plug values into a function — just replace the variable with a certain number.

$f(-2) = (-2)^2 + 1 = 5$

$f(0) = (0)^2 + 1 = 1$

$f(252) = (252)^2 + 1 = 63505$

$g(-90°) = 2 - \sin(-180°) = 2 - 0 = 2$

$g(0°) = 2 - \sin 0° = 2 - 0 = 2$

$g(45°) = 2 - \sin 90° = 2 - 1 = 1$

Exam questions use functions all the time. They generally don't have that much to do with the actual question. It's just a bit of terminology to get comfortable with.

Multiplication and Division

There's three different ways of showing MULTIPLICATION:

1) with good old-fashioned "times" signs (×):

$f(x) = (2x \times 6y) + (2x \times \sin x) + (z \times y)$

The multiplication signs and the variable x are easily confused.

2) or sometimes just use a little dot:

$f(x) = 2x.6y + 2x.\sin x + z.y$

Dots are better for long expressions — they're less confusing and easier to read.

3) but you often don't need anything at all:

$f(x) = 12xy + 2x\sin x + zy$

And there's three different ways of showing DIVISION:

1) $\dfrac{x + 2}{3}$

2) $(x + 2) \div 3$

3) $(x + 2)/3$

Equations and Identities

This is an IDENTITY:

$x^2 - y^2 \equiv (x + y)(x - y)$

But this is an EQUATION:

$y = x^2 + x$

Make up any values you like for x and y, and it's always true. The left-hand side always equals the right-hand side.

The difference is that the identity's true for all values of x and y, but the equation's only true for certain values.

NB: If it's an identity, use the $\equiv$ sign instead of =.

This has at most two possible solutions for each value of y. e.g. if y = O, x can only be O or -1.

Laws of Indices

You use the laws of indices a helluva lot in maths — when you're integrating, differentiating and ...er... well loads of other places. So take the time to get them sorted <u>now</u>.

Three mega-important Laws of Indices

You <u>must</u> know these three rules. I can't make it any clearer than that.

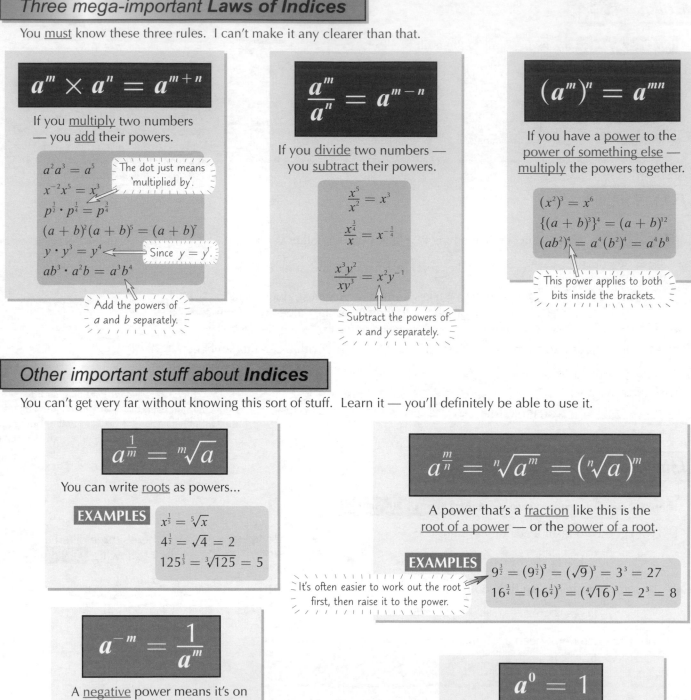

$$a^m \times a^n = a^{m+n}$$

If you <u>multiply</u> two numbers — you <u>add</u> their powers.

$a^2 a^3 = a^5$
$x^{-2} x^5 = x^3$
$p^{\frac{1}{2}} \cdot p^{\frac{1}{4}} = p^{\frac{3}{4}}$
$(a+b)^2 (a+b)^5 = (a+b)^7$
$y \cdot y^3 = y^4$
$ab^3 \cdot a^2 b = a^3 b^4$

The dot just means 'multiplied by'.

Since $y = y'$.

Add the powers of a and b separately.

$$\frac{a^m}{a^n} = a^{m-n}$$

If you <u>divide</u> two numbers — you <u>subtract</u> their powers.

$\dfrac{x^5}{x^2} = x^3$

$\dfrac{x^{\frac{3}{4}}}{x} = x^{-\frac{1}{4}}$

$\dfrac{x^3 y^2}{xy^3} = x^2 y^{-1}$

Subtract the powers of x and y separately.

$$(a^m)^n = a^{mn}$$

If you have a <u>power</u> to the <u>power of something else</u> — <u>multiply</u> the powers together.

$(x^2)^3 = x^6$
$\{(a+b)^3\}^4 = (a+b)^{12}$
$(ab^2)^4 = a^4 (b^2)^4 = a^4 b^8$

This power applies to both bits inside the brackets.

Other important stuff about Indices

You can't get very far without knowing this sort of stuff. Learn it — you'll definitely be able to use it.

$$a^{\frac{1}{m}} = \sqrt[m]{a}$$

You can write <u>roots</u> as powers...

EXAMPLES
$x^{\frac{1}{5}} = \sqrt[5]{x}$
$4^{\frac{1}{2}} = \sqrt{4} = 2$
$125^{\frac{1}{3}} = \sqrt[3]{125} = 5$

$$a^{\frac{m}{n}} = \sqrt[n]{a^m} = \left(\sqrt[n]{a}\right)^m$$

A power that's a <u>fraction</u> like this is the <u>root of a power</u> — or the <u>power of a root</u>.

EXAMPLES
$9^{\frac{3}{2}} = (9^{\frac{1}{2}})^3 = (\sqrt{9})^3 = 3^3 = 27$
$16^{\frac{3}{4}} = (16^{\frac{1}{4}})^3 = (\sqrt[4]{16})^3 = 2^3 = 8$

It's often easier to work out the root first, then raise it to the power.

$$a^{-m} = \frac{1}{a^m}$$

A <u>negative</u> power means it's on the bottom line of a fraction.

EXAMPLES
$x^{-2} = \dfrac{1}{x^2}$
$2^{-3} = \dfrac{1}{2^3} = \dfrac{1}{8}$
$(x+1)^{-1} = \dfrac{1}{x+1}$

$$a^0 = 1$$

This works for <u>any</u> number or letter.

EXAMPLES
$x^0 = 1$
$2^0 = 1$
$(a+b)^0 = 1$

Indices, indices — de fish all live indices...

What can I say that I haven't said already? Blah, blah, important. Blah, blah, learn these. Blah, blah, use them all the time. Mmm, that's about all that needs to be said really. So I'll be quiet and let you <u>get</u> on with what you need to do.

Surds

A surd is a number like $\sqrt{2}$, $\sqrt[3]{12}$ or $5\sqrt{3}$ — one that's written with the $\sqrt{}$ sign. They're important because you can give <u>exact</u> answers where you'd otherwise have to round to a certain number of decimal places.

Surds are sometimes the only way to give an *Exact Answer*

Put $\sqrt{2}$ into a calculator and you'll get something like 1.414213562...
But square 1.414213562 and you get 1.999999999.

And no matter how many decimal places you use, you'll never get <u>exactly</u> 2.
The only way to write the exact, spot-on value is to <u>use surds</u>.

So, as you're not allowed a calculator for your C1 exam, leave your answer as a <u>surd</u>.

There are basically *Three Rules* for using *Surds*

There are three <u>rules</u> you'll need to know to be able to use surds properly. Check out the 'Rules of Surds' box below.

EXAMPLES   (i) Simplify $\sqrt{12}$ and $\sqrt{\frac{3}{16}}$.   (ii) Show that $\frac{9}{\sqrt{3}} = 3\sqrt{3}$.   (iii) Find $(2\sqrt{5} + 3\sqrt{6})^2$.

(i) <u>Simplifying</u> surds means making the number in the $\sqrt{}$ sign <u>smaller</u>, or getting rid of a <u>fraction</u> in the $\sqrt{}$ sign.

$$\sqrt{12} = \sqrt{4 \times 3} = \sqrt{4} \times \sqrt{3} = 2\sqrt{3}$$

$$\sqrt{\frac{3}{16}} = \frac{\sqrt{3}}{\sqrt{16}} = \frac{\sqrt{3}}{4}$$

Using $\sqrt{\frac{a}{b}} = \frac{\sqrt{a}}{\sqrt{b}}$.

Using $\sqrt{ab} = \sqrt{a}\sqrt{b}$.

(ii) For questions like these, you have to write a number (here, it's 3) as $3 - (\sqrt{3})^2 - \sqrt{3} \times \sqrt{3}$

$$\frac{9}{\sqrt{3}} = \frac{3 \times 3}{\sqrt{3}} = \frac{3 \times \sqrt{3} \times \sqrt{3}}{\sqrt{3}} = 3\sqrt{3}$$

Cancelling $\sqrt{3}$ from the top and bottom lines.

(iii) Multiply surds very <u>carefully</u> — it's easy to make a silly mistake.

$$\begin{aligned}(2\sqrt{5} + 3\sqrt{6})^2 &= (2\sqrt{5} + 3\sqrt{6})(2\sqrt{5} + 3\sqrt{6}) \\ &= (2\sqrt{5})^2 + 2 \times (2\sqrt{5}) \times (3\sqrt{6}) + (3\sqrt{6})^2 \\ &= (2^2 \times \sqrt{5}^2) + (2 \times 2 \times 3 \times \sqrt{5} \times \sqrt{6}) + (3^2 \times \sqrt{6}^2) \\ &= 20 + 12\sqrt{30} + 54 \\ &= 74 + 12\sqrt{30}\end{aligned}$$

$= 4 \times 5 = 20$ $= 9 \times 6 = 54$ $= 12\sqrt{5}\sqrt{6} = 12\sqrt{30}$

Rules of Surds

There's not really very much to remember.

$$\sqrt{ab} = \sqrt{a}\sqrt{b}$$

$$\sqrt{\frac{a}{b}} = \frac{\sqrt{a}}{\sqrt{b}}$$

$$a = (\sqrt{a})^2 = \sqrt{a}\sqrt{a}$$

Remove surds from fractions by *Rationalising the Denominator*

Surds are pretty darn complicated.

So they're the last thing you want at the bottom of a fraction.

But have no fear — <u>Rationalise the Denominator</u>...

Yup, you heard... (it means getting rid of the surds from the bottom of a fraction).

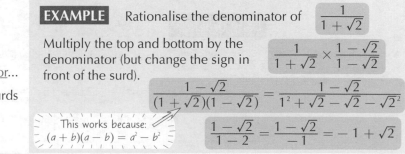

EXAMPLE   Rationalise the denominator of $\frac{1}{1 + \sqrt{2}}$

Multiply the top and bottom by the denominator (but change the sign in front of the surd).

$$\frac{1}{1 + \sqrt{2}} \times \frac{1 - \sqrt{2}}{1 - \sqrt{2}}$$

$$\frac{1 - \sqrt{2}}{(1 + \sqrt{2})(1 - \sqrt{2})} = \frac{1 - \sqrt{2}}{1^2 + \sqrt{2} - \sqrt{2} - \sqrt{2}^2}$$

This works because:
$(a + b)(a - b) = a^2 - b^2$

$$\frac{1 - \sqrt{2}}{1 - 2} = \frac{1 - \sqrt{2}}{-1} = -1 + \sqrt{2}$$

Surely the pun is mightier than the surd...

You'll need to work with surds in your <u>non-calculator C1 exam</u>, as roots are nigh on impossible (well, very tricky) to work out without a calculator. Learn the rules in the box so you can write them down without thinking — then get <u>loads</u> of practice.

Multiplying Out Brackets

In this horrific nightmare that is AS-level maths, you need to manipulate and simplify expressions <u>all the time</u>.

Remove brackets by **Multiplying** them out

Here are the basic types you have to deal with. You'll have seen them before. But there's no harm in reminding you, eh?

<u>Multiply Your Brackets Here — we do all shapes and sizes</u>

Single Brackets

$a(b + c + d) = ab + ac + ad$

Squared Brackets

$(a + b)^2 = (a + b)(a + b) = a^2 + 2ab + b^2$

Use the middle stage until you're comfortable with it. Just <u>never</u> make this <u>mistake</u>: $(a + b)^2 = a^2 + b^2$

Double Brackets

$(a + b)(c + d) = ac + ad + bc + bd$

Long Brackets

Write it out again with <u>each term</u> from one bracket separately multiplied by the <u>other bracket</u>.

$(x + y + z)(a + b + c + d)$

$= x(a + b + c + d) + y(a + b + c + d) + z(a + b + c + d)$

Then <u>multiply out each</u> of these <u>brackets</u>, one at a time.

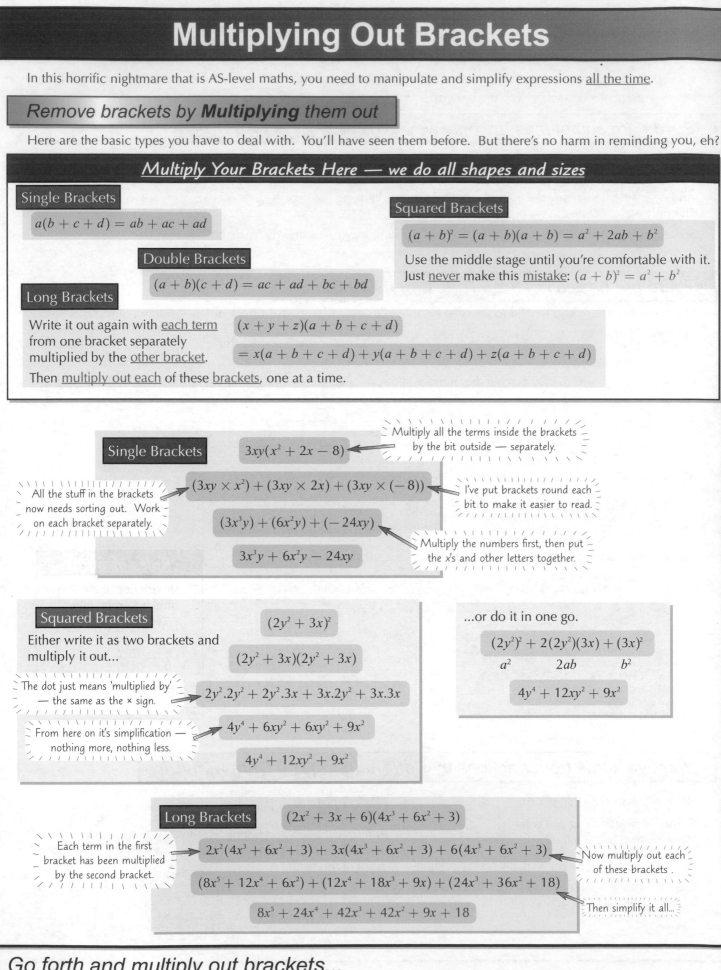

Single Brackets

$3xy(x^2 + 2x - 8)$

Multiply all the terms inside the brackets by the bit outside — separately.

$(3xy \times x^2) + (3xy \times 2x) + (3xy \times (-8))$

All the stuff in the brackets now needs sorting out. Work on each bracket separately.

I've put brackets round each bit to make it easier to read.

$(3x^3y) + (6x^2y) + (-24xy)$

Multiply the numbers first, then put the x's and other letters together.

$3x^3y + 6x^2y - 24xy$

Squared Brackets

Either write it as two brackets and multiply it out...

$(2y^2 + 3x)^2$

$(2y^2 + 3x)(2y^2 + 3x)$

The dot just means 'multiplied by' — the same as the × sign.

$2y^2.2y^2 + 2y^2.3x + 3x.2y^2 + 3x.3x$

From here on it's simplification — nothing more, nothing less.

$4y^4 + 6xy^2 + 6xy^2 + 9x^2$

$4y^4 + 12xy^2 + 9x^2$

...or do it in one go.

$(2y^2)^2 + 2(2y^2)(3x) + (3x)^2$
$\quad a^2 \qquad\quad 2ab \qquad\quad b^2$

$4y^4 + 12xy^2 + 9x^2$

Long Brackets

$(2x^2 + 3x + 6)(4x^3 + 6x^2 + 3)$

Each term in the first bracket has been multiplied by the second bracket.

$2x^2(4x^3 + 6x^2 + 3) + 3x(4x^3 + 6x^2 + 3) + 6(4x^3 + 6x^2 + 3)$

Now multiply out each of these brackets .

$(8x^5 + 12x^4 + 6x^2) + (12x^4 + 18x^3 + 9x) + (24x^3 + 36x^2 + 18)$

Then simplify it all...

$8x^5 + 24x^4 + 42x^3 + 42x^2 + 9x + 18$

Go forth and multiply out brackets...

OK, so this is obvious, but I'll say it anyway — if you've got 3 or more brackets together, multiply them out 2 at a time. Then you'll be turning a really hard problem into two easy ones. You can do that loads in maths. In fact, writing the same thing in different ways is what maths is about. That and sitting in classrooms with tacky 'maths can be fun' posters...

Taking Out Common Factors

Common factors need to be hunted down, and taken outside the brackets. They are a danger to your exam mark.

Spot those **Common Factors**

A bit which is in each term of an expression is a <u>common factor</u>.

Spot Those Common Factors

$$2x^3z + 4x^2yz + 14x^2y^2z$$

Look for any bits that are in each term.

<u>Numbers</u>: there's a common factor of 2 here because 2 divides into 2, 4 and 14.

<u>Variables</u>: there's at least an x^2 in each term and there's a z in each term.

So there's a common factor of $2x^2z$ in this expression.

And Take Them Outside a Bracket

If you spot a common factor you can "<u>take it out</u>":

$$2x^2z(x + 2y + 7y^2)$$

Write the common factor outside a bracket.

...and put what's left of each term inside the bracket.

Afterwards, always <u>multiply back out</u> to check you did it right:

Check by Multiplying Out Again

$$2x^2z(x + 2y + 7y^2) = 2x^3z + 4x^2yz + 14x^2y^2z$$

But it's not just numbers and variables you need to look for...

Brackets:

$$(y + a)^2(x - a)^3 + (x - a)^2$$

$(x-a)^2$ is a common factor
— it comes out to give:

$$(x - a)^2((y + a)^2(x - a) + 1)$$

Look for **Common Factors** when **Simplifying Expressions**

EXAMPLE Simplify... $(x + 1)(x - 2) + (x + 1)^2 - x(x + 1)$

There's an $(x + 1)$ factor in each term, so we can take this out as a common factor (hurrah).

$$(x + 1)\{(x - 2) + (x + 1) - x\}$$

The terms inside the big bracket are the old terms with an $(x + 1)$ removed.

At this point you should check that this multiplies out to give the original expression. (You can just do this in your head, if you trust it.)

Then simplify the big bracket's innards:

$$(x + 1)(\cancel{x} - 2 + x + 1 - \cancel{x})$$

$$= (x + 1)(x - 1)$$

Get this answer by multiplying out the two brackets (or by using the "difference of two squares").

$$= x^2 - 1$$

Bored of spotting trains or birds? Try common factors...

You'll be doing this business of taking out common factors a lot — so get your head round this. It's just a case of looking for things that are in all the different terms of an expression, i.e. <u>bits they have in common</u>. And if something's in all the different terms, save yourself some time and ink, and write it once — instead of two, three or more times.

Algebraic Fractions

No one likes fractions. But just like Mondays, you can't put them off forever. Face those fears. Here goes...

The first thing you've got to know about fractions:

You can just add the stuff on the top lines because the bottom lines are all the same.

$$\frac{a}{x} + \frac{b}{x} + \frac{c}{x} \equiv \frac{a + b + c}{x}$$

x is called a common denominator — a fancy way of saying 'the bottom line of all the fractions is x'.

Add fractions by putting them over a **Common Denominator**...

Finding a common denominator just means 'rewriting some fractions so all their bottom lines are the same'.

EXAMPLE Simplify $\frac{1}{2x} - \frac{1}{3x} + \frac{1}{5x}$

You need to rewrite these so that all the bottom lines are equal. What you want is something that all these bottom lines divide into.

Put it over a Common Denominator

30 is the lowest number that 2, 3 and 5 go into. So the common denominator is $30x$.

$$\frac{15}{30x} - \frac{10}{30x} + \frac{6}{30x}$$

Always check that these divide out to give what you started with.

$$\frac{15 - 10 + 6}{30x} = \frac{11}{30x}$$

...even **horrible** looking ones

Yep, finding a common denominator even works for those fraction nasties — like these:

EXAMPLE Simplify $\frac{3}{x + 2} + \frac{5}{x - 3}$

Find the Common Denominator

Take all the individual 'bits' from the bottom lines and multiply them together. Only use each bit once unless something on the bottom line is squared.

The individual 'bits' here are $(x + 2)$ and $(x - 3)$.

$$(x + 2)(x - 3)$$

Put Each Fraction over the Common Denominator

Make the denominator of each fraction into the common denominator.

$$\frac{3(x - 3)}{(x + 2)(x - 3)} + \frac{5(x + 2)}{(x + 2)(x - 3)}$$

Multiply the top and bottom lines of each fraction by whatever makes the bottom line the same as the common denominator.

Combine into One Fraction

Once everything's over the common denominator you can just add the top lines together.

$$= \frac{3(x - 3) + 5(x + 2)}{(x + 2)(x - 3)}$$

All the bottom lines are the same — so you can just add the top lines.

All you need to do now is tidy up the top.

$$= \frac{3x - 9 + 5x + 10}{(x + 2)(x - 3)} = \frac{8x + 1}{(x + 2)(x - 3)}$$

So much prettier now all the terms are <u>together</u>. Simple.

Well put me over a common denominator and pickle my walrus...

Adding fractions — turning lots of fractions into one fraction. Sounds pretty good to me, since it means you don't have to write as much. Better do it carefully, though — otherwise you can watch those marks shoot straight down the toilet.

Rewriting Expressions

I know this is basic stuff but if you don't get really comfortable with it you <u>will</u> make silly mistakes. You will.

Cancelling stuff on the top and bottom lines

Cancelling stuff is good — because it means you've got rid of something, and you don't have to write as much.

EXAMPLE Simplify $\dfrac{ax + ay}{az}$

You can do this in two ways. Use whichever you prefer — but make sure you understand the ideas behind both.

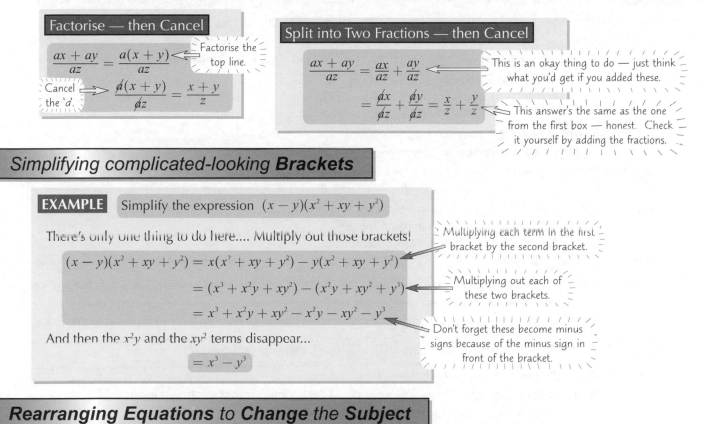

Factorise — then Cancel

$$\frac{ax + ay}{az} = \frac{a(x + y)}{az}$$ — Factorise the top line.

Cancel → $\dfrac{\cancel{a}(x + y)}{\cancel{a}z} = \dfrac{x + y}{z}$
the 'a'.

Split into Two Fractions — then Cancel

$$\frac{ax + ay}{az} = \frac{ax}{az} + \frac{ay}{az}$$ ← This is an okay thing to do — just think what you'd get if you added these.

$$= \frac{\cancel{a}x}{\cancel{a}z} + \frac{\cancel{a}y}{\cancel{a}z} = \frac{x}{z} + \frac{y}{z}$$ ← This answer's the same as the one from the first box — honest. Check it yourself by adding the fractions.

Simplifying complicated-looking Brackets

EXAMPLE Simplify the expression $(x - y)(x^2 + xy + y^2)$

There's only one thing to do here.... Multiply out those brackets!

$(x - y)(x^2 + xy + y^2) = x(x^2 + xy + y^2) - y(x^2 + xy + y^2)$ — Multiplying each term in the first bracket by the second bracket.

$= (x^3 + x^2y + xy^2) - (x^2y + xy^2 + y^3)$ — Multiplying out each of these two brackets.

$= x^3 + x^2y + xy^2 - x^2y - xy^2 - y^3$ — Don't forget these become minus signs because of the minus sign in front of the bracket.

And then the x^2y and the xy^2 terms disappear...

$= x^3 - y^3$

Rearranging Equations to Change the Subject

Changing the subject means taking an equation in terms of <u>one variable</u> and rewriting it in terms of <u>another</u>, e.g. $y = f(x)$ can also be written as $x = g(y)$. It's time to put those <u>mad algebra skills</u> to the test...

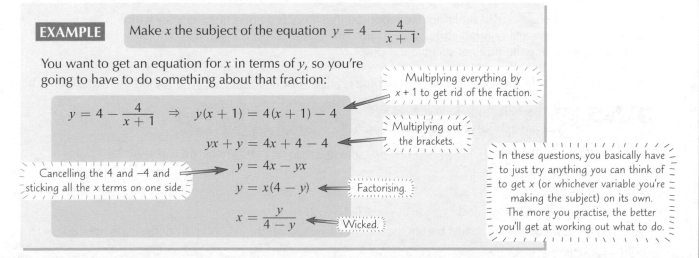

EXAMPLE Make x the subject of the equation $y = 4 - \dfrac{4}{x + 1}$.

You want to get an equation for x in terms of y, so you're going to have to do something about that fraction:

$$y = 4 - \frac{4}{x + 1} \Rightarrow y(x + 1) = 4(x + 1) - 4$$ — Multiplying everything by $x + 1$ to get rid of the fraction.

$$yx + y = 4x + 4 - 4$$ — Multiplying out the brackets.

$$y = 4x - yx$$ — Cancelling the 4 and −4 and sticking all the x terms on one side.

$$y = x(4 - y)$$ — Factorising.

$$x = \frac{y}{4 - y}$$ — Wicked.

In these questions, you basically have to just try anything you can think of to get x (or whichever variable you're making the subject) on its own. The more you practise, the better you'll get at working out what to do.

Don't look at me like that...

Choose a word, any word at all. Like "Simple". Now stare at it. Keep staring at it. Does it look weird? No? Stare a bit longer. Now does it look weird? Yes? Why is that? I don't understand.

Proof

Every now and then, the examiners like to throw in a <u>crazy question</u> where they ask you to '<u>prove</u>' whether something is true or false. And when they say prove, they don't mean 'try out a couple of examples and that'll do' — you have to back up your answer with a proper '<u>mathematical argument</u>'. So here goes...

You can **Prove** something by **Exhaustion**, **Contradiction** or **Counter-example**

In <u>proof by exhaustion</u> you break things down into two or more <u>cases</u>. You have to make sure that your cases cover <u>all possible situations</u>, then prove <u>separately</u> that the statement is true for <u>each case</u>. Sounds tiring.

EXAMPLE   Prove the following statement: "For any integer x, the value of $f(x) = x^3 + x + 1$ is an odd integer."

To prove the statement, split the situation into <u>two cases</u>: (i) x is an <u>even number</u>, and (ii) x is an <u>odd number</u>

(i) If x is an <u>even integer</u>, then it can be written as $\underline{x = 2n}$, for some integer n (this is the definition of an even number).

Substitute $x = 2n$ into the function: $f(2n) = (2n)^3 + 2n + 1 = 8n^3 + 2n + 1 = 2(4n^3 + n) + 1$

n is an integer $\Rightarrow (4n^3 + n)$ is an integer (as the sum or product of any integers are also integers)
$\Rightarrow 2(4n^3 + n)$ is an even integer (because 2× an integer is the definition of an even number)
$\Rightarrow 2(4n^3 + n) + 1$ is an <u>odd integer</u> (as even + odd = odd)

So $f(x)$ is <u>odd</u> when x is <u>even</u>.

(ii) If x is an <u>odd integer</u>, then it can be written as $\underline{x = 2m + 1}$, for some integer m. (This is the definition of an odd number.)

Substitute $x = 2m + 1$ into the function: $f(2m + 1) = (2m + 1)^3 + (2m + 1) + 1 = (8m^3 + 12m^2 + 6m + 1) + 2m + 1 + 1$
$= 8m^3 + 12m^2 + 8m + 3 = 2(4m^3 + 6m^2 + 4m) + 3$

m is an integer $\Rightarrow (4m^3 + 6m^2 + 4m)$ is an integer
$\Rightarrow 2(4m^3 + 6m^2 + 4m)$ is an even integer
$\Rightarrow 2(4m^3 + 6m^2 + 4m) + 3$ is an <u>odd integer</u>

So $f(x)$ is <u>odd</u> when x is <u>odd</u>.

As any integer x <u>must</u> be odd or even, and we've shown that $f(x)$ is <u>odd</u> when x is odd or even, $f(x)$ is <u>odd</u> for <u>any</u> integer x.

To prove a statement by <u>contradiction</u>, you suppose the statement <u>isn't true</u>, then wait for everything to go wrong...

EXAMPLE   Prove the following statement: "If x^2 is even, then x must be even."

We can prove the statement by contradiction.
Suppose the statement is <u>not true</u>. Then there must be an <u>odd number</u> x for which x^2 is <u>even</u>.
If x is odd, then you can write x as $\underline{2k + 1}$, where k is an integer.
Now, $x^2 = (2k + 1)^2 = 4k^2 + 4k + 1$
$4k^2 + 4k = 2(2k^2 + 2k)$ is <u>even</u> because it is 2× an integer
$\Rightarrow 4k^2 + 4k + 1$ is <u>odd</u> (since even + odd = odd).
So if x is odd, then x^2 is also odd. But we supposed that there is an odd number x for which x^2 is even — we have a <u>contradiction</u>. So we can conclude that if x^2 is <u>even</u>, then x must also be <u>even</u>, hence the original statement is <u>true</u>.

A <u>counter-example</u> is the best way to show something is <u>false</u>. Just find <u>one case</u> where the statement doesn't hold.

EXAMPLE   Disprove the following statement:
"For any pair of real numbers x and y, if $x > y$, then $x^2 + x > y^2 + y$."

To <u>disprove</u> the statement, it's enough to find just <u>one example</u> of x and y where $x > y$, but $x^2 + x \leq y^2 + y$.
Let $x = 2$ and $y = -4$.
Then $2 > -4 \Rightarrow x > y$
but $x^2 + x = 2^2 + 2 = 6$ and $y^2 + y = (-4)^2 + (-4) = 12$, so $x^2 + x < y^2 + y$
So when $x = 2$ and $y = -4$, the first part of the statement holds, but the second part of the statement doesn't.
So the statement is <u>not true</u>.

And that's the proof, the whole proof, and nothing but the proof...

These questions are mental, I know. They've gotta be done though. And it's back to normality in the next section, I promise...

C1 Section 1 — Practice Questions

So that was the first section. Now, before you get stuck into Section Two, test yourself with these questions. Go on. If you thought this section was a doddle, you should be able to fly through them...

Warm-up Questions

1) Pick out the constants and the variables from the following equations:
   a) $(ax + 6)^2 = 2b + 3$
   b) $f(x) = 12a + 3b^3 - 2$
   c) $y = \dfrac{-b \pm \sqrt{b^2 - 4ac}}{2a}$
   d) $\dfrac{dy}{dx} = x^2 + ax + 2$

2) What symbol should be used instead of the equals sign in identities?

3) Which of these are identities (i.e. true for all variable values)?

   A $(x + b)(y - b) = xy + b(y - x) - b^2$ B $(2y + x^2) = 10$

   C $a^2 - b^2 = (a - b)(a + b)$ D $a^3 + b^3 = (a + b)(a^2 - ab + b^2)$

4) Simplify these:
   a) $x^3 . x^5$ b) $a^7 . a^8$ c) $\dfrac{x^8}{x^2}$ d) $(a^2)^4$ e) $(xy^2).(x^3yz)$ f) $\dfrac{a^2b^4c^6}{a^3b^2c}$

5) Work out the following:
   a) $16^{1/2}$ b) $8^{1/3}$ c) $16^{3/4}$ d) x^0 e) $49^{-1/2}$

6) Find exact answers to these equations:
   a) $x^2 - 5 = 0$ b) $(x + 2)^2 - 3 = 0$

7) Simplify: a) $\sqrt{28}$ b) $\sqrt{\dfrac{5}{36}}$ c) $\sqrt{18}$ d) $\sqrt{\dfrac{9}{16}}$

8) Show that a) $\dfrac{8}{\sqrt{2}} = 4\sqrt{2}$, and b) $\dfrac{\sqrt{2}}{2} = \dfrac{1}{\sqrt{2}}$

9) Find $(6\sqrt{3} + 2\sqrt{7})^2$

10) Rationalise the denominator of: $\dfrac{2}{3 + \sqrt{7}}$

11) Remove the brackets and simplify the following expressions:
    a) $(a + b)(a - b)$ b) $(a + b)(a + b)$
    c) $35xy + 25y(5y + 7x) - 100y^2$ d) $(x + 3y + 2)(3x + y + 7)$

12) Take out the common factors from the following expressions:
    a) $2x^2y + axy + 2xy^2$ b) $a^2x + a^2b^2x^2$
    c) $16y + 8yx + 56x$ d) $x(x - 2) + 3(2 - x)$

13) Put the following expressions over a common denominator:
    a) $\dfrac{2x}{3} + \dfrac{y}{12} + \dfrac{x}{5}$ b) $\dfrac{5}{xy^2} - \dfrac{2}{x^2y}$ c) $\dfrac{1}{x} + \dfrac{x}{x + y} + \dfrac{y}{x - y}$

14) Simplify these expressions:
    a) $\dfrac{2a}{b} - \dfrac{a}{2b}$ b) $\dfrac{2p}{p + q} + \dfrac{2q}{p - q}$ c) "A bird in the hand is worth two in the bush"

C1 Section 1 — Practice Questions

The warm-up questions should have been a <u>walk in the park</u>, so now for the main event — <u>exam-style questions</u>. The questions on this page are like the ones you'll get <u>in your exam</u>, so make sure you can do them before moving on.

Exam Questions

1   a)   Write down the value of $27^{\frac{1}{3}}$.

(1 mark)

      b)   Find the value of $27^{\frac{4}{3}}$.

(2 marks)

2   Simplify

      a) $(5\sqrt{3})^2$

(1 mark)

      b) $(5 + \sqrt{6})(2 - \sqrt{6})$

(2 marks)

3   Given that $10000\sqrt{10} = 10^{k}$, find the value of k.

(3 marks)

4   Express $\dfrac{5 + \sqrt{5}}{3 - \sqrt{5}}$ in the form $a + b\sqrt{5}$, where a and b are integers.

(4 marks)

5   Factorise completely

$$2x^4 - 32x^2.$$

(3 marks)

6   Write

$$\frac{x + 5x^3}{\sqrt{x}}$$

    in the form $x^m + 5x^n$, where m and n are constants.

(2 marks)

7   Show that

$$\frac{(5 + 4\sqrt{x})^2}{2x}$$

    can be written as $\dfrac{25}{2}x^{-1} + Px^{-\frac{1}{2}} + Q$, and find the value of the integers P and Q.

(3 marks)

Sketching Quadratic Graphs

If a question doesn't seem to make sense, or you can't see how to go about solving a problem, try drawing a <u>graph</u>. It sometimes helps if you can actually <u>see</u> what the problem is, rather than just reading about it.

Sketch the graphs of the following quadratic functions:

① $y = 2x^2 - 4x + 3$

② $y = 8 - 2x - x^2$

Quadratic graphs are **Always** u-shaped or n-shaped

A) The first thing you need to know is whether the graph's going to be u-shaped or n-shaped (upside down). To decide, look at the <u>coefficient of x^2</u>.

$y = 2x^2 - 4x + 3$

The coefficient of x^2 here is <u>positive</u>... ...so the graph's u-shaped. → +ve

$y = 8 - 2x - x^2$

The coefficient of x^2 here is <u>negative</u>... ...so the graph's upside down (n-shaped). → −ve

B) Now find the places where the graph crosses the <u>axes</u> (both the y-axis and the x-axis).

(i) Put $x = 0$ to find where it meets the <u>y-axis</u>.

$y = 2x^2 - 4x + 3$

$y = (2 \times 0^2) - (4 \times 0) + 3$ so $y = 3$

That's where it crosses the y-axis.

(ii) Solve $y = 0$ to find where it meets the <u>x-axis</u>.

$2x^2 - 4x + 3 = 0$

$b^2 - 4ac = -8 < 0$

You could use the formula. But first check $b^2 - 4ac$ to see if $y = 0$ has any roots.

So it has no solutions, and doesn't cross the x-axis.

For more info, see page 17.

(i) Put $x = 0$.

$y = 8 - 2x - x^2$

$y = 8 - (2 \times 0) - 0^2$ so $y = 8$

(ii) Solve $y = 0$.

$8 - 2x - x^2 = 0$

$\Rightarrow (2 - x)(x + 4) = 0$

$\Rightarrow x = 2$ or $x = -4$

This equation factorises easily...

The minimum or maximum of the graph is always at $x = \frac{-b}{2a}$

The maximum value is <u>halfway</u> between the roots — the graph's symmetrical.

C) Finally, find the <u>minimum</u> or <u>maximum</u> (i.e. the <u>vertex</u>).

Since $y = 2(x - 1)^2 + 1$

By <u>completing the square</u> (see page 14).

the minimum value is $y = 1$, which occurs at $x = 1$.

The maximum value is at $x = -1$

So the maximum is $y = 8 - (2 \times -1) - (-1)^2$

i.e. the graph has a maximum at the point (–1, 9).

Sketching Quadratic Graphs

A) <u>up or down</u> — decide which direction the curve points in.

B) <u>axes</u> — find where the curve crosses them.

C) <u>max / min</u> — find the vertex.

Van Gogh, Monet — all the greats started out sketching graphs...

So there are <u>three steps</u> here to learn. Simple enough. You can do the third step (finding the max/min point) by either a) completing the square, which is covered a bit later, or b) using the fact that the graph's symmetrical — so once you've found the points where it crosses the x-axis, the point halfway between them will be the max/min. It's all laughs here...

Factorising a Quadratic

Factorising a quadratic means putting it into <u>two brackets</u> — and is useful if you're trying to draw a graph of a quadratic or solve a quadratic equation. It's pretty easy if $a = 1$ (in $ax^2 + bx + c$ form), but can be a real pain otherwise.

$$x^2 - x - 12 = (x - 4)(x + 3)$$

The graph of $x^2 - x - 12$ will cross the x-axis when $y = 0$. i.e. when $x = 4$ and $x = -3$.

Factorising's not so bad when *a = 1*

EXAMPLE Solve $x^2 - 8 = 2x$ by factorising.

A Put into $ax^2 + bx + c = 0$ Form

$x^2 - 2x - 8 = 0$ ⟵ So $a = 1$, $b = -2$, $c = -8$.

Write down the two brackets with x's in: $x^2 - 2x - 8 = (x \quad)(x \quad)$

B Find the Two Numbers

Find two numbers that <u>multiply</u> together to make c but which also <u>add</u> or <u>subtract</u> to give b (you can ignore any minus signs for now).

1 and 8 multiply to give 8 — and add / subtract to give 9 and 7.
2 and 4 multiply to give 8 — and add / subtract to give 6 and 2.

This is the value for b you're after — so this is the right combination: 2 and 4.

C Find the Signs

Now all you have to do is put in the plus or minus signs.

If c is negative, then the signs must be different.

$x^2 - 2x - 8 = (x \quad 4)(x \quad 2)$

$x^2 - 2x - 8 = (x + 2)(x - 4)$

It must be +2 and −4 because $2 \times (-4) = -8$ and $2 + (-4) = 2 - 4 = -2$

D Solve the Equation

All you've done so far is to factorise the equation — you've still got to solve it.

$(x + 2)(x - 4) = 0$

$\Rightarrow x + 2 = 0$ or $x - 4 = 0$

Don't forget this last step. The factors aren't the answer.

$\Rightarrow x = -2$ or $x = 4$

Factorising Quadratics

A) **Rearrange the equation into the standard $ax^2 + bx + c$ form.**

B) **Write down the two brackets:**
   $(x \quad)(x \quad)$

C) **Find two numbers that multiply to give 'c' and add/subtract to give 'b' (ignoring signs).**

D) **Put the numbers in the brackets and choose their signs.**

Another *Example...*

EXAMPLE Solve $x^2 + 4x - 21 = 0$ by factorising.

This equation is already in the standard format — you can write down the brackets straight away.

$x^2 + 4x - 21 = (x \quad)(x \quad)$

1 and 21 multiply to give 21 — and add / subtract to give 22 and 20.
3 and 7 multiply to give 21 — and add / subtract to give 10 and 4.

This is the value of 'b' you're after — 3 and 7 are the right numbers.

$x^2 + 4x - 21 = (x + 7)(x - 3)$

And solving the equation to find x gives... $\Rightarrow x = -7$ or $x = 3$

Scitardauq Gnisirotcaf — you should know it backwards...

Factorising quadratics — this is <u>very</u> basic stuff. You've really got to be comfortable with it. If you're even slightly rusty, you need to practise it until it's second nature. Remember why you're doing it — you don't factorise simply for the pleasure it gives you — it's so you can <u>solve</u> quadratic equations. Well, that's the theory anyway...

Factorising a Quadratic

It's not over yet...

Factorising a quadratic when $a \neq 1$

These can be a real pain. The basic method's the same as on the previous page — but it can be a bit more awkward.

EXAMPLE Factorise $3x^2 + 4x - 15$

A ### Write Down Two Brackets

As before, write down two brackets — but instead of just having x in each, you need two things that will multiply to give $3x^2$.

It's got to be $3x$ and x here.

$$3x^2 + 4x - 15 = (3x \qquad)(x \qquad)$$

B ### The Fiddly Bit

You need to find two numbers that multiply together to make 15 — but which will give you $4x$ when you multiply them by x and $3x$, and then add / subtract them.

$(3x \quad 1)(x \quad 15) \Rightarrow x$ and $45x$ which then add or subtract to give $46x$ and $44x$.

$(3x \quad 15)(x \quad 1) \Rightarrow 15x$ and $3x$ which then add or subtract to give $18x$ and $12x$.

$(3x \quad 3)(x \quad 5) \Rightarrow 3x$ and $15x$ which then add or subtract to give $18x$ and $12x$.

$(3x \quad 5)(x \quad 3) \Rightarrow 5x$ and $9x$ which then add or subtract to give $14x$ and $4x$.

This is the value you're after — so this is the right combination.

C ### Add the Signs

You know the brackets must be like these... $\Rightarrow (3x \quad 5)(x \quad 3) = 3x^2 + 4x - 15$

So all you have to do is put in the plus or minus signs.

'c' is negative — that means the signs in the brackets are different.

You've only got two choices — if you're unsure, just multiply them out to see which one's right.

$$(3x + 5)(x - 3) = 3x^2 - 4x - 15$$
or...
$$(3x - 5)(x + 3) = 3x^2 + 4x - 15 \quad \Leftarrow \text{ So it's this one.}$$

Sometimes it's best just to **Cheat** and use the **Formula**

Here are two final points to bear in mind:

See page 16 for all you need to know about the quadratic formula.

1) It won't always factorise.

2) Sometimes factorising is so messy that it's easier to just use the quadratic formula...

So if the question doesn't tell you to factorise, don't assume it will factorise.
And if it's something like this thing below, don't bother trying to factorise it...

EXAMPLE Solve $6x^2 + 87x - 144 = 0$

This will actually factorise, but there are 2 possible bracket forms to try.
$(6x \quad)(x \quad)$ or $(3x \quad)(2x \quad)$ And for each of these, there are 8 possible ways of making 144 to try.

And you can quote me on that...

"He who can properly do quadratic equations is considered a god."
Plato

"Quadratic equations are the music of reason."
James J Sylvester

Completing the Square

Completing the Square is a handy little trick that you should <u>definitely</u> know how to use.
It can be a bit fiddly — but it gives you <u>loads</u> of information about a quadratic really quickly.

Take any old quadratic and put it in a **Special Form**

Completing the square can be really confusing. For starters, what does "Completing the Square" <u>mean</u>?
<u>What</u> is the square? <u>Why</u> does it need completing? Well, there is <u>some</u> logic to it:

1)   The <u>square</u> is something like this: $(x + \text{something})^2$ It's basically the factorised equation (with the factors both the same), but there's something missing...

2)   ...So you need to '<u>complete</u>' it by adding a number to the square to make it equal to the original equation. $(x + \text{something})^2 + d$

You'll start with something like this...   ...sort the *x*-coefficients...   ...and you'll end up with something like this.

$$2x^2 + 8x - 5 \quad \Longrightarrow \quad 2(x + 2)^2 + ? \quad \Longrightarrow \quad 2(x + 2)^2 - 13$$

Lovely!

Make completing the square a bit **Easier**

There are only a few stages to completing the square — if you can't be bothered trying to understand it,
just <u>learn how to do it</u>. But I reckon it's worth spending a bit more time to get your head round it <u>properly</u>.

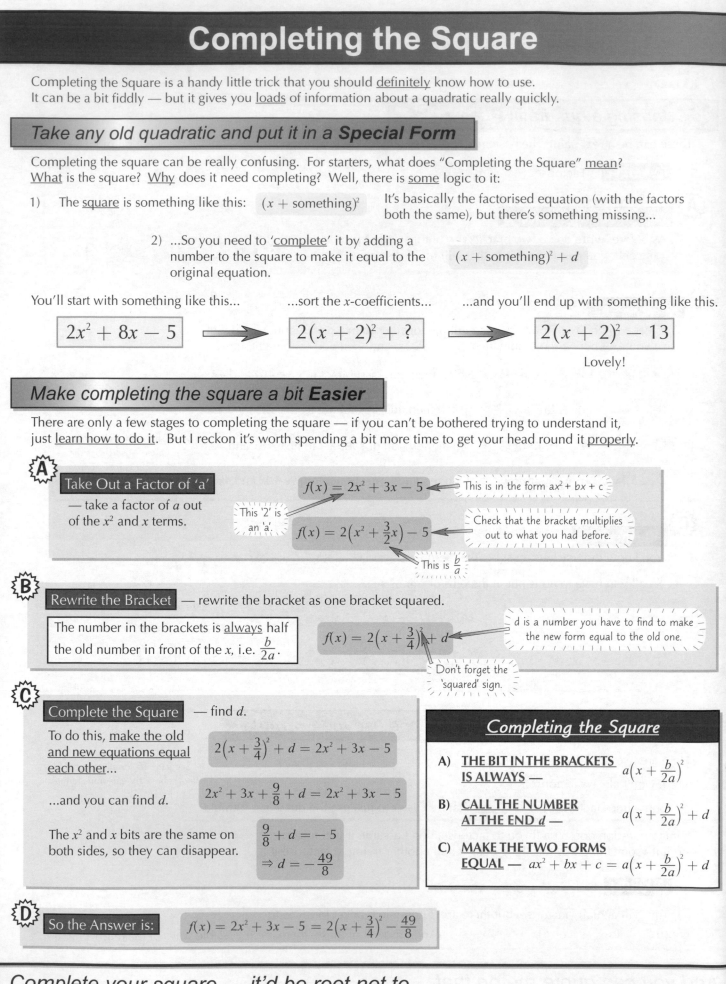

A   Take Out a Factor of 'a'
— take a factor of *a* out of the x^2 and *x* terms.

This '2' is an 'a'.

$f(x) = 2x^2 + 3x - 5$ This is in the form $ax^2 + bx + c$

$f(x) = 2\left(x^2 + \frac{3}{2}x\right) - 5$ Check that the bracket multiplies out to what you had before.

This is $\frac{b}{a}$

B   Rewrite the Bracket — rewrite the bracket as one bracket squared.

The number in the brackets is <u>always</u> half the old number in front of the *x*, i.e. $\frac{b}{2a}$.

$f(x) = 2\left(x + \frac{3}{4}\right)^2 + d$

d is a number you have to find to make the new form equal to the old one.

Don't forget the 'squared' sign.

C   Complete the Square — find *d*.

To do this, <u>make the old and new equations equal each other</u>...

$2\left(x + \frac{3}{4}\right)^2 + d = 2x^2 + 3x - 5$

...and you can find *d*.

$2x^2 + 3x + \frac{9}{8} + d = 2x^2 + 3x - 5$

The x^2 and *x* bits are the same on both sides, so they can disappear.

$\frac{9}{8} + d = -5$

$\Rightarrow d = -\frac{49}{8}$

Completing the Square

A)   **THE BIT IN THE BRACKETS IS ALWAYS** — $a\left(x + \frac{b}{2a}\right)^2$

B)   **CALL THE NUMBER AT THE END *d*** — $a\left(x + \frac{b}{2a}\right)^2 + d$

C)   **MAKE THE TWO FORMS EQUAL** — $ax^2 + bx + c = a\left(x + \frac{b}{2a}\right)^2 + d$

D   So the Answer is: $f(x) = 2x^2 + 3x - 5 = 2\left(x + \frac{3}{4}\right)^2 - \frac{49}{8}$

Complete your square — it'd be root not to...

Remember — you're basically trying to write the expression as one bracket squared, but it doesn't quite work. So you have
to add a number (*d*) to make it work. It's a bit confusing at first, but once you've learnt it you won't forget it in a hurry.

Completing the Square

Once you've completed the square, you can very quickly say <u>loads</u> about a quadratic function. And it all relies on the fact that a squared number can <u>never</u> be less than zero... <u>ever</u>.

Completing the square can sometimes be *Useful*

This is a quadratic written as a completed square. As it's a quadratic function and the coefficient of x^2 is positive, it's a u-shaped graph.

This is a square — it can never be negative. The smallest it can be is O.

$$f(x) = 3x^2 - 6x - 7 = 3(x-1)^2 - 10$$

A Find the Minimum — make the bit in the brackets equal to zero.

When the squared bit is zero, $f(x)$ reaches its minimum value. This means the graph reaches its lowest point.

$$f(x) = 3(x-1)^2 - 10$$

This number here is the minimum.

$$f(1) = 3(1-1)^2 - 10$$

$f(1)$ means using $x = 1$ in the function.

$$f(1) = 3(0)^2 - 10 = -10$$

So the minimum is −10, when $x = 1$

These notes are all about graphs with positive coefficients in front of the x^2. But if the coefficient is negative, then the graph is flipped upside down (n-shaped, not u-shaped).

With this information, you can easily sketch the graph...

Vertex is at (1, −10).

$f(x) = 3x^2 - 6x - 7$

B Where Does $f(x)$ Cross the x-axis? — i.e. find x.

Make the completed square function equal zero.

$$3(x-1)^2 - 10 = 0$$

Solve it to find where $f(x)$ crosses the x-axis.

$$\Rightarrow (x-1)^2 = \frac{10}{3}$$

da-de-dah ... rearranging again.

$$\Rightarrow x - 1 = \pm\sqrt{\frac{10}{3}}$$

$$\Rightarrow x = 1 \pm \sqrt{\frac{10}{3}}$$

So $f(x)$ crosses the x-axis when...

$$x = 1 + \sqrt{\frac{10}{3}} \quad \text{or} \quad x = 1 - \sqrt{\frac{10}{3}}$$

Graphs of Completed Squares

The graph of $f(x) = a(x+p)^2 + q$ will have a vertex at $(-p, q)$ and a line of symmetry at $x = -p$.

Some functions don't have *Real Roots*

By completing the square, you can also quickly tell if the graph of a quadratic function ever crosses the x-axis. It'll only cross the x-axis if the function changes sign (i.e. goes from positive to negative or vice versa). Take this function...

'Roots' are just the solutions to the equation. You can also think of them as 'where the graph crosses the x-axis'.

Check for Roots

$$f(x) = x^2 + 4x + 7$$

$$f(x) = (x+2)^2 + 3$$

This number's positive.

The smallest this bit can be is zero (at $x = -2$).

$(x+2)^2$ is never less than zero so $f(x)$ is never less than three.

This means that:

a) $f(x)$ can <u>never</u> be negative.
b) The graph of $f(x)$ <u>never</u> crosses the x-axis.

If the coefficient of x^2 is negative, you can do the same sort of thing to check whether $f(x)$ ever becomes positive.

Don't forget — two wrongs don't make a root...

You'll be pleased to know that that's the end of me trying to tell you how to do something you probably really don't want to do. Now you can push it to one side and run off to roll around in a bed of nettles... much more fun.

The Quadratic Formula

Unlike factorising, the quadratic formula <u>always</u> works... no ifs, no buts, no butts, no nothing...

The **Quadratic Formula** — a reason to be cheerful, but careful...

If you want to solve a quadratic equation $ax^2 + bx + c = 0$,
then the answers are given by this formula:

$$x = \frac{-b \pm \sqrt{b^2 - 4ac}}{2a}$$

The formula's a godsend — but use the power wisely...

If any of the coefficients (i.e. if a, b or c) in your quadratic equation are negative — be <u>especially</u> careful.

Always take things nice and <u>slowly</u> — don't try to rush it.

It's a good idea to write down what a, b and c are <u>before</u> you start plugging them into the formula.

There are a couple of minus signs in the formula — which can catch you out if you're not paying <u>attention</u>.

I shall teach you the ways of the **Formula**

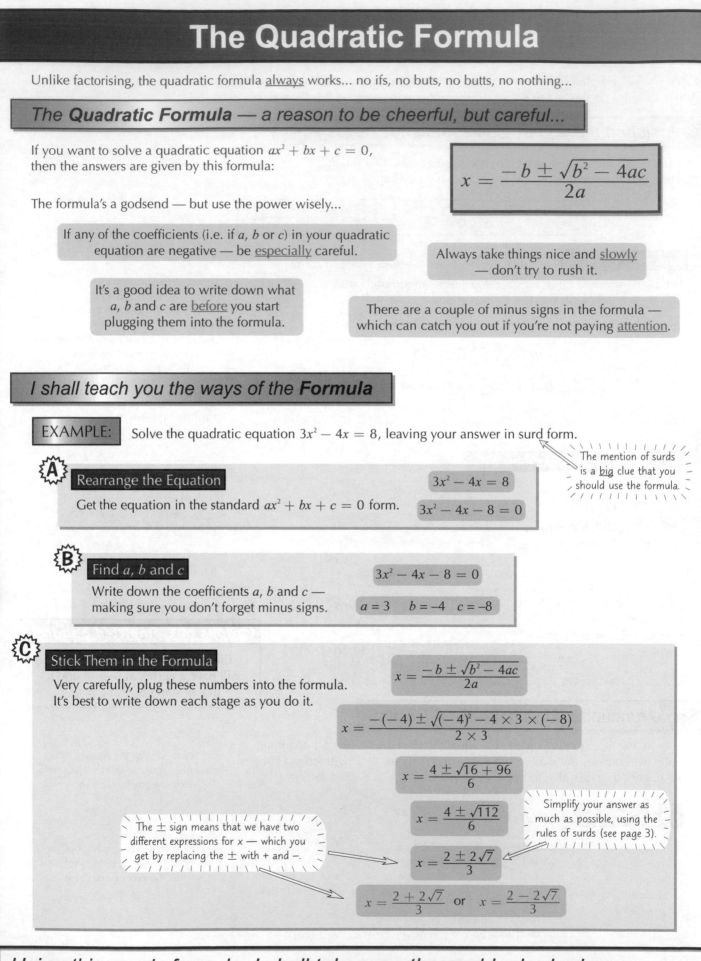

EXAMPLE: Solve the quadratic equation $3x^2 - 4x = 8$, leaving your answer in surd form.

The mention of surds is a <u>big</u> clue that you should use the formula.

A Rearrange the Equation

Get the equation in the standard $ax^2 + bx + c = 0$ form.

$3x^2 - 4x = 8$

$3x^2 - 4x - 8 = 0$

B Find a, b and c

Write down the coefficients a, b and c — making sure you don't forget minus signs.

$3x^2 - 4x - 8 = 0$

$a = 3 \quad b = -4 \quad c = -8$

C Stick Them in the Formula

Very carefully, plug these numbers into the formula. It's best to write down each stage as you do it.

$$x = \frac{-b \pm \sqrt{b^2 - 4ac}}{2a}$$

$$x = \frac{-(-4) \pm \sqrt{(-4)^2 - 4 \times 3 \times (-8)}}{2 \times 3}$$

$$x = \frac{4 \pm \sqrt{16 + 96}}{6}$$

$$x = \frac{4 \pm \sqrt{112}}{6}$$

Simplify your answer as much as possible, using the rules of surds (see page 3).

The $\pm$ sign means that we have two different expressions for x — which you get by replacing the $\pm$ with + and −.

$$x = \frac{2 \pm 2\sqrt{7}}{3}$$

$$x = \frac{2 + 2\sqrt{7}}{3} \text{ or } x = \frac{2 - 2\sqrt{7}}{3}$$

Using this magic formula, I shall take over the world... ha ha ha...

Okay, maybe it's not <u>quite</u> that good... but it's really important. So learn it properly — which means spending enough time until you can just say it out loud the whole way through, with no hesitations. Or perhaps you could try singing it as loud as you can to the tune of your favourite cheesy song. Sha-la-la-la-la-la-la-ha... La-di-da... Sha-la-la-la-la-la-la-ha...

The Discriminant

By using part of the quadratic formula, you can quickly tell if a quadratic equation has two solutions, one solution, or no solutions at all. Tell me more, I hear you cry...

How Many Roots? Check the b² – 4ac bit...

$$x = \frac{-b \pm \sqrt{b^2 - 4ac}}{2a}$$

When you try to find the roots of a quadratic function, this bit in the square-root sign ($b^2 - 4ac$) can be positive, zero, or negative. It's <u>this</u> that tells you if a quadratic function has two roots, one root, or no roots.

The $b^2 - 4ac$ bit is called the <u>discriminant</u>.

<u>Because</u> — if the discriminant is positive, the formula will give you two different values — when you add or subtract the $\sqrt{b^2 - 4ac}$ bit.

<u>But</u> if it's zero, you'll only get one value, since adding or subtracting zero doesn't make any difference.

<u>And</u> if it's negative, you don't get any (real) values because you can't take the square root of a negative number.

Well, not in C1. In some areas of maths, you can actually take the square root of negative numbers and get 'imaginary' numbers. That's why we say no 'real' roots — because there are 'imaginary' roots!

It's good to be able to picture what this means:

A root is just the value of x when $y = 0$, so it's where the graph touches or crosses the x-axis.

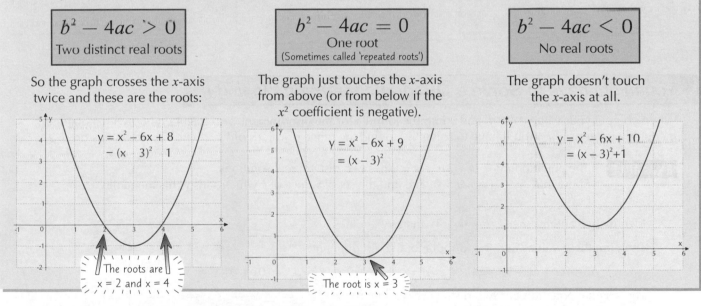

$b^2 - 4ac > 0$	$b^2 - 4ac = 0$	$b^2 - 4ac < 0$
Two distinct real roots	One root (Sometimes called 'repeated roots')	No real roots

So the graph crosses the x-axis twice and these are the roots:

The graph just touches the x-axis from above (or from below if the x^2 coefficient is negative).

The graph doesn't touch the x-axis at all.

$y = x^2 - 6x + 8$
$= (x - 3)^2 - 1$

The roots are
$x = 2$ and $x = 4$

$y = x^2 - 6x + 9$
$= (x - 3)^2$

The root is $x = 3$

$y = x^2 - 6x + 10$
$= (x - 3)^2 + 1$

Identify a, b and c to find the Discriminant

The <u>first</u> thing you have to do when you're given a quadratic is to <u>work out</u> what a, b and c are. Make sure you get them the <u>right way round</u> — it's easy to get mixed up if the quadratic's in a <u>different order</u>.

EXAMPLE Find the discriminant of $15 - x - 2x^2$. How many real roots does $15 - x - 2x^2$ have?

First, identify a, b and c: $a = -2$, $b = -1$ and $c = 15$ (NOT $a = 15$, $b = -1$ and $c = -2$).

Then put these values into the formula for the discriminant:

$b^2 - 4ac = (-1)^2 - (4 \times -2 \times 15) = 1 + 120 = 121$.

The discriminant is > 0, so $15 - x - 2x^2$ has two distinct real roots.

ha ha ha ha haaaaaa... ha ha ha... ha ha ha... ha ha ha........

The Discriminant

The discriminant often comes up in exam questions — but sometimes they'll be sneaky and not actually tell you that's what you have to find. Any question that mentions roots of a quadratic will probably mean that you need to find the discriminant.

a, *b* and *c* might be **Unknown**

In exam questions, you're often given a <u>quadratic</u> where one or more of *a*, *b* and *c* are given in terms of an <u>unknown</u> (usually *k*, but sometimes *p* or *q*). This means that you'll end up with an <u>equation</u> or <u>inequality</u> for the discriminant <u>in terms of the unknown</u> — you might have to <u>solve</u> it to find the <u>value</u> or <u>range of values</u> of the unknown.

EXAMPLE Find the range of values of *k* for which: a) f(*x*) has 2 distinct roots, b) f(*x*) has 1 root, c) f(*x*) has no real roots, where f(*x*) = $3x^2 + 2x + k$.

First, decide what *a*, *b* and *c* are: $a = 3, b = 2, c = k$

Then work out what the discriminant is:
$$b^2 - 4ac = 2^2 - 4 \times 3 \times k$$
$$= 4 - 12k$$

These calculations are exactly the same as in a). You don't need to do them if you've done a) because the only difference is the (in)equality symbol.

a) <u>Two distinct roots</u> means:
$$b^2 - 4ac > 0 \Rightarrow 4 - 12k > 0$$
$$\Rightarrow 4 > 12k$$
$$\Rightarrow k < \tfrac{1}{3}$$

b) <u>One root</u> means:
$$b^2 - 4ac = 0 \Rightarrow 4 - 12k = 0$$
$$\Rightarrow 4 = 12k$$
$$\Rightarrow k = \tfrac{1}{3}$$

c) <u>No roots</u> means:
$$b^2 - 4ac < 0 \Rightarrow 4 - 12k < 0$$
$$\Rightarrow 4 < 12k$$
$$\Rightarrow k > \tfrac{1}{3}$$

You might have to **Solve** a **Quadratic Inequality** to find *k*

When you put your values of *a*, *b* and *c* into the formula for the <u>discriminant</u>, you might end up with a <u>quadratic inequality</u> in terms of *k*. You'll have to solve this to find the range of values of *k* — there's more on this on p. 24.

EXAMPLE The equation $kx^2 + (k + 3)x + 4 = 0$ has two distinct real solutions. Show that $k^2 - 10k + 9 > 0$, and find the set of values of *k* which satisfy this inequality.

Identify *a*, *b* and *c*: $a = k, b = (k + 3)$ and $c = 4$

Then put these values into the formula for the discriminant:
$$b^2 - 4ac = (k + 3)^2 - (4 \times k \times 4) = k^2 + 6k + 9 - 16k = k^2 - 10k + 9.$$

The original equation has two distinct real solutions, so the discriminant must be > 0.

So $k^2 - 10k + 9 > 0.$

Now, to find the set of values for *k*, you have to factorise the quadratic:
$$k^2 - 10k + 9 = (k - 1)(k - 9).$$

The solutions of this equation are $k = 1$ and $k = 9$. From the graph, you can see that this is a u-shaped quadratic which is > 0 when

$k < 1$ or when $k > 9$.

$y = k^2 - 10k + 9$
$= (k - 1)(k - 9)$

I'll try not to discriminate...

Don't panic if you're not sure how to solve quadratic inequalities — they're covered in more detail on p. 24. Chances are you'll get a discriminant question in the exam, so you need to know what to do. Although it might be tempting to hide under your exam desk and hope it doesn't find you, there's no escaping these questions — so get practising.

'Almost' Quadratic Equations

Sometimes you'll be asked to solve equations that look really difficult, like the ones on this page. But with a bit of rearrangement and fiddling you can get them to look just like an ordinary quadratic you can solve.

Some **Nasty-looking** equations are just **Quadratics**

$$x^4 - 6x^2 + 9 = 0$$

Arrrgh. How on earth are you supposed to solve something like that? Well the answer is... with great difficulty — that's if you don't spot that you can turn it into quadratic form like this:

$$(x^2)^2 - 6(x^2) + 9 = 0$$

It still looks weird. But, if those x^2's were y's:

$$y^2 - 6y + 9 = 0$$

Now it's a just a simple quadratic that you could solve in your sleep — or the exam, which would probably be more useful.

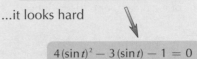

$$4\sin^2 t - 3\sin t - 1 = 0$$

...it looks hard

$$4(\sin t)^2 - 3(\sin t) - 1 = 0$$

...still looks hard

$$4y^2 - 3y - 1 = 0$$

...looks easy.

Just make a **Substitution** to **Simplify**

EXAMPLE: $2x^6 - 11x^3 + 5 = 0$

1 Spot That It's a Quadratic

Put it in the form: a(something)^2 + b(same thing) + (number) = 0.

$$2(x^3)^2 - 11(x^3) + 5 = 0$$

Now substitute x^3 for y to make it like a normal quadratic.

2 Substitute

let $x^3 = y$ $2y^2 - 11y + 5 = 0$

And solve this quadratic to find the values of y.

3 Solve it $2y^2 - 11y + 5 = 0$

$$(2y - 1)(y - 5) = 0$$

$$y = \frac{1}{2}, \text{ or } 5$$

Now you've got the values of y, you can get the values of x.

4 Find the Original Unknown x

$y = \frac{1}{2}$, or 5   but... $y = x^3$ ← This comes from stage 2.

Which means... $x^3 = \frac{1}{2}$, or 5

So the answer is... $x = \sqrt[3]{\frac{1}{2}}$, or $\sqrt[3]{5}$

Be careful with the number of solutions you get here. Depending on your substitution, you might get more than one solution for each value of y. e.g. if you make the substitution $y = x^2$, there's a good chance you'll get four possible values for x. You have been warned...

Disguised Quadratics

1) **Put the equation in the FORM:** a(something)^2+b(same thing)+(number)=0

2) **SUBSTITUTE a new variable for the something in the brackets to get a normal-looking quadratic.**

3) **SOLVE the quadratic in the usual way — i.e. by factorising or using the quadratic formula.**

4) **Stick your answers in the substitution equation to get the values for the ORIGINAL unknown.**

Almost quadratics — almost worthwhile, almost interesting, almost...

Quadratics with delusions of grandeur. Whatever next. Anyway, there isn't much to add to what's already on this page. All you need to do is spot the substitution you can use to make your life easier — then things will be, well, easier.

Cows

The stuff on this page isn't strictly on the syllabus. But I've included it anyway because I reckon it's really important stuff that you ought to know.

There are loads of *Different Types* of Cows

Dairy Cattle

Every day a dairy cow can produce up to 128 pints of milk — which can be used to make 14 lbs of cheese, 5 gallons of ice cream, or 6 lbs of butter.

The Jersey
The Jersey is a small breed best suited to pastures in high rainfall areas. It is kept for its creamy milk.

Advantages
1) Can produce creamy milk until old age.
2) Milk is the highest in fat of any dairy breed (5.2%).
3) Fairly docile, although bulls can't be trusted.
Disadvantages
1) Produces less milk than most other breeds.

The Holstein-Friesian
This breed can be found in many areas.
It is kept mainly for milk.

Advantages
1) Produce more milk than any breed.
2) The breed is large, so bulls can be sold for beef.
Disadvantages
1) Milk is low in fat (3.5%).

Beef Cattle

Cows are sedentary animals who spend up to 8 hours a day chewing the cud while standing still or lying down to rest after grazing. Getting fat for people to eat.

The Angus
The Angus is best suited to areas where there is moderately high rainfall.

Advantages
1) Early maturing.
2) High ratio of meat to body weight.
3) Forages well.
4) Adaptable.

The Hereford
The Hereford matures fairly early, but later than most shorthorn breeds. All Herefords have white faces, and if a Hereford is crossbred with any other breed of cow, all the offspring will have white or partially white faces.

Advantages
1) Hardy.
2) Adaptable to different feeds.
Disadvantages
1) Susceptible to eye diseases.

You will often see cows with pieces of grass sticking out of their mouths.

Milk comes from Cows

This is <u>really</u> important — try not to forget it.

Milk is an emulsion of butterfat suspended in a solution of water (roughly 80%), lactose, proteins and salts. Cow's milk has a specific gravity of around 1.03.
It's pasteurised by heating it to 63° C for 30 minutes. It's then rapidly cooled and stored below 10° C.

Louis Pasteur began his experiments into 'pasteurisation' in 1856. By 1946, the vacuum pasteurisation method had been perfected, and in 1948, UHT (ultra heat-treated) pasteurisation was introduced.

$$cow + grass = fat \ cow$$
$$fat \ cow + milking \ machine \Rightarrow milk$$

\ \ \ \ \ \ | \ | \ | \ | \ | \ / \ / \ / \ / \ /
SOME IMPORTANT FACTS TO REMEMBER:
• A newborn calf can walk on its own an hour after birth.
• A cow's teeth are only on the bottom of her mouth.
• While some cows can live up to 40 years, they generally don't live beyond 20.

Famous Cows and Cow Songs

Famous Cows

1) Ermintrude from the Magic Roundabout.
2) The Laughing Cow.
3) Other TV commercial cows — Anchor, Dairylea.
4) The cow that jumped over the moon.
5) Greek mythology was full of gods turning themselves and their girlfriends into cattle.

Cows in Pop Music

1) Boom Boom Cow — Black Eyed Peas
2) Saturday Night at the Moo-vies — The Drifters
3) I Kissed a Cow — Katy Perry
4) Take a Cow — Rihanna
5) Cows Don't Lie — Shakira

Pantomime Cows aren't Real

If you go to see a pantomime around Christmas time, you may see a cow on stage. Don't get concerned about animal rights and exploitation of animals — it's not a real cow. Pantomime cows are just two people wearing a cow costume. Sometimes it'll be a pantomime horse instead.

The Cow
The cow is of the bovine ilk;
One end is moo, the other, milk.
— Ogden Nash

Where's me Jersey — I'm Friesian...

Cow-milking — an underrated skill, in my opinion. As Shakespeare once wrote, 'Those who can milk cows are likely to get pretty good grades in maths exams, no word of a lie'. Well, he probably would've written something like that if he was into cows. And he would've written it because cows are helpful when you're trying to work out what a question's all about — and once you know that, you can decide the best way forward. And if you don't believe me, remember the saying of the ancient Roman Emperor Julius Caesar — 'If in doubt, draw a cow'.

C1 Section 2 — Practice Questions

Mmmm, well, quadratic equations — not exactly designed to make you fall out of your chair through laughing so hard, are they? But (and that's a huge 'but') they'll get you <u>plenty of marks</u> come that fine morning when you march confidently into the exam hall — if you know <u>what you're doing</u>. Time for some <u>practice questions</u> methinks...

Warm-up Questions

1) Factorise the following expressions. While you're doing this, <u>sing a jolly song</u> to show how much you enjoy it.
   a) $x^2 + 2x + 1$,   b) $x^2 - 13x + 30$,   c) $x^2 - 4$,
   d) $3 + 2x - x^2$,   e) $2x^2 - 7x - 4$,   f) $5x^2 + 7x - 6$.

2) Solve the following equations. And <u>sing verse two</u> of your jolly song.
   a) $x^2 - 3x + 2 = 0$,   b) $x^2 + x - 12 = 0$,   c) $2 + x - x^2 = 0$,   d) $x^2 + x - 16 = x$,
   e) $3x^2 - 15x - 14 = 4x$,   f) $4x^2 - 1 = 0$,   g) $6x^2 - 11x + 9 = 2x^2 - x + 3$.

3) Rewrite these quadratics by <u>completing the square</u>. Then state their <u>maximum</u> or <u>minimum</u> value and the <u>value of x</u> where this occurs. Also, say if and where they <u>cross the x-axis</u> — just for a laugh, like.
   a) $x^2 - 4x - 3$,   b) $3 - 3x - x^2$,   c) $2x^2 - 4x + 11$,   d) $4x^2 - 28x + 48$.

4) How many <u>roots</u> do these quadratics have? <u>Sketch</u> their graphs.
   a) $x^2 - 2x - 3 = 0$,   b) $x^2 - 6x + 9 = 0$,   c) $2x^2 + 4x + 3 = 0$.

5) Solve these quadratic equations, leaving your answers in <u>surd form</u> where necessary.
   a) $3x^2 - 7x + 3 = 0$,   b) $2x^2 - 6x - 2 = 0$,   c) $x^2 + 4x + 6 = 12$.

   I have a peek at p.24 for help on solving a quadratic inequality.

6) If the quadratic equation $x^2 + kx + 4 = 0$ has <u>two roots</u>, what are the possible values of k?

7) Solve the equation $4x^4 - 5x^2 + 1 = 0$.

The warm-up questions will only get you as far as the <u>third floor</u>. And you'll have to use the stairs.
To get all the way to the <u>top floor</u>, you need to take the <u>express lift</u> that is this lovely set of exam questions...

Exam Questions

1   The equation $x^2 + 2kx + 4k = 0$, where k is a non-zero integer, has equal roots.

   Find the value of k.

   (4 marks)

2   The equation $px^2 + (p + 3)x + 4 = 0$ has 2 distinct real solutions for x (p is a constant).

   a)   Show that $p^2 - 10p + 9 > 0$.

   (3 marks)

   b)   Hence find the range of possible values for p.

   (4 marks)

3   Solve the equation $2x^{\frac{2}{5}} - 3x^{\frac{1}{5}} - 2 = 0$.

   (4 marks)

C1 Section 2 — Practice Questions

Three exam questions are <u>never enough</u> — so here are a few more...

4   Given that

$$5x^2 + nx + 14 \equiv m(x + 2)^2 + p,$$

find the values of the integers m, n and p.

(3 marks)

5   a)   Rewrite $x^2 - 12x + 15$ in the form $(x - a)^2 + b$, for integers a and b.

(2 marks)

     b)   (i)   Find the minimum value of $x^2 - 12x + 15$.

(1 mark)

          (ii)   State the value of x at which this minimum occurs.

(1 mark)

6   a)   Use the quadratic formula to solve the equation $x^2 - 14x + 25 = 0$.
Leave your answer in simplified surd form.

(3 marks)

     b)   Sketch the curve of $y = x^2 - 14x + 25$, giving the coordinates of the
point where the curve crosses the x- and y-axis.

(3 marks)

     c)   Hence solve the inequality $x^2 - 14x + 25 \leq 0$.

(1 mark)

7   a)   (i)   Express $10x - x^2 - 27$ in the form $-(m - x)^2 + n$, where m and n are integers.

(2 marks)

          (ii)   Hence show that $10x - x^2 - 27$ is always negative.

(1 mark)

     b)   (i)   State the coordinates of the maximum point of the curve $y = 10x - x^2 - 27$.

(2 marks)

          (ii)   Sketch the curve, showing where the curve crosses the y-axis.

(2 marks)

8   The quadratic equation $(p - 2)x^2 + px + 2 = 0$ has only one root. Find the value of p.

(4 marks)

Linear Inequalities

Solving <u>inequalities</u> is very similar to solving equations. You've just got to be really careful that you keep the inequality sign pointing the <u>right</u> way.

> Find the ranges of x that satisfy these inequalities:
>
> (i) $x - 3 < -1 + 2x$ (ii) $8x + 2 \geq 2x + 17$ (iii) $4 - 3x \leq 16$ (iv) $36x < 6x^2$

Sometimes the inequality sign *Changes Direction*

Like I said, these are pretty similar to solving equations — because whatever you do to one side, you have to do to the other. But multiplying or dividing by <u>negative</u> numbers <u>changes</u> the direction of the inequality sign.

<u>Adding</u> or <u>subtracting</u> doesn't change the direction of the inequality sign

<u>Multiplying</u> or <u>dividing</u> by something <u>positive</u> doesn't affect the inequality sign

EXAMPLE If you <u>add</u> or <u>subtract</u> something from both sides of an inequality, the inequality sign <u>doesn't</u> change direction.

EXAMPLE Multiplying or dividing both sides of an inequality by a <u>positive</u> number <u>doesn't</u> affect the direction of the inequality sign.

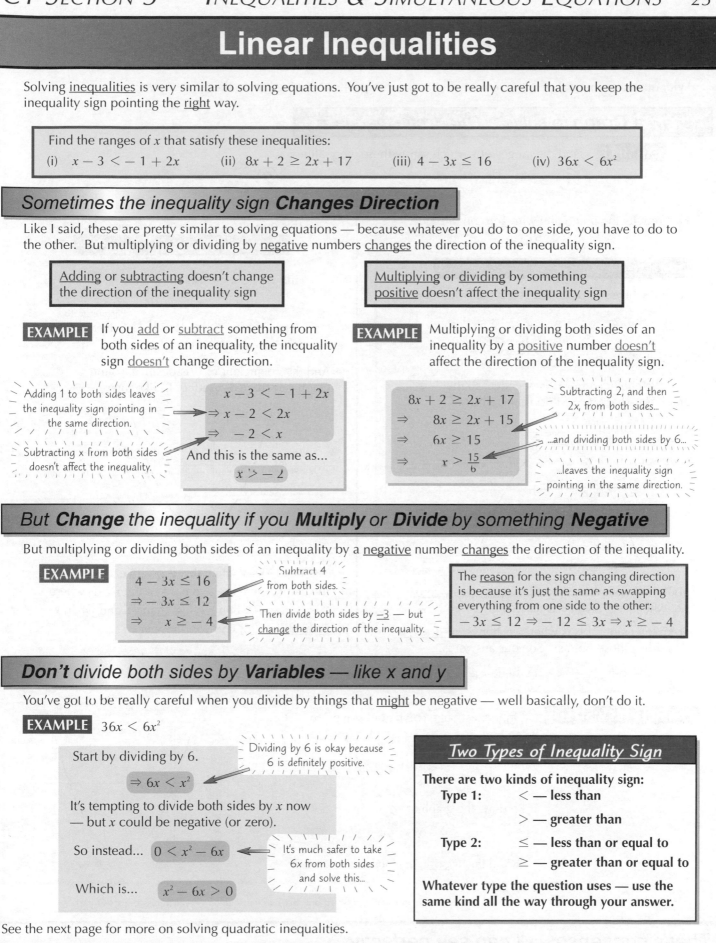

Adding 1 to both sides leaves the inequality sign pointing in the same direction.

$$x - 3 < -1 + 2x$$
$$\Rightarrow x - 2 < 2x$$
$$\Rightarrow -2 < x$$

Subtracting x from both sides doesn't affect the inequality.

And this is the same as...

$$x > -2$$

$$8x + 2 \geq 2x + 17$$
$$\Rightarrow \quad 8x \geq 2x + 15$$
$$\Rightarrow \quad 6x \geq 15$$
$$\Rightarrow \quad x > \frac{15}{6}$$

Subtracting 2, and then 2x, from both sides...

...and dividing both sides by 6...

...leaves the inequality sign pointing in the same direction.

But *Change* the inequality if you *Multiply* or *Divide* by something *Negative*

But multiplying or dividing both sides of an inequality by a <u>negative</u> number <u>changes</u> the direction of the inequality.

EXAMPLE

$$4 - 3x \leq 16$$
$$\Rightarrow -3x \leq 12$$
$$\Rightarrow \quad x \geq -4$$

Subtract 4 from both sides.

Then divide both sides by –3 — but <u>change</u> the direction of the inequality.

The <u>reason</u> for the sign changing direction is because it's just the same as swapping everything from one side to the other:
$$-3x \leq 12 \Rightarrow -12 \leq 3x \Rightarrow x \geq -4$$

Don't divide both sides by *Variables* — like x and y

You've got to be really careful when you divide by things that <u>might</u> be negative — well basically, don't do it.

EXAMPLE $36x < 6x^2$

Start by dividing by 6.

$$\Rightarrow 6x < x^2$$

Dividing by 6 is okay because 6 is definitely positive.

It's tempting to divide both sides by x now — but x could be negative (or zero).

So instead... $0 < x^2 - 6x$

It's much safer to take 6x from both sides and solve this...

Which is... $x^2 - 6x > 0$

Two Types of Inequality Sign

There are two kinds of inequality sign:

Type 1: $<$ — **less than**

$>$ — **greater than**

Type 2: $\leq$ — **less than or equal to**

$\geq$ — **greater than or equal to**

Whatever type the question uses — use the same kind all the way through your answer.

See the next page for more on solving quadratic inequalities.

So no one knows we've arrived safely — splendid...

So just remember — inequalities are just like normal equations except that you have to reverse the sign when multiplying or dividing by a negative number. And <u>don't</u> divide both sides by variables. (You should know not to do this with normal equations anyway because the variable could be <u>zero</u>.) OK — lecture's over.

Quadratic Inequalities

With quadratic inequalities, you're best off drawing the graph and taking it from there.

Draw a **Graph** to solve a **Quadratic** inequality

EXAMPLE Find the ranges of x which satisfy these inequalities:

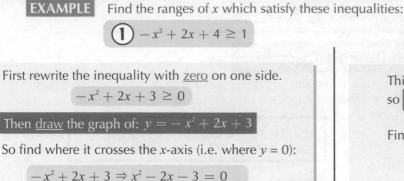

① $-x^2 + 2x + 4 \geq 1$

② $2x^2 - x - 3 > 0$

First rewrite the inequality with zero on one side.

$$-x^2 + 2x + 3 \geq 0$$

Then draw the graph of: $y = -x^2 + 2x + 3$

So find where it crosses the x-axis (i.e. where $y = 0$):

$$-x^2 + 2x + 3 \Rightarrow x^2 - 2x - 3 = 0$$
$$\Rightarrow (x + 1)(x - 3) = 0$$
$$\Rightarrow x = -1 \text{ or } x = 3$$

And the coefficient of x^2 is negative, so the graph is n-shaped. So it looks like this:

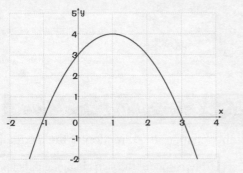

You're interested in when this is positive or zero, i.e. when it's above the x-axis.

From the graph, this is when x is between −1 and 3 (including those points). So your answer is...

$$-x^2 + 2x + 4 \geq 1 \text{ when } -1 \leq x \leq 3.$$

This one already has zero on one side, so draw the graph of $y = 2x^2 - x - 3$.

Find where it crosses the x-axis:

$$2x^2 - x - 3 = 0$$
$$\Rightarrow (2x - 3)(x + 1) = 0$$
$$\Rightarrow x = \tfrac{3}{2} \text{ or } x = -1$$

Factorise it to find the roots.

And the coefficient of x^2 is positive, so the graph is u-shaped. And looks like this:

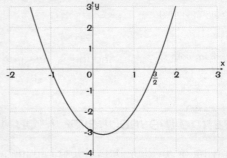

You need to say when this is positive. Looking at the graph, there are two parts of the x-axis where this is true — when x is less than −1 and when x is greater than 3/2. So your answer is:

$$2x^2 - x - 3 > 0 \text{ when } x < -1 \text{ or } x > \tfrac{3}{2}.$$

EXAMPLE (REVISITED) On the last page you had to solve $36x < 6x^2$.

$$36x < 6x^2$$
equation 1 $\Rightarrow 6x < x^2$
$$\Rightarrow 0 < x^2 - 6x$$

So draw the graph of

$$y = x^2 - 6x = x(x - 6)$$

And this is positive when $x < 0$ or $x > 6$.

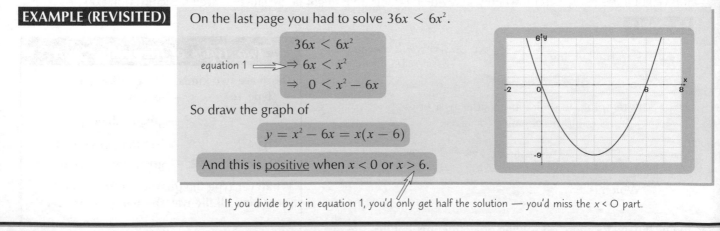

If you divide by x in equation 1, you'd only get half the solution — you'd miss the $x < 0$ part.

That's nonsense — I can see perfectly...

Call me sad, but I reckon these questions are pretty cool. They look a lot more difficult than they actually are and you get to draw a picture. Wow! When you do the graph, the important thing is to find where it crosses the x-axis (you don't need to know where it crosses the y-axis) and make sure you draw it the right way up. Then you just need to decide which bit of the graph you want. It'll either be the range(s) of x where the graph is below the x-axis or the range(s) where it's above. And this depends on the inequality sign.

Simultaneous Equations

Solving simultaneous equations means finding the answers to two equations <u>at the same time</u> — i.e. finding values for x and y for which both equations are true. And it's one of those things that you'll have to do <u>again and again</u> — so it's definitely worth practising them until you feel <u>really confident</u>.

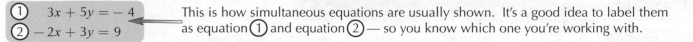

① $3x + 5y = -4$
② $-2x + 3y = 9$

This is how simultaneous equations are usually shown. It's a good idea to label them as equation ① and equation ② — so you know which one you're working with.

But they'll look different sometimes, maybe like this. Make sure you rearrange them as '$ax + by = c$'.

$4 + 5y = -3x$
$-2x = 9 - 3y$

rearrange as
$ax + by = c$

$3x + 5y = -4$
$-2x + 3y = 9$

Solving them by *Elimination*

Elimination is a lovely method. It's really quick when you get the hang of it — you'll be doing virtually all of it in your head.

EXAMPLE:

① $3x + 5y = -4$
② $-2x + 3y = 9$

To get the x's to match, you need to multiply the first equation by 2 and the second by 3:

①×2 $6x + 10y = -8$
②×3 $-6x + 9y = 27$

Add the equations together to eliminate the x's.

①+② $19y = 19$
$y = 1$

So y is 1. Now stick that value for y into one of the equations to find x:

$y = 1$ in ① $\Rightarrow 3x + 5 = -4$
$3x = -9$
$x = -3$

So the solution is $x = -3$, $y = 1$.

A Match the Coefficients

Multiply the equations by numbers that will make either the x's or the y's match in the two equations. (Ignoring minus signs.)

Go for the lowest common multiple (LCM). e.g. LCM of 2 and 3 is 6.

B Eliminate to Find One Variable

If the coefficients are the <u>same</u> sign, you'll need to <u>subtract</u> one equation from the other.

If the coefficients are <u>different</u> signs, you need to <u>add</u> the equations.

C Find the Variable You Eliminated

When you've found one variable, put its value into one of the original equations so you can find the other variable.

But you should always...

D Check Your Answer

...by putting these values into the other equation.

② $-2x + 3y = 9$
$x = -3$
$y = 1$

If these two numbers are the same, then the values you've got for the variables are right.

$-2 \times (-3) + 3 \times 1 = 6 + 3 = 9$

Elimination Method

1) **Match the coefficients**

2) **Eliminate and then solve for one variable**

3) **Find the other variable (that you eliminated)**

4) **Check your answer**

Eliminate your social life — do AS-level maths

This is a fairly basic method that won't be new to you. So make sure you know it. The only possibly tricky bit is <u>matching the coefficients</u> — work out the lowest common multiple of the coefficients of x, say, then multiply the equations to get this number in front of each x.

Simultaneous Equations with Quadratics

Elimination is great for simple equations. But it won't always work. Sometimes one of the equations has not just x's and y's in it — but bits with x^2 and y^2 as well. When this happens, you can <u>only</u> use the <u>substitution</u> method.

Use Substitution if one equation is **Quadratic**

EXAMPLE: $-x + 2y = 5$ ——Ⓛ ← The <u>linear</u> equation — with only x's and y's in.
 $x^2 + y^2 = 25$ ——Ⓠ ← The <u>quadratic</u> equation — with some x^2 and y^2 bits in.

Rearrange the <u>linear equation</u> so that either x or y is on its own on one side of the equals sign.

Ⓛ $-x + 2y = 5$
$\Rightarrow x = 2y - 5$

Substitute this expression into the <u>quadratic equation</u>...

Sub into Ⓠ: $x^2 + y^2 = 25$
$\Rightarrow (2y - 5)^2 + y^2 = 25$

...and then rearrange this into the form $ax^2 + bx + c = 0$, so you can solve it — either by <u>factorising</u> or using the <u>quadratic formula</u>.

$\Rightarrow (4y^2 - 20y + 25) + y^2 = 25$
$\Rightarrow 5y^2 - 20y = 0$
$\Rightarrow 5y(y - 4) = 0$
$\Rightarrow y = 0$ or $y = 4$

One Quadratic and One Linear Eqn

1) **Isolate variable in linear equation**
   Rearrange the linear equation
   to get either x or y on its own.

2) **Substitute into quadratic equation**
   — to get a quadratic equation
   in just one variable.

3) **Solve to get values for one variable**
   — either by factorising or using
   the quadratic formula.

4) **Stick these values in the linear equation**
   — to find corresponding values
   for the other variable.

Finally put both these values back into the <u>linear equation</u> to find corresponding values for x:

When $y = 0$: $-x + 2y = 5$ Ⓛ
 $\Rightarrow x = -5$

When $y = 4$: $-x + 2y = 5$ Ⓛ
 $\Rightarrow -x + 8 = 5$
 $\Rightarrow x = 3$

So the solutions to the simultaneous equations are: $x = -5$, $y = 0$ and $x = 3$, $y = 4$.

As usual, <u>check your answers</u> by putting these values back into the original equations.

Check Your Answer

$x = -5$, $y = 0$: $-(-5) + 2 \times 0 = 5$ ✓
$ (-5)^2 + 0^2 = 25$ ✓

$x = 3$, $y = 4$: $-(3) + 2 \times 4 = 5$ ✓
$ 3^2 + 4^2 = 25$ ✓

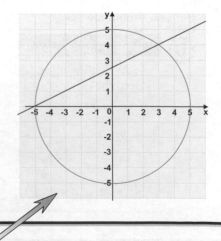

$y = x^2$ — a match-winning substitution...

The quadratic equation above is actually a <u>circle</u> about the origin with radius 5. (There's plenty more about circles on pages 35 and 36) The linear equation is just a standard straight line. So what you're actually finding here are the two points where the line passes through the circle. And these turn out to be (–5, 0) and (3, 4). See the graph. (I thought you might appreciate seeing a graph that wasn't a line or a parabola for a change.)

Geometric Interpretation

When you have to interpret something <u>geometrically</u>, you have to draw a picture to show what's going on.

Two Solutions — Two points of Intersection

EXAMPLE

$$y = x^2 - 4x + 5 \quad \textcircled{1}$$
$$y = 2x - 3 \quad \textcircled{2}$$

Geometric Interpretation

So from solving the simultaneous equations, you know that the graphs meet in <u>two places</u> — the points (2, 1) and (4, 5).

SOLUTION

Substitute expression for y from $\textcircled{2}$ into $\textcircled{1}$:

$$2x - 3 = x^2 - 4x + 5$$

Rearrange and solve:

$$x^2 - 6x + 8 = 0$$
$$(x - 2)(x - 4) = 0$$
$$x = 2 \text{ or } x = 4$$

In $\textcircled{2}$ gives:

$$x = 2 \Rightarrow y = 2 \times 2 - 3 = 1$$
$$x = 4 \Rightarrow y = 2 \times 4 - 3 = 5$$

There are 2 pairs of solutions: $x = 2$, $y = 1$ and $x = 4$, $y = 5$

One Solution — One point of Intersection

EXAMPLE

$$y = x^2 - 4x + 5 \quad \textcircled{1}$$
$$y = 2x - 4 \quad \textcircled{2}$$

Geometric Interpretation

Since the equations have only one solution, the two graphs only meet at one point — (3, 2). The straight line is a <u>tangent</u> to the curve.

SOLUTION

Substitute $\textcircled{2}$ in $\textcircled{1}$:

$$2x - 4 = x^2 - 4x + 5$$

Rearrange and solve:

$$x^2 - 6x + 9 = 0$$
$$(x - 3)^2 = 0$$
$$x = 3$$

Double root — i.e. you only get 1 solution from the quadratic.

In Equation $\textcircled{2}$ gives:

$$y = 2 \times 3 - 4$$
$$y = 2$$

There's 1 solution: $x = 3$, $y = 2$

No Solutions means the Graphs Never Meet

EXAMPLE

$$y = x^2 - 4x + 5 \quad \textcircled{1}$$
$$y = 2x - 5 \quad \textcircled{2}$$

Geometric Interpretation

The equations have no solutions — the graphs never meet.

SOLUTION

Substitute $\textcircled{2}$ in $\textcircled{1}$:

$$2x - 5 = x^2 - 4x + 5$$

Rearrange and try to solve with the quadratic formula:

$$x^2 - 6x + 10 = 0$$
$$b^2 - 4ac = (-6)^2 - 4 \cdot 10$$
$$= 36 - 40 = -4$$

$b^2 - 4ac < 0$, so the quadratic has no roots.
So the simultaneous equations have no solutions.

Geometric Interpretation? Frankly my dear, I don't give a damn...

This stuff also works the other way round. If you're given the graphs of two equations, then the points where they intersect are the solutions to the simultaneous equations — which is pretty handy 'cos then you can avoid doing lots of algebra. Nice.

C1 Section 3 — Practice Questions

What's that I hear you cry? You want practice questions — and lots of them. Well, it just so happens I've got a few here. For quadratic inequalities, my advice is, 'if you're not sure, draw a picture — even if it's not accurate'. And as for simultaneous equations — well, just don't rush them.

Warm-up Questions

1) Solve a) $7x - 4 > 2x - 42$,   b) $12y - 3 \leq 4y + 4$,   c) $9y - 4 \geq 17y + 2$.

2) Find the ranges of x that satisfy these inequalities:
     a) $x + 6 < 5x - 4$,   b) $4x - 2 > x - 14$,   c) $7 - x \leq 4 - 2x$

3) Find the ranges of x that satisfy the following inequalities. (And watch that you use the right kind of inequality sign in your answers.)
     a) $3x^2 - 5x - 2 \leq 0$,   b) $x^2 + 2x + 7 > 4x + 9$,   c) $3x^2 + 7x + 4 \geq 2(x^2 + x - 1)$.

4) Find the ranges of x that satisfy these jokers:
     a) $x^2 + 3x - 1 \geq x + 2$,   b) $2x^2 > x + 1$,   c) $3x^2 - 12 < x^2 - 2x$

5) Solve these sets of simultaneous equations:
     a) $3x - 4y = 7$ and $-2x + 7y = -22$,   b) $2x - 3y = \frac{11}{12}$ and $x + y = -\frac{7}{12}$

6) Find where possible (and that's a bit of a clue) the solutions to these sets of simultaneous equations. Interpret your answers geometrically.
     a) $y = x^2 - 7x + 4$ b) $y = 30 - 6x + 2x^2$ c) $x^2 + 2y^2 - 3 = 0$
         $2x - y - 10 = 0$ $y = 2(x + 11)$ $y = 2x + 4$

7) A bit trickier — find where the following lines meet:
     a) $y = 3x - 4$ and $y = 7x - 5$
     b) $y = 13 - 2x$ and $7x - y - 23 = 0$
     c) $2x - 3y + 4 = 0$ and $x - 2y + 1 = 0$

I know, I know. Those questions weren't enough for you. Not to worry, there are plenty more — and the next set are exam-style questions. Try to contain your excitement.

Exam Questions

1   For the inequalities below, find the set of values for x:

     a) $3x + 2 \leq x + 6$,

(2 marks)

     b) $20 - x - x^2 > 0$,

(4 marks)

     c) $3x + 2 \leq x + 6$ and $20 - x - x^2 > 0$.

(1 mark)

C1 Section 3 — Practice Questions

The world is full of inequality and injustice. We need to <u>put a stop to it now</u>. The first thing we need to do is...
Oh, sorry, that's not what they meant by "solve the inequality". And I'd just come up with a solution for world peace.

2   Solve the inequalities:

    a) $3 \leq 2p + 5 \leq 15$,

(3 marks)

    b) $q^2 - 9 > 0$.

(4 marks)

3   a)   Factorise $3x^2 - 13x - 10$.

(1 mark)

    b)   Hence, or otherwise, solve $3x^2 - 13x - 10 \leq 0$.

(3 marks)

4   Find the coordinates of intersection for the following curve and line:
$$x^2 + 2y^2 = 36, \quad x + y = 6$$

(6 marks)

5   The curve C has equation $y = -x^2 + 3$ and the line l has equation $y = -2x + 4$.

    a)   Find the coordinates of the point (or points) of intersection of C and l.

(4 marks)

    b)   Sketch the graphs of C and l on the same axes, clearly showing
    where the graphs intersect the x- and y- axcs.

(5 marks)

6   The line l has equation $y = 2x - 3$ and the curve C has equation $y = (x + 2)(x - 4)$.

    a)   Sketch the line l and the curve C on the same axes, showing the coordinates
    of the x- and y- intercepts.

(5 marks)

    b)   Show that the x-coordinates of the points of intersection of l and C satisfy the equation
    $x^2 - 4x - 5 = 0$.

(2 marks)

    c)   Hence, or otherwise, find the points of intersection of l and C.

(4 marks)

Coordinate Geometry

Welcome to geometry club... nice — today I shall be mostly talking about straight lines...

Finding the equation of a line Through Two Points

If you get through your exam without having to find the equation of a line through two points, I'm a Dutchman.

EXAMPLE Find the equation of the line that passes through the points (–3, 10) and (1, 4), and write it in the forms:

$$y - y_1 = m(x - x_1)$$

$$y = mx + c$$

$$ax + by + c = 0$$

— where a, b and c are <u>integers</u>.

You might be asked to write the equation of a line in <u>any</u> of these forms — but they're all similar.
Basically, if you find an equation in one form — you can easily <u>convert</u> it into either of the others.

The **Easiest** to find is $y - y_1 = m(x - x_1)$...

To sketch a line from its equation, just plug in a couple of x-values, use the y-values that you get to plot two points, and draw a line through them. Piece of cake.

Point 1 is (–3, 10) and Point 2 is (1, 4).

Label the Points Label Point 1 as (x_1, y_1) and Point 2 as (x_2, y_2).

Point 1 — $(x_1, y_1) = (-3, 10)$

Point 2 — $(x_2, y_2) = (1, 4)$

It doesn't matter which way round you label them.

Find the Gradient Find the <u>gradient</u> of the line m — this is $m = \frac{y_2 - y_1}{x_2 - x_1}$.

$$m = \frac{4 - 10}{1 - (-3)} = \frac{-6}{4} = -\frac{3}{2}$$

Be careful here, y goes on the top, x on the bottom.

Write Down the Equation <u>Write down</u> the equation of the line, using the coordinates x_1 and y_1 — this is just $y - y_1 = m(x - x_1)$.

$x_1 = -3$ and $y_1 = 10$ ⟹

$$y - 10 = -\frac{3}{2}(x - (-3))$$

$$y - 10 = -\frac{3}{2}(x + 3)$$

...and **Rearrange** this to get the other two forms:

For the form $y = mx + c$, take everything except the y over to the right.

$$y - 10 = -\frac{3}{2}(x + 3)$$

$$\Rightarrow y = -\frac{3}{2}x - \frac{9}{2} + 10$$

$$\Rightarrow y = -\frac{3}{2}x + \frac{11}{2}$$

To find the form $ax + by + c = 0$, take everything over to one side — and then get rid of any fractions.

Multiply the whole equation by 2 to get rid of the 2's on the bottom line.

$$y = -\frac{3}{2}x + \frac{11}{2}$$

$$\Rightarrow \frac{3}{2}x + y - \frac{11}{2} = 0$$

$$\Rightarrow 3x + 2y - 11 = 0$$

Equations of Lines

1) **LABEL** the points (x_1, y_1) and (x_2, y_2).

2) **GRADIENT** — find it and call it m.

3) **WRITE DOWN THE EQUATION** using $y - y_1 = m(x - x_1)$

4) **CONVERT** to one of the other forms, if necessary.

If you end up with an equation like $\frac{3}{2}x - \frac{4}{3}y + 6 = 0$, where you've got a 2 and a 3 on the bottom of the fractions — multiply everything by the <u>lowest common multiple</u> of 2 and 3, i.e. 6.

There ain't nuffink to this geometry lark, Mister...

This is the sort of stuff that looks hard but is actually pretty easy. Finding the equation of a line in that first form really is a piece of cake — the only thing you have to be careful of is when a point has a <u>negative coordinate</u> (or two). In that case, you've just got to make sure you do the subtractions properly when you work out the gradient. See, this stuff ain't so bad...

Coordinate Geometry

This page is based around two really important facts that you've got to know — one about <u>parallel lines</u>, one about <u>perpendicular lines</u>. It's really a page of unparalleled excitement...

Two more lines...

Line l_1
$3x - 4y - 7 = 0$
$y = \frac{3}{4}x - \frac{7}{4}$

Line l_2
$x - 3y - 3 = 0$
$y = \frac{1}{3}x - 1$

...and two points...

Point A (3, –1)

Point B (–2, 4)

Parallel lines have equal Gradient

That's what makes them parallel — the fact that the gradients are the same.

EXAMPLE Find the line parallel to l_1 that passes through the point A (3, –1).

Parallel lines have the <u>same gradient</u>.

The original equation is this: $y = \frac{3}{4}x - \frac{7}{4}$

So the new equation will be this: $y = \frac{3}{4}x + c$

We just need to find c.

We know that the line passes through A, so at this point x will be 3, and y will be –1.

Stick these values into the equation to find c.

$-1 = \frac{3}{4} \times 3 + c$

$\Rightarrow c = -1 - \frac{9}{4} = -\frac{13}{4}$

So the equation of the line is... $y = \frac{3}{4}x - \frac{13}{4}$

And if you're only given the $ax + by + c = 0$ form it's even easier:

The <u>original</u> line is: $3x - 4y - 7 = 0$

So the <u>new</u> line is: $3x - 4y - k = 0$

Then just use the values of x and y at the point A to find k...

$3 \times 3 - 4 \times (-1) - k = 0$

$\Rightarrow 13 - k = 0$

$\Rightarrow k = 13$

So the equation is: $3x - 4y - 13 = 0$

The gradient of a Perpendicular line is: –1 ÷ the Other Gradient

Finding <u>perpendicular</u> lines (or '<u>normals</u>') is just as easy as finding parallel lines — as long as you remember the gradient of the perpendicular line is <u>–1 ÷ the gradient of the other one</u>.

EXAMPLE Find the line perpendicular to l_2 that passes through the point B (–2, 4).

l_2 has equation: $y = \frac{1}{3}x - 1$

So if the equation of the new line is $y = mx + c$, then

$m = -1 \div \frac{1}{3}$

$\Rightarrow m = -3$

Since the gradient of a perpendicular line is: –1 ÷ the other one.

Also... $4 = (-3) \times (-2) + c$

$\Rightarrow c = 4 - 6 = -2$

Putting the coordinates of B(–2, 4) into $y = mx + c$.

So the equation of the line is...

$y = -3x - 2$

Or if you start with: l_2 $x - 3y - 3 = 0$

To find a perpendicular line, swap these two numbers around, and change the sign of <u>one of them</u>. (So here, 1 and –3 become 3 and 1.)

So the new line has equation...

$3x + y + d = 0$

Or you could have used $-3x - y + d = 0$.

But... $3 \times (-2) + 4 + d = 0$

$\Rightarrow d = 2$

Using the coordinates of point B.

And so the equation of the <u>perpendicular</u> line is...

$3x + y + 2 = 0$

Wowzers — parallel lines on the same graph dimension...

This looks more complicated than it actually is. All you're doing is finding the equation of a straight line through a <u>certain point</u> — the only added complication is that you have to find the gradient first. And there's another way to remember how to find the gradient of a normal — just remember that the gradients of perpendicular lines multiply together to make –1.

Equations of Straight Lines

Once you've got your straight line segment, you're probably going to want to do all sorts of cool stuff — like find its length, or the coordinates of its mid-point. Luckily for you, this page tells you exactly how to do that...

Find the **Mid-Point** by Finding the **Average** of the **End Points**

In the exam you could be asked to find the mid-point of a line segment.
To do this, just <u>add</u> the coordinates of the end-points of the line segment together, then <u>divide by two</u>:

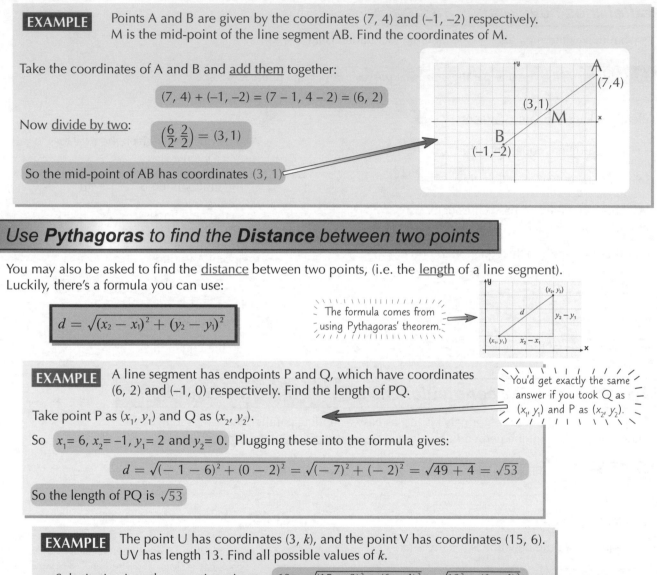

EXAMPLE Points A and B are given by the coordinates (7, 4) and (–1, –2) respectively. M is the mid-point of the line segment AB. Find the coordinates of M.

Take the coordinates of A and B and <u>add them</u> together:

$$(7, 4) + (-1, -2) = (7 - 1, 4 - 2) = (6, 2)$$

Now <u>divide by two</u>: $\left(\frac{6}{2}, \frac{2}{2}\right) = (3, 1)$

So the mid-point of AB has coordinates (3, 1)

Use **Pythagoras** to find the **Distance** between two points

You may also be asked to find the <u>distance</u> between two points, (i.e. the <u>length</u> of a line segment). Luckily, there's a formula you can use:

$$d = \sqrt{(x_2 - x_1)^2 + (y_2 - y_1)^2}$$

The formula comes from using Pythagoras' theorem.

EXAMPLE A line segment has endpoints P and Q, which have coordinates (6, 2) and (–1, 0) respectively. Find the length of PQ.

You'd get exactly the same answer if you took Q as (x_1, y_1) and P as (x_2, y_2).

Take point P as (x_1, y_1) and Q as (x_2, y_2).

So $x_1 = 6, x_2 = -1, y_1 = 2$ and $y_2 = 0$. Plugging these into the formula gives:

$$d = \sqrt{(-1 - 6)^2 + (0 - 2)^2} = \sqrt{(-7)^2 + (-2)^2} = \sqrt{49 + 4} = \sqrt{53}$$

So the length of PQ is $\sqrt{53}$

EXAMPLE The point U has coordinates (3, k), and the point V has coordinates (15, 6). UV has length 13. Find all possible values of k.

Substituting into the equation gives: $13 = \sqrt{(15 - 3)^2 + (6 - k)^2} = \sqrt{12^2 + (6 - k)^2}$

Squaring both sides:

$13^2 = 12^2 + (6 - k)^2$

$169 = 144 + (6 - k)^2$

$25 = (6 - k)^2$

$25 = 36 - 12k + k^2$

$k^2 - 12k + 11 = 0$

$(k - 1)(k - 11) = 0$ So $k = 1$ or $k = 11$

You could take square roots at this stage instead: $\pm 5 = 6 - k$ and so $k = 1$ or $k = 11$. It's up to you.

CGP — Coordinate Geometry Practitioners...

As long as you know how to add, subtract, square and square root then you should be fine with the stuff on this page. If not, then you could always try drawing the line and measuring it with a ruler — although it probably won't get you the right answer. Or any marks. Actually, you're best off steering clear of that method altogether.

Curve Sketching

A picture speaks a thousand words... and <u>graphs</u> are what pass for pictures in maths. They're dead useful for getting your head round tricky questions, and time spent learning how to sketch graphs is time well spent.

The graph of $y = kx^n$ is a different shape for different k and n

Usually, you only need a <u>rough</u> sketch of a graph — so just knowing the basic shapes of these graphs will do.

Don't confuse <u>sketching</u> with <u>plotting</u> — they're totally different beasts. We're only really interested about the shape of the curve and where it crosses the axes here, not working out every exact point that the graph passes through.

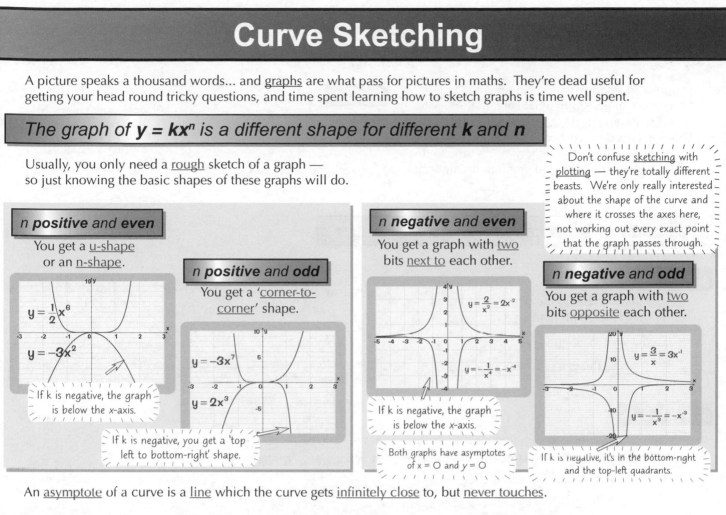

n *positive* and *even*

You get a <u>u-shape</u> or an <u>n-shape</u>.

$y = \frac{1}{2}x^6$

$y = -3x^2$

If k is negative, the graph is below the x-axis.

n *positive* and *odd*

You get a 'corner-to-corner' shape.

$y = -3x^7$

$y = 2x^3$

If k is negative, you get a 'top left to bottom-right' shape.

n *negative* and *even*

You get a graph with <u>two</u> bits <u>next to</u> each other.

$y = \frac{2}{x^2} = 2x^{-2}$

$y = -\frac{1}{x^4} = -x^{-4}$

If k is negative, the graph is below the x-axis.

Both graphs have asymptotes of $x = 0$ and $y = 0$

n *negative* and *odd*

You get a graph with <u>two</u> bits <u>opposite</u> each other.

$y = \frac{3}{x} = 3x^{-1}$

$y = -\frac{1}{x^3} = -x^{-3}$

If k is negative, it's in the bottom-right and the top-left quadrants.

An <u>asymptote</u> of a curve is a <u>line</u> which the curve gets <u>infinitely close</u> to, but <u>never touches</u>.

If you know the **Factors** of a cubic — the graph's easy to **Sketch**

A cubic function has an x^3 term in it, and all cubics have '<u>bottom-left to top-right</u>' shape — or a '<u>top-left to bottom-right</u>' shape if the coefficient of x^3 is <u>negative</u>.

If you know the <u>factors</u> of a cubic, the graph is easy to sketch — just find where the function is <u>zero</u>.

EXAMPLE Sketch the graphs of the following <u>cubic</u> functions.

(i) $f(x) = x(x-1)(2x+1)$ (ii) $g(x) = (1-x)(x^2-2x+2)$ (iii) $h(x) = (x-3)^2(x+1)$ (iv) $m(x) = (2-x)^3$

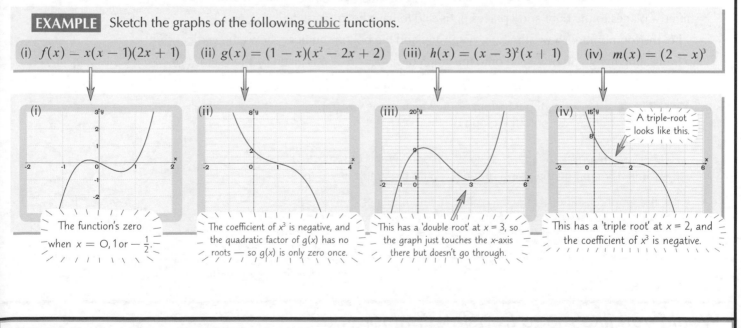

(i) The function's zero when $x = 0, 1$ or $-\frac{1}{2}$.

(ii) The coefficient of x^3 is negative, and the quadratic factor of $g(x)$ has no roots — so $g(x)$ is only zero once.

(iii) This has a 'double root' at $x = 3$, so the graph just touches the x-axis there but doesn't go through.

(iv) A triple-root looks like this.

This has a 'triple root' at $x = 2$, and the coefficient of x^3 is negative.

Graphs, graphs, graphs — you can never have too many graphs...

It may seem like a lot to remember, but graphs can really help you get your head round a question — a quick sketch can throw a helluva lot of light on a problem that's got you completely stumped. So being able to draw these graphs won't just help with an actual graph-sketching question — it could help with loads of others too. Got to be worth learning.

Graph Transformations

Suppose you start with any old function $f(x)$. Then you can transform (change) it in three ways — by translating it, stretching or reflecting it. You don't need to worry about stretches or reflections until C2, but right now, it's time to dive into the wonderful world of graph translations...

$y = f(x)$

I'll use this graph of $y = f(x)$ as an example, where $f(x) = x(x + 2)(x − 2)$, i.e. $f(x) = x^3 − 4x$.

Translations are caused by Adding things

$y = f(x) + a$

Adding a number to the whole function translates the graph in the y-direction.

1) If $a > 0$, the graph goes upwards.

2) If $a < 0$, the graph goes downwards.

The green graph is $y = x(x + 2)(x − 2) + 2$, i.e. $y = x^3 − 4x + 2$.

The blue graph is $y = x(x + 2)(x − 2) − 4$, i.e. $y = x^3 − 4x − 4$.

$y = f(x + a)$

Writing '$x + a$' instead of 'x' means the graph moves sideways ("translated in the x-direction").

1) If $a > 0$, the graph goes to the left.

2) If $a < 0$, the graph goes to the right.

The green graph is $y = (x − 1)^3 − 4(x − 1)$, i.e. $y = x^3 − 3x^2 − x + 3$.

The blue graph is $y = (x + 2)^3 − 4(x + 2)$, i.e. $y = x^3 + 6x^2 + 8x$.

Translations can be written as Column Vectors

The top number is called the horizontal component and the bottom number is called the vertical component.

In the exam you might be given a translation in vector form. A graph which has been shifted k places to the right and l places up is said to have been translated through $\binom{k}{l}$ 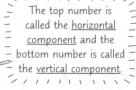 — i.e. the top number shows the horizontal shift and the bottom number shows the vertical shift.

So translating the graph of $y = f(x)$ onto the graph of $y = f(x − a) + b$ is given by the vector $\binom{a}{b}$.

EXAMPLE Describe the transformation which maps the graph of $y = x^2$ onto the graph of $y = (x − 1)^2 − 4$.

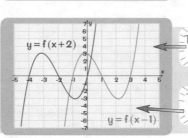

$f(x) = x^2$, so mapping the graph of $y = x^2$ onto the graph of $y = (x − 1)^2 − 4$ is the same as mapping the graph of $y = f(x)$ onto the graph of $y = f(x − 1) − 4$.

i.e. the graph is shifted 1 place to the right and 4 places downwards.

So the graph has been translated through $\binom{1}{−4}$.

If the graph moves to the left, then the top number in the vector will be negative. Similarly, if the graph moves down, then the bottom number will negative.

Would you like me to translate that for you?

The trickiest part of this stuff is getting the positives and negatives right. For the translation $y = f(x + a)$, if a is positive, then the graph moves to the left, which means the horizontal component of the column vector will be negative. On the other hand, for the translation $y = f(x) + b$, if b is positive, then the graph moves upwards, and so the vertical component of the column vector will also be positive. It's not too difficult, but it's easy to get wrong, so don't rush in there all guns blazing.

Circles

I always say a <u>beautiful shape</u> deserves a <u>beautiful formula</u>, and here you've got one of my favourite double-acts...

Equation of a circle: $(x - a)^2 + (y - b)^2 = r^2$

The equation of a circle looks complicated, but it's all based on Pythagoras' theorem.
Take a look at the circle below, with centre (6, 4) and radius 3.

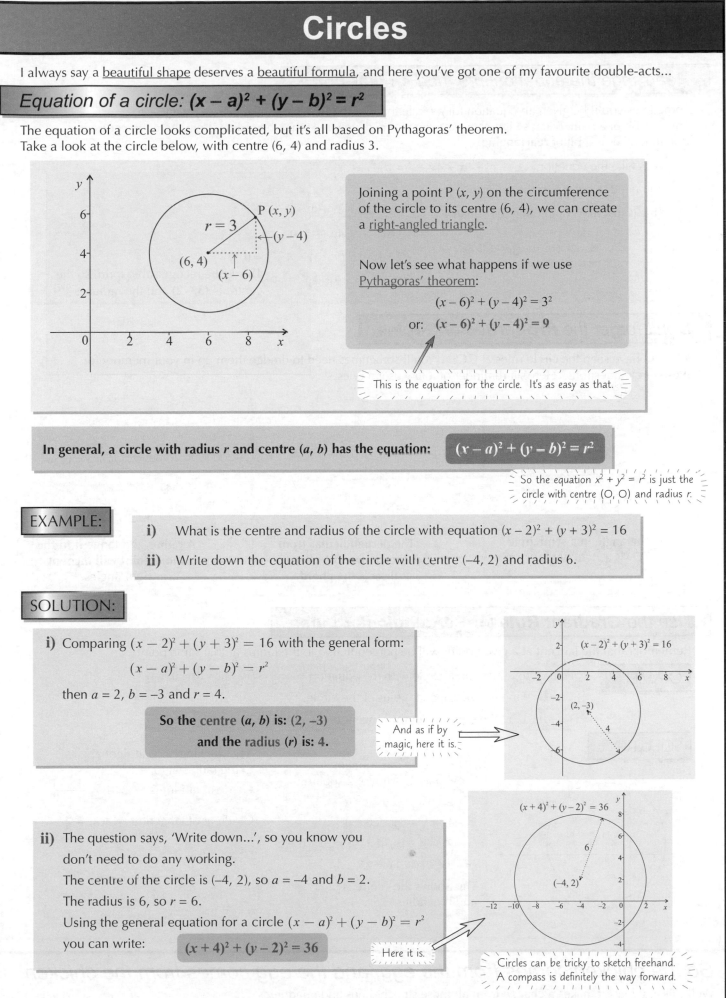

Joining a point P (x, y) on the circumference of the circle to its centre (6, 4), we can create a <u>right-angled triangle</u>.

Now let's see what happens if we use <u>Pythagoras' theorem</u>:

$$(x - 6)^2 + (y - 4)^2 = 3^2$$

or: $(x - 6)^2 + (y - 4)^2 = 9$

This is the equation for the circle. It's as easy as that.

In general, a circle with radius r and centre (a, b) has the equation: $\quad (x - a)^2 + (y - b)^2 = r^2$

So the equation $x^2 + y^2 = r^2$ is just the circle with centre (O, O) and radius r.

EXAMPLE:

i) What is the centre and radius of the circle with equation $(x - 2)^2 + (y + 3)^2 = 16$

ii) Write down the equation of the circle with centre (−4, 2) and radius 6.

SOLUTION:

i) Comparing $(x - 2)^2 + (y + 3)^2 = 16$ with the general form:

$$(x - a)^2 + (y - b)^2 = r^2$$

then $a = 2$, $b = -3$ and $r = 4$.

> So the **centre** (a, b) is: **(2, −3)**
> and the **radius** (r) is: **4.**

And as if by magic, here it is.

$(x - 2)^2 + (y + 3)^2 = 16$

$(2, -3)$

ii) The question says, 'Write down...', so you know you don't need to do any working.

The centre of the circle is (−4, 2), so $a = -4$ and $b = 2$.

The radius is 6, so $r = 6$.

Using the general equation for a circle $(x - a)^2 + (y - b)^2 = r^2$ you can write: $\quad (x + 4)^2 + (y - 2)^2 = 36$

Here it is.

$(x + 4)^2 + (y - 2)^2 = 36$

$(-4, 2)$

Circles can be tricky to sketch freehand. A compass is definitely the way forward.

This is pretty much all you need to learn. Everything on the next page uses stuff you should know already.

Circles

Rearrange the equation into the Familiar Form

Sometimes you'll be given an equation for a circle that doesn't look much like $(x - a)^2 + (y - b)^2 = r^2$.
This is a bit of a pain, because it means you can't immediately tell what the **radius** is or where the **centre** is.
But all it takes is a bit of **rearranging**.

Let's take the equation: $x^2 + y^2 - 6x + 4y + 4 = 0$

You need to get it into the form $(x - a)^2 + (y - b)^2 = r^2$.

This is just like completing the square.

> Have a look at pages 14-15 for more on completing the square.

$$x^2 + y^2 - 6x + 4y + 4 = 0$$
$$x^2 - 6x + y^2 + 4y + 4 = 0$$
$$(x - 3)^2 - 9 + (y + 2)^2 - 4 + 4 = 0$$
$$(x - 3)^2 + (y + 2)^2 = 9 \implies$$

This is the recognisable form, so the centre is **(3, –2)** and the radius is $\sqrt{9} = $ **3**.

Don't forget the Properties of Circles

You will have seen the circle rules at GCSE. You'll sometimes need to dredge them up in your memory for these circle questions. Here's a reminder of a few useful ones.

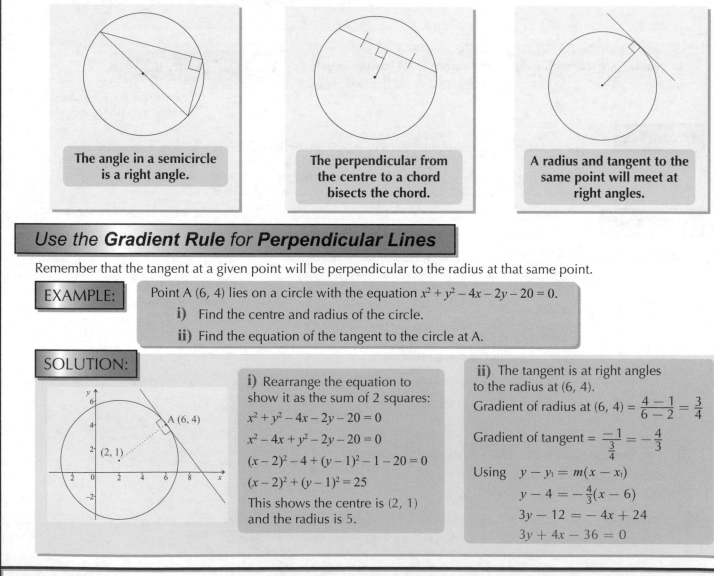

The angle in a semicircle is a right angle.

The perpendicular from the centre to a chord bisects the chord.

A radius and tangent to the same point will meet at right angles.

Use the Gradient Rule for Perpendicular Lines

Remember that the tangent at a given point will be perpendicular to the radius at that same point.

EXAMPLE:
Point A (6, 4) lies on a circle with the equation $x^2 + y^2 - 4x - 2y - 20 = 0$.
  i) Find the centre and radius of the circle.
  ii) Find the equation of the tangent to the circle at A.

SOLUTION:

i) Rearrange the equation to show it as the sum of 2 squares:
$$x^2 + y^2 - 4x - 2y - 20 = 0$$
$$x^2 - 4x + y^2 - 2y - 20 = 0$$
$$(x - 2)^2 - 4 + (y - 1)^2 - 1 - 20 = 0$$
$$(x - 2)^2 + (y - 1)^2 = 25$$
This shows the centre is (2, 1) and the radius is 5.

ii) The tangent is at right angles to the radius at (6, 4).
Gradient of radius at (6, 4) $= \dfrac{4 - 1}{6 - 2} = \dfrac{3}{4}$

Gradient of tangent $= \dfrac{-1}{\frac{3}{4}} = -\dfrac{4}{3}$

Using $y - y_1 = m(x - x_1)$
$$y - 4 = -\tfrac{4}{3}(x - 6)$$
$$3y - 12 = -4x + 24$$
$$3y + 4x - 36 = 0$$

So the chicken comes from the egg, and the egg comes from the chicken...

Well folks, at least it makes a change from all those straight lines and quadratics.
I reckon if you know the **formula** and **what it means**, you should be absolutely **fine** with questions on circles.

C1 Section 4 — Practice Questions

There you go then... a section on <u>various geometrical things</u>. And in a way it was quite exciting, I'm sure you'll agree. Though as you're probably aware, we mathematicians take our excitement from wherever we can get it. Anyway, I'll leave you alone now to <u>savour</u> these practice questions. <u>Don't skip the warm-up</u> — you don't want to hurt yourself...

Warm-up Questions

1) Find the <u>equations</u> of the <u>straight lines</u> that pass through the points

   a) $(2, -1)$ and $(-4, -19)$,   b) $\left(0, -\frac{1}{3}\right)$ and $\left(5, \frac{2}{3}\right)$.

   Write each of them in the forms
   (i) $y - y_1 = m(x - x_1)$,
   (ii) $y = mx + c$,
   (iii) $ax + by + c = 0$, where a, b and c are integers.

2) a) The line l has equation $y = \frac{3}{2}x - \frac{2}{3}$. Find the equation of the lovely, cuddly line <u>parallel to l</u>, passing through the point with coordinates $(4, 2)$. Name this line <u>Lilly</u>.

   b) The line m (whose name is actually Mike) passes through the point $(6, 1)$ and is <u>perpendicular</u> to $2x - y - 7 = 0$. What is the equation of m?

3) The coordinates of points R and S are $(1, 9)$ and $(10, 3)$ respectively. Find the equation of the line <u>perpendicular</u> to RS, passing through the point $(1, 9)$.

4) Point A has coordinates $(2, 5)$ and point B has coordinates $(12, -1)$.
   M is the mid-point of the line segment AB. Find:

   a) The coordinates of M,

   b) The length of AM, leaving your answer in surd form.

5) It's lovely, lovely <u>curve-sketching time</u> — so draw rough sketches of the following curves:
   a) $y = -2x^4$,   b) $y = \frac{1}{x^2}$,   c) $y = -5x^3$,   d) $y = -\frac{2}{x^5}$.

6) Admit it — you <u>love</u> curve-sketching. We all do — and like me, you probably can't get enough of it. So more power to your elbow, and sketch these <u>cubic graphs</u>:

   a) $y = (x - 4)^3$,   b) $y = (3 - x)(x + 2)^2$,

   c) $y = (1 - x)(x^2 - 6x + 8)$,   d) $y = (x - 1)(x - 2)(x - 3)$.

7) Right — now it's time to get serious. Put your <u>thinking head on</u>, and use the graph of $f(x)$ to sketch what these graphs would look like after they've been '<u>transformed</u>'. Also give the vectors which describe the transformation.

   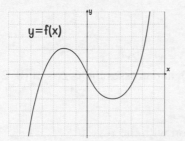

   a) (i) $y = f(x + a)$,

       (ii) $y = f(x - a)$,   where $a > 0$,

   b) (i) $y = f(x) + a$,

       (ii) $y = f(x) - a$,   where $a > 0$.

8) Give the radius and the coordinates of the centre of the circles with the following equations:
   a) $x^2 + y^2 = 9$ b) $(x - 2)^2 + (y + 4)^2 = 4$ c) $x(x + 6) = y(8 - y)$

C1 Section 4 — Practice Questions

The excitement continues on this page, with a <u>thrilling selection</u> of the finest exam questions <u>money can buy</u>. If you're asked to sketch a graph in your exam, it's worth taking a bit of time. They won't expect your graph to be <u>100% accurate</u>, but just make sure you've got the <u>general shape</u> right and that it crosses the axes in the <u>right places</u>.

Exam Questions

1 The line PQ has equation $4x + 3y = 15$.

a) Find the gradient of PQ.

(2 marks)

b) The point R lies on PQ and has coordinates $(3, 1)$. Find the equation of the line which passes through the point R and is perpendicular to PQ, giving your answer in the form $y = mx + c$. *(3 marks)*

2 The curve C has the equation

$$y = (2x + 1)(x - 2)^2.$$

Sketch C, clearly showing the points at which the curve meets the x- and y- axes.

(4 marks)

3

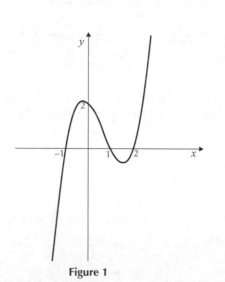

Figure 1

Figure 1 shows a sketch of the function $y = f(x)$, where $f(x) = x^3 - 2x^2 - x + 2$. The function crosses the x-axis at $(-1, 0)$, $(1, 0)$ and $(2, 0)$, and crosses the y-axis at $(0, 2)$.

On separate diagrams, sketch the following:

a) $y = f(x - 4)$, clearly labelling any points of intersection with the x-axis,

(2 marks)

b) $y = f(x) - 2$, clearly labelling any points of intersection with the y-axis.

(2 marks)

C1 Section 4 — Practice Questions

Worry ye not, I'm not going to leave you wanting more — here are a few
more exam questions for you to sink your teeth into.

4   a)   Sketch the curve $y = f(x)$, where $f(x) = x^2 - 4$, showing clearly the points of intersection
            with the x- and y- axes.

(2 marks)

     b)   Describe fully the transformation that transforms the curve $y = f(x)$ to the curve $y = f(x + 2)$.

(1 marks)

     c)   The curve $y = f(x)$ is translated vertically two units upwards. State the vector that describes
            this transformation and give the equation of the curve after it has been transformed, in the
            form $y = x^2 + ax + b$, where a and b are constants to be determined.

(2 marks)

5   The line l passes through the point $S\,(7, -3)$ and has gradient -2.

     a)   Find an equation of l, giving your answer in the form $y = mx + c$.

(3 marks)

     b)   The point T has coordinates $(5, 1)$. Show that T lies on l.

(1 mark)

6

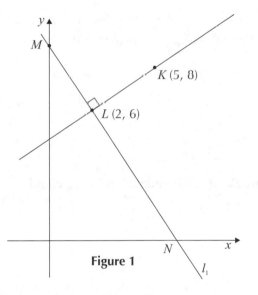

Figure 1

The points L and K have coordinates $(2, 6)$ and $(5, 8)$ respectively. The line l_1 passes through the point L
and is perpendicular to the line LK, as shown in **Figure 1**.

     a)   Find an equation for l_1 in the form $ax + by + c = 0$, where a, b, and c are integers.

(4 marks)

The line l_1 intersects the y-axis at the point M and the x-axis at the point N.

     b)   Find the coordinates of M.

(2 marks)

     c)   Find the coordinates of N.

(2 marks)

C1 Section 4 — Practice Questions

Yet more questions. You lucky, lucky people.

7   The line PQ satisfies the equation $2x - 14y + 6 = 0$.
Points P and Q have coordinates $(-3, 0)$ and $(k, 1)$ respectively.

   a)   Find the value of k.

   (2 marks)

   b)   Find the length of PQ, leaving your answer in surd form.

   (3 marks)

   c)   Find the equation of the line through Q which is parallel to the
        line $2x + y + 5 = 0$.

   (3 marks)

8   C is a circle with the equation: $x^2 + y^2 - 2x - 10y + 21 = 0$.

   a)   Find the centre and radius of C.

   (5 marks)

   The line joining $P(3, 6)$ and $Q(q, 4)$ is a diameter of C.

   b)   Show that $q = -1$.

   (3 marks)

   c)   Find the equation of the tangent to C at Q, giving your answer in the form $ax + by + c = 0$, where
        a, b and c are integers.

   (5 marks)

9   The diagram shows a circle C, with centre P. M is the midpoint of AB, a chord.

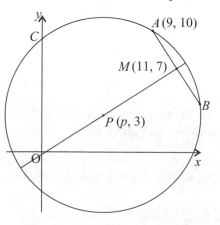

   a)   Show that $p = 5$.

   (5 marks)

   b)   Find the equation of circle C.

   (4 marks)

Factorising Cubics

Factorising a quadratic function is okay — but you might also be asked to <u>factorise a cubic</u> (something with x^3 in it). And that takes a bit more time — there are more steps, so there are more chances to make mistakes.

Factorising a cubic given **One Factor**

$$f(x) = 2x^3 + x^2 - 8x - 4$$

Factorising a cubic means exactly what it meant with a quadratic — putting brackets in.
When they ask you to factorise a cubic equation, they'll usually tell you one of the factors.

> **EXAMPLE**   Given that $(x+2)$ is a factor of $f(x) = 2x^3 + x^2 - 8x - 4$, express $f(x)$ as the product of three linear factors.

① The first step is to find a quadratic factor. So write down the factor you know, along with another set of brackets.

$$(x + 2)(\qquad) = 2x^3 + x^2 - 8x - 4$$

Put the x^2 bit in this new set of brackets.
These have to <u>multiply together</u> to give you this.

$$(x + 2)(2x^2 \qquad - 2) = 2x^3 + x^2 - 8x - 4$$

② Find the number for the second set of brackets.
These have to <u>multiply together</u> to give you this.

$$(x + 2)(2x^2 \qquad - 2) = 2x^3 + x^2 - 8x - 4$$

③ These multiplied give you $-2x$, but there's $-8x$ in $f(x)$ — so you need an 'extra' $-6x$.
And that's what this $-3x$ is for.

$$(x + 2)(2x^2 - 3x - 2) = 2x^3 + x^2 - 8x - 4$$

> You only need $-3x$ because it's
> going to be multiplied by 2
> — which makes $-6x$.

> If you wanted to solve a cubic, you'd do it
> exactly the same way — put it in the form
> $ax^3 + bx^2 + cx + d = 0$ and factorise.

Factorising Cubics

1) **Write down the factor $(x-k)$.**

2) **Put in the x^2 term.**

3) **Put in the constant.**

4) **Put in the x term by comparing the number of x's on both sides.**

5) **Check there are the same number of x^2's on both sides.**

6) **Factorise the quadratic you've found — if that's possible.**

> If every term in the cubic contains an 'x'
> (i.e. $ax^3 + bx^2 + cx$) then just take out x
> as your first factor before factorising the
> remaining quadratic as usual.

④ Before you go any further, check that there are the same number of x^2's on <u>both</u> sides.

$4x^2$ from here...

$$(x + 2)(2x^2 - 3x - 2) = 2x^3 + x^2 - 8x - 4$$

...and $-3x^2$ from here...   ...add together to give this x^2.

If this is okay, factorise the quadratic into two linear factors.

$$(2x^2 - 3x - 2) = (2x + 1)(x - 2)$$

<u>And so...</u> $2x^3 + x^2 - 8x - 4 = (x + 2)(2x + 1)(x - 2)$

I love the smell of fresh factorised cubics in the morning...

Factorising cubics is exactly the same as learning to unicycle... It's impossible at first. But when you finally manage it, it's really easy from then onwards and you'll never forget it. Probably. To tell the truth, I can't unicycle at all. So don't believe a word I say.

Algebraic Division

Algebraic division is one of those things that you have to learn when you're studying maths.
You'll probably never use it again once you've entered the 'real world', but hey ho... such is life.

Do **Algebraic Division** by means of **Subtraction**

$$(2x^3 - 3x^2 - 3x + 7) \div (x - 2) = ?$$

The trick with this is to see how many times you can subtract $(x - 2)$ from $(2x^3 - 3x^2 - 3x + 7)$.
The idea is to keep subtracting lumps of $(x - 2)$ until you've got rid of all the powers of x.

Do the subtracting in **Stages**

At each stage, always try to get rid of the highest power of x.
Then start again with whatever you've got left.

(1) Start with $2x^3 - 3x^2 - 3x + 7$, and subtract $2x^2$ lots of $(x - 2)$ to get rid of the x^3 term.

$(2x^3 - 3x^2 - 3x + 7) - 2x^2(x - 2)$
$(2x^3 - 3x^2 - 3x + 7) - 2x^3 + 4x^2$
$\qquad = x^2 - 3x + 7$

$2x^3 \div x = 2x^2$

This is what's left — so now you have to get rid of the x^2 term.

(2) Now start again with $x^2 - 3x + 7$.
The highest power of x is the x^2 term.
So subtract x lots of $(x - 2)$ to get rid of that.

$(x^2 - 3x + 7) - x(x - 2)$
$(x^2 - 3x + 7) - x^2 + 2x$
$\qquad = -x + 7$

Now start again with this — and get rid of the x term.

(3) All that's left now is $-x + 7$.
Get rid of the $-x$ by subtracting -1 times $(x - 2)$.

$(-x + 7) - (-1(x - 2))$
$(-x + 7) + x - 2$
$\qquad = 5$

There are no more powers of x to get rid of — so stop here.

The remainder's 5.

Interpreting the results...

Time to work out exactly what all that meant...

Started with: $2x^3 - 3x^2 - 3x + 7$

Subtracted: $2x^2(x - 2) + x(x - 2) - 1(x - 2)$

$\qquad = (x - 2)(2x^2 + x - 1)$

Remainder: $= 5$

So... $2x^3 - 3x^2 - 3x + 7 = (x - 2)(2x^2 + x - 1) + 5$

...or to put that another way...

$$\frac{2x^3 - 3x^2 - 3x + 7}{x - 2} = 2x^2 + x - 1 \text{ with remainder 5.}$$

$2x^2 + x - 1$ is called the quotient.

Algebraic Division

$$(ax^3 + bx^2 + cx + d) \div (x - k) = ?$$

1) SUBTRACT a multiple of $(x - k)$ to get rid of the highest power of x.

2) REPEAT step 1 until you've got rid of all the powers of x.

3) WORK OUT how many lumps of $(x - k)$, you've subtracted, and the REMAINDER.

Algebraic division is a beautiful thing that we should all cherish...

Revising algebraic division isn't the most enjoyable way to spend an afternoon, it's true, but it's in the specification, and so you need to be comfortable with it. It involves the same process you use when you're doing long division with numbers — so if you're having trouble following the above, do $4863 \div 7$ really slowly. What you're doing at each stage is subtracting multiples of 7, and you do this until you can't take any more 7s away, which is when you get your remainder.

The Remainder and Factor Theorems

The Remainder Theorem and the Factor Theorem are easy, and possibly quite useful.

The **Remainder Theorem** is an easy way to work out **Remainders**

> When you divide f(x) by ($x - a$), the remainder is f(a).

So in the example on the previous page, you could have worked out the remainder dead easily.

1) f(x) = $2x^3 - 3x^2 - 3x + 7$.

2) You're dividing by ($x - 2$), so $a = 2$.

3) So the remainder must be f(2) = $(2 \times 8) - (3 \times 4) - (3 \times 2) + 7 = 5$.

Careful now... when you're dividing by something like ($x + 7$), a is negative — so here, a = –7.

If you want the remainder after dividing by something like (ax − b), there's an extension to the remainder theorem...

> When you divide f(x) by ($ax - b$), the remainder is f$\left(\dfrac{b}{a}\right)$.

> **EXAMPLE** Find the remainder when you divide $2x^3 - 3x^2 - 3x + 7$ by $2x - 1$.
>
> f(x) = $2x^3 - 3x^2 - 3x + 7$. You're dividing by $2x - 1$, so $a = 2$ and $b = 1$.
>
> So the remainder must be: f$\left(\frac{1}{2}\right) = 2\left(\frac{1}{8}\right) - 3\left(\frac{1}{4}\right) - 3\left(\frac{1}{2}\right) + 7 = 5$

The **Factor Theorem** is just the Remainder Theorem with a **Zero Remainder**

If you get a remainder of zero when you divide f(x) by ($x - a$), then ($x - a$) must be a factor. That's the Factor Theorem.

> If f(x) is a polynomial, and f(a) = 0, then ($x - a$) is a factor of f(x).
>
> In other words: If you know the roots, you also know the factors — and vice versa.

> **EXAMPLE** Show that $(2x + 1)$ is a factor of f(x) = $2x^3 - 3x^2 + 4x + 3$.
>
> The question's giving you a big hint here. Notice that $2x + 1 = 0$ when $x = -\frac{1}{2}$. So plug this value of x into f(x).
> If you show that f$\left(-\frac{1}{2}\right) = 0$, then the factor theorem says that $(x + \frac{1}{2})$ is a factor — which means that
> $2 \times (x + \frac{1}{2}) = (2x + 1)$ is also a factor.
>
> f(x) = $2x^3 - 3x^2 + 4x + 3$ and so f$\left(-\frac{1}{2}\right) = 2 \times \left(-\frac{1}{8}\right) - 3 \times \frac{1}{4} + 4 \times \left(-\frac{1}{2}\right) + 3 = 0$
>
> So, by the factor theorem, $(x + \frac{1}{2})$ is a factor of f(x), and so $(2x + 1)$ is also a factor.

(x − 1) is a Factor if the coefficients **Add Up To 0**

This works for all polynomials — no exceptions. It could save a fair whack of time in the exam.

> **EXAMPLE** Factorise the polynomial f(x) = $6x^2 - 7x + 1$
>
> The coefficients (6, –7 and 1) add up to 0. That means f(1) = 0, and so $(x - 1)$ is a factor. Easy.
>
> Then just factorise it like any quadratic to get this: f(x) = $6x^2 - 7x + 1 = (6x - 1)(x - 1)$

Factorising a **Cubic** given **No Factors**

If the question doesn't give you any factors, the best way to find a factor of a cubic is to guess — use trial and error.

First, add up the coefficients to check if ($x - 1$) is a factor.

If that doesn't work, keep trying small numbers (find f(–1), f(2), f(–2), f(3) and so on) until you find a number that gives you zero when you put it in the cubic. Call that number k. ($x - k$) is a factor of the cubic.
Then finish factorising the cubic using the method on page 41.

Binomial Expansions

If you're feeling a bit stressed, just take a couple of minutes to relax before trying to get your head round this page — it's a bit of a stinker in places. Have a cup of tea and think about something else for a couple of minutes. Ready...

Writing *Binomial Expansions* is all about *Spotting Patterns*

Doing binomial expansions just involves <u>multiplying out</u> brackets. It would get nasty when you raise the brackets to <u>higher powers</u> — but once again I've got a <u>cunning plan</u>...

$$(1 + x)^0 = \qquad\qquad 1$$
$$(1 + x)^1 = \qquad\qquad 1 + x$$
$$(1 + x)^2 = \qquad\qquad 1 + 2x + x^2$$
$$(1 + x)^3 = \qquad 1 + 3x + 3x^2 + x^3$$
$$(1 + x)^4 = 1 + 4x + 6x^2 + 4x^3 + x^4$$

Anything to the power of O is 1.

$$(1 + x)^3 = (1 + x)(1 + x)^2$$
$$= (1 + x)(1 + 2x + x^2)$$
$$= 1 + 2x + x^2 + x + 2x^2 + x^3$$
$$= 1 + 3x + 3x^2 + x^3$$

A Frenchman named Pascal spotted the pattern in the coefficients and wrote them down in a <u>triangle</u>.
So it was called '<u>Pascal's Triangle</u>' (imaginative, eh?).
The pattern's easy — each number is the <u>sum</u> of the two above it.

So, the next line will be: **1 5 10 10 5 1**
giving $(1 + x)^5 = 1 + 5x + 10x^2 + 10x^3 + 5x^4 + x^5$.

```
              1
           1     1
        1     2     1
      1    3      3   + 1
   1     4     6    = 4    1
```

You *Don't* need to write out Pascal's Triangle for *Higher Powers*

There's a formula for the numbers in the triangle. The formula looks <u>horrible</u> (one of the worst in AS maths) so don't try to learn it letter by letter — look for the <u>patterns</u> in it instead. Here's an example:

> **EXAMPLE**   Expand $(1 + x)^{10}$, giving the first four terms only.

So you can use this formula for any power, the power is called *n*. In this example *n* = 10.

$$(1 + x)^n = 1 + \frac{n}{1}x + \frac{n(n-1)}{1 \times 2}x^2 + \boxed{\frac{n(n-1)(n-2)}{1 \times 2 \times 3}x^3} + \;.................\; + x^n$$

Here's a closer look at the term in the black box above:

There are <u>three things</u> multiplied together on the top row. If n = 10, this would be 10 × 9 × 8.

$$\frac{n(n-1)(n-2)}{1 \times 2 \times 3}x^3$$

<u>Start here</u>. The power of x is 3 and everything else here is based on 3.

There are <u>three integers</u> here multiplied together. 1 × 2 × 3 is written as 3! and called 3 <u>factorial</u>.

This means, if *n* = 10 and you were asked for '<u>the term in x^7</u>' you should write $\dfrac{10 \times 9 \times 8 \times 7 \times 6 \times 5 \times 4}{1 \times 2 \times 3 \times 4 \times 5 \times 6 \times 7}x^7$.

This can be <u>simplified</u> to $\dfrac{10!}{7!3!}x^7$

$10 \times 9 \times 8 \times 7 \times 6 \times 5 \times 4 = \dfrac{10!}{3!}$ because it's the numbers from 10 to 1 multiplied together, divided by the numbers from 3 to 1 multiplied together.

Believe it or not, there's an even <u>shorter</u> form: $\dfrac{10!}{7!3!}$ is written as $^{10}C_7$ or $\binom{10}{7}$

$$^nC_r = \binom{n}{r} = \frac{n!}{r!(n-r)!}$$

So, to finish the example, $(1 + x)^{10} = 1 + \dfrac{10}{1}x + \dfrac{10 \times 9}{1 \times 2}x^2 + \dfrac{10 \times 9 \times 8}{1 \times 2 \times 3}x^3 + ...$ $= 1 + 10x + 45x^2 + 120x^3 + ...$

Don't forget that C1 is a <u>non-calculator</u> exam. Don't panic though — tricky-looking calculations like this will normally cancel down to something a bit nicer: $\dfrac{10 \times 9 \times 8}{1 \times 2 \times 3} = 5 \times 3 \times 8 = 40 \times 3 = 120$. Phew!

Binomial Expansions

It's slightly more complicated when the **Coefficient** of x isn't 1

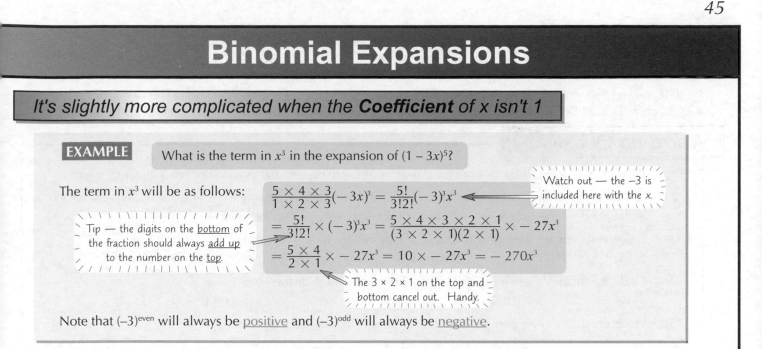

EXAMPLE What is the term in x^3 in the expansion of $(1 - 3x)^5$?

The term in x^3 will be as follows:

Watch out — the -3 is included here with the x.

$$\frac{5 \times 4 \times 3}{1 \times 2 \times 3}(-3x)^3 = \frac{5!}{3!2!}(-3)^3 x^3$$

Tip — the digits on the <u>bottom</u> of the fraction should always <u>add up</u> to the number on the <u>top</u>.

$$= \frac{5!}{3!2!} \times (-3)^3 x^3 = \frac{5 \times 4 \times 3 \times 2 \times 1}{(3 \times 2 \times 1)(2 \times 1)} \times -27x^3$$

$$= \frac{5 \times 4}{2 \times 1} \times -27x^3 = 10 \times -27x^3 = -270x^3$$

The $3 \times 2 \times 1$ on the top and bottom cancel out. Handy.

Note that $(-3)^{\text{even}}$ will always be <u>positive</u> and $(-3)^{\text{odd}}$ will always be <u>negative</u>.

Some **Binomials** contain **More Complicated Expressions**

The binomials so far have all had a <u>1</u> in the brackets — things get tricky when there's a <u>number other than 1</u>. Don't panic, though. The method is the same as before once you've done a bit of <u>factorising</u>.

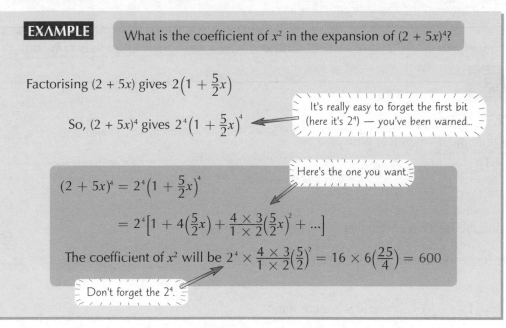

EXAMPLE What is the coefficient of x^2 in the expansion of $(2 + 5x)^4$?

Factorising $(2 + 5x)$ gives $2\left(1 + \frac{5}{2}x\right)$

So, $(2 + 5x)^4$ gives $2^4\left(1 + \frac{5}{2}x\right)^4$

It's really easy to forget the first bit (here it's 2^4) — you've been warned...

$$(2 + 5x)^4 = 2^4\left(1 + \frac{5}{2}x\right)^4$$

Here's the one you want.

$$= 2^4\left[1 + 4\left(\frac{5}{2}x\right) + \frac{4 \times 3}{1 \times 2}\left(\frac{5}{2}x\right)^2 + ...\right]$$

The coefficient of x^2 will be $2^4 \times \frac{4 \times 3}{1 \times 2}\left(\frac{5}{2}\right)^2 = 16 \times 6\left(\frac{25}{4}\right) = 600$

Don't forget the 2^4.

So, there's <u>no need</u> to work out all of the terms.
In fact, you could have gone <u>directly</u> to the term in x^2 by using the method on page 44.

> Note: the question asked for the <u>coefficient of x^2</u> in the expansion, so <u>don't include any x's</u> in your answer. If you'd been asked for the <u>term in x^2</u> in the expansion, then you <u>should</u> have included the x^2 in your answer.
>
> <u>Always</u> read the question very carefully.

Pascal was fine at maths but rubbish at music — he only played the triangle...

All in all quite a tricky couple of pages — thanks in no small part to that nightmare formula. As I said before, trying to spot patterns will make using it a bit easier and quicker. And always try to simplify those big fractions when doing calculations — it will save you a lot of grief in the exam. Other than that, practice makes perfect — so it's on to the practice questions...

C1 Section 5 — Practice Questions

Well, if you've been working through these sections in order, then that's C1 all done. I hope you've enjoyed it as much as I have. Before you move onto the practice exams, have a goosey at these questions.

Warm-up Questions

1) Given that $(x + 1)$ is a factor of $f(x) = x^3 + 6x^2 + 11x + 6$, express $f(x)$ as a product of 3 linear factors.

2) Write the following functions f(x) in the form $f(x) = (x + 2)g(x) +$ remainder (where g(x) is a quadratic):
   a) $f(x) = 3x^3 - 4x^2 - 5x - 6$, b) $f(x) = x^3 + 2x^2 - 3x + 4$, c) $f(x) = 2x^3 + 6x - 3$

3) Find the remainder when the following are divided by: (i) $(x + 1)$, (ii) $(x - 1)$, (iii) $(x - 2)$
   a) $f(x) = 6x^3 - x^2 - 3x - 12$, b) $f(x) = x^4 + 2x^3 - x^2 + 3x + 4$, c) $f(x) = x^5 + 2x^2 - 3$

4) Find the remainder when $f(x) = x^4 - 3x^3 + 7x^2 - 12x + 14$ is divided by:
   a) $x + 2$ b) $2x + 4$ c) $x - 3$ d) $2x - 6$

5) Which of the following are factors of $f(x) = x^5 - 4x^4 + 3x^3 + 2x^2 - 2$?
   a) $x - 1$ b) $x + 1$ c) $x - 2$ d) $2x - 2$

6) Find the values of c and d so that $2x^4 + 3x^3 + 5x^2 + cx + d$ is exactly divisible by $(x - 2)(x + 3)$.

7) Write down the sixth row of Pascal's Triangle. (Hint: it starts with a '1'.)

8) Give the first four terms in the expansion of $(1 + x)^{12}$.

9) What is the term in x^2 in the expansion of $(1 - 2x)^{16}$?

10) Find the coefficient of x^2 in the expansion of $(2 + 3x)^5$.

There now, that wasn't so bad, was it? Now take a deep breath and have a go at some exam style questions.

Exam Questions

1   $f(x) = 2x^3 - 5x^2 - 4x + 3$

   a) Find the remainder when f(x) is divided by

      (i) $(x - 1)$

(2 marks)

      (ii) $(2x + 1)$

(2 marks)

   b) Show using the factor theorem that $(x + 1)$ is a factor of f(x).

(2 marks)

   c) Factorise f(x) completely.

(4 marks)

2   $f(x) = (4x^2 + 3x + 1)(x - p) + 5$, where p is a constant.

   a) State the value of f(p).

(1 mark)

   b) Find the value of p, given that when f(x) is divided by $(x + 1)$, the remainder is -1.

(2 marks)

   c) Find the remainder when f(x) is divided by $(x - 1)$.

(1 mark)

3   Find the coefficient of x^4 in the binomial expansion of $(4 + 3x)^5$.

(4 marks)

4   $f(x) = x^3 + px + 4$ has a factor of $(x + 4)$.

   a) Find the value of p.

(2 marks)

   b) Hence find the roots of the equation $f(x) = 0$.

(3 marks)

General Certificate of Education
Advanced Subsidiary (AS) and Advanced Level

Core Mathematics C1 — Practice Exam One

Time Allowed: 1 hour 30 min

Calculators may **not** be used for this exam

There are 72 marks available for this paper.

Section A (36 marks)

1 Find the remainder when $f(x) = x^3 + x^2 - 3x - 1$ is divided by $(x + 2)$.

(2 marks)

2 a) Write down the exact value of $36^{-\frac{1}{2}}$.

(2 marks)

  b) Simplify $\dfrac{a^6 \times a^3}{\sqrt{a^4}} \div a^{\frac{1}{2}}$.

(3 marks)

3 Make x the subject of the equation $y = \dfrac{x-1}{x} + 3$.

(3 marks)

4 Express $\left(5\sqrt{5} + 2\sqrt{3}\right)^2$ in the form $a + b\sqrt{c}$, where a, b and c are integers to be found.

(4 marks)

5 a) Write down the first four terms in the expansion of $(1 + ax)^{10}$, $a > 0$.

(2 marks)

  b) Find the coefficient of x^2 in the expansion of $(2 + 3x)^5$.

(2 marks)

6 a) Express $x^2 - 6x + 5$ in the form $(x + a)^2 + b$.

(2 marks)

  b) Factorise the expression $x^2 - 6x + 5$.

(2 marks)

7 The line AB is part of the line with equation $y + 2x - 5 = 0$.
  A is the point with coordinates $(1, 3)$ and B is the point with coordinates $(4, k)$.

  a) Find the value of k.

(1 mark)

  b) What is the equation of the line perpendicular to AB, that passes through A?

(4 marks)

8   The equation $x^2 - 4x + (k - 1) = 0$, where k is a constant, has no real roots.
    Find the set of possible values of k.

    (4 marks)

9   a)   Solve the inequality $4x + 7 > 7x + 4$.

    (2 marks)

    b)   Find the values of k, such that $(x - 5)(x - 3) > k$, for all possible values of x.

    (3 marks)

Section B (36 marks)

10 a)   Find the coordinates of the intersection points of the graphs of $y = 7 - x$ and $y = x^2 + 3x - 5$.

    (5 marks)

    b)   Express $y = x^2 + 3x - 5$ in the form $y = (x + a)^2 + b$.

    (3 marks)

    c)   Sketch the graph of $y = x^2 + 3x - 5$, showing the coordinates of any turning points and points of intersection with the x-axis.

    (3 marks)

11 a)   Rewrite the following equation in the form $f(x) = 0$,
         where $f(x)$ is of the form $f(x) = ax^3 + bx^2 + cx + d$:
         $$(x - 1)(x^2 + x + 1) = 2x^2 - 17$$

    (2 marks)

    b)   Show that $(x + 2)$ is a factor of $f(x)$.

    (3 marks)

    c)   Hence factorise $f(x)$ as the product of a linear factor and a quadratic factor.

    (3 marks)

    d)   Divide the polynomial $x^3 - 2x^2 + 3x - 3$ by $(x - 1)$, showing both the quotient and remainder.

    (4 marks)

12 A circle, C, has equation $x^2 - 6x + y^2 = 3$.

    a)   Find the exact coordinates of the points where C intersects the x-axis.

    (4 marks)

    b)   Rearrange the equation of C into the form $(x - a)^2 + (y - b)^2 = c$.

    (2 marks)

    c)   Write down the radius, r, and the coordinates of Q, the centre of the circle.
         Where appropriate, give your answer in simplified surd form.

    (2 marks)

    d)   (i)   Find the distance from Q to the point P with coordinates $(5, 4)$.
              Where appropriate, give your answers in simplified surd form.

    (3 marks)

        (ii) Does P lie inside C? Give a reason for your answer.

    (2 marks)

General Certificate of Education
Advanced Subsidiary (AS) and Advanced Level

Core Mathematics C1 — Practice Exam Two

Time Allowed: 1 hour 30 min

Calculators may **not** be used for this exam

There are 72 marks available for this paper.

Section A (36 marks)

1   A function is defined by $f(x) = x^3 - 4x^2 - 7x + 10$. $(x - 1)$ is a factor of $f(x)$.
    Solve the equation $x^3 - 4x^2 - 7x + 10 = 0$.

(4 marks)

2   a)   Simplify $(\sqrt{3} + 1)(\sqrt{3} - 1)$.

(2 marks)

    b)   Rationalise the denominator of the expression $\dfrac{\sqrt{3} - 1}{\sqrt{3} + 1}$.

(3 marks)

3   a)   Express $x^2 - 7x + 17$ in the form $(x - m)^2 + n$, where m and n are constants.

(3 marks)

    b)   Hence state the maximum value of $f(x) = \dfrac{1}{x^2 - 7x + 17}$.

(2 marks)

4   Find the set of possible values of x which satisfy the equation $9x^2 + 4x < 0$.

(3 marks)

5   Find the coefficient of x^3 in the expansion of $(2 + x)^5$.

(3 marks)

6   Prove that, when n is an odd integer, $3n^2 - 12$ is always odd, and when n is an even integer,
    $3n^2 - 12$ is always even.

(3 marks)

7   Find the possible values of k if the equation $g(x) = 0$ is to have only one root,
    where $g(x)$ is given by $g(x) = 3x^2 + kx + 12$.

(3 marks)

8   By making the substitution $y = x^2$, solve the equation $x^4 - 6x^2 + 8 = 0$.

(5 marks)

9   a)   Find the value of:

(i) 10^0,

(1 mark)

(ii) $81^{-\frac{1}{2}}$,

(2 marks)

b)   Simplify the expression $\frac{a^2 b}{a^3} - \frac{b}{a} + \frac{b^2 c^3 d}{bc^2}$.

(2 marks)

Section B (36 marks)

10 a)   Find the remainder when the function $f(x) = x^3 - 6x^2 - x + 30$ is divided by:

(i) $(x + 3)$

(2 marks)

(ii) $(2x - 1)$

(2 marks)

b)   Using the factor theorem, show that $(x - 3)$ is a factor of $f(x)$.

(2 marks)

c)   Factorise $f(x)$ completely.

(4 marks)

d)   The graph of $y = x^3 - 6x^2 - x + 30$ is translated through $\binom{1}{0}$. Find the equation of the resulting graph, in the form $y = x^3 + ax^2 + bx + c$.

(3 marks)

11   The circle with equation $x^2 - 6x + y^2 - 4y = 0$ crosses the y-axis at the origin and the point A.

a)   Find the coordinates of A.

(2 marks)

b)   Rearrange the equation of the circle in the form: $(x - a)^2 + (y - b)^2 = c$.

(3 marks)

c)   Write down the radius and the coordinates of the centre of the circle.

(2 marks)

d)   Find the equation of the tangent to the circle at A.

(4 marks)

12 a)   Find the coordinates of the point A, when A lies at the intersection of the lines l_1 and l_2, and when the equations of l_1 and l_2 respectively are $x - y + 1 = 0$ and $2x + y - 8 = 0$.

(3 marks)

b)   The points B and C have coordinates $(6, -4)$ and $\left(-\frac{4}{3}, -\frac{1}{3}\right)$ respectively, and D is the midpoint of AC. Find the equation of the line BD in the form $ax + by + c = 0$, where a, b and c are integers.

(6 marks)

c)   Show that the triangle ABD is a right-angled triangle.

(3 marks)

Logs

Don't be put off by your parents or grandparents telling you that logs are hard. <u>Logarithm</u> is just a fancy word for <u>power</u>, and once you know how to use them you can solve all sorts of equations.

You need to be able to **Switch** between **Different Notations**

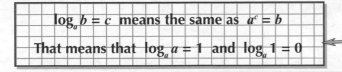

$\log_a b = c$ means the same as $a^c = b$

That means that $\log_a a = 1$ and $\log_a 1 = 0$

The little number 'a' after 'log' is called the <u>base</u>. Logs can be to any base, but <u>base 10</u> is the most common. The <u>button</u> marked '<u>log</u>' on your calculator uses base 10.

EXAMPLE   Index notation: $10^2 = 100$ log notation: $\log_{10} 100 = 2$

The <u>base</u> goes here but it's usually left out if it's 10.

So the <u>logarithm</u> of 100 to the <u>base 10</u> is 2, because 10 raised to the <u>power</u> of 2 is 100.

EXAMPLES

Write down the values of the following:

a) $\log_2 8$ b) $\log_9 3$ c) $\log_5 5$

a)   8 is 2 raised to the power of 3, so $2^3 = 8$ and $\log_2 8 = 3$

b)   3 is the square root of 9, or $9^{1/2} = 3$, so $\log_9 3 = 1/2$

c)   Anything to the power of 1 is itself, so $\log_5 5 = 1$

Write the following using log notation:

a) $5^3 = 125$ b) $3^0 = 1$

You just need to make sure you get things in the right place.

a)   3 is the power or <u>logarithm</u> that 5 (the <u>base</u>) is raised to to get 125, so $\log_5 125 = 3$

b)   You'll need to remember this one: $\log_3 1 = 0$

The **Laws of Logarithms** are **Unbelievably Useful**

Whenever you have to deal with <u>logs</u>, you'll end up using the <u>laws</u> below. That means it's no bad idea to <u>learn them</u> by heart right now.

Laws of Logarithms

$$\log_a x + \log_a y = \log_a (xy)$$

$$\log_a x - \log_a y = \log_a \left(\frac{x}{y}\right)$$

$$\log_a x^k = k \log_a x$$

So $\log_a \frac{1}{x} = -\log_a x$

Use the **Laws** to **Manipulate Logs**

EXAMPLE   Write each expression in the form $\log_a n$, where n is a number.

a) $\log_a 5 + \log_a 4$ b) $2 \log_a 6 - \log_a 9$

a) $\log_a x + \log_a y = \log_a (xy)$

You just have to <u>multiply</u> the numbers together:

$\log_a 5 + \log_a 4 = \log_a (5 \times 4)$
$= \log_a 20$

b) $\log_a x^k = k \log_a x$

and

$\log_a x - \log_a y = \log_a \left(\frac{x}{y}\right)$

$2 \log_a 6 = \log_a 6^2 = \log_a 36$

$\log_a 36 - \log_a 9 = \log_a (36 \div 9)$
$= \log_a 4$

It's sometimes hard to see the wood for the trees — especially with logs...

Tricky, tricky, tricky... I think of $\log_a b$ as 'the <u>power</u> I have to raise a to if I want to end up with b' — that's all it is. And the log laws make a bit more sense if you think of 'log' as meaning 'power'. For example, you know that $2^a \times 2^b = 2^{a+b}$ — this just says that if you multiply the two numbers, you add the powers. Well, the first law of logs is saying the same thing. Any road, even if you don't really understand why they work, make sure you know the log laws like you know your own navel.

Exponentials and Logs

Okay, you've done the theory of logs. So now it's a bit of stuff about <u>exponentials</u> (the opposite of logs, kind of), and then it'll be time to get your calculator out for a bit of button pressing...

Graphs of a^x Never Reach Zero

All the graphs of $y = a^x$ (exponential graphs) where $a > 1$ have the <u>same basic shape</u>. The graphs for $a = 2$, $a = 3$ and $a = 4$ are shown on the right.

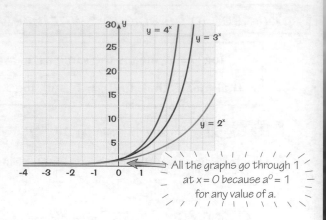

- All the a's are greater than 1 — so <u>y increases as x increases</u>.

- The <u>bigger</u> a is, the <u>quicker</u> the graphs increase.

- As x <u>decreases</u>, y <u>decreases</u> at a <u>smaller and smaller rate</u> — y will approach zero, but never actually get there.

All the graphs go through 1 at $x = 0$ because $a^0 = 1$ for any value of a.

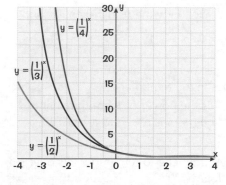

The graphs on the left are for $y = a^x$ where $a < 1$ (they're for $a = \frac{1}{2}$, $\frac{1}{3}$ and $\frac{1}{4}$).

- All the a's are less than 1 — meaning <u>y decreases as x increases</u>.

- As x <u>increases</u>, y <u>decreases</u> at a <u>smaller and smaller rate</u> — again, y will approach zero, but never actually get there.

You can use Exponentials and Logs to Solve Equations

EXAMPLE   1)   Solve $2^{4x} = 3$ to 3 significant figures.

You want x on its own, so take logs of both sides (by writing 'log' in front of both sides):

$$\log 2^{4x} = \log 3$$

Now use one of the laws of logs: $\log x^k = k \log x$:

$$4x \log 2 = \log 3$$

You can now divide both sides by '4 log 2' to get x on its own:

$$x = \frac{\log 3}{4 \log 2}$$

But $\frac{\log 3}{4 \log 2}$ is just a number you can find using a calculator:

$$x = 0.396 \text{ (to 3 s.f.)}$$

I don't know about you, but I enjoyed that more than the biggest, fastest rollercoaster. You want another? OK then...

EXAMPLE   2)   Solve $7 \log_{10} x = 5$ to 3 significant figures.

You want x on its own, so begin by dividing both sides by 7:

$$\log_{10} x = \frac{5}{7}$$

You now need to take exponentials of both sides by doing '10 to the power of both sides' (since the log is to base 10):

$$10^{\log_{10} x} = 10^{\frac{5}{7}}$$

Logs and exponentials are inverse functions, so they cancel out:

$$x = 10^{\frac{5}{7}}$$

Again, $10^{\frac{5}{7}}$ is just a number you can find using a calculator:

$$x = 5.18 \text{ (to 3 s.f.)}$$

Exponentials and Logs

Use the **Calculator Log Button** Whenever You Can

> **EXAMPLE** Use logarithms to solve the following for x, giving the answers to 4 s.f.
>
> a) $10^{3x} = 4000$ b) $7^x = 55$ c) $\log_2 x = 5$

You've got the magic buttons on your calculator, but you'd better <u>follow the instructions</u> and show that you know how to use the <u>log rules</u> covered earlier.

a) $10^{3x} = 4000$ — there's an 'unknown' in the power, so <u>take logs of both sides</u>.
(In theory, it doesn't matter what <u>base</u> you use, but your calculator has a '$\log_{10}$' button, so base 10 is usually a good idea. But whatever base you use, <u>use the same one for both sides</u>.)

So taking logs to base 10 of both sides of the above equation gives:

$$\log 10^{3x} = \log 4000$$
$$\text{i.e. } 3x \log 10 = \log 4000$$

Since $\log_{10} 10 = 1$ ⟹ i.e. $3x = \log 4000$, so $x = 1.201$ (to 4 sig. fig.)

b) $7^x = 55$. Again, take logs of both sides, and use the log rules: $x \log_{10} 7 = \log_{10} 55$, so $x = \dfrac{\log_{10} 55}{\log_{10} 7} = 2.059$

c) $\log_2 x = 5$ — to get rid of a log, you 'take exponentials', meaning you do '2 (the base) to the power of each side'.

Think of 'taking logs' and 'taking exponentials' as opposite processes — one cancels the other out: $2^{\log_2 x} = 2^5$
i.e. $x = 32$

You might have to **Combine** the **Laws of Logs** to **Solve** equations

If the examiners are feeling particularly mean, they might make you use <u>more than one</u> law to solve an equation.

> **EXAMPLE** Solve the equation $\log_3(2 - 3x) - 2\log_3 x = 2$.

First, combine the log terms into one term (you can do this because they both have the same base): $\log_3 \dfrac{2 - 3x}{x^2} = 2$

Remember that $2\log x = \log x^2$.

Then take exponentials of both sides: $3^{\log_3 \frac{2-3x}{x^2}} = 3^2 \Rightarrow \dfrac{2 - 3x}{x^2} = 9$

Finally, rearrange the equation and solve for x: $2 - 3x = 9x^2 \Rightarrow 0 = 9x^2 + 3x - 2$
$\Rightarrow 0 = (3x - 1)(3x + 2)$

Ignore the negative solution because you can't take logs of a negative number.

So $x = \dfrac{1}{3}$.

Exponential Growth and **Decay** Applies to **Real-life** Problems

Logs can even be used to solve real-life problems.

> **EXAMPLE** The radioactivity of a substance decays by 20 per cent over a year. The initial level of radioactivity is 400. Find the time taken for the radioactivity to fall to 200 (the half-life).

$R = 400 \times 0.8^T$ where R is the <u>level of radioactivity</u> at time T years.
We need $R = 200$, so solve $200 = 400 \times 0.8^T$

The 0.8 comes from $1 - 20\%$ decay.

$0.8^T = \dfrac{200}{400} = 0.5 \Rightarrow T \log 0.8 = \log 0.5 \Rightarrow T = \dfrac{\log 0.5}{\log 0.8} = 3.106$ years

If in doubt, take the log of something — that usually works...

The thing about exponential growth is that it's really useful, as it happens in real life all over the place. Money in a bank account earns interest at <u>a certain percentage per year</u>, and so the balance rises <u>exponentially</u> (if you don't spend or save anything). Likewise, if you got 20% cleverer for every week you studied, that would also be exponential... and impressive.

Exponentials and Logs

Logarithms can be handy if you want to turn a dodgy looking equation into something nice and easy to work with.

Exponential Equations can be **Reduced to Linear Form**

Equations like $y = ax^n$ and $y = ab^x$ can be a bit awkward to use. Fortunately, using the laws of logs, they can be rewritten in a form you know and love — that old $y = mx + c$ chestnut. Just take logs of both sides and rearrange:

$$y = ax^n \Rightarrow \log_{10}y = n\log_{10}x + \log_{10}a$$

$$y = ab^x \Rightarrow \log_{10}y = x\log_{10}b + \log_{10}a$$

The equations look pretty horrendous now, I'll admit. But look at them carefully — they're just a nasty looking version of $y = mx + c$.

Once the equations are in the form $y = mx + c$, you can draw their straight line graphs to your heart's content, and use those graphs to easily work out all kinds of things that would have been really tricky to do with exponential graphs.

EXAMPLE The number of employees, p, working for a company t years after it was founded can be modelled by the equation $p = at^b$. The table below shows the number of employees the company has:

Age of company (t years)	2	5	8	13	25
Number of employees (p)	3	7	10	16	29

a) Show that $p = at^b$ can be written in the form $\log p = b\log t + \log a$.

b) Plot a graph of $\log t$ against $\log p$ and draw a line of best fit for your graph.

c) Find the values of a and b in the equation $p = at^b$.

a) Starting with $p = at^b$, take logs of both sides:

$\log p = \log at^b$

Now use laws of logs to rearrange into required form:

$\log p = \log a + \log t^b = b\log t + \log a$ — as required.

See page 51 if you've forgotten the laws of logs already. Shame on you.

b) Make a table of the values of $\log t$ and $\log p$, using p and t as given in the question:

$\log t$	0.301	0.699	0.903	1.114	1.398
$\log p$	0.477	0.845	1.000	1.204	1.462

Now plot a graph of $\log t$ against $\log p$ and draw a line of best fit:

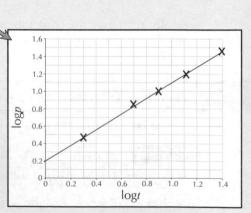

c) From part a), the graph has equation $\log p = b\log t + \log a$.

Compare this to $y = mx + c$:

b is the gradient of the line and
$\log a$ is the vertical intercept of the line.

Use the coordinates of two points on the line to find the gradient:
E.g. use coordinates (1.0, 1.1) and (0, 0.2):

$b = \dfrac{y_2 - y_1}{x_2 - x_1} = \dfrac{1.1 - 0.2}{1.0 - 0} = 0.9.$

You can also read the vertical intercept off the graph — 0.2.

BUT this value is equal to $\log a$, so take exponentials of both sides to find $a = 10^{0.2} = 1.585$ (3 d.p.).

So $b = 0.9$ and $a = 1.585$, and the original equation $p = at^b$ is $p = 1.585t^{0.9}$.

Reducing to linear form — as easy as falling off an exponential...

The results you get with the method shown in the example will depend on your line of best fit, so make sure you draw it carefully. It doesn't hurt to check your final answer using the values in the original table to see how well it fits the data. And don't forget that the vertical intercept is a log — you'll need to take exponentials to get the value you want.

C2 Section 1 — Practice Questions

Logs and exponentials are <u>surprisingly useful</u> things. As well as being in your exam they pop up all over the place in real life — <u>savings</u>, <u>radioactive decay</u>, growth of <u>bacteria</u> — all logarithmic.
And now for something (marginally) different:

Warm-up Questions

1) Write down the values of the following:
   a) $\log_3 27$
   b) $\log_3 (1 \div 27)$
   c) $\log_3 18 - \log_3 2$

2) Simplify the following:
   a) $\log 3 + 2 \log 5$
   b) $\tfrac{1}{2} \log 36 - \log 3$
   c) $\log 2 - \tfrac{1}{4} \log 16$

3) Simplify $\log_b (x^2 - 1) - \log_b (x - 1)$

4) a) Copy and complete the table for the function $y = 4^x$:

x	–3	–2	–1	0	1	2	3
y							

   b) Using suitable scales, plot a graph of $y = 4^x$ for $-3 < x < 3$.
   c) Use the graph to solve the equation $4^x = 20$.

5) Solve these little jokers:
   a) $10^x = 240$
   b) $\log_{10} x = 5.3$
   c) $10^{2x+1} = 1500$
   d) $4^{(x-1)} = 200$

6) Find the smallest integer P such that $1.5^P > 1\,000\,000$.

Time for some practice at the <u>real thing</u>. On your marks... Get set... Go.

Exam Questions

1   a)   Solve the equation
$$2^x = 9$$
giving your answer to 2 decimal places.

(3 marks)

   b)   Hence, or otherwise, solve the equation
$$2^{2x} - 13(2^x) + 36 = 0$$
giving each solution to an appropriate degree of accuracy.

(5 marks)

2   Solve the equation
$$\log_7 (y + 3) + \log_7 (2y + 1) = 1$$
where $y > 0$.

(5 marks)

3   a)   Solve the equation:
$$\log_3 x = -\frac{1}{2}$$
leaving your answer as an exact value.

(3 marks)

   b)   Find x, where
$$2 \log_3 x = -4$$
leaving your answer as an exact value.

(2 marks)

C2 Section 1 — Practice Questions

4   a)   Find x, if

$$6^{(3x+2)} = 9$$

giving your answer to 3 significant figures.

(3 marks)

     b)   Find y, if

$$3^{(y^2-4)} = 7^{(y+2)}$$

giving your answer to 3 significant figures.

(5 marks)

5   For the positive integers p and q,

$$\log_4 p - \log_4 q = \frac{1}{2}$$

     a)   Show that $p = 2q$.

(3 marks)

     b)   Solve the equation for p and q

$$\log_2 p + \log_2 q = 7$$

(5 marks)

6   a)   Write the following expressions in the form $\log_a n$, where n is an integer:

        (i) $\log_a 20 - 2\log_a 2$

(3 marks)

        (ii) $\frac{1}{2}\log_a 16 + \frac{1}{3}\log_a 27$

(3 marks)

     b)   Find the value of:

        (i) $\log_2 64$

(1 mark)

        (ii) $2\log_3 9$

(2 marks)

     c)   Calculate the value of the following, giving your answer to 4 d.p.

        (i) $\log_6 25$

(1 mark)

        (ii) $\log_3 10 + \log_3 2$

(2 marks)

7   The yearly income from book sales of a particular author has tended to increase with time. The table below shows his income from book sales over the first five years after his book was published.

Number of years after book published (t)	1	2	3	4	5
Income (£p thousand)	10	13	17	24	35

The relationship is modelled by the equation $p = ab^t$, where a and b are constants to be found.

     a)   Complete the following table, giving values correct to 3 d.p.:

t	1	2	3	4	5
$\log_{10}p$	1	1.114			

(1 mark)

     b)   Plot a graph of $\log_{10}p$ against t. Draw by eye a line of best fit for your graph.

(2 marks)

     c)   State, in terms of a and b, the gradient and vertical-axis intercept of your graph.
        Hence use your graph to find an equation for p in terms of t.

(8 marks)

     d)   Calculate the author's predicted income 10 years after his book was published.

(1 mark)

Sequences

A sequence is a list of numbers that follow a <u>certain pattern</u>. Sequences can be <u>finite</u> or <u>infinite</u> (infinity — oooh), and they're usually generated in one of two ways. And guess what? You have to know everything about them.

A **Sequence** can be defined by its nth **Term**

You almost definitely covered this stuff at GCSE, so <u>no excuses</u> for mucking it up.

The point of all this is to show how you can work out any <u>value</u> (<u>the nth term</u>) from its <u>position</u> in the sequence (<u>n</u>).

> **EXAMPLE**   Find the nth term of the sequence 5, 8, 11, 14, 17, ...
>
> | 1st | 2nd | 3rd | 4th | 5th |
> |------|------|------|------|------|
> | 5 | 8 | 11 | 14 | 17 |
>
> +3   +3   +3   +3
>
> Each term is <u>3 more</u> than the one before it. That means that you need to start by <u>multiplying n by 3</u>.
>
> Take the first term (where $n = 1$). If you multiply n by 3, you still have to <u>add 2</u> to get 5.
>
> The same goes for $n = 2$. To get 8 you need to multiply n by 3, then add 2.
> Every term in the sequence is worked out exactly the same way.
>
> So n^{th} term is $3n + 2$.

You can define a sequence by a **Recurrence Relation** too

Don't be put off by the fancy name — recurrence relations are pretty <u>easy</u> really.

> The main thing to remember is:
>
> a_k **just means the kth term of the sequence**

The <u>next term</u> in the sequence is a_{k+1}. You need to describe how to <u>work out</u> a_{k+1} if you're given a_k.

> **EXAMPLE**   Find the recurrence relation of the sequence 5, 8, 11, 14, 17, ...
>
> From the example above, you know that each term equals the one before it, plus 3.
>
> This is written like this: $a_{k+1} = a_k + 3$
>
> So, if $k = 5$, $a_k = a_5$ which stands for the 5th term, and $a_{k+1} = a_6$ which stands for the 6th term.
>
> In everyday language, $a_{k+1} = a_k + 3$ means that the sixth term equals the fifth term plus 3.
>
> <u>BUT</u> $a_{k+1} = a_k + 3$ on its own <u>isn't enough</u> to describe 5, 8, 11, 14, 17, ...
> For example, the sequence 87, 90, 93, 96, 99, ... <u>also</u> has each term being 3 more than the one before.
>
> The description needs to be more <u>specific</u>, so you've got to <u>give one term</u> in the sequence, as well as the recurrence relation. You almost always give the <u>first value</u>, a_1.
>
> Putting all of this together gives 5, 8, 11, 14, 17, ... as $a_{k+1} = a_k + 3$, $a_1 = 5$.

Sequences

Some sequences involve **Multiplying**

You've done the easy 'adding' business. Now it gets really tough — <u>multiplying</u>. Are you sure you're ready for this...

EXAMPLE A sequence is defined by $a_{k+1} = 2a_k - 1$, $a_2 = 5$. List the first five terms.

OK, you're told the second term, $a_2 = 5$. Just plug that value into the equation, and carry on from there.

$a_3 = 2 \times 5 - 1 = 9$ *From the equation $a_k = a_2$ so $a_{k+1} = a_3$*

$a_4 = 2 \times 9 - 1 = 17$ *Now use a_3 to find $a_{k+1} = a_4$ and so on...*

$a_5 = 2 \times 17 - 1 = 33$

Now to find the first term, a_1: $a_2 = 2a_1 - 1$ *Just make $a_k = a_1$*
$$5 = 2a_1 - 1$$
$$2a_1 = 6$$
$$a_1 = 3$$

So the first five terms of the sequence are $3, 5, 9, 17, 33$.

Some Sequences have a **Certain Number** of terms — others go on **Forever**

Some sequences are only defined for a <u>certain number</u> of terms.   *It's the $1 \le k \le 20$ bit that tells you it's finite.*

For example, $a_{k+1} = a_k + 3$, $a_1 = 1$, $1 \le k \le 20$ will be 1, 4, 7, 10, ..., 58 and will contain 20 terms.
This is a finite sequence.

Other sequences <u>don't</u> have a specified number of terms and could go on <u>forever</u>.

For example, $u_{k+1} = u_k + 2$, $u_1 = 5$, will be 5, 7, 9, 11, 13, ... and won't have a final term.
This is an infinite sequence.

While others are <u>periodic</u>, and just revisit the same values over and over again.

For example, $u_k = u_{k-3}$, $u_1 = 1$, $u_2 = 4$, $u_3 = 2$, will be 1, 4, 2, 1, 4, 2, 1, 4, 2,...
This is a periodic sequence with period 3.

Convergent Sequences have a **Limit**

The terms of some sequences get <u>closer and closer</u> to a <u>limit</u> without ever reaching it — these sequences are called <u>convergent sequences</u>. If a sequence does not approach a limit, it is called a <u>divergent sequence</u>. For a convergent sequence defined by a relation $a_{k+1} = f(a_k)$, the limit can be found by solving $L = f(L)$.

EXAMPLE A sequence is defined by the relation $a_{k+1} = -\frac{1}{2}a_k + 2$. Find L, the limit of a_k as k tends to infinity.

You probably won't have to do this calculation in the exam, but you do need to know the difference between convergent and divergent sequences — so you still need to understand what's going on.

Here, $f(a_k) = -\frac{1}{2}a_k + 2$

Now take $L = f(L)$, which gives $L = -\frac{1}{2}L + 2$

'As k tends to infinity' just means 'as k gets really ruddy big'. You might also see it written as $k \to \infty$.

Rearranging: $\frac{3}{2}L = 2 \Rightarrow L = \frac{4}{3}$ So, the limit of the sequence as k tends to infinity is $\frac{4}{3}$.

Like maths teachers, sequences can go on and on and on and on...

If you know the formula for the nth term, you can work out any term using a single formula, so it's kind of easy. If you only know a recurrence relation, then you can only work out the <u>next</u> term. So if you want the 20th term, and you only know the first one, then you have to use the recurrence relation 19 times. (So it'd be quicker to work out a formula really.)

Arithmetic Progressions

Right, you've got basic sequences tucked under your belt now — time to step it up a notch (sounds painful).
When the terms of a sequence progress by adding a fixed amount each time, this is called an arithmetic progression.

It's all about **Finding** the nth Term

The first term of a sequence is given the symbol **a**. The amount you add each time is called the common difference, or **d**. The position of any term in the sequence is called **n**.

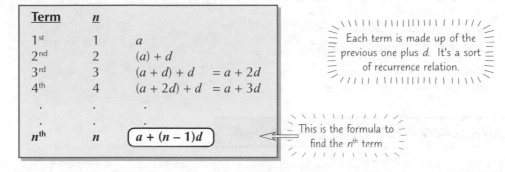

Term	n		
1st	1	a	
2nd	2	$(a) + d$	
3rd	3	$(a + d) + d$	$= a + 2d$
4th	4	$(a + 2d) + d$	$= a + 3d$
.	.	.	
.	.	.	
.	.	.	
nth	n	$\boxed{a + (n-1)d}$	

Each term is made up of the previous one plus d. It's a sort of recurrence relation.

This is the formula to find the nth term

EXAMPLE   Find the 20th term of the arithmetic progression 2, 5, 8, 11, … and find the formula for the nth term.

Here $a = 2$ and $d = 3$.

To get d, just find the difference between two terms next to each other — e.g. 11 − 8 = 3

So 20th term $= a + (20 - 1)d$
$= 2 + 19 \times 3$
$= 59$

The general term is the nth term, i.e.
$a + (n - 1)d$
$= 2 + (n - 1)3$
$= 3n - 1$

A **Series** is when you **Add the Terms** to **Find the Total**

S_n is the total of the first n terms of the arithmetic progression:

$$S_n = a + (a + d) + (a + 2d) + (a + 3d) + \ldots + (a + (n - 1)d)$$

There's a really neat version of the same formula too:

$$\boxed{S_n = n \times \frac{(a + l)}{2}}$$

The l stands for the last value in the progression. You work it out as $l = a + (n - 1)d$

Nobody likes formulas, so think of it as the average of the first and last terms multiplied by the number of terms.

EXAMPLE   Find the sum of the series with first term 3, last term 87 and common difference 4.

Here you know a, d and l, but you don't know n yet.

Use the information about the last value, l: $a + (n - 1)d = 87$

Then plug in the other values: $3 + 4(n - 1) = 87$

$4n - 4 = 84$

$n = 22$ means that there are 22 terms in the progression.

$4n = 88$

$n = 22$

$$S_{22} = 22 \times \frac{(3 + 87)}{2} \qquad S_{22} = 990$$

Arithmetic Series and Sigma Notation

They **Won't** always give you the **Last Term**...

...but don't panic — there's a formula to use when the <u>last term is unknown</u>. But you knew I'd say that, didn't you?

You know $l = a + (n - 1)d$ and $S_n = n \times \dfrac{(a + l)}{2}$.

Plug l into S_n and rearrange to get the formula in the box:

$$S_n = \frac{n}{2}[2a + (n - 1)d]$$

EXAMPLE For the sequence $-5, -2, 1, 4, 7, \ldots$
find the sum of the first 20 terms.

So $a = -5$ and $d = 3$.
The question says $n = 20$ too.

$$S_{20} = \frac{20}{2}[2 \times -5 + (20 - 1) \times 3]$$
$$= 10[-10 + 19 \times 3]$$
$$S_{20} = 470$$

There's **Another** way of **Writing Series**, too

So far, the letter S has been used for the sum. The Greeks did a lot of work on this — their capital letter for S is Σ or <u>sigma</u>. This is used today, together with the general term, to mean the <u>sum</u> of the series.

EXAMPLE

...and ending with $n = 15$

Find $\displaystyle\sum_{n=1}^{15}(2n + 3)$

Starting with $n = 1$...

This means you have to find the sum of the <u>first 15 terms</u> of the series with n^{th} term $2n + 3$.

The first term ($n = 1$) is 5, the second term ($n = 2$) is 7, the third is 9, ... and the last term ($n = 15$) is 33.

In other words, you need to find $5 + 7 + 9 + \ldots + 33$. This gives $a = 5$, $d = 2$, $n = 15$ and $l = 33$.

You know all of a, d, n and l, so you can use either formula:

$$S_n = n\frac{(a + l)}{2}$$
$$S_{15} = 15\frac{(5 + 33)}{2}$$
$$S_{15} = 15 \times 19$$
$$S_{15} = 285$$

It makes no difference which method you use.

$$S_n = \frac{n}{2}[2a + (n - 1)d]$$
$$S_{15} = \frac{15}{2}[2 \times 5 + 14 \times 2]$$
$$S_{15} = \frac{15}{2}[10 + 28]$$
$$S_{15} = 285$$

Use **Arithmetic Progressions** to add up the **First n Whole Numbers**

The <u>sum of the first n natural numbers</u> looks like this:

$$S_n = 1 + 2 + 3 + \ldots + (n - 2) + (n - 1) + n$$

So $a = 1$, $l = n$ and also $n = n$.
Now just plug those values into the formula:

Natural numbers are just positive whole numbers.

$$S_n = n \times \frac{(a + l)}{2} \implies S_n = \frac{1}{2}n(n + 1)$$

EXAMPLE

Add up all the whole numbers from 1 to 100.

Sounds pretty hard, but all you have to do is stick it into the formula:

$S_{100} = \frac{1}{2} \times 100 \times 101$. So $S_{100} = 5050$

It's pretty easy to <u>prove</u> this:

1) Say, $S_n = 1 + 2 + 3 + \ldots + (n - 2) + (n - 1) + n$ ①

2) ① is just addition, so it's also true that:
$S_n = n + (n - 1) + (n - 2) + \ldots + 3 + 2 + 1$ ②

3) Add ① and ② together to get:
$2S_n = (n + 1) + (n + 1) + (n + 1) + \ldots + (n + 1) + (n + 1) + (n + 1)$
$\Rightarrow 2S_n = n(n + 1) \Rightarrow S_n = \frac{1}{2}n(n + 1)$. Voilà.

This sigma notation is all Greek to me... (Ho ho ho)

A <u>sequence</u> is just a list of numbers (with commas between them) — a <u>series</u> on the other hand is when you add all the terms together. It doesn't sound like a big difference, but mathematicians get all hot under the collar when you get the two mixed up. Remember that Black<u>ADD</u>er was a great TV <u>series</u> — not a TV sequence. (Sounds daft, but I bet you remember it now.)

Geometric Progressions

You have a geometric progression when each term in a sequence is found by multiplying the previous term by a (constant) number. Let me explain...

Geometric Progressions Multiply by a Constant each time

Geometric progressions work like this: the next term in the sequence is obtained by multiplying the previous one by a constant value. Couldn't be easier.

$$u_1 = a \qquad\qquad = a$$
$$u_2 = a \times r \qquad\quad = ar$$
$$u_3 = a \times r \times r \quad = ar^2$$
$$u_4 = a \times r \times r \times r = ar^3$$

The first term (u_1) is called 'a'.

The number you multiply by each time is called 'the common ratio', symbolised by 'r'.

Here's the formula describing any term in the geometric progression:

$$u_n = ar^{n-1}$$

EXAMPLE

There is a chessboard with a 1p piece on the first square, 2p on the second square, 4p on the third, 8p on the fourth and so on until the board is full. Calculate how much money is on the board.

This is a geometric progression, where you get the next term in the sequence by multiplying the previous one by 2.

So $a = 1$ (because you start with 1p on the first square) and $r = 2$.

So $u_1 = 1$, $u_2 = 2$, $u_3 = 4$, $u_4 = 8...$

To be continued... (once we've gone over how to sum the terms of a geometric progression).

A Sequence becomes a Series when you Add the Terms to find the Total

S_n stands for the sum of the first underline{n} terms of the geometric progression.
In the example above, you're told to work out S_{64} (because there are 64 squares on a chessboard).

To work out the formula for the sum of a G.P. you use two series and subtract.

For a G.P.:
$$S_n = a + ar + ar^2 + ar^3 + ... + ar^{n-1}$$

Multiplying by r gives:
$$rS_n = ar + ar^2 + ar^3 + ... + ar^{n-2} + ar^{n-1} + ar^n$$

Subtracting gives:
$$S_n - rS_n = a - ar^n$$

Factorising:
$$(1-r)S_n = a(1-r^n) \implies \boxed{S_n = \frac{a(1-r^n)}{1-r}}$$

If the series were subtracted the other way around you'd get
$$S_n = \frac{a(r^n - 1)}{r-1}.$$
Both versions are correct.

So, back to the chessboard example:

$$a = 1, \; r = 2, \; n = 64 \quad S_{64} = \frac{1(1 - 2^{64})}{1-2}$$
$$S_{64} = 1.84 \times 10^{19} \text{ pence or } £1.84 \times 10^{17}$$

The whole is more than the sum of the parts — hmm, not in maths, it ain't...

You really need to understand the difference between arithmetic and geometric progressions — it's not hard, but it needs to be fixed firmly in your head. There are only a few formulas for sequences and series (the nth term of a sequence, the sum of the first n terms of a series), and these are in the formula book they give you — but make sure you know how to use them.

Geometric Progressions

Geometric progressions can either Grow or Shrink

In the chessboard example, each term was <u>bigger</u> than the previous one: 1, 2, 4, 8, 16, ...
You can create a series where each term is <u>smaller</u> than the previous one by using a <u>small value of r</u>.

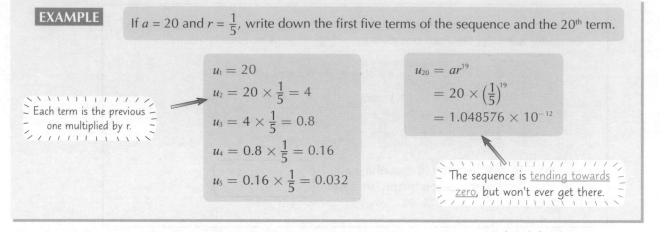

EXAMPLE   If $a = 20$ and $r = \frac{1}{5}$, write down the first five terms of the sequence and the 20th term.

$u_1 = 20$

$u_2 = 20 \times \frac{1}{5} = 4$

$u_3 = 4 \times \frac{1}{5} = 0.8$

$u_4 = 0.8 \times \frac{1}{5} = 0.16$

$u_5 = 0.16 \times \frac{1}{5} = 0.032$

Each term is the previous one multiplied by r.

$u_{20} = ar^{19}$

$= 20 \times \left(\frac{1}{5}\right)^{19}$

$= 1.048576 \times 10^{-12}$

The sequence is <u>tending towards zero</u>, but won't ever get there.

In general, for each term to be <u>smaller</u> than the one before, you need $|r| < 1$.
A sequence with $|r| < 1$ is <u>convergent</u>, since the terms converge to a limit.

$|r|$ means the modulus (or size) of r, <u>ignoring the sign</u> of the number. So $|r| < 1$ means that $-1 < r < 1$.

A Convergent Series has a Sum to Infinity

In other words, if you just <u>kept</u> adding terms to a <u>convergent series</u>, you'd get <u>closer and closer</u> to a certain number, but you'd never actually reach it.

If $|r| < 1$ and n is very, very <u>big</u>, then r^n will be very, very <u>small</u> — or to put it technically, $r^n \to 0$. (Try working out $(\frac{1}{2})^{100}$ on your calculator if you don't believe me.)

This means $(1 - r^n)$ is really, really close to 1.

So, as $n \to \infty$, $S_n \to \dfrac{a}{1-r}$.

It's easier to remember as $\boxed{S_\infty = \dfrac{a}{1-r}}$

S_∞ just means 'sum to infinity'.

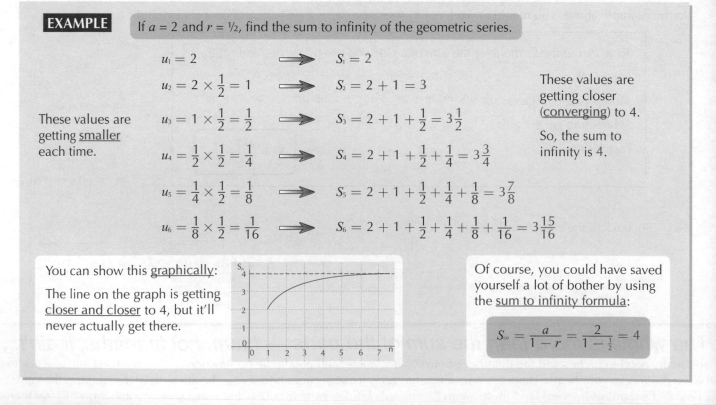

EXAMPLE   If $a = 2$ and $r = \frac{1}{2}$, find the sum to infinity of the geometric series.

$u_1 = 2$ $\Longrightarrow$ $S_1 = 2$

$u_2 = 2 \times \frac{1}{2} = 1$ $\Longrightarrow$ $S_2 = 2 + 1 = 3$

These values are getting <u>smaller</u> each time.

$u_3 = 1 \times \frac{1}{2} = \frac{1}{2}$ $\Longrightarrow$ $S_3 = 2 + 1 + \frac{1}{2} = 3\frac{1}{2}$

$u_4 = \frac{1}{2} \times \frac{1}{2} = \frac{1}{4}$ $\Longrightarrow$ $S_4 = 2 + 1 + \frac{1}{2} + \frac{1}{4} = 3\frac{3}{4}$

$u_5 = \frac{1}{4} \times \frac{1}{2} = \frac{1}{8}$ $\Longrightarrow$ $S_5 = 2 + 1 + \frac{1}{2} + \frac{1}{4} + \frac{1}{8} = 3\frac{7}{8}$

$u_6 = \frac{1}{8} \times \frac{1}{2} = \frac{1}{16}$ $\Longrightarrow$ $S_6 = 2 + 1 + \frac{1}{2} + \frac{1}{4} + \frac{1}{8} + \frac{1}{16} = 3\frac{15}{16}$

These values are getting closer (<u>converging</u>) to 4.

So, the sum to infinity is 4.

You can show this <u>graphically</u>:

The line on the graph is getting <u>closer and closer</u> to 4, but it'll never actually get there.

Of course, you could have saved yourself a lot of bother by using the <u>sum to infinity formula</u>:

$S_\infty = \dfrac{a}{1-r} = \dfrac{2}{1-\frac{1}{2}} = 4$

Geometric Progressions

A Divergent series Doesn't have a sum to infinity

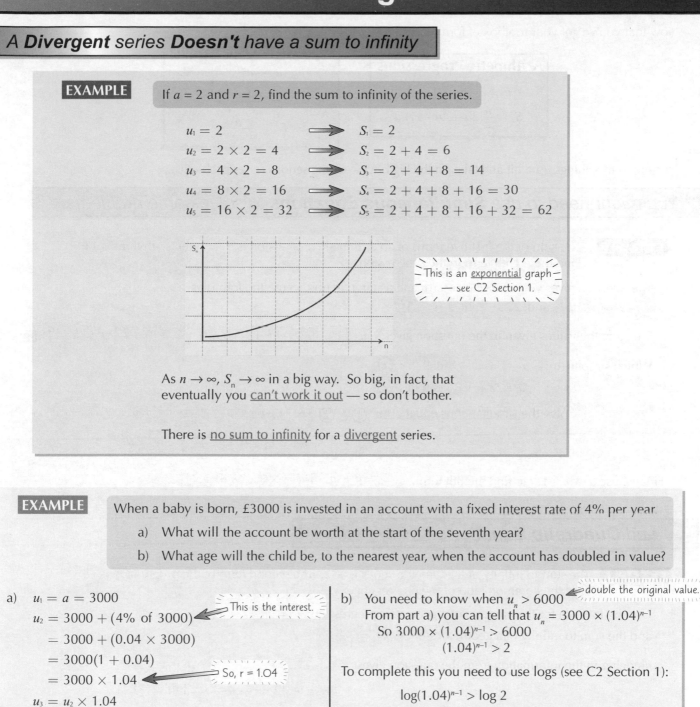

EXAMPLE If $a = 2$ and $r = 2$, find the sum to infinity of the series.

$u_1 = 2$ $\implies$ $S_1 = 2$
$u_2 = 2 \times 2 = 4$ $\implies$ $S_2 = 2 + 4 = 6$
$u_3 = 4 \times 2 = 8$ $\implies$ $S_3 = 2 + 4 + 8 = 14$
$u_4 = 8 \times 2 = 16$ $\implies$ $S_4 = 2 + 4 + 8 + 16 = 30$
$u_5 = 16 \times 2 = 32$ $\implies$ $S_5 = 2 + 4 + 8 + 16 + 32 = 62$

This is an <u>exponential</u> graph — see C2 Section 1.

As $n \to \infty$, $S_n \to \infty$ in a big way. So big, in fact, that eventually you <u>can't work it out</u> — so don't bother.

There is <u>no sum to infinity</u> for a <u>divergent</u> series.

EXAMPLE When a baby is born, £3000 is invested in an account with a fixed interest rate of 4% per year.

a) What will the account be worth at the start of the seventh year?

b) What age will the child be, to the nearest year, when the account has doubled in value?

a) $u_1 = a = 3000$

$u_2 = 3000 + (4\% \text{ of } 3000)$ ← This is the interest.

$= 3000 + (0.04 \times 3000)$

$= 3000(1 + 0.04)$

$= 3000 \times 1.04$ ← So, r = 1.04

$u_3 = u_2 \times 1.04$

$= (3000 \times 1.04) \times 1.04$

$= 3000 \times (1.04)^2$

$u_4 = 3000 \times (1.04)^3$

I've missed out some steps here — check that you understand what's happened.

$\vdots \qquad \vdots \qquad \vdots$

$u_7 = 3000 \times (1.04)^6$

$= £3795.96$ (to the nearest penny)

b) You need to know when $u_n > 6000$ ← double the original value.

From part a) you can tell that $u_n = 3000 \times (1.04)^{n-1}$

So $3000 \times (1.04)^{n-1} > 6000$

$(1.04)^{n-1} > 2$

To complete this you need to use logs (see C2 Section 1):

$\log(1.04)^{n-1} > \log 2$

$(n - 1) \log(1.04) > \log 2$

$n - 1 > \dfrac{\log 2}{\log 1.04}$

$n - 1 > 17.67$

$n > 18.67$ (to 2 d.p.)

So u_{19} (the amount at the start of the 19th year) will be more than double the original amount — plenty of time to buy a Porsche for the 21st birthday.

So tell me — if my savings earn 4% per year, when will I be rich...

Now here's a funny thing — you can have a convergent geometric series if the common ratio is small enough. I find this odd — that I can keep adding things to a sum forever, but the sum never gets really really big.

Sequence and Series Problems

Now that you've got your toolbox of formulas:

Arithmetic Progressions

$u_n = a + (n-1)d$

$S_n = \frac{n}{2}[2a + (n-1)d]$

Geometric Progressions

$u_n = ar^{n-1}$

$S_n = \frac{a(1-r^n)}{1-r}$

$S_\infty = \frac{a}{1-r}$

It's time to mix things up a bit and take on the big boys — some serious series problems...

You might need to use *Simultaneous Equations* to solve some problems...

EXAMPLE The sum of the first five terms of an arithmetic progression is 5, and the sixth term is 13. Find the eighth term in the progression.

The question gives you a particular term and a sum of terms, so use the formulas
$u_n = a + (n-1)d$ and $S_n = \frac{n}{2}[2a + (n-1)d]$.

Plugging the values given in the question gives: $u_6 = a + (6-1)d = 13$ and $S_5 = 5 = \frac{5}{2}[2a + (5-1)d]$

Which simplify to: $a + 5d = 13$, call this ①

$a + 2d = 1$, call this ②

Solve the <u>simultaneous equations</u>: ① − ② ⇒ $3d = 12$ ⇒ $d = 4$

$d = 4$ in ② ⇒ $a = 1 - 8 = -7$

Finally, use $a + (n-1)d$ to find the 8th term: $u_8 = a + (n-1)d = -7 + (7 \times 4) = 21$

... and *Quadratic Equations* to solve others

EXAMPLE The sum to infinity of a geometric series is −32. The second term of the progression is −8. Find the common ratio of the progression.

Use the formula for the *n*th term of a geometric progression: $u_n = ar^{n-1}$

and the sum to infinity of a geometric series: $S_\infty = \frac{a}{1-r}$

Plugging in the information from the question gives: $u_2 = ar = -8$, call this ①

$S_\infty = -32 = \frac{a}{1-r}$, call this ②

Rearrange ① into the form $a = -\frac{8}{r}$ in order to eliminate *a* from ②:

If you were trying to find *a*, then you would rearrange to eliminate *r* instead.

$$-32 = \frac{\left(\frac{-8}{r}\right)}{1-r}$$

$$-32(1-r) = \frac{(-8)}{r}$$

$$-32r + 32r^2 = -8$$

$$4r^2 - 4r + 1 = 0$$

$$(2r-1)^2 = 0$$

$$\Rightarrow 2r = 1, \quad r = \frac{1}{2}$$

This quadratic only has one root. If you get a quadratic with two roots, pick the one for which $|r| < 1$, as a series with a sum to infinity must be convergent.

At last – the series finalé...

Make sure you know which formulas apply to arithmetic and which to geometric progressions. You might have to use different combinations of them in the exam to get your simultaneous equations. Just look at what you are given in the question and what you are being asked to do, and use the corresponding formulas. That's all there is to it really.

C2 Section 2 — Practice Questions

What's that I hear you cry? You want revision questions — and lots of them. Well it just so happens I've got a few here. With sequences and series, get a <u>clear idea</u> in your head before you start, or you could go in completely the <u>wrong direction</u>. That would be bad.

Warm-up Questions

1) Find the <u>nth term</u> for the following sequences:

   a) 2, 6, 10, 14, ...

   b) 0.2, 0.7, 1.2, 1.7, ...

   c) 21, 18, 15, 12, ...

   d) 76, 70, 64, 58, ...

2) Find the <u>sum</u> of the arithmetic series that <u>begins with</u> 5, 8, ... and <u>ends with</u> 65.

3) An arithmetic series has <u>first term</u> 7 and <u>5th term</u> 23.

   Find: a) the common difference,   b) the 15th term,   and   c) the sum of the first 10 terms.

4) Find $\displaystyle\sum_{n=1}^{10}(48 - 5n)$

5) For the geometric progression 2, –6, 18, ..., find:

   a) the 10th term,

   b) the sum of the first 10 terms.

6) Find the sum of the first 12 terms of the following geometric series:

   a) 2 + 8 + 32 + ...

   b) 30 + 15 + 7.5 + ...

7) A geometric progression begins 2, 6, ...
   Which term of the geometric progression equals 1458?

More <u>lovingly crafted</u> questions, wrought from the <u>finest numbers</u> and <u>quality equations</u> for our valued customers...

Exam Questions

1   A sequence is defined by the recurrence relation: $h_{n+1} = 2h_n + 2$ when $n \geq 1$.

   a)   Given that $h_1 = 5$, find the values of h_2, h_3, and h_4.

   (3 marks)

   b)   Calculate the value of $\displaystyle\sum_{r=3}^{6} h_r$.

   (3 marks)

C2 Section 2 — Practice Questions

I like sequences, they're shiny and colourful and sparkly and... wait, what? ... Oh. Fiddlesticks.

2   A sequence $a_1, a_2, a_3, \ldots$ is defined by $a_1 = k$, $a_{n+1} = 3a_n + 11$, $n \geq 1$, where k is a constant.

     a)   Show that $a_4 = 27k + 143$.

(3 marks)

     b)   Find the value of k, given that $\displaystyle\sum_{r=1}^{4} a_r = 278$.

(3 marks)

3   Ned has 15 cuboidal pots that need filling with soil. Each pot is taller than the one before it. The different capacities of his 15 pots form an arithmetic sequence with first term (representing the smallest pot) a ml and the common difference d ml. The 7th pot is 580 ml and he will need a total of exactly 9525 ml of soil to fill all of them.

     Find the value of a and the value of d.

(7 marks)

4   The first term of an arithmetic sequence is 22 and the common difference is -1.1.

     a)   Find the value of the 31st term.

(2 marks)

     b)   If the kth term of the sequence is 0, find k.

(2 marks)

     c)   The sum to n terms of the sequence is S_n.
        Find the value of n at which S_n first becomes negative.

(4 marks)

5   David's personal trainer has given him a timetable to improve his upper-body strength, which gradually increases the amount of push-ups David does each day.

     The timetable for the first four days is shown below:

Day:	Mon	Tue	Wed	Thur
Number of push-ups:	6	14	22	30

     a)   Find an expression, in terms of n, for the number of push-ups he will have to do on day n.

(3 marks)

     b)   David follows his exercise routine for 10 days. Calculate how many push-ups he has done in total over the 10 days.

(3 marks)

     His personal trainer recommends that David takes a break from his exercise routine when he has done a cumulative total of 2450 push-ups. Given that David completes his exercises on day k, but reaches the recommended limit part-way through day $(k + 1)$,

     c)   Show that k satisfies $(2k - 49)(k + 25) < 0$.

(3 marks)

     d)   Find the value of k.

(2 marks)

C2 Section 2 — Practice Questions

Here come the final few...

6   A geometric series has the first term 12 and is defined by: $u_{n+1} = 12 \times 1.3^n$.

     a)   Is the series convergent or divergent?

(1 mark)

     b)   Find the values of the 3rd and 10th terms.

(2 marks)

7   In a geometric series, $a = 20$ and $r = \frac{3}{4}$.

     Find values for the following, giving your answers to 3 significant figures where necessary:

     a) S_∞

(2 marks)

     b) u_{15}

(2 marks)

     c)   The smallest value of n for which $S_n > 79.76$.

(5 marks)

8   To raise money for charity, Alex, Chris and Heather were sponsored £1 for each kilometre they ran over a 10-day period. They receive sponsorship proportionally for partial kilometres completed.

     Alex ran 3 km every day.

     Chris ran 2 km on day 1 and on each subsequent day ran 20% further than the day before.

     Heather ran 1 km on day 1 and on each subsequent day, she ran 50% further than the previous day.

     a)   How far did Heather run on day 5, to the nearest 10 metres?

(2 marks)

     b)   Show that day 10 is the first day that Chris runs further than 10 km.

(3 marks)

     c)   Find the total amount raised by the end of the 10 days, to the nearest penny.

(4 marks)

9   Two different geometric series have the same second term and sum to infinity:

         $u_2 = 5$ and $S_\infty = 36$.

     a)   Show that $36r^2 - 36r + 5 = 0$, where r represents the two possible ratios.

(4 marks)

     b)   Hence find the values of r, and the corresponding first terms, for both geometric series.

(4 marks)

Arc Length and Sector Area

Arc lengths and sector areas are easier than you'd think — once you've learnt two simple(ish) formulas.

Always work in **Radians** for **Arc Length** and **Sector Area Questions**

Remember — for arc length and sector area questions you've got to measure all the angles in radians.

The main thing is that you know how radians relate to degrees.
In short, 180 degrees = π radians. The table below shows you how to convert between the two units:

Converting angles	
Radians to degrees:	Degrees to radians:
Divide by π, multiply by 180.	Divide by 180, multiply by π.

Here's a table of some of the common angles you're going to need — in degrees and radians:

Degrees	0	30	45	60	90	120	180	270	360
Radians	0	$\frac{\pi}{6}$	$\frac{\pi}{4}$	$\frac{\pi}{3}$	$\frac{\pi}{2}$	$\frac{2\pi}{3}$	π	$\frac{3\pi}{2}$	2π

If you have part of a circle (like a section of pie chart), you can work out the length of the curved side, or the area of the 'slice of pie' — as long as you know the angle at the centre (θ) and the length of the radius (r). Read on...

You can find the **Length** of an **Arc** using a nice easy formula...

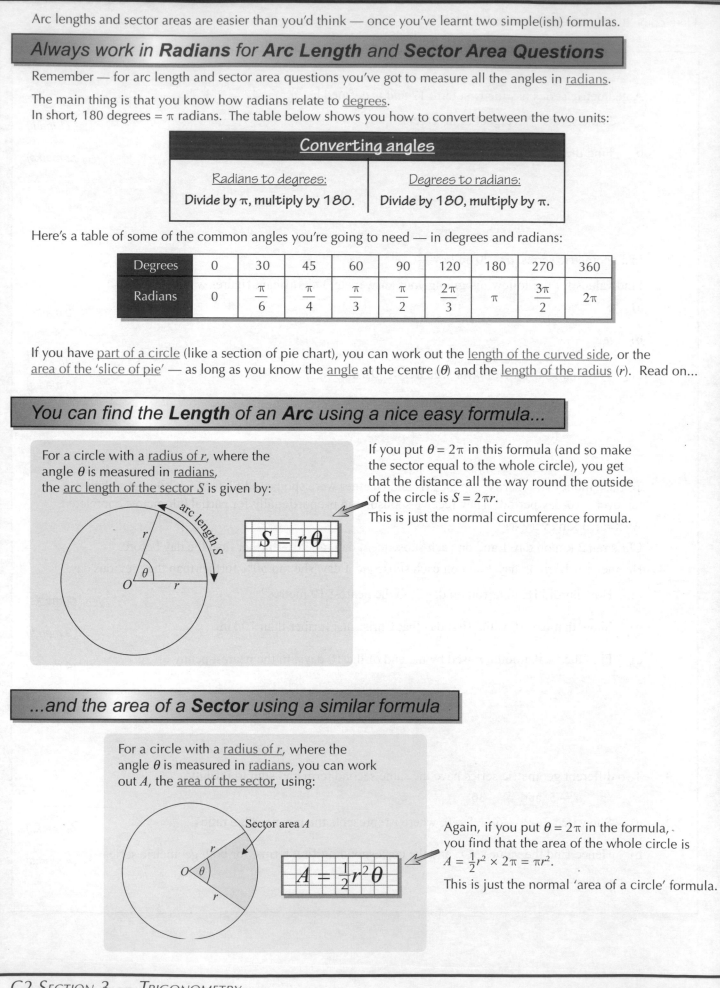

For a circle with a radius of r, where the angle θ is measured in radians, the arc length of the sector S is given by:

$$S = r\theta$$

If you put $\theta = 2\pi$ in this formula (and so make the sector equal to the whole circle), you get that the distance all the way round the outside of the circle is $S = 2\pi r$.

This is just the normal circumference formula.

...and the area of a **Sector** using a similar formula

For a circle with a radius of r, where the angle θ is measured in radians, you can work out A, the area of the sector, using:

Sector area A

$$A = \frac{1}{2}r^2\theta$$

Again, if you put $\theta = 2\pi$ in the formula, you find that the area of the whole circle is $A = \frac{1}{2}r^2 \times 2\pi = \pi r^2$.

This is just the normal 'area of a circle' formula.

Arc Length and Sector Area

Questions on <u>trigonometry</u> quite often use the same angles — so it makes life easier if you know the sin, cos and tan of these commonly used angles. Or to put it another way, examiners expect you to know them — so learn them.

Draw Triangles to remember sin, cos and tan of the Important Angles

You should know the values of <u>sin</u>, <u>cos</u> and <u>tan</u> at 30°, 60° and 45°. But to help you remember, you can draw these two groovy triangles. It may seem a complicated way to learn a few numbers, but it does make it easier. Honest.

The idea is you draw the triangles below, putting in their angles and side lengths. Then you can use them to work out special trig values like <u>sin 45°</u> or <u>cos 60°</u> more accurately than any calculator (which only gives a few decimal places).

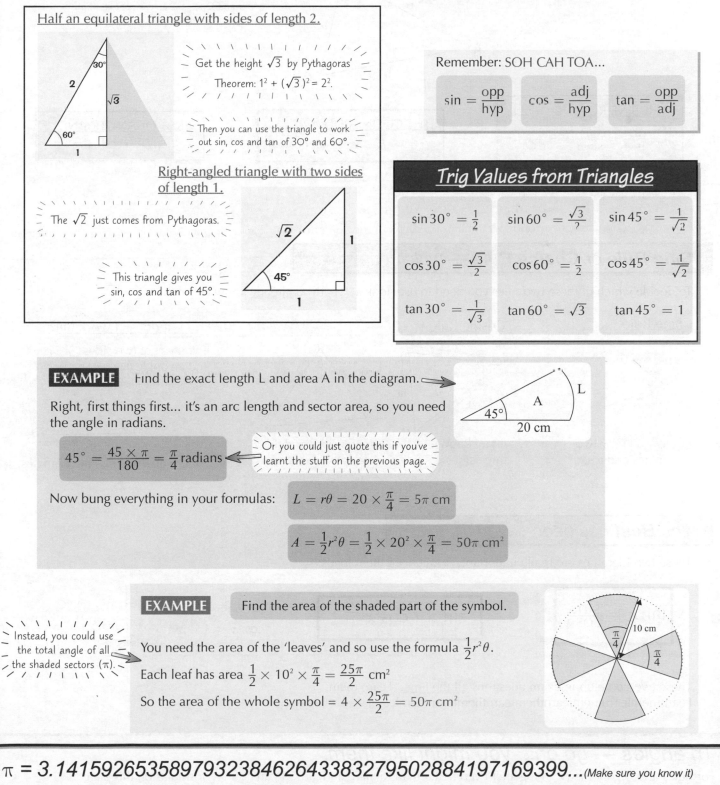

<u>Half an equilateral triangle with sides of length 2.</u>

Get the height $\sqrt{3}$ by Pythagoras' Theorem: $1^2 + (\sqrt{3})^2 = 2^2$.

Then you can use the triangle to work out sin, cos and tan of 30° and 60°.

<u>Right-angled triangle with two sides of length 1.</u>

The $\sqrt{2}$ just comes from Pythagoras.

This triangle gives you sin, cos and tan of 45°.

Remember: SOH CAH TOA...

$$\sin = \frac{opp}{hyp} \qquad \cos = \frac{adj}{hyp} \qquad \tan = \frac{opp}{adj}$$

Trig Values from Triangles

$\sin 30° = \frac{1}{2}$	$\sin 60° = \frac{\sqrt{3}}{2}$	$\sin 45° = \frac{1}{\sqrt{2}}$
$\cos 30° = \frac{\sqrt{3}}{2}$	$\cos 60° = \frac{1}{2}$	$\cos 45° = \frac{1}{\sqrt{2}}$
$\tan 30° = \frac{1}{\sqrt{3}}$	$\tan 60° = \sqrt{3}$	$\tan 45° = 1$

EXAMPLE Find the exact length L and area A in the diagram.

Right, first things first... it's an arc length and sector area, so you need the angle in radians.

$$45° = \frac{45 \times \pi}{180} = \frac{\pi}{4} \text{ radians}$$

Or you could just quote this if you've learnt the stuff on the previous page.

Now bung everything in your formulas:

$$L = r\theta = 20 \times \frac{\pi}{4} = 5\pi \text{ cm}$$

$$A = \frac{1}{2}r^2\theta = \frac{1}{2} \times 20^2 \times \frac{\pi}{4} = 50\pi \text{ cm}^2$$

EXAMPLE Find the area of the shaded part of the symbol.

Instead, you could use the total angle of all the shaded sectors (π).

You need the area of the 'leaves' and so use the formula $\frac{1}{2}r^2\theta$.

Each leaf has area $\frac{1}{2} \times 10^2 \times \frac{\pi}{4} = \frac{25\pi}{2}$ cm²

So the area of the whole symbol $= 4 \times \frac{25\pi}{2} = 50\pi$ cm²

$\pi = 3.14159265358979323846264338327950288419716939...$ *(Make sure you know it)*

It's worth repeating, just to make sure — those formulas for arc length and sector area only work if the angle is in <u>radians</u>.

The Trig Formulas You Need to Know

There are some more trig formulas you <u>need to know</u> for the exam.
So here they are — learn them or you're seriously stuffed. Worse than an aubergine.

The **Sine Rule** and **Cosine Rule** work for **Any** triangle

Remember, these three formulas work for <u>ANY</u> triangle, not just right-angled ones.

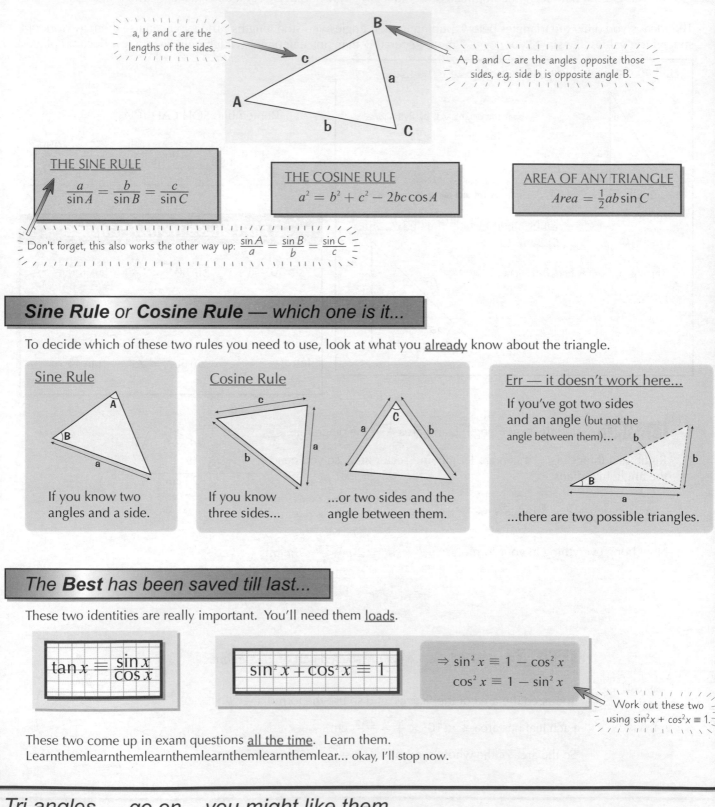

a, b and c are the lengths of the sides.

A, B and C are the angles opposite those sides, e.g. side b is opposite angle B.

THE SINE RULE
$$\frac{a}{\sin A} = \frac{b}{\sin B} = \frac{c}{\sin C}$$

THE COSINE RULE
$$a^2 = b^2 + c^2 - 2bc\cos A$$

AREA OF ANY TRIANGLE
$$Area = \tfrac{1}{2}ab\sin C$$

Don't forget, this also works the other way up: $\frac{\sin A}{a} = \frac{\sin B}{b} = \frac{\sin C}{c}$

Sine Rule or **Cosine Rule** — which one is it...

To decide which of these two rules you need to use, look at what you <u>already</u> know about the triangle.

Sine Rule

If you know two angles and a side.

Cosine Rule

If you know three sides...

...or two sides and the angle between them.

Err — it doesn't work here...

If you've got two sides and an angle (but not the angle between them)...

...there are two possible triangles.

The **Best** has been saved till last...

These two identities are really important. You'll need them <u>loads</u>.

$$\tan x \equiv \frac{\sin x}{\cos x}$$

$$\sin^2 x + \cos^2 x \equiv 1$$

$$\Rightarrow \sin^2 x \equiv 1 - \cos^2 x$$
$$\cos^2 x \equiv 1 - \sin^2 x$$

Work out these two using $\sin^2 x + \cos^2 x \equiv 1$.

These two come up in exam questions <u>all the time</u>. Learn them.
Learnthemlearnthemlearnthemlearnthemlearnthemlear... okay, I'll stop now.

Tri angles — go on... you might like them.

Formulas and trigonometry go together even better than Richard and Judy. I can count 7 formulas on this page.
That's not many, so please, just make sure you know them. If you haven't learnt them I will cry for you. I will sob. ♦ ☹ ♦

Using the Sine and Cosine Rules

This page is about "solving" triangles, which just means finding all their <u>sides</u> and <u>angles</u> when you already know a few.

EXAMPLE   Solve $\triangle ABC$, in which $A = 40°$, $a = 27$ m, $B = 73°$. Then find the area.

Draw a quick sketch first — don't worry if it's not deadly accurate, though.

You're given 2 angles and a side, so you need the Sine Rule.

> Make sure you put side *a* opposite angle A.

First of all, get the other angle: $\angle C = (180 - 40 - 73)° = 67°$

Then find the other sides, one at a time:

$$\frac{a}{\sin A} = \frac{b}{\sin B} \Rightarrow \frac{27}{\sin 40°} = \frac{b}{\sin 73°}$$
$$\Rightarrow b = \frac{\sin 73°}{\sin 40°} \times 27 = \underline{40.2\,\text{m}}$$

$$\frac{c}{\sin C} = \frac{a}{\sin A} \Rightarrow \frac{c}{\sin 67°} = \frac{27}{\sin 40°}$$
$$\Rightarrow c = \frac{\sin 67°}{\sin 40°} \times 27 = \underline{38.7\,\text{m}}$$

Now just use the formula to find its area.   Area of $\triangle ABC = \frac{1}{2}ab\sin C$

$$= \frac{1}{2} \times 27 \times 40.169 \times \sin 67°$$
$$= 499.2\,\text{m}^2$$

> Use a more accurate value for *b* here, rather than the rounded value 40.2.

EXAMPLE   Find X, Y and z.

6.5 cm   Y°   z   35°   X°   10 cm

You've been given 2 sides and the angle between them, so you're first going to need the Cosine Rule to find side z.

$$a^2 = b^2 + c^2 - 2bc\cos A$$

$$z^2 = (6.5)^2 + 10^2 - 2(6.5)(10)\cos 35°$$
$$\Rightarrow z^2 = 142.25 - 130\cos 35°$$
$$\Rightarrow z^2 = 35.7602$$
$$\Rightarrow z = \underline{5.98\,\text{cm}}$$

> In this case, angle A is 35°, and side *a* is actually z.

Now that you've got all the sides and one angle, you can use the Sine Rule to find the other two angles.

$$\frac{a}{\sin A} = \frac{b}{\sin B} = \frac{c}{\sin C}$$

> Remember — if $\frac{a}{\sin A} = \frac{b}{\sin B}$ then $\frac{\sin A}{a} = \frac{\sin B}{b}$

$$\frac{\sin X}{6.5} = \frac{\sin 35°}{5.9800}$$
$$\Rightarrow \sin X = 0.6235$$
$$\Rightarrow X = \sin^{-1} 0.6235$$
$$\Rightarrow X = \underline{38.6°}$$

> $\sin^{-1}$ is also called 'arcsin'.

$$\frac{\sin Y}{10} = \frac{\sin 35°}{5.9800}$$
$$\Rightarrow \sin Y = 0.9592$$
$$\Rightarrow Y = \sin^{-1} 0.9592$$
$$\Rightarrow Y = \underline{73.6°} \text{ or } \underline{106.4°}$$

> This is the answer you need. <u>Be careful</u>: your calculator only gives you values for $\sin^{-1}$ between $-90°$ and $90°$. See page 74.

Check your answers by adding up all the angles in the triangle. If they don't add up to 180°, you've gone wrong somewhere.

Graphs of Trig Functions

Before you leave this page, you should be able to close your eyes and picture these three graphs in your head, properly labelled and everything. If you can't, you need to learn them more. I'm not kidding.

sin x and cos x are always in the range –1 to 1

<u>sin x</u> and <u>cos x</u> are similar — they just bob up and down between –1 and 1.

sin x and cos x are both <u>periodic</u> (repeat themselves) with period 360°

$$\cos(x + 360°) = \cos x \qquad \sin(x + 360°) = \sin x$$

They bounce up and down from –1 to 1 — they can <u>never</u> have a value outside this range.

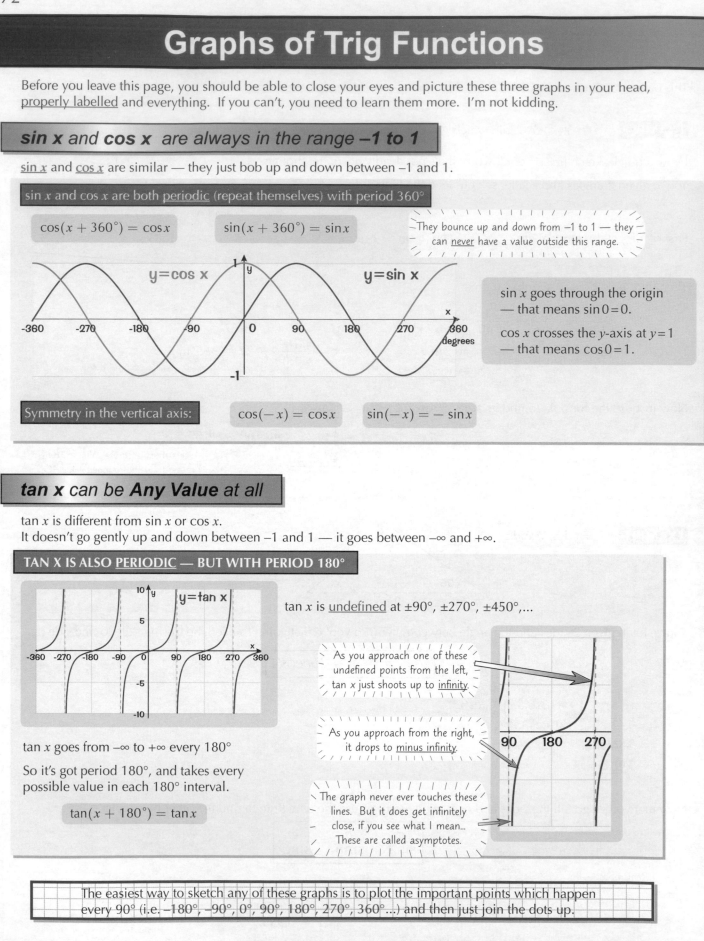

sin x goes through the origin — that means $\sin 0 = 0$.

cos x crosses the y-axis at y = 1 — that means $\cos 0 = 1$.

Symmetry in the vertical axis: $\qquad \cos(-x) = \cos x \qquad \sin(-x) = -\sin x$

tan x can be Any Value at all

tan x is different from sin x or cos x.
It doesn't go gently up and down between –1 and 1 — it goes between –∞ and +∞.

TAN X IS ALSO PERIODIC — BUT WITH PERIOD 180°

tan x is <u>undefined</u> at ±90°, ±270°, ±450°,...

As you approach one of these undefined points from the left, tan x just shoots up to <u>infinity</u>.

As you approach from the right, it drops to <u>minus infinity</u>.

The graph never ever touches these lines. But it does get infinitely close, if you see what I mean... These are called asymptotes.

tan x goes from –∞ to +∞ every 180°

So it's got period 180°, and takes every possible value in each 180° interval.

$$\tan(x + 180°) = \tan x$$

The easiest way to sketch any of these graphs is to plot the important points which happen every 90° (i.e. –180°, –90°, 0°, 90°, 180°, 270°, 360°...) and then just join the dots up.

Sin and cos can make your life worthwhile — give them a chance...

It's really really really really really important that you can draw the trig graphs on this page, and get all the labels right. Make sure you know what value sin, cos and tan have at the interesting points — i.e. 0°, 90°, 180°, 270°, 360°. It's easy to remember what the graphs look like, but you've got to know exactly <u>where</u> they're max, min, zero, etc.

Graph Transformations

Remember the graph <u>translations</u> you saw back in C1? Well there are a couple of other kinds of graph transformations you need to know about. Happily, all these transformations work <u>just the same</u> for trig graphs as they do for <u>all the other</u> different kinds of functions you've seen so far.

Stretches and *Reflections* are caused by *Multiplying* things

$y = af(x)$ <u>Multiplying</u> the <u>whole function</u> <u>stretches</u>, <u>squeezes</u> or <u>reflects</u> the graph <u>vertically</u>.

1) <u>Negative</u> values of 'a' <u>reflect</u> the basic shape in the <u>x-axis</u>.

2) If $a > 1$ or $a < -1$ (i.e. $|a| > 1$) the graph is <u>stretched vertically</u>.

3) If $-1 < a < 1$ (i.e. $|a| < 1$) the graph is <u>squashed vertically</u>.

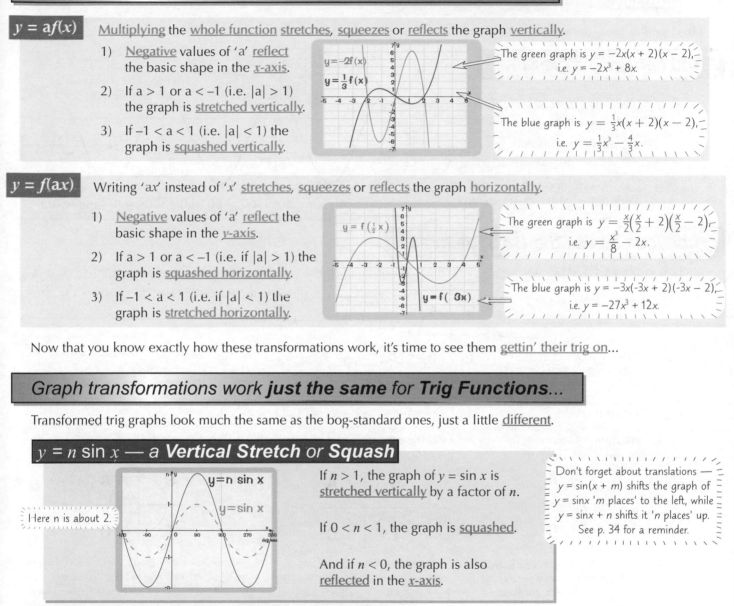

The green graph is $y = -2x(x + 2)(x - 2)$, i.e. $y = -2x^3 + 8x$.

The blue graph is $y = \frac{1}{3}x(x + 2)(x - 2)$, i.e. $y = \frac{1}{3}x^3 - \frac{4}{3}x$.

$y = f(ax)$ Writing 'ax' instead of 'x' <u>stretches</u>, <u>squeezes</u> or <u>reflects</u> the graph <u>horizontally</u>.

1) <u>Negative</u> values of 'a' <u>reflect</u> the basic shape in the <u>y-axis</u>.

2) If $a > 1$ or $a < -1$ (i.e. if $|a| > 1$) the graph is <u>squashed horizontally</u>.

3) If $-1 < a < 1$ (i.e. if $|a| < 1$) the graph is <u>stretched horizontally</u>.

The green graph is $y = \frac{x}{2}\left(\frac{x}{2} + 2\right)\left(\frac{x}{2} - 2\right)$, i.e. $y = \frac{x^3}{8} - 2x$.

The blue graph is $y = -3x(-3x + 2)(-3x - 2)$, i.e. $y = -27x^3 + 12x$.

Now that you know exactly how these transformations work, it's time to see them <u>gettin' their trig on</u>...

Graph transformations work *just the same* for *Trig Functions*...

Transformed trig graphs look much the same as the bog-standard ones, just a little <u>different</u>.

$y = n \sin x$ — a *Vertical Stretch* or *Squash*

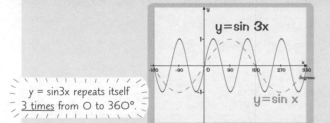

Here n is about 2.

If $n > 1$, the graph of $y = \sin x$ is <u>stretched vertically</u> by a factor of n.

If $0 < n < 1$, the graph is <u>squashed</u>.

And if $n < 0$, the graph is also <u>reflected</u> in the <u>x-axis</u>.

Don't forget about translations — $y = \sin(x + m)$ shifts the graph of $y = \sin x$ 'm places' to the left, while $y = \sin x + n$ shifts it 'n places' up. See p. 34 for a reminder.

$y = \sin nx$ — a *Horizontal Squash* or *Stretch*

$y = \sin 3x$ repeats itself 3 times from O to 360°.

If $n > 1$, the graph of $y = \sin x$ is <u>squashed horizontally</u> by a factor of n.

If $0 < n < 1$, the graph is <u>stretched</u>.

And if $n < 0$, the graph is also <u>reflected</u> in the <u>y-axis</u>.

Curling up on the sofa with 2cos x — that's my idea of cosiness ☺

One thing you've got to be ever so careful about here is making sure you transform the graphs in the <u>right</u> direction. It can get a bit confusing with the horizontal and vertical stretching and squashing — in the trig transformations above, $n > 1$ means a <u>vertical stretch</u> but a <u>horizontal squash</u>. Other than that, it's not too difficult — so just sit back and enjoy.

Solving Trig Equations in a Given Interval

I used to really hate trig stuff like this. But once I'd got the hang of it, I just couldn't get enough. I stopped going out, lost interest in the opposite sex — the CAST method became my life. Learn it, but be careful. It's addictive.

There are **Two Ways** to find Solutions in an **Interval**...

EXAMPLE Solve $\cos x = \frac{1}{2}$ for $-360° \leq x \leq 720°$.

Like I said — there are two ways to solve this kind of question. Just use the one you prefer...

You can draw a **graph**...

Your calculator gives you a solution of 60°. Then you have to work out what the others will be.

The other solutions are 60° either side of the graph's peaks.

1) Draw the graph of $y = \cos x$ for the range you're interested in...

2) Get the first solution from your calculator and mark this on the graph,

3) Use the symmetry of the graph to work out what the other solutions are:

So the solutions are: $-300°$, $-60°$, $60°$, $300°$, $420°$ and $660°$.

...or you can use the **CAST** diagram

CAST stands for COS, ALL, SIN, TAN — and the CAST diagram shows you where these functions are positive:

Between 90° and 180°, only SIN is positive.

Between 0 and 90°, ALL of sin, cos and tan are positive.

Between 180° and 270°, only TAN is positive.

Between 270° and 360°, only COS is positive.

This is positive — so you're only interested in where cos is positive.

First, to find all the values of x between 0° and 360° where $\cos x = \frac{1}{2}$ — you do this:

Put the first solution onto the CAST diagram.	Find the other angles between 0° and 360° that might be solutions.	Ditch the ones that are the wrong sign.

The angle from your calculator goes anticlockwise from the x-axis (unless it's negative — then it would go clockwise into the 4th quadrant).

The other possible solutions come from making the same angle from the horizontal axis in the other 3 quadrants.

$\cos x = ½$, which is positive. The CAST diagram tells you cos is positive in the 4th quadrant — but not the 2nd or 3rd — so ditch those two angles.

So you've got solutions 60° and 300° in the range 0° to 360°. But you need all the solutions in the range $-360°$ to 720°. Get these by repeatedly adding or subtracting 360° onto each until you go out of range:

$x = 60° \Rightarrow$ (adding 360°) $x = 420°$, 780° (too big)

and (subtracting 360°) $x = -300°$, $-660°$ (too small)

$x = 300° \Rightarrow$ (adding 360°) $x = 660°$, 1020° (too big)

and (subtracting 360°) $x = -60°$, $-420°$ (too small)

So the solutions are: $x = -300°$, $-60°$, $60°$, $300°$, $420°$ and $660°$.

And I feel that love is dead, I'm loving angles instead...

Suppose the first solution you get is negative, let's say $-d°$, then you'd measure it clockwise on the CAST diagram. So it'd be $d°$ in the 4th quadrant. Then you'd work out the other 3 possible solutions in exactly the same way, rejecting the ones which weren't the right sign. Got that? No? Got that? No? Got that? Yes? Good!

Solving Trig Equations in a Given Interval

Sometimes it's a bit more complicated. But only a bit.

Sometimes you end up with *sin kx = number*

For these, it's definitely easier to draw the <u>graph</u> rather than use the CAST method —
that's one reason why being able to sketch trig graphs properly is so important.

EXAMPLE Solve: $\sin 3x = -\dfrac{1}{\sqrt{2}}$ for $0° \leq x \leq 360°$.

You could get a question like this involving cos kx or tan kx instead — the method's the same as for sin, but make sure you're happy dealing with all three.

1) You've got $3x$ instead of x, which means the range you need to find solutions
    in is $0° \leq 3x \leq 1080°$. So draw the graph of $y = \sin x$ between $0°$ and $1080°$.

2) Use your calculator to find the first solution. You'll get $3x = -45°$ — but this
    is outside the range for $3x$, so use the pattern of the graph to find a solution in the
    range. As the sin curve repeats every $360°$, there'll be a solution at $360 - 45 = 315°$.

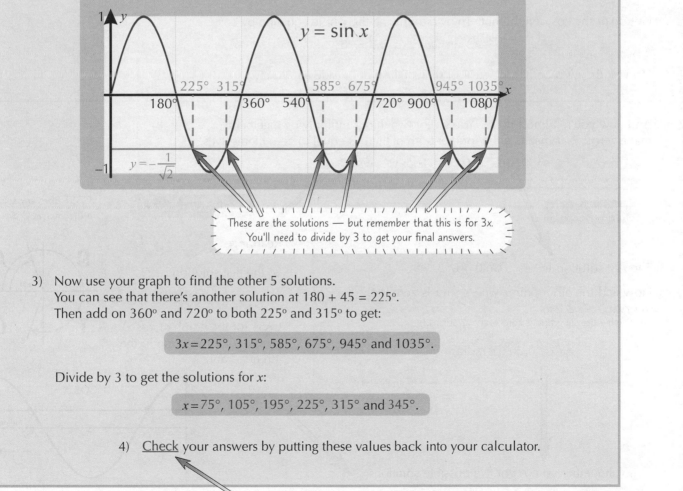

*These are the solutions — but remember that this is for $3x$.
You'll need to divide by 3 to get your final answers.*

3) Now use your graph to find the other 5 solutions.
    You can see that there's another solution at $180 + 45 = 225°$.
    Then add on $360°$ and $720°$ to both $225°$ and $315°$ to get:

    $$3x = 225°, 315°, 585°, 675°, 945° \text{ and } 1035°.$$

    Divide by 3 to get the solutions for x:

    $$x = 75°, 105°, 195°, 225°, 315° \text{ and } 345°.$$

4) <u>Check</u> your answers by putting these values back into your calculator.

*It really is mega-important that you check these
answers — it's dead easy to make a silly mistake.
They should all be in the range $0° \leq x \leq 360°$.*

Live a life of sin (and cos and tan)...

Yep, the example on this page is pretty fiddly. The most important bit is actually getting the sketch right for your new range.
If you don't, you're in big trouble. Then you've just got to carefully use the sketch to work out the other solutions.
It's tricky, but you'll feel better about yourself when you've got it mastered. Ah you will, you will, you will ...

Solving Trig Equations in a Given Interval

Now for something really exciting — trig identities. Mmm, well, maybe exciting was the wrong word. But they can be dead useful, so here goes...

For equations with **tan x** in, it often helps to use this...

$$\tan x \equiv \frac{\sin x}{\cos x}$$

This is a handy thing to know — and one the examiners love testing. Basically, if you've got a trig equation with a tan in it, together with a sin or a cos — chances are you'll be better off if you rewrite the tan using this formula.

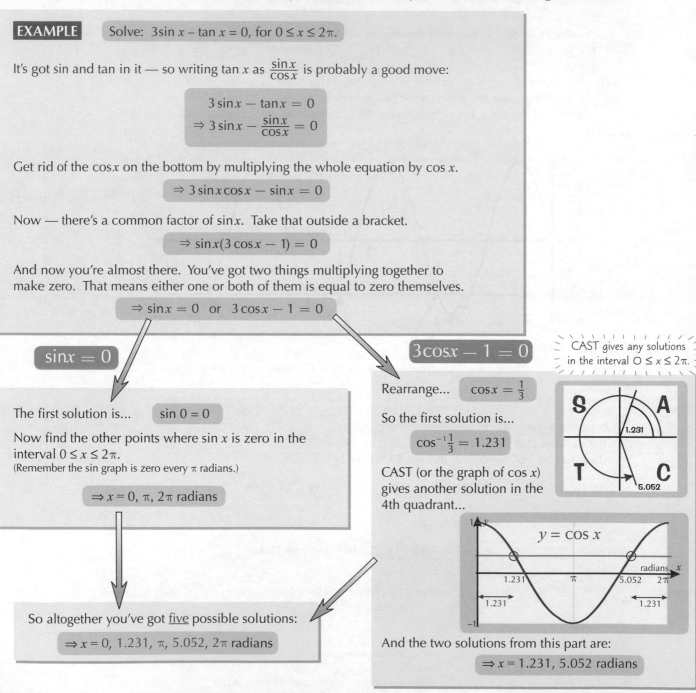

EXAMPLE   Solve: $3\sin x - \tan x = 0$, for $0 \le x \le 2\pi$.

It's got sin and tan in it — so writing $\tan x$ as $\frac{\sin x}{\cos x}$ is probably a good move:

$$3\sin x - \tan x = 0$$
$$\Rightarrow 3\sin x - \frac{\sin x}{\cos x} = 0$$

Get rid of the $\cos x$ on the bottom by multiplying the whole equation by $\cos x$.

$$\Rightarrow 3\sin x \cos x - \sin x = 0$$

Now — there's a common factor of $\sin x$. Take that outside a bracket.

$$\Rightarrow \sin x(3\cos x - 1) = 0$$

And now you're almost there. You've got two things multiplying together to make zero. That means either one or both of them is equal to zero themselves.

$$\Rightarrow \sin x = 0 \quad \text{or} \quad 3\cos x - 1 = 0$$

$\sin x = 0$

The first solution is... $\sin 0 = 0$

Now find the other points where $\sin x$ is zero in the interval $0 \le x \le 2\pi$.
(Remember the sin graph is zero every π radians.)

$$\Rightarrow x = 0, \pi, 2\pi \text{ radians}$$

So altogether you've got <u>five</u> possible solutions:

$$\Rightarrow x = 0, 1.231, \pi, 5.052, 2\pi \text{ radians}$$

$3\cos x - 1 = 0$

CAST gives any solutions in the interval $0 \le x \le 2\pi$.

Rearrange... $\cos x = \frac{1}{3}$

So the first solution is...

$$\cos^{-1}\frac{1}{3} = 1.231$$

CAST (or the graph of $\cos x$) gives another solution in the 4th quadrant...

$y = \cos x$

And the two solutions from this part are:

$$\Rightarrow x = 1.231, 5.052 \text{ radians}$$

Trigonometry is the root of all evil...

What a page — you don't have fun like that every day, do you? No, trig equations are where it's at. This is a really useful trick, though — and can turn a nightmare of an equation into a bit of a pussycat. <u>Rewriting</u> stuff using <u>different</u> formulas is always worth trying if it feels like you're getting stuck — even if you're not sure why when you're doing it. You might have a flash of inspiration when you see the new version.

Solving Trig Equations in a Given Interval

Another trig identity — and it's a good 'un — examiners love it. And it's not difficult either.

And if you have a **sin² x** or a **cos² x**, think of this straight away...

$$\sin^2 x + \cos^2 x \equiv 1 \implies \begin{array}{l} \sin^2 x \equiv 1 - \cos^2 x \\ \cos^2 x \equiv 1 - \sin^2 x \end{array}$$

Use this identity to get rid of a sin² or a cos² that's making things awkward...

EXAMPLE   Solve: $2\sin^2 x + 5\cos x = 4$, for $0° \leq x \leq 360°$.

You can't do much while the equation's got both sin's and cos's in it. So replace the sin²x bit with 1 − cos²x.

$$2(1 - \cos^2 x) + 5\cos x = 4$$

Multiply out the bracket and rearrange it so that you've got zero on one side — and you get a quadratic in cosx:

Now the only trig function is cos.

$$\Rightarrow 2 - 2\cos^2 x + 5\cos x - 4$$
$$\Rightarrow 2\cos^2 x - 5\cos x + 2 = 0$$

This is a quadratic in cosx. It's easier to factorise this if you make the substitution $y = \cos x$.

$$2y^2 - 5y + 2 = 0$$
$$\Rightarrow (2y - 1)(y - 2) = 0$$
$$\Rightarrow (2\cos x - 1)(\cos x - 2) = 0$$

$2y^2 - 5y + 2 = (2y\ ?)(y\ ?)$
$= (2y - 1)(y - 2)$

Now one of the brackets must be 0. So you get 2 equations as usual:

You've already done this example on page 74.

$$2\cos x - 1 = 0 \quad \text{or} \quad \cos x - 2 = 0$$

This is a bit weird. cos x is always between −1 and 1. So you don't get any solutions from this bracket.

$$\cos x = \tfrac{1}{2} \Rightarrow x = 60° \quad \text{or} \quad x = 300° \quad \text{and} \quad \cos x = 2$$

So at the end of all that, the only solutions you get are $x = 60°$ and $x = 300°$. How boring.

Use the **Trig Identities** to prove something is the **Same** as something else

Another use for these trig identities is proving that two things are the same.

EXAMPLE   Show that $\dfrac{\cos^2\theta}{1 + \sin\theta} = 1 - \sin\theta$

The identity sign ≡ means that this is true for all θ, rather than just certain values.

Prove things like this by playing about with one side of the equation until you get the other side.

$$\underline{\text{Left-hand side}}: \frac{\cos^2\theta}{1 + \sin\theta}$$

The only thing I can think of doing here is replacing cos² θ with 1 − sin² θ. (Which is good because it works.)

$$\equiv \frac{1 - \sin^2\theta}{1 + \sin\theta}$$

The next trick is the hardest to spot. Look at the top — does that remind you of anything?

The top line is a difference of two squares:

$$\equiv \frac{(1 + \sin\theta)(1 - \sin\theta)}{1 + \sin\theta}$$

$1 - a^2 = (1 + a)(1 - a)$
$\Rightarrow 1 - \sin^2\theta = (1 + \sin\theta)(1 - \sin\theta)$

$$\equiv 1 - \sin\theta, \underline{\text{the right-hand side}}.$$

Trig identities — the path to a brighter future...

That was a pretty miserable section. But it's over. These trig identities aren't exactly a barrel of laughs, but they are a definite source of marks — you can bet your last penny they'll be in the exam. That substitution trick to get rid of a sin² or a cos² and end up with a quadratic in sin x or cos x is a real examiners' favourite. Those identities can be a bit daunting, but it's always worth having a few tricks in the back of your mind — always look for things that factorise, or fractions that can be cancelled down, or ways to use those trig identities. Ah, it's all good clean fun.

C2 Section 3 — Practice Questions

I know, I know — that was a long section. And, rather predictably, it's followed by lots of <u>practice questions</u>. <u>Brace yourself</u> for the warm-up — this is going to be a <u>heavy session</u>...

Warm-up Questions

1) Write down the exact values of cos 30°, sin 30°, tan 30°, cos 45°, sin 45°, tan 45°, cos 60°, sin 60° and tan 60°.

2) Draw a triangle $\triangle XYZ$ with sides of length x, y and z. Write down the Sine and Cosine Rules for this triangle. Write down an expression for its area.

3) What is tan x in terms of cos x and sin x? What is $\cos^2 x$ in terms of $\sin^2 x$?

4) Solve: a) $\triangle ABC$ in which A = 30°, C = 25°, $b = 6$ m, and find its area.
   b) $\triangle PQR$ in which $p = 3$ km, $q = 23$ km, R = 10°. (Answers to 2 d.p.)

5) My pet triangle Freda has sides of length 10, 20 and 25. Find her angles (in degrees to 1 d.p.)

6) Find the 2 possible triangles $\triangle ABC$ which satisfy $b = 5$, $a = 3$, A = 35°. (This is tricky: Try sketching it first, and see if you can work out how to make 2 different triangles satisfying the data given.)

7) Sketch the graphs for sin$x$, cos$x$ and tan$x$. Make sure you label all the max/min/zero/undefined points.

8) Sketch the following graphs:
   a) $y = \frac{1}{2}\cos x$ (for $0° \leq x \leq 360°$)   b) $y = \tan 3x$ (for $0° \leq x \leq 180°$)

9) a) Solve each of these equations for $0° \leq \theta \leq 360°$:
   (i) $\sin\theta = -\frac{\sqrt{3}}{2}$ (ii) $\tan\theta = -1$ (iii) $\cos\theta = -\frac{1}{\sqrt{2}}$
   b) Solve each of these equations for $-180° \leq \theta \leq 180°$ (giving your answer to 1 d.p.):
   (i) $\cos 4\theta = -\frac{2}{3}$ (ii) $\sin 2\theta = 0.3$ (iii) $\tan\left(\frac{1}{2}\theta\right) = 500$

10) Find all the solutions to $6\sin^2 x = \cos x + 5$ in the range $0° \leq x \leq 360°$ (answers to 1 d.p.).

11) Solve $3\tan x + 2\cos x = 0$ for $-90° \leq x \leq 90°$

12) Simplify: $(\sin y + \cos y)^2 + (\cos y - \sin y)^2$

13) Show that $\frac{\sin^4 x + \sin^2 x \cos^2 x}{\cos^2 x - 1} \equiv -1$

Well after that vigorous warm-up you should be more than ready to tackle this <u>mental marathon</u> of exam-style questions. Take your time to work out <u>what each question wants</u> — if it looks impossible, there's probably a way of simplifying it somehow. A picture paints a thousand words, so <u>sketch it out</u> if you're totally confused.

Exam Questions

1   For an angle x, $3\cos x = 2\sin x$.

   a)   Find tan x.
                                                                                    (2 marks)

   b)   Hence, or otherwise, find all the values of x, in the interval $0 \leq x \leq 360°$, for which $3\cos x = 2\sin x$, giving your answers to 1 d.p.
                                                                                    (2 marks)

C2 Section 3 — Practice Questions

Okay, okay — since you asked so nicely, here are another two whole pages of exam questions.
Don't say I never give you anything.

2

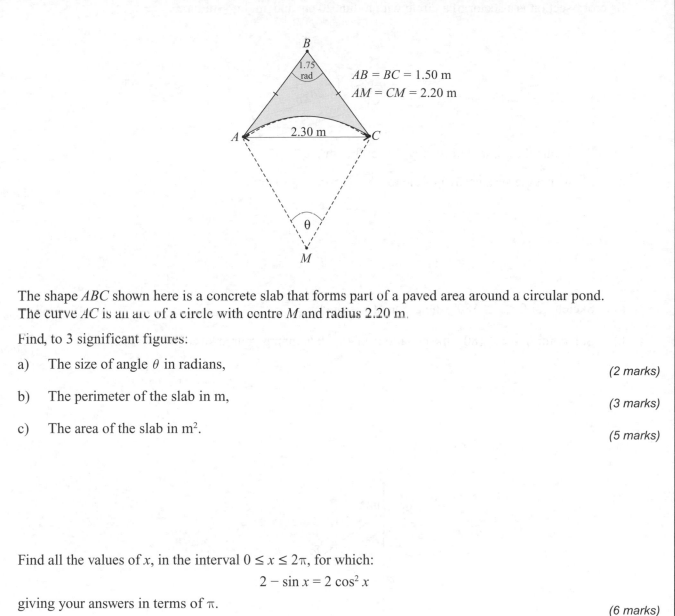

The shape *ABC* shown here is a concrete slab that forms part of a paved area around a circular pond. The curve *AC* is an arc of a circle with centre *M* and radius 2.20 m.

Find, to 3 significant figures:

a) The size of angle θ in radians,

(2 marks)

b) The perimeter of the slab in m,

(3 marks)

c) The area of the slab in m².

(5 marks)

3 Find all the values of *x*, in the interval $0 \leq x \leq 2\pi$, for which:
$$2 - \sin x = 2 \cos^2 x$$
giving your answers in terms of π.

(6 marks)

4 Solve the following equations, for $-\pi \leq x \leq \pi$:

a) $(1 + 2 \cos x)(3 \tan^2 x - 1) = 0$

(6 marks)

b) $3 \cos^2 x = \sin^2 x$

(4 marks)

5   The diagram below shows the dimensions of a child's wooden toy. The toy is a prism with height 10 cm. Its cross-section is a sector of a circle with radius 20 cm and angle $\frac{\pi}{4}$ radians.

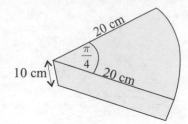

a)   Show that the volume of the toy, $V = 500\pi$ cm³.

(3 marks)

b)   Show that the surface area of the toy, $S = (150\pi + 400)$ cm².

(5 marks)

6   a)   Sketch, for $0 \le x \le 180°$, the graph of $y = \sin 4x$.

(2 marks)

b)   Solve, for $0 \le x \le 180°$, the equation $\sin 4x = 0.5$, giving your answers in degrees.

(4 marks)

7

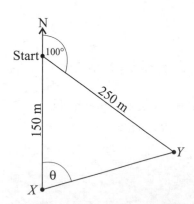

The diagram shows the locations of two walkers, X and Y, after walking in different directions from the same start position.

X walked due south for 150 m. Y walked 250 m on a bearing of 100°.

a)   Calculate the distance between the two walkers to the nearest m.

(2 marks)

b)   Show that $\dfrac{\sin\theta}{\sin 80°} = 0.93$ to 2 decimal places.

(3 marks)

Differentiation

Brrrrr... differentiation is a bad one — it really is. Not because it's that hard, but because it comes up all over the place in exams. So if you don't know it perfectly, you're asking for trouble. <u>Differentiation</u> is a great way to work out <u>gradients</u> of graphs. You take a function, differentiate it, and you can quickly tell <u>how steep</u> a graph is. It's magic.

Use this formula to differentiate **Powers of x**

$\frac{d}{dx}$ just means 'the derivative of the thing in the brackets with respect to x'.

$$\frac{d}{dx}(x^n) = nx^{n-1}$$

<u>Derivative</u> just means 'the thing you get when you differentiate something'.

Equations are much easier to differentiate when they're written as <u>powers of x</u> — like writing $\sqrt{x}$ as $x^{\frac{1}{2}}$.

When you've done this, you can use the formula (the thing in the red box above) to differentiate the equation.

Use the differentiation formula...

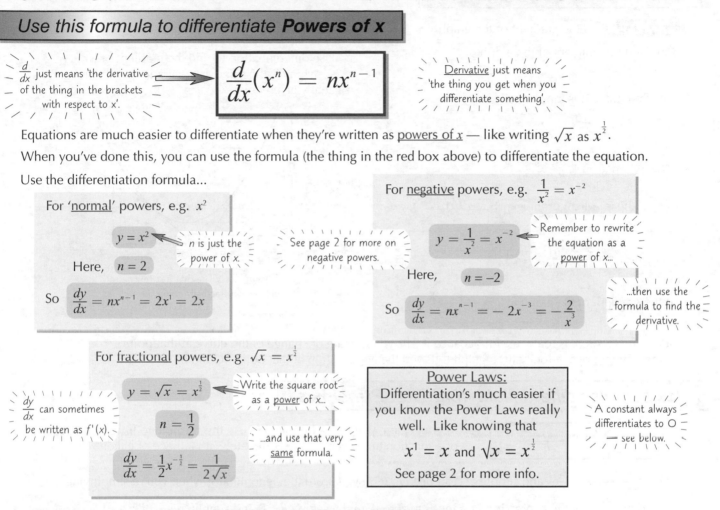

For '<u>normal</u>' powers, e.g. x^2

$$y = x^2$$

n is just the power of x.

See page 2 for more on negative powers.

Here, $n = 2$

So $\frac{dy}{dx} = nx^{n-1} = 2x^1 = 2x$

For <u>negative</u> powers, e.g. $\frac{1}{x^2} = x^{-2}$

$$y = \frac{1}{x^2} = x^{-2}$$

Remember to rewrite the equation as a <u>power</u> of x...

Here, $n = -2$

So $\frac{dy}{dx} = nx^{n-1} = -2x^{-3} = -\frac{2}{x^3}$

...then use the formula to find the derivative.

For <u>fractional</u> powers, e.g. $\sqrt{x} = x^{\frac{1}{2}}$

$$y = \sqrt{x} = x^{\frac{1}{2}}$$

Write the square root as a <u>power</u> of x...

$\frac{dy}{dx}$ can sometimes be written as $f'(x)$.

$$n = \frac{1}{2}$$

...and use that very <u>same</u> formula.

$$\frac{dy}{dx} = \frac{1}{2}x^{-\frac{1}{2}} = \frac{1}{2\sqrt{x}}$$

Power Laws:
Differentiation's much easier if you know the Power Laws really well. Like knowing that
$$x^1 = x \text{ and } \sqrt{x} = x^{\frac{1}{2}}$$
See page 2 for more info.

A constant always differentiates to O — see below.

Differentiate each term in an equation **Separately**

This formula is better than cake — even better than that really nice sticky black chocolate one from that place in town.

Even if there are loads of terms in the equation, it doesn't matter. Differentiate each bit separately and you'll be fine. Here are a couple of examples...

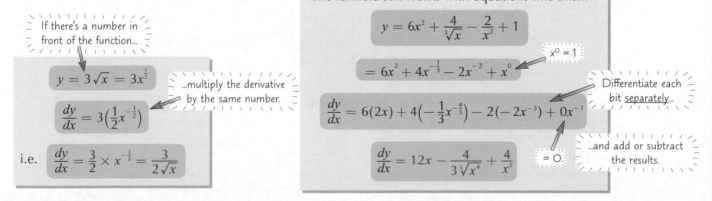

If there's a number in front of the function...

$$y = 3\sqrt{x} = 3x^{\frac{1}{2}}$$

...multiply the derivative by the same number.

$$\frac{dy}{dx} = 3\left(\frac{1}{2}x^{-\frac{1}{2}}\right)$$

i.e. $\frac{dy}{dx} = \frac{3}{2} \times x^{-\frac{1}{2}} = \frac{3}{2\sqrt{x}}$

The formula still works with equations like this...

$$y = 6x^2 + \frac{4}{\sqrt[3]{x}} - \frac{2}{x^2} + 1$$

$$= 6x^2 + 4x^{-\frac{1}{3}} - 2x^{-2} + x^0$$

$x^0 = 1$

$$\frac{dy}{dx} = 6(2x) + 4\left(-\frac{1}{3}x^{-\frac{4}{3}}\right) - 2(-2x^{-3}) + 0x^{-1}$$

Differentiate each bit <u>separately</u>...

$$\frac{dy}{dx} = 12x - \frac{4}{3\sqrt[3]{x^4}} + \frac{4}{x^3}$$

= O.

...and add or subtract the results.

Dario Gradient — differentiating Crewe from the rest...

If you're going to bother doing maths, you've got to be able to differentiate things. Simple as that. But luckily, once you can do the simple stuff, you should be all right. Big long equations are just made up of loads of simple little terms, so they're not really that much harder. Learn the formula, and make sure you can use it by practising all day and all night forever.

Differentiation

Differentiation is what you do if you need to find a gradient. Excited yet?

Differentiate to find **Gradients**

EXAMPLE   Find the gradient of the graph $y = x^2$ at $x = 1$ and $x = -2$...

You need the gradient of the graph of...

$$y = x^2$$

So differentiate this function to get...

$$\frac{dy}{dx} = 2x$$

Now when $x = 1$, $\frac{dy}{dx} = 2$,

And so the gradient of the graph at $x = 1$ is 2.

And when $x = -2$, $\frac{dy}{dx} = -4$,

So the gradient of the graph at $x = -2$ is –4.

Use differentiation to find the gradient of a curve — which is the same as the gradient of the tangent at any given point.

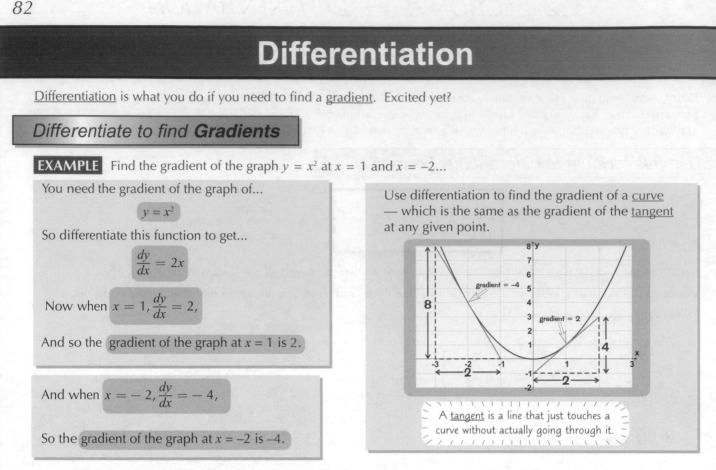

A tangent is a line that just touches a curve without actually going through it.

Finding the gradient is really useful because it tells you the rate of change of the curve at that point, e.g. the gradient of a velocity-time graph tells you the acceleration at that point. Good eh?

You can also differentiate from **First Principles**

$$f'(x) = \lim_{h \to 0}\left(\frac{f(x + h) - f(x)}{h}\right)$$

In your exam, you might be asked to use this formula to find the derivative of a function at a given point. Fortunately, it's a piece of cake:

1) Find $\frac{f(x + h) - f(x)}{h}$ and simplify. (You need to remove h from the denominator when you're simplifying.)

2) Find the limit of the expression as h tends to zero ($\lim_{h \to 0}$) by setting $h = 0$ and simplifying.

3) Whack the x-value for your given point into the expression, and out pops the derivative of $f(x)$ at that point.

As always, a good way of picturing this is by drawing a graph:

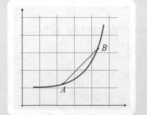

- The diagram shows part of a curve, $f(x)$.

- The chord AB is basically just a straight line which joins two points, A and B, that lie on the curve.

- You can find the gradient of this chord using the usual formula, $m = \frac{y_2 - y_1}{x_2 - x_1}$ (see C1 Section 4).

- As B gets closer and closer to A, the gradient of the chord will get closer and closer to the gradient of the tangent of $f(x)$ at A.

- It's the same idea as in the formula above, $f'(x) = \lim_{h \to 0}\left(\frac{f(x + h) - f(x)}{h}\right)$.
  You're just finding the gradient of AB as h (AB's length) gets closer and closer to zero.

Help me Differentiation — You're my only hope...

There's not really that much hard maths on this page — but there are a couple of very important ideas that you need to get your head round pretty blinkin' soon. Understanding that differentiating gives the gradient of the graph is even more important than washing regularly — AND THAT'S IMPORTANT. Or so I've been told. Personally I'm not so sure.

Finding Tangents and Normals

What's a tangent? Beats me. Oh no, I remember, it's one of those thingies on a curve. Ah, yes... I remember now...

Tangents *Just* touch a curve

To find the equation of a tangent or a normal to a curve, you first need to know its gradient —
so differentiate. Then complete the line's equation using the coordinates of one point on the line.

EXAMPLE Find the tangent to the curve $y = (4 - x)(x + 2)$ at the point (2, 8).

Tangents and Normals...

A tangent just touches the curve but doesn't go through it — it has the same gradient as the curve.

A normal is a line perpendicular (at right angles) to a curve.

To find the curve's (and the tangent's) gradient, first write the equation in a form you can differentiate...

$$y = 8 + 2x - x^2$$

...and then differentiate it.

$$\frac{dy}{dx} = 2 - 2x$$

The gradient of the tangent will be the gradient of the curve at $x = 2$.

At $x = 2$, $\frac{dy}{dx} = -2$,

So the tangent has equation,

$$y - y_1 = -2(x - x_1)$$

in $y - y_1 = m(x - x_1)$ form. See page 30.

And since it passes through the point (2, 8), this becomes

$$y - 8 = -2(x - 2), \text{ or } y = -2x + 12.$$

You can also write it in $y = mx + c$ form.

Normals are at *Right Angles* to a curve

EXAMPLE Find the normal to the curve $y = \dfrac{(x + 2)(x + 4)}{6\sqrt{x}}$ at the point (4, 4).

There's more info on parallel and perpendicular lines on p. 31.

Write the equation of the curve in a form you can differentiate.

$$y = \frac{x^2 + 6x + 8}{6x^{\frac{1}{2}}} = \frac{1}{6}x^{\frac{3}{2}} + x^{\frac{1}{2}} + \frac{4}{3}x^{-\frac{1}{2}}$$

Dividing everything on the top line by everything on the bottom line.

Differentiate it...

$$\frac{dy}{dx} = \frac{1}{6}\left(\frac{3}{2}x^{\frac{1}{2}}\right) + \frac{1}{2}x^{-\frac{1}{2}} + \frac{4}{3}\left(-\frac{1}{2}x^{-\frac{3}{2}}\right)$$

$$= \frac{1}{4}\sqrt{x} + \frac{1}{2\sqrt{x}} - \frac{2}{3\sqrt{x^3}}$$

Find the gradient at the point you're interested in. At $x = 4$,

$$\frac{dy}{dx} = \frac{1}{4} \times 2 + \frac{1}{2 \times 2} - \frac{2}{3 \times 8} = \frac{2}{3}$$

Because the gradient of the normal multiplied by the gradient of the curve must be -1.

So the gradient of the normal is $-\frac{3}{2}$.

And the equation of the normal is $y - y_1 = -\frac{3}{2}(x - x_1)$.

Finally, since the normal goes through the point (4, 4), the equation of the normal must be $y - 4 = -\frac{3}{2}(x - 4)$, or after rearranging, $y = -\frac{3}{2}x + 10$.

Finding Tangents and Normals

1) **Differentiate the function.**

2) **Find the gradient, m, of the tangent or normal.** This is,

   for a tangent: the gradient of the curve

   for a normal: $\dfrac{-1}{\text{gradient of the curve}}$

3) **Write the equation** of the tangent or normal in the form $y - y_1 = m(x - x_1)$, or $y = mx + c$.

4) **Complete the equation** of the line using the coordinates of a point on the line.

Repeat after me... "I adore tangents and normals..."

Examiners can't stop themselves saying the words 'Find the tangent...' and 'Find the normal...'. They love the words. These phrases are music to their ears. They can't get enough of them. I just thought it was my duty to tell you that. And so now you know, you'll definitely be wanting to learn how to do the stuff on this page. Of course you will.

Stationary Points

Differentiation is how you find gradients of curves. So you can use differentiation to find a <u>stationary point</u> (where a graph 'levels off') — that means finding where the <u>gradient</u> becomes <u>zero</u>.

Stationary Points are when the gradient is Zero

EXAMPLE Find the stationary points on the curve $y = 2x^3 - 3x^2 - 12x + 5$, and work out the nature of each one.

A <u>stationary point</u> can be...

(i) a <u>maximum</u>,

or (iii) something like <u>this</u>.

O (ii) a <u>minimum</u>,

At stationary points, the gradient = 0, which means $\frac{dy}{dx} = 0$.

This kind of stationary point is called a 'point of inflection'.

You need to find where $\frac{dy}{dx} = f'(x) = 0$. So first, <u>differentiate</u> the function.

$$y = 2x^3 - 3x^2 - 12x + 5 \Rightarrow \frac{dy}{dx} = 6x^2 - 6x - 12$$

This is the expression for the gradient.

And then set this derivative equal to <u>zero</u>.

$f'(x)$ (pronounced "f-dash of x") is just another way to write a derivative.

$$6x^2 - 6x - 12 = 0$$
$$\Rightarrow x^2 - x - 2 = 0$$
$$\Rightarrow (x - 2)(x + 1) = 0$$
$$\Rightarrow x = 2 \ or \ x = -1$$

So the graph has <u>two</u> stationary points, at $x = 2$ and $x = -1$.

The stationary points are actually at $(2, -15)$ and $(-1, 12)$.

Substitute the x values into the function to find the y-coordinates.

Decide if it's a Maximum or a Minimum by differentiating Again

Once you've found where the stationary points are, you have to decide whether each of them is a <u>maximum</u> or <u>minimum</u> — this is all a question means when it says, '...determine the nature of the turning points'.

A turning point is a another name for a maximum or a minimum.

To decide whether a stationary point is a <u>maximum</u> or a <u>minimum</u> — just differentiate again to find $\frac{d^2y}{dx^2}$ (or $f''(x)$).

This is called a <u>second-order derivative</u> — because you've differentiated twice.

If $\frac{d^2y}{dx^2} < 0$, it's a <u>maximum</u>.

If $\frac{d^2y}{dx^2} > 0$, it's a <u>minimum</u>.

But if $\frac{d^2y}{dx^2} = 0$, you can't tell what type of stationary point it is.

You've just found that $\frac{dy}{dx} = 6x^2 - 6x - 12$.

So differentiating again gives $\frac{d^2y}{dx^2} = 12x - 6$.

Stick in the x-coordinates of the stationary points.

At $x = -1$, $\frac{d^2y}{dx^2} = -18$, which is <u>negative</u> — so $x = -1$ is a <u>maximum</u>.

And at $x = 2$, $\frac{d^2y}{dx^2} = 18$, which is <u>positive</u> — so $x = 2$ is a <u>minimum</u>.

And since a cubic graph (where the coefficient of x^3 is <u>positive</u>) goes from <u>bottom-left to top-right</u>...

...you can draw a rough sketch of the graph, even though the roots would be hard to find.

Stationary Points

1) **Find stationary points by solving**
$$\frac{dy}{dx} = 0.$$

2) **Differentiate again to decide whether a point is a maximum or a minimum.**

3) **If** $\frac{d^2y}{dx^2} < 0$ — **it's a maximum.**

 If $\frac{d^2y}{dx^2} > 0$ — **it's a minimum.**

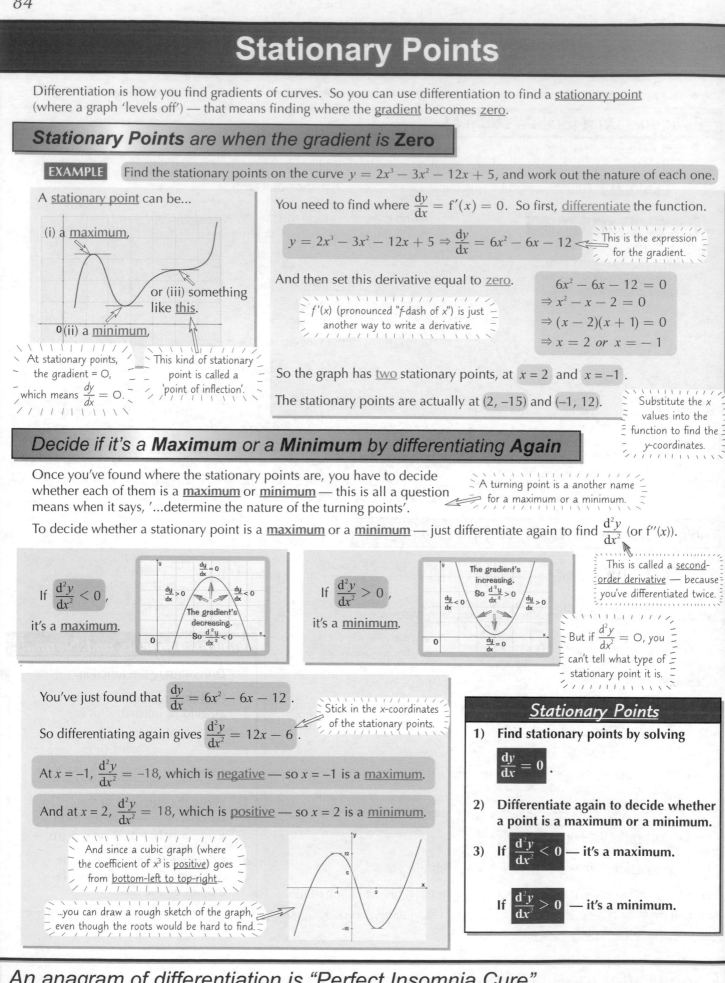

An anagram of differentiation is "Perfect Insomnia Cure"...

No joke, is it — this differentiation business — but it's a dead important topic in maths. It's so important to know how to find whether a stationary point is a max or a min — but it can get a bit confusing. Try remembering MINMAX — which is short for 'MINUS means a MAXIMUM'. Or make up some other clever way to remember what means what.

Increasing and Decreasing Functions

Differentiation is all about finding gradients. Which means that you can find out where a graph is going up...
...and where it's going down. Lovely.

Find out if a function is *Increasing* or *Decreasing*

You can use differentiation to work out exactly where a function is <u>increasing</u> or <u>decreasing</u> — and how quickly.

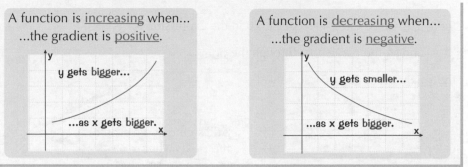

A function is <u>increasing</u> when...
...the gradient is <u>positive</u>.

y gets bigger...

...as x gets bigger.

A function is <u>decreasing</u> when...
...the gradient is <u>negative</u>.

y gets smaller...

...as x gets bigger.

And there's more...

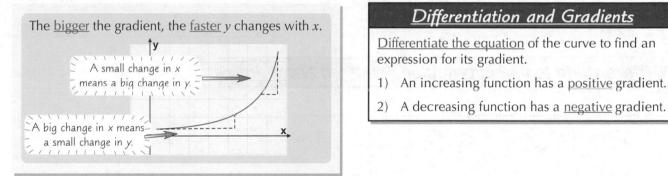

The <u>bigger</u> the gradient, the <u>faster</u> y changes with x.

A small change in x means a big change in y.

A big change in x means a small change in y.

Differentiation and Gradients

<u>Differentiate the equation</u> of the curve to find an expression for its gradient.

1) An increasing function has a <u>positive</u> gradient.

2) A decreasing function has a <u>negative</u> gradient.

EXAMPLE The path of a ball thrown through the air is described by the equation $y = 10x - 5x^2$, where y is the height of the ball above the ground and x is the horizontal distance from its starting point. Find where the height of the ball is increasing and where it's decreasing.

You have the equation for the path of the ball, and you need to know where y is increasing and where it's decreasing. That makes this a question about <u>gradients</u> — so <u>differentiate</u>.

$$y = 10x - 5x^2 \text{ so } \frac{dy}{dx} = 10 - 10x$$

This is an <u>increasing</u> function when: $10 - 10x > 0$, i.e. when $x < 1$, so the ball's height is increasing for $0 \leq x < 1$.

And it's a <u>decreasing</u> function when: $10 - 10x < 0$, i.e. when $x > 1$, so its height decreases for $x > 1$ (until it lands).

Just to check: The gradient of the ball's path is given by $\frac{dy}{dx} = 10 - 10x$.

There's a turning point (i.e. the ball's flight levels out) when $x = 1$.

Differentiating again gives $\frac{d^2y}{dx^2} = -10$, which is <u>negative</u> — and so the turning point is a <u>maximum</u>.

This is what you'd expect — the ball goes <u>up then down</u>, not the other way round.

Decreasing function — also known as ironing...

Basically, you can tell whether a function is getting bigger or smaller by looking at the derivative. To make it more interesting, I wrote it as a nursery rhyme: the f(*duke of york*) = 10 000x, and when they were up the derivative was positive, and when they were down the derivative was negative, and when they were only halfway up at a stationary point the derivative was neither negative nor positive, it was zero. Catchy eh?

Curve Sketching

You'll even be asked to do some drawing in the exam... but don't get too excited — it's just drawing graphs... great.

Find where the curve crosses the Axes

Sketch the graph of $f(x) = \frac{x^2}{2} - 2\sqrt{x}$, for $x \geq 0$.

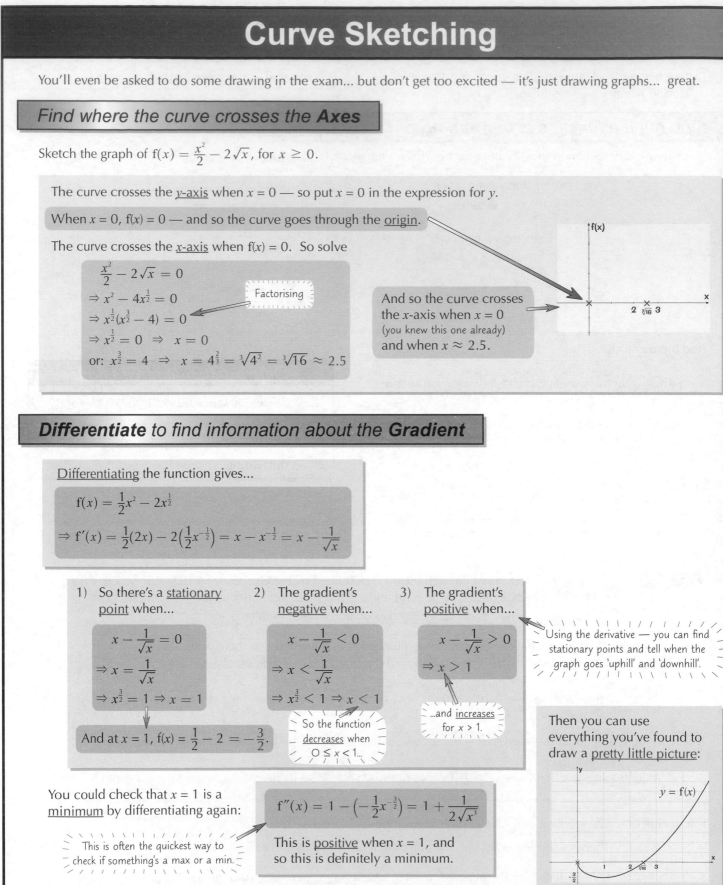

The curve crosses the y-axis when $x = 0$ — so put $x = 0$ in the expression for y.

When $x = 0$, $f(x) = 0$ — and so the curve goes through the origin.

The curve crosses the x-axis when $f(x) = 0$. So solve

$$\frac{x^2}{2} - 2\sqrt{x} = 0$$
$$\Rightarrow x^2 - 4x^{\frac{1}{2}} = 0$$
$$\Rightarrow x^{\frac{1}{2}}(x^{\frac{3}{2}} - 4) = 0$$

Factorising

$$\Rightarrow x^{\frac{1}{2}} = 0 \Rightarrow x = 0$$
$$\text{or: } x^{\frac{3}{2}} = 4 \Rightarrow x = 4^{\frac{2}{3}} = \sqrt[3]{4^2} = \sqrt[3]{16} \approx 2.5$$

And so the curve crosses the x-axis when $x = 0$ (you knew this one already) and when $x \approx 2.5$.

Differentiate to find information about the Gradient

Differentiating the function gives...

$$f(x) = \frac{1}{2}x^2 - 2x^{\frac{1}{2}}$$
$$\Rightarrow f'(x) = \frac{1}{2}(2x) - 2\left(\frac{1}{2}x^{-\frac{1}{2}}\right) = x - x^{-\frac{1}{2}} = x - \frac{1}{\sqrt{x}}$$

1) So there's a stationary point when...

$$x - \frac{1}{\sqrt{x}} = 0$$
$$\Rightarrow x = \frac{1}{\sqrt{x}}$$
$$\Rightarrow x^{\frac{3}{2}} = 1 \Rightarrow x = 1$$

And at $x = 1$, $f(x) = \frac{1}{2} - 2 = -\frac{3}{2}$.

2) The gradient's negative when...

$$x - \frac{1}{\sqrt{x}} < 0$$
$$\Rightarrow x < \frac{1}{\sqrt{x}}$$
$$\Rightarrow x^{\frac{3}{2}} < 1 \Rightarrow x < 1$$

So the function decreases when $0 \leq x < 1$...

3) The gradient's positive when...

$$x - \frac{1}{\sqrt{x}} > 0$$
$$\Rightarrow x > 1$$

...and increases for $x > 1$.

Using the derivative — you can find stationary points and tell when the graph goes 'uphill' and 'downhill'.

Then you can use everything you've found to draw a pretty little picture:

You could check that $x = 1$ is a minimum by differentiating again:

$$f''(x) = 1 - \left(-\frac{1}{2}x^{-\frac{3}{2}}\right) = 1 + \frac{1}{2\sqrt{x^3}}$$

This is often the quickest way to check if something's a max or a min.

This is positive when $x = 1$, and so this is definitely a minimum.

Curve sketching's important — but don't take my word for it...

Curve sketching — an underrated skill, in my opinion. As Shakespeare once wrote, 'Those who can do fab sketches of graphs and stuff are likely to get pretty good grades in maths exams, no word of a lie'. Well, he probably would've written something like that if he was into maths. And he would've written it because graphs are helpful when you're trying to work out what a question's all about — and once you know that, you can decide the best way forward. And if you don't believe me, remember the saying of the ancient Roman Emperor Julius Caesar, 'If in doubt, draw a graph'.

Real-life Problems

Differentiation isn't just mathematical daydreaming. It can be applied to <u>real-life</u> problems. For instance, you can use differentiation to find out the <u>maximum possible volume</u> of a box, given a limited amount of cardboard. Thrilling.

Finding *Maximum / Minimum Values* for *Volume* and *Area*

To find the maximum for a shape's volume, all you need is an equation for the volume <u>in terms of only one variable</u> — then just <u>differentiate as normal</u>. But examiners don't hand it to you on a plate — there's usually one too many variables chucked in. So you've got to know how to manipulate the information to get rid of that unwanted variable.

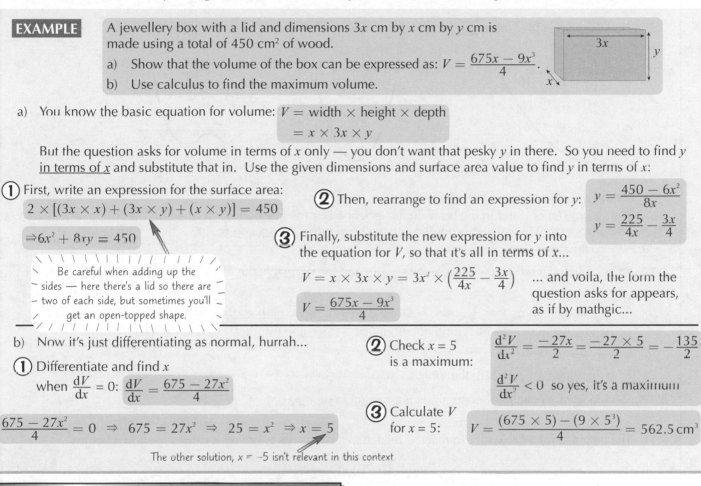

EXAMPLE   A jewellery box with a lid and dimensions $3x$ cm by x cm by y cm is made using a total of 450 cm² of wood.

a)   Show that the volume of the box can be expressed as: $V = \dfrac{675x - 9x^3}{4}$.

b)   Use calculus to find the maximum volume.

a)   You know the basic equation for volume: $V = \text{width} \times \text{height} \times \text{depth}$
$$= x \times 3x \times y$$

But the question asks for volume in terms of x only — you don't want that pesky y in there. So you need to find y <u>in terms of x</u> and substitute that in. Use the given dimensions and surface area value to find y in terms of x:

① First, write an expression for the surface area:
$$2 \times [(3x \times x) + (3x \times y) + (x \times y)] = 450$$
$$\Rightarrow 6x^2 + 8xy = 450$$

Be careful when adding up the sides — here there's a lid so there are two of each side, but sometimes you'll get an open-topped shape.

② Then, rearrange to find an expression for y: $y = \dfrac{450 - 6x^2}{8x}$
$$y = \dfrac{225}{4x} - \dfrac{3x}{4}$$

③ Finally, substitute the new expression for y into the equation for V, so that it's all in terms of x...
$$V = x \times 3x \times y = 3x^2 \times \left(\dfrac{225}{4x} - \dfrac{3x}{4}\right)$$
$$V = \dfrac{675x - 9x^3}{4}$$
... and voila, the form the question asks for appears, as if by mathgic...

b)   Now it's just differentiating as normal, hurrah...

① Differentiate and find x when $\dfrac{dV}{dx} = 0$: $\dfrac{dV}{dx} = \dfrac{675 - 27x^2}{4}$
$$\dfrac{675 - 27x^2}{4} = 0 \Rightarrow 675 = 27x^2 \Rightarrow 25 = x^2 \Rightarrow x = 5$$

The other solution, $x = -5$ isn't relevant in this context

② Check $x = 5$ is a maximum: $\dfrac{d^2V}{dx^2} = \dfrac{-27x}{2} = \dfrac{-27 \times 5}{2} = -\dfrac{135}{2}$
$$\dfrac{d^2V}{dx^2} < 0 \text{ so yes, it's a maximum}$$

③ Calculate V for $x = 5$: $V = \dfrac{(675 \times 5) - (9 \times 5^3)}{4} = 562.5 \text{ cm}^3$

Differentiation works for *Any Shape*

EXAMPLE   Ned uses a circular tin to bake his pies in. The tin is t cm high with a d cm diameter. The volume of the pie tin is 1000 cm³.

a)   Prove that the surface area of the tin, $A = \dfrac{\pi}{4}d^2 + \dfrac{4000}{d}$.

b)   Find the minimum surface area.

a) $A = $ area of tin's base + area of tin's curved face
$$\Rightarrow \pi\left(\dfrac{d}{2}\right)^2 + (\pi d \times t).$$ But you can't have t in there.
So, use the given value of volume to find an expression for t in terms of d:

This shape is open-topped, so only count the area of the circle once.

$$V = \pi\left(\dfrac{d}{2}\right)^2 t = 1000$$
$$\Rightarrow t = \dfrac{1000}{\pi\left(\dfrac{d}{2}\right)^2} = \dfrac{4000}{\pi d^2}$$

Substitute your expression for t into the equation for surface area:
$$A = \dfrac{\pi}{4}d^2 + \left(\pi d \times \dfrac{4000}{\pi d^2}\right) \Rightarrow A = \dfrac{\pi}{4}d^2 + \dfrac{4000}{d}$$

b)   Differentiate and find the stationary point:
$$\dfrac{dA}{dd} = \dfrac{\pi}{2}d - \dfrac{4000}{d^2} \Rightarrow \dfrac{\pi}{2}d - \dfrac{4000}{d^2} = 0 \Rightarrow d^3 = \dfrac{8000}{\pi}$$
$$\Rightarrow d = \dfrac{20}{\sqrt[3]{\pi}}$$

Check it's a minimum:
$$\dfrac{d^2A}{dd^2} = \dfrac{\pi}{2} + \dfrac{8000}{d^3} = \dfrac{\pi}{2} + \dfrac{8000}{\left(\dfrac{8000}{\pi}\right)} = \dfrac{3\pi}{2}$$

Positive, so it is a minimum.

Calculate the area for that value of d:
$$A = \dfrac{\pi}{4}\left(\dfrac{20}{\sqrt[3]{\pi}}\right)^2 + \left(\dfrac{4000}{\left(\dfrac{20}{\sqrt[3]{\pi}}\right)}\right) = 439 \text{ cm}^2 \text{ (to 3 s.f.)}$$

C2 Section 4 — Practice Questions

That's what <u>differentiation</u> is all about. Yes, there are <u>fiddly things</u> to remember — but overall, it's not as bad as all that. And just think of all the <u>lovely marks</u> you'll get if you can answer questions like these in the exam...

1) <u>Differentiate</u> these functions with respect to x:
   a) $y = x^2 + 2$,   b) $y = x^4 + \sqrt{x}$,   c) $y = \frac{7}{x^2} - \frac{3}{\sqrt{x}} + 12x^3$

2) Find the <u>gradients</u> of these <u>graphs</u> at $x = 2$:

   a)
   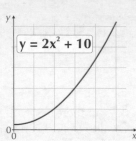
   $y = 2x^2 + 10$

   b)
   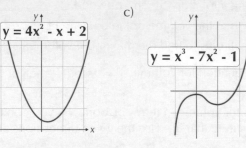
   $y = 4x^2 - x + 2$

   c)
   $y = x^3 - 7x^2 - 1$

3) 1 litre of water is poured into a bowl.
   The <u>volume (v)</u> of water in the bowl (in ml) is defined by the <u>function</u>: $v = 17t^2 - 10t$.
   Find the <u>rate</u> at which water is poured into the bowl when $\underline{t = 4 \text{ seconds}}$.

4) Yawn, yawn. Find the equations of the <u>tangent</u> and the <u>normal</u> to the curve $y = \sqrt{x^3} - 3x - 10$ at $x = 16$.

5) Show that the curves $y = \frac{x^3}{3} - 2x^2 - 4x + \frac{86}{3}$ and $y = \sqrt{x}$ <u>both go through</u> the point (4, 2), and are <u>perpendicular</u> at that point. Good question, that — <u>nice and exciting</u>, just the way you like 'em.

6) Find the stationary points of the function $y = x^3 + \frac{3}{x}$.
   Decide whether each stationary point is a <u>minimum</u> or a <u>maximum</u>.

7) The height (h m) a firework can reach is related to the mass (m g) of fuel it carries as shown below:
   $$h = \frac{m^2}{10} - \frac{m^3}{800}$$
   Find the <u>mass of fuel</u> required to achieve the <u>maximum height</u> and state what the maximum height is.

8) Points A (2, 2) and B (4, 6) lie on the curve $y = f(x)$.
   a) Find the gradient of the chord AB.
   b) How would you find a closer approximation to the gradient of $y = f(x)$ at point A than your answer to part a)?

If you get all the answers right, then well done... go <u>get yourself a pie</u>. But if you get any wrong, read the section again, work out where you went wrong, and then <u>try the questions again</u>.

1   Find the gradient of the curve $y = \frac{1}{\sqrt{x}} + \frac{1}{x}$ at the point $\left(4, \frac{3}{4}\right)$.

(5 marks)

Hopefully that question wasn't too much for you, because there's <u>plenty more</u> where that came from...

2   Given that $y = x^7 + \dfrac{2}{x^3}$, find:

    a) $\dfrac{\mathrm{d}y}{\mathrm{d}x}$

(2 marks)

    b) $\dfrac{\mathrm{d}^2y}{\mathrm{d}x^2}$

(2 marks)

3   a)   Given that $f(x) = x^2 + 8$, show that $f(2 + h) = h^2 + 4h + 12$

(1 mark)

    b)   Hence find and simplify $\dfrac{f(2 + h) - f(2)}{h}$.

(2 marks)

    c)   Use your answer to part b) to find the gradient of $f(x)$ when $x = 2$.

(2 marks)

4   The curve C is given by the equation $y = mx^3 - x^2 + 8x + 2$, for a constant m.

    a)   Find $\dfrac{\mathrm{d}y}{\mathrm{d}x}$.

(2 marks)

    The point P lies on C, and has the x-value 5. The normal to C at P is parallel to the line given by the equation $y + 4x - 3 = 0$.

    b)   Find the gradient of curve C at P.

(3 marks)

    Hence or otherwise, find:

    c)   (i)   the value of m.

(3 marks)

           (ii)   the y-value at P.

(2 marks)

5   The curve C is given by the equation $y = 2x^3 - 4x^2 - 4x + 12$.

    a)   Find $\dfrac{\mathrm{d}y}{\mathrm{d}x}$.

(2 marks)

    b)   Write down the gradient of the tangent to the curve at the point where $x = 2$.

(1 mark)

    c)   Hence or otherwise find an equation for the normal to the curve at this point.

(3 marks)

6   A steam train travels between Haverthwaite and Eskdale at a speed of x miles per hour and burns y units of coal, where y is given by: $2\sqrt{x} + \dfrac{27}{x}$, for $x > 2$.

    a)   Find the speed that gives the minimum coal consumption.

(5 marks)

    b)   Find $\dfrac{\mathrm{d}^2y}{\mathrm{d}x^2}$, and hence show that this speed gives the minimum coal consumption.

(2 marks)

    c)   Calculate the minimum coal consumption.

(1 mark)

C2 Section 4 — Practice Questions

7   a)   Find $\dfrac{dy}{dx}$ for the curve $y = 6 + \dfrac{4x^3 - 15x^2 + 12x}{6}$.

(3 marks)

     b)   Hence, find the coordinates of the stationary points on the curve.

(5 marks)

     c)   Determine the nature of each stationary point.

(3 marks)

8   a)   Determine the coordinates of the stationary points for the curve $y = (x - 1)(3x^2 - 5x - 2)$.

(4 marks)

     b)   Find whether each of these points is a maximum or minimum.

(3 marks)

     c)   Sketch the curve of y.

(3 marks)

9   Ayesha is building a closed-back bookcase. She uses a total of 72 m² of wood (not including shelving) to make a bookcase that is x metres high, $\frac{x}{2}$ metres wide and d metres deep, as shown.

     a)   Show that the full capacity of the bookcase is given by: $V = 12x - \dfrac{x^3}{12}$.

(4 marks)

     b)   Find the value of x for which V is stationary, leaving your answer in surd form.

(4 marks)

     c)   Show that this is a maximum point and hence calculate the maximum V.

(4 marks)

10   a)   Show that the equation $\dfrac{x^2 + 3x^{\frac{3}{2}}}{\sqrt{x}}$ can be written in the form $x^p + 3x^q$, and state the values of p and q.

(3 marks)

     b)   Now let $y = 3x^3 + 5 + \dfrac{x^2 + 3x^{\frac{3}{2}}}{\sqrt{x}}$. Find $\dfrac{dy}{dx}$, giving each coefficient in its simplest form.

(4 marks)

11   Function $f(x) = \frac{1}{2}x^4 - 3x$ has a single stationary point.

     a)   Find the coordinates of the stationary point.

(3 marks)

     b)   Determine the nature of the stationary point.

(2 marks)

     c)   State the range of values of x for which $f(x)$ is:

       (i)   increasing,

(1 mark)

       (ii)   decreasing.

(1 mark)

     d)   Sketch the curve for the function $f(x) = \frac{1}{2}x^4 - 3x$.

(2 marks)

Integration

Integration is the 'opposite' of differentiation — and so if you can differentiate, you can be pretty confident you'll be able to integrate too. There's just one extra thing you have to remember — the constant of integration...

You need the constant because there's More Than One right answer

When you integrate something, you're trying to find a function that returns to what you started with when you differentiate it. And when you add the constant of integration, you're just allowing for the fact that there's more than one possible function that does this...

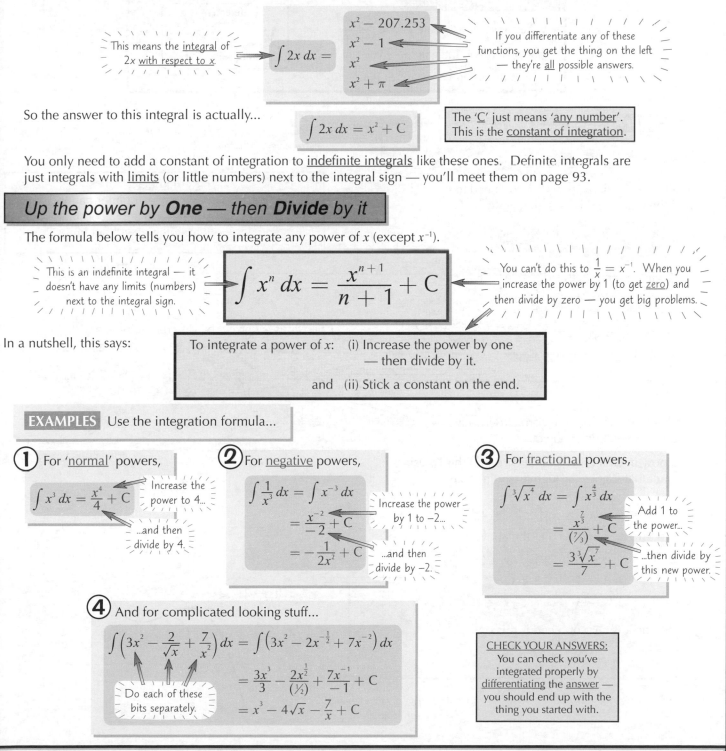

This means the integral of $2x$ with respect to x.

$$\int 2x\,dx = \quad \begin{matrix} x^2 - 207.253 \\ x^2 - 1 \\ x^2 \\ x^2 + \pi \end{matrix}$$

If you differentiate any of these functions, you get the thing on the left — they're all possible answers.

So the answer to this integral is actually...

$$\int 2x\,dx = x^2 + C$$

The 'C' just means 'any number'. This is the constant of integration.

You only need to add a constant of integration to indefinite integrals like these ones. Definite integrals are just integrals with limits (or little numbers) next to the integral sign — you'll meet them on page 93.

Up the power by One — then Divide by it

The formula below tells you how to integrate any power of x (except x^{-1}).

This is an indefinite integral — it doesn't have any limits (numbers) next to the integral sign.

$$\int x^n\,dx = \frac{x^{n+1}}{n+1} + C$$

You can't do this to $\frac{1}{x} = x^{-1}$. When you increase the power by 1 (to get zero) and then divide by zero — you get big problems.

In a nutshell, this says:

To integrate a power of x: (i) Increase the power by one — then divide by it.

and   (ii) Stick a constant on the end.

EXAMPLES   Use the integration formula...

① For 'normal' powers,

$$\int x^3\,dx = \frac{x^4}{4} + C$$

Increase the power to 4...

...and then divide by 4.

② For negative powers,

$$\int \frac{1}{x^3}\,dx = \int x^{-3}\,dx$$
$$= \frac{x^{-2}}{-2} + C$$
$$= -\frac{1}{2x^2} + C$$

Increase the power by 1 to −2...

...and then divide by −2.

③ For fractional powers,

$$\int \sqrt[3]{x^4}\,dx = \int x^{\frac{4}{3}}\,dx$$
$$= \frac{x^{\frac{7}{3}}}{(\frac{7}{3})} + C$$
$$= \frac{3\sqrt[3]{x^7}}{7} + C$$

Add 1 to the power...

...then divide by this new power.

④ And for complicated looking stuff...

$$\int\left(3x^2 - \frac{2}{\sqrt{x}} + \frac{7}{x^2}\right)dx = \int\left(3x^2 - 2x^{-\frac{1}{2}} + 7x^{-2}\right)dx$$
$$= \frac{3x^3}{3} - \frac{2x^{\frac{1}{2}}}{(\frac{1}{2})} + \frac{7x^{-1}}{-1} + C$$
$$= x^3 - 4\sqrt{x} - \frac{7}{x} + C$$

Do each of these bits separately.

CHECK YOUR ANSWERS:
You can check you've integrated properly by differentiating the answer — you should end up with the thing you started with.

Indefinite integrals — joy without limits...

This integration lark isn't so bad then — there's only a couple of things to remember and then you can do it no problem. But that constant of integration catches loads of people out — it's so easy to forget — and you'll definitely lose marks if you do forget it. You have been warned. Other than that, there's not much to it. Hurray.

Integration

By now, you're probably aware that maths isn't something you do unless you're a bit of a <u>thrill-seeker</u>. You know, sometimes they even ask you to find a curve with a certain derivative that goes through a certain point.

*You sometimes need to find the **Value** of the **Constant of Integration***

When they tell you something else about the curve in addition to its derivative, you can work out the value of that <u>constant of integration</u>. Usually the something is the <u>coordinates</u> of one of the points the curve goes through.

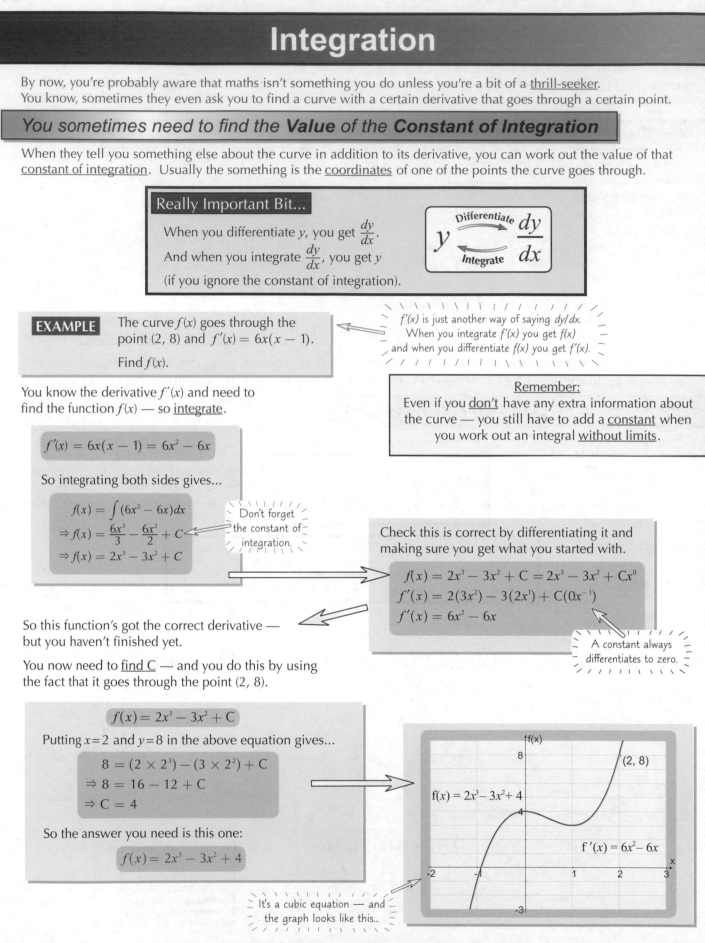

Really Important Bit...

When you differentiate y, you get $\frac{dy}{dx}$.

And when you integrate $\frac{dy}{dx}$, you get y

(if you ignore the constant of integration).

$$y \xrightarrow{\text{Differentiate}} \frac{dy}{dx}$$
$$y \xleftarrow{\text{Integrate}} \frac{dy}{dx}$$

EXAMPLE The curve $f(x)$ goes through the point $(2, 8)$ and $f'(x) = 6x(x - 1)$.

Find $f(x)$.

$f'(x)$ is just another way of saying dy/dx. When you integrate $f'(x)$ you get $f(x)$ and when you differentiate $f(x)$ you get $f'(x)$.

You know the derivative $f'(x)$ and need to find the function $f(x)$ — so <u>integrate</u>.

<u>Remember:</u>
Even if you <u>don't</u> have any extra information about the curve — you still have to add a <u>constant</u> when you work out an integral <u>without limits</u>.

$$f'(x) = 6x(x - 1) = 6x^2 - 6x$$

So integrating both sides gives...

$$f(x) = \int (6x^2 - 6x)dx$$
$$\Rightarrow f(x) = \frac{6x^3}{3} - \frac{6x^2}{2} + C$$
$$\Rightarrow f(x) = 2x^3 - 3x^2 + C$$

Don't forget the constant of integration.

Check this is correct by differentiating it and making sure you get what you started with.

$$f(x) = 2x^3 - 3x^2 + C = 2x^3 - 3x^2 + Cx^0$$
$$f'(x) = 2(3x^2) - 3(2x^1) + C(0x^{-1})$$
$$f'(x) = 6x^2 - 6x$$

So this function's got the correct derivative — but you haven't finished yet.

A constant always differentiates to zero.

You now need to <u>find C</u> — and you do this by using the fact that it goes through the point $(2, 8)$.

$$f(x) = 2x^3 - 3x^2 + C$$

Putting $x = 2$ and $y = 8$ in the above equation gives...

$$8 = (2 \times 2^3) - (3 \times 2^2) + C$$
$$\Rightarrow 8 = 16 - 12 + C$$
$$\Rightarrow C = 4$$

So the answer you need is this one:

$$f(x) = 2x^3 - 3x^2 + 4$$

It's a cubic equation — and the graph looks like this...

Maths and alcohol don't mix — so never drink and derive...

That's another page under your belt and — go on, admit it — there was nothing too horrendous on it. If you can do the stuff from the previous page and then substitute some numbers into an equation, you can do everything from this page too. So if you think this is boring, you'd be right. But if you think it's much harder than the stuff before, you'd be wrong.

Integration

Some integrals have <u>limits</u> (i.e. little numbers) next to the integral sign. You integrate them in exactly the same way — but you <u>don't</u> need a constant of integration. Much easier. And scrummier and yummier too.

A *Definite Integral* finds the *Area Under a Curve*

This definite integral tells you the <u>area</u> between the graph of $y = x^3$ and the x-axis between $x = -2$ and $x = 2$:

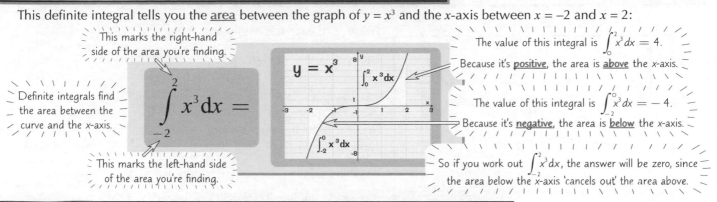

This marks the right-hand side of the area you're finding.

Definite integrals find the area between the curve and the x-axis.

$$\int_{-2}^{2} x^3 \, dx =$$

This marks the left-hand side of the area you're finding.

The value of this integral is $\int_{0}^{2} x^3 \, dx = 4$.
Because it's <u>positive</u>, the area is <u>above</u> the x-axis.

The value of this integral is $\int_{-2}^{0} x^3 \, dx = -4$.
Because it's <u>negative</u>, the area is <u>below</u> the x-axis.

So if you work out $\int_{-2}^{2} x^3 \, dx$, the answer will be zero, since the area below the x-axis 'cancels out' the area above.

Do the integration in the same way — then use the *Limits*

Finding a definite integral isn't really any harder than an indefinite one — there's just an <u>extra</u> stage you have to do. After you've integrated the function you have to work out the value of this new function by sticking in the <u>limits</u>.

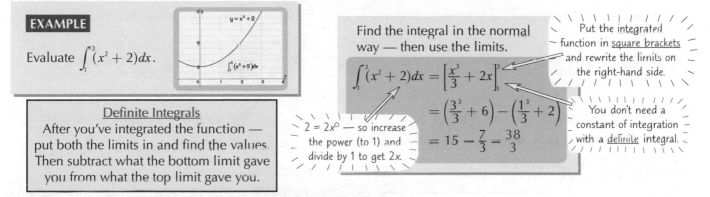

EXAMPLE

Evaluate $\int_{1}^{3} (x^2 + 2) \, dx$.

Find the integral in the normal way — then use the limits.

Put the integrated function in <u>square brackets</u> and rewrite the limits on the right-hand side.

$$\int_{1}^{3} (x^2 + 2) \, dx = \left[\frac{x^3}{3} + 2x\right]_{1}^{3}$$

$$= \left(\frac{3^3}{3} + 6\right) - \left(\frac{1^3}{3} + 2\right)$$

$$= 15 - \frac{7}{3} = \frac{38}{3}$$

$2 = 2x^0$ — so increase the power (to 1) and divide by 1 to get $2x$.

You don't need a constant of integration with a <u>definite</u> integral.

<u>Definite Integrals</u>
After you've integrated the function — put both the limits in and find the values. Then subtract what the bottom limit gave you from what the top limit gave you.

Integrate 'to Infinity' with the ∞ (infinity) sign

And you can integrate all the way to <u>infinity</u> as well. Just use the ∞ symbol as your upper limit. Or use $-\infty$ as your lower limit if you want to integrate to '<u>minus infinity</u>'.

EXAMPLE Find the area under the curve $y = \dfrac{15}{x^2} - \dfrac{30}{x^3}$ for $x \geq 2$.

For this, you need to integrate from $x = 2$ up to infinity (∞).

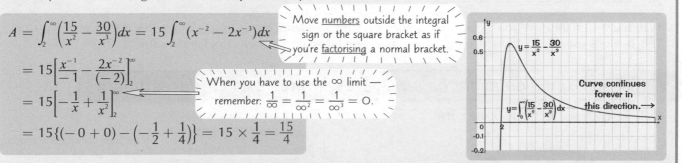

$$A = \int_{2}^{\infty} \left(\frac{15}{x^2} - \frac{30}{x^3}\right) dx = 15 \int_{2}^{\infty} (x^{-2} - 2x^{-3}) \, dx$$

$$= 15 \left[\frac{x^{-1}}{-1} - \frac{2x^{-2}}{(-2)}\right]_{2}^{\infty}$$

$$= 15 \left[-\frac{1}{x} + \frac{1}{x^2}\right]_{2}^{\infty}$$

$$= 15 \left\{(-0 + 0) - \left(-\frac{1}{2} + \frac{1}{4}\right)\right\} = 15 \times \frac{1}{4} = \frac{15}{4}$$

Move <u>numbers</u> outside the integral sign or the square bracket as if you're <u>factorising</u> a normal bracket.

When you have to use the ∞ limit — remember: $\frac{1}{\infty} = \frac{1}{\infty^2} = \frac{1}{\infty^3} = 0$.

$y = \frac{15}{x^2} - \frac{30}{x^3}$

Curve continues forever in this direction. →

$y = \int_{0}^{\infty} \left(\frac{15}{x^2} - \frac{30}{x^3}\right) dx$

My hobbies? Well I'm really inte grating. Especially carrots.

It's still integration — but this time you're putting two numbers into an expression afterwards. So although this may not be the wild and crazy fun-packed time your teachers promised you when they were trying to persuade you to take AS maths, you've got to admit that a lot of this stuff is pretty similar — and if you can do one bit, you can use that to do quite a few other bits too. Maths is like that. But I admit it's probably not as much fun as a big banana-and-toffee cake.

The Trapezium Rule

Sometimes <u>integrals</u> can be just <u>too hard</u> to do using the normal methods — then you need to know other ways to solve them. That's where the <u>Trapezium Rule</u> comes in.

The **Trapezium Rule** is Used to Find the **Approximate Area** Under a Curve

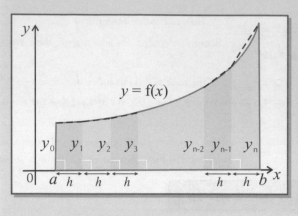

The area of each trapezium is $A = \frac{h}{2}(y_n + y_{n+1})$

The area represented by $\int_a^b y \, dx$ is approximately:

$$\int_a^b y \, dx \approx \frac{1}{2}h[(y_0 + y_n) + 2(y_1 + y_2 + \ldots + y_{n-1})]$$

where **n** is the number of strips or intervals and **h** is the width of each strip.

You can find the width of each strip using $\quad h = \dfrac{b-a}{n}$

$y_0, y_1, y_2, \ldots, y_n$ are the heights of the sides of the trapeziums — you get these by putting the x-values into the equation of the curve.

So basically the formula for approximating $\int_a^b y \, dx$ works like this:

'Add the first and last heights $(y_0 + y_n)$ and add this to <u>twice</u> all the other heights added up — then multiply by $\frac{1}{2}h$.'

EXAMPLE Find an approximate value for $\int_0^2 \sqrt{4 - x^2} \, dx$ using 4 strips. Give your answer to 4 s.f.

Start by working out the width of each strip: $h = \dfrac{b-a}{n} = \dfrac{2-0}{4} = 0.5$

This means the x-values are $x_0 = 0$, $x_1 = 0.5$, $x_2 = 1$, $x_3 = 1.5$ and $x_4 = 2$ (the question specifies 4 strips, so $n = 4$).

Set up a table and work out the y-values or heights using the equation in the integral.

x	$y = \sqrt{4 - x^2}$
$x_0 = 0$	$y_0 = \sqrt{4 - 0^2} = 2$
$x_1 = 0.5$	$y_1 = \sqrt{4 - 0.5^2} = \sqrt{3.75} = 1.936491673$
$x_2 = 1.0$	$y_2 = \sqrt{4 - 1.0^2} = \sqrt{3} = 1.732050808$
$x_3 = 1.5$	$y_3 = \sqrt{4 - 1.5^2} = \sqrt{1.75} = 1.322875656$
$x_4 = 2.0$	$y_4 = \sqrt{4 - 2.0^2} = 0$

Now put all the y-values into the formula with h and n:

$$\int_a^b y \, dx \approx \frac{0.5}{2}[2 + 0 + 2(1.9365 + 1.7321 + 1.3229)]$$
$$\approx 0.25[2 + 2 \times 4.9915]$$
$$\approx 2.996 \text{ to 4 s.f.}$$

Watch out — if they ask you to work out a question with 5 y-values (or '<u>ordinates</u>') then this is the <u>same</u> as 4 strips. The x-values usually go up in <u>nice jumps</u> — if they don't then <u>check</u> your calculations carefully.

The Approximation might be an **Overestimate** or an **Underestimate**

It all depends on the shape of the curve...

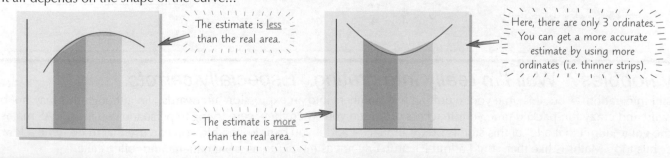

The estimate is <u>less</u> than the real area.

The estimate is <u>more</u> than the real area.

Here, there are only 3 ordinates. You can get a more accurate estimate by using more ordinates (i.e. thinner strips).

The Trapezium Rule

These are usually popular questions with examiners — as long as you're careful there are <u>plenty of marks</u> to be had.

The *Trapezium Rule* is in the *Formula Booklet*

...so don't try any heroics — always <u>look it up</u> and use it with these questions.

EXAMPLE   Use the trapezium rule with 7 ordinates to find an approximation to $\int_1^{2.2} 2\log_{10}x\,dx$

Remember, <u>7 ordinates</u> means <u>6 strips</u> — so $n = 6$.

Calculate the width of the strips: $h = \dfrac{b-a}{n} = \dfrac{2.2-1}{6} = 0.2$

Set up a table and work out the y-values using $y = 2\log_{10}x$: $\Longrightarrow$

x	$y = 2\log_{10}x$
$x_0=1.0$	$y_0=2\log_{10}1=0$
$x_1=1.2$	$y_1=2\log_{10}1.2=0.15836$
$x_2=1.4$	$y_2=0.29226$
$x_3=1.6$	$y_3=0.40824$
$x_4=1.8$	$y_4=0.51055$
$x_5=2.0$	$y_5=0.60206$
$x_6=2.2$	$y_6=0.68485$

Putting all these values in the formula gives:

$$\int_a^b y\,dx \approx \frac{0.2}{2}[0 + 0.68485 + 2(0.15836 + 0.29226 + 0.40824 + 0.51055 + 0.60206)]$$

$$\approx 0.1 \times [0.68485 + 2 \times 1.97147]$$

$$\approx 0.462779$$

$$\approx 0.463 \text{ to 3 d.p.}$$

EXAMPLE   Use the trapezium rule with 8 intervals to find an approximation to $\int_0^\pi \sin x\,dx$

Whenever you get a calculus question using <u>trig functions</u>, you <u>have</u> to use <u>radians</u>. You'll probably be given a limit with π in, which is a pretty good reminder.

There are 8 intervals, so $n = 8$.

Keep your x-values in terms of π.

Calculate the width of the strips: $h = \dfrac{b-a}{n} = \dfrac{\pi-0}{8} = \dfrac{\pi}{8}$

Set up a table and work out the y-values:

So, putting all this in the formula gives:

x	$y = \sin x$
$x_0=0$	$y_0=\sin 0 = 0$
$x_1=\dfrac{\pi}{8}$	$y_1=0.38268$
$x_2=\dfrac{\pi}{4}$	$y_2=0.70711$
$x_3=\dfrac{3\pi}{8}$	$y_3=0.92388$
$x_4=\dfrac{\pi}{2}$	$y_4=1$
$x_5=\dfrac{5\pi}{8}$	$y_5=0.92388$
$x_6=\dfrac{3\pi}{4}$	$y_6=0.70711$
$x_7=\dfrac{7\pi}{8}$	$y_7=0.38268$
$x_8=\pi$	$y_8=0$

$$\int_a^b y\,dx \approx \frac{1}{2}\cdot\frac{\pi}{8}[0 + 0 + 2(0.383 + 0.707 + 0.924 + 1 + 0.924 + 0.707 + 0.383)]$$

$$\approx \frac{\pi}{16} \times [2 \times 5.028]$$

$$\approx 1.97 \text{ to 3 s.f.}$$

These values are quicker to work-out if you know that the graph is symmetrical.

Maths rhyming slang #3: Dribble and drool — Trapezium rule...

Take your time with trapezium rule questions — it's so easy to make a mistake with all those numbers flying around. Make a nice table showing all your ordinates (careful — this is always one more than the number of strips). Then add up y_1 to y_{n-1} and multiply the answer by 2. Add on y_0 and y_n. Finally, multiply what you've got so far by the width of a strip and divide by 2. It's a good idea to write down what you get after each stage, by the way — then if you press the wrong button (easily done) you'll be able to pick up from where you went wrong. They're not hard — just fiddly.

Areas Between Curves

With a bit of thought, you can use integration to find all kinds of areas — even ones that look quite tricky at first. The best way to work out what to do is draw a <u>picture</u>. Then it'll seem easier. I promise you it will.

Sometimes you have to **Add** integrals...

This looks pretty hard — until you draw a picture and see what it's all about.

> **EXAMPLE**   Find the area enclosed by the curve $y = x^2$, the line $y = 2 - x$ and the x-axis.

Find out where the graphs meet by <u>solving</u> $x^2 = 2 - x$ — they meet at $x = 1$ (they also meet at $x = -2$, but this isn't in A).

You have to find area A — but you'll need to <u>split</u> it into two smaller pieces.

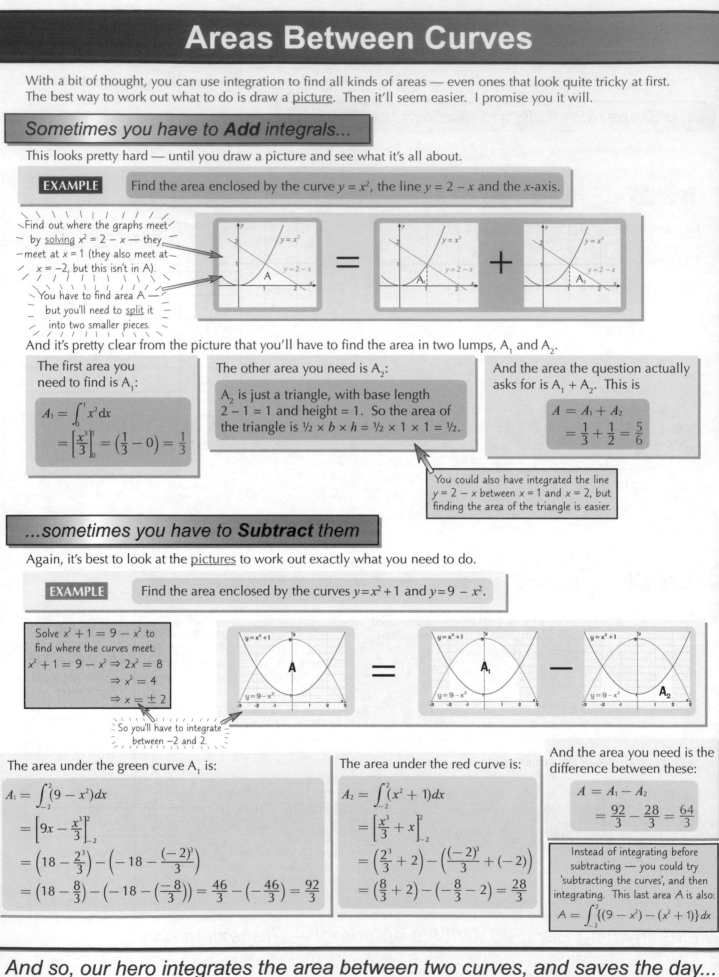

And it's pretty clear from the picture that you'll have to find the area in two lumps, A_1 and A_2.

The first area you need to find is A_1:

$$A_1 = \int_0^1 x^2 dx$$
$$= \left[\frac{x^3}{3}\right]_0^1 = \left(\frac{1}{3} - 0\right) = \frac{1}{3}$$

The other area you need is A_2:

A_2 is just a triangle, with base length $2 - 1 = 1$ and height = 1. So the area of the triangle is $\frac{1}{2} \times b \times h = \frac{1}{2} \times 1 \times 1 = \frac{1}{2}$.

And the area the question actually asks for is $A_1 + A_2$. This is

$$A = A_1 + A_2$$
$$= \frac{1}{3} + \frac{1}{2} = \frac{5}{6}$$

You could also have integrated the line $y = 2 - x$ between $x = 1$ and $x = 2$, but finding the area of the triangle is easier.

...sometimes you have to **Subtract** them

Again, it's best to look at the <u>pictures</u> to work out exactly what you need to do.

> **EXAMPLE**   Find the area enclosed by the curves $y = x^2 + 1$ and $y = 9 - x^2$.

Solve $x^2 + 1 = 9 - x^2$ to find where the curves meet.
$x^2 + 1 = 9 - x^2 \Rightarrow 2x^2 = 8$
$\Rightarrow x^2 = 4$
$\Rightarrow x = \pm 2$

So you'll have to integrate between −2 and 2.

The area under the green curve A_1 is:

$$A_1 = \int_{-2}^{2}(9 - x^2)dx$$
$$= \left[9x - \frac{x^3}{3}\right]_{-2}^{2}$$
$$= \left(18 - \frac{2^3}{3}\right) - \left(-18 - \frac{(-2)^3}{3}\right)$$
$$= \left(18 - \frac{8}{3}\right) - \left(-18 - \left(\frac{-8}{3}\right)\right) = \frac{46}{3} - \left(-\frac{46}{3}\right) = \frac{92}{3}$$

The area under the red curve is:

$$A_2 = \int_{-2}^{2}(x^2 + 1)dx$$
$$= \left[\frac{x^3}{3} + x\right]_{-2}^{2}$$
$$= \left(\frac{2^3}{3} + 2\right) - \left(\frac{(-2)^3}{3} + (-2)\right)$$
$$= \left(\frac{8}{3} + 2\right) - \left(-\frac{8}{3} - 2\right) = \frac{28}{3}$$

And the area you need is the difference between these:

$$A = A_1 - A_2$$
$$= \frac{92}{3} - \frac{28}{3} = \frac{64}{3}$$

Instead of integrating before subtracting — you could try 'subtracting the curves', and then integrating. This last area A is also:

$$A = \int_{-2}^{2}\{(9 - x^2) - (x^2 + 1)\} dx$$

And so, our hero integrates the area between two curves, and saves the day...

That's the basic idea of finding the area enclosed by curves and lines — just draw a picture and then break the area down into <u>smaller, easier chunks</u>. And of course it's always a good idea to keep an eye out for anything <u>symmetrical</u> that could save you a bit of work. Questions like this aren't too hard — but they can sometimes take quite a long time. Great.

C2 Section 5 — Practice Questions

Penguins evolved with a layer of blubber under their skin to keep them warm.
They should've saved themselves the effort and done these questions instead — mmm, toasty warm...

Warm-up Questions

1) Integrate these: a) $\int 10x^4 dx$,   b) $\int (3x + 5x^2) dx$,   c) $\int (x^2(3x + 2)) dx$

2) Work out the equation of the curve that has derivative $\frac{dy}{dx} = 6x - 7$ and goes through the point (1, 0).

3) How can you tell whether an integral is a definite one or an indefinite one?
   (It's easy really — it just sounds difficult.)

4) Evaluate the following definite integrals:

   a) $\int_0^1 (4x^3 + 3x^2 + 2x + 1) dx$ b) $\int_1^2 \left(\frac{8}{x^5} + \frac{3}{\sqrt{x}} \right) dx$ c) $\int_1^6 \frac{3}{x^2} dx$.

5) Evaluate: a) $\int_{-3}^3 (9 - x^2) dx$ b) $\int_1^\infty \frac{3}{x^2} dx$.

   Sketch the areas represented by these integrals.

6) Find area A in the diagram below:

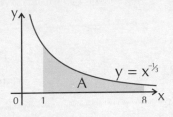

7) Use the trapezium rule with n intervals to estimate:

   a) $\int_0^3 (9 - x^2)^{\frac{1}{2}} dx$ with $n = 3$ b) $\int_{0.2}^{1.2} x^{x^2} dx$ with $n = 5$

8) Use integration to find the yellow area in each of these graphs:

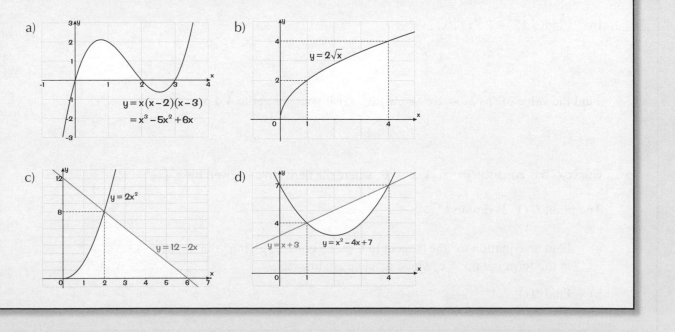

C2 Section 5 — Practice Questions

They think it's all over...

Exam Questions

1   Find $f(x)$ in each case below. Give each term in its simplest form.

   a) $f'(x) = x^{-\frac{1}{2}} + 4 - 5x^3$

                                         (3 marks)

   b) $f'(x) = 2x + \dfrac{3}{x^2}$

                                         (2 marks)

   c) $f'(x) = 6x^2 - \dfrac{1}{3\sqrt{x}}$

                                         (2 marks)

2   The curve C has the equation $y = f(x)$, $x > 0$. $f'(x)$ is given as $2x + 5\sqrt{x} + \dfrac{6}{x^2}$.

   A point P on curve C has the coordinates $(3, 7)$.

   Find $f(x)$, giving your answer in its simplest form.

                                         (6 marks)

3   $f'(x) = \dfrac{1}{\sqrt{36x}} - 2\left(\sqrt{\dfrac{1}{x^3}}\right)$ where $x > 0$.

   a)   Show that $f'(x) = Ax^{-\frac{1}{2}} - Bx^{-\frac{3}{2}}$ and give the values of A and B.

                                         (3 marks)

   b)   The curve C is given by $y = f(x)$ and goes through point $P(1, 7)$.
       Find the equation of the curve.

                                         (4 marks)

4   a)   Show that $(5 + 2\sqrt{x})^2$ can be written in the form $a + b\sqrt{x} + cx$, stating the values of the
       constants a, b and c.

                                         (3 marks)

   b)   Find $\displaystyle\int (5 + 2\sqrt{x})^2 \, dx$.

                                         (3 marks)

5   Find the value of $\displaystyle\int_{2}^{7} (2x - 6x^2 + \sqrt{x}) \, dx$. Give your answer to 4 d.p.

                                         (5 marks)

6   Curve C has equation $y = f(x)$, $x \neq 0$, where the derivative is given by $f'(x) = x^3 - \dfrac{2}{x^2}$.

   The point $P(1, 2)$ lies on C.

   a)   Find an equation for the tangent to C at the point P, giving your answer
       in the form $y = mx + c$, where m and c are integers.

                                         (4 marks)

   b)   Find $f(x)$.

                                         (5 marks)

C2 Section 5 — Practice Questions

7   a)   Using the trapezium rule with n intervals, estimate the values of:

   (i) $\int_{2}^{8}\left(\sqrt{3x^3} + \dfrac{2}{\sqrt{x}}\right)dx$, $n = 3$ *(4 marks)*

   (ii) $\int_{1}^{5}\left(\dfrac{x^3 - 2}{4}\right)dx$, $n = 4$ *(4 marks)*

   b)   How could you change your application of the trapezium rule to get better approximations?   *(1 mark)*

8   $f'(x) = (x - 1)(3x - 1)$ where $x > 0$.

   a)   The curve C is given by $f(x)$ and goes through point P (3, 10). Find $f(x)$.   *(6 marks)*

   b)   The equation for the normal to C at the point P can be written in the form $y = \dfrac{a - x}{b}$
       where a and b are integers. Find the values of a and b.   *(4 marks)*

9   Complete the table and hence use the trapezium rule with 6 ordinates to estimate $\int_{1.5}^{4} y\, dx$.

x	$x_0 = 1.5$	$x_1 =$	$x_2 =$	$x_3 =$	$x_4 = 3.5$	$x_5 = 4.0$
$y = 3x - \sqrt{2^x}$	$y_0 =$	$y_1 = 4$	$y_2 = 5.12156$	$y_3 =$	$y_4 =$	$y_5 = 8.0$

(7 marks)

10   Curve C, $y = (x - 3)^2 (x + 1)$, is sketched on the diagram below:

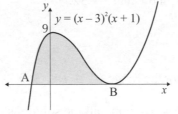

Calculate the shaded area between point A, where C intersects the x-axis, and point B,
where C touches the x-axis.   *(8 marks)*

11   The diagram shows the curve $y = (x + 1)(x - 5)$.
    Points J (–1, 0) and K (4, –5) lie on the curve.

   a)   Find the equation of the straight line joining J and K
       in the form $y = mx + c$.   *(2 marks)*

   b)   Calculate $\int_{-1}^{4}(x + 1)(x - 5)\,dx$.   *(5 marks)*

   c)   Find the area of the shaded region.   *(4 marks)*

...it is now.

General Certificate of Education
Advanced Subsidiary (AS) and Advanced Level

Core Mathematics C2 — Practice Exam One

Time Allowed: 1 hour 30 min

Graphical calculators may be used for this exam.

Give any non-exact numerical answers to an appropriate degree of accuracy.

There are 72 marks available for this paper.

Section A (36 marks)

1   You are given that $\cos\theta = \dfrac{\sqrt{3}}{2}$.

    a)   Use a right-angled triangle to give an exact value for $\sin\theta$.

(3 marks)

    b)   Hence find an exact value for $\tan\theta$.

(1 mark)

2   Find the gradient of the curve given by $y = \sqrt{x} - \dfrac{1}{x^3}$ at the point where $x = 1$.

(3 marks)

3   a)   Write down the value of $\log_3 3$.

(1 mark)

    b)   Given that $\log_a x = \log_a 4 + 3\log_a 2$, show that $x = 32$.

(2 marks)

4   a)   Sketch the graph of $y = \tan 2t$ for the range $0° \le t < 360°$.

(2 marks)

    b)   Solve the equation $\sin 2t = \sqrt{2}\cos 2t$, giving all the solutions in the range $0° \le t < 360°$.

(3 marks)

5   Show that the equation

$$\tan^2\theta + \frac{\tan\theta}{\cos\theta} = 1$$

can be written in the form $2\sin^2\theta + \sin\theta - 1 = 0$.

(3 marks)

6   Find $\displaystyle\int_1^4 (3x^2 + \sqrt{x})\,dx$.

(3 marks)

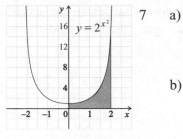

7 a) The diagram shows the graph of $y = 2^{x^2}$. Use the trapezium rule with 5 ordinates (4 strips) to find an estimate for the area of the region bounded by the axes, the curve and the line $x = 2$.

(4 marks)

b) State whether your answer is an underestimate or overestimate, justifying your answer.

(1 mark)

8 You are given that $f(x) = x^2 - 1$.

a) Find and simplify $\dfrac{f(x + h) - f(x)}{h}$.

(2 marks)

b) Use your answer to find the gradient of $f(x)$ at the point where $x = 2$, showing your reasoning.

(3 marks)

9 A geometric series has 3rd term 81. The sum to infinity of the series is 10 times greater than the first term of the series. Find:

a) the common ratio of the series,

(3 marks)

b) the first term of the series,

(2 marks)

Section B (36 marks)

10 The diagram shows the graphs of the curve $y = x^2 - 4x + 6$ and the line $y = -x + 4$.

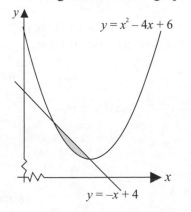

a) Find the coordinates of the points where the line and curve intersect.

(5 marks)

b) Evaluate the integral $\displaystyle\int_{1}^{2} (x^2 - 4x + 6)\,dx$.

(3 marks)

c) Hence, or otherwise, show that the total area enclosed by the curve $y = x^2 - 4x + 6$ and the line $y = -x + 4$ is equal to $\frac{1}{6}$.

(4 marks)

11 A new symmetrical mini-stage is to be built according to the design shown below. The design consists of a rectangle of length q metres and width $2r$ metres, two sectors of radius r and angle θ radians (shaded), and an isosceles triangle.

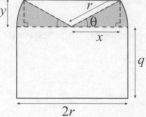

a) Show that distance x is given by $x = r\cos\theta$ and find a similar expression for distance y.

(1 mark)

b) Find, in terms of r, q and θ, expressions for the perimeter P, and the area A, of the stage.

(4 marks)

c) If the perimeter of the stage is to be 40 metres, and $\theta = \frac{\pi}{3}$, show that A is given approximately by $A = 40r - 3.614r^2$.

(4 marks)

d) Use your answer to part c) to find all possible values of r if the area of the stage is to be 12 m².

(3 marks)

12 The number of supporters of a local football team has tended to increase in recent years. The following table shows the average home game attendance for the club in recent seasons.

Season	05/06	06/07	07/08	08/09	09/10
Attendance (in hundreds, to the nearest hundred)	1	2	4	8	14

This increase may be modelled by an equation of the form $y = ab^t$, where y is the average attendance in hundreds, t is the number of years after the 04/05 season and a and b are constants to be determined.

a) Show that $y = ab^t$ may be written in the form $\log_{10}y = t\log_{10}b + \log_{10}a$.

(2 marks)

b) Complete the following table, giving values correct to 3 d.p.:

t	1	2	3	4	5
$\log_{10}y$	0	0.301			

(1 mark)

c) Plot a graph of $\log_{10}y$ against t. Draw by eye a line of best fit for your data.

(2 marks)

d) Using your graph, find values of $\log_{10}a$ and $\log_{10}b$. Hence calculate a and b.

(4 marks)

e) The chairman has promised a new stadium for the club when the average attendance reaches 5000. According to your model, in which season will the attendance reach this value?

(3 marks)

General Certificate of Education
Advanced Subsidiary (AS) and Advanced Level

Core Mathematics C2 — Practice Exam Two

Time Allowed: 1 hour 30 min

Graphical calculators may be used for this exam.

Give any non-exact numerical answers to an appropriate degree of accuracy.

There are 72 marks available for this paper.

Section A (36 marks)

1   Express $225°$ in radians.

(2 marks)

2   Find the values of x for which the function $f(x) = x^2 - 3x + 1$ is increasing.

(3 marks)

3   a)   Write down the value of $\log_a a$.

(1 mark)

    b)   Solve the equation $4^{2x+1} = 9$.

(3 marks)

4   Sketch the graphs of $y = \sin x$ and $y = \sin \frac{x}{2}$ in the range $0° \leq x \leq 720°$ on the same set of axes, showing the points at which the graphs cross the x-axis.

(3 marks)

5   The diagram shows a sector of a circle of radius 4 cm and angle 0.2 radians.
Find:

    a)   the area of the sector,

(2 marks)

    b)   the perimeter of the sector.

0.2   4 cm

(3 marks)

6 Find the equation of the curve with gradient $\frac{dy}{dx} = \frac{1}{x^2} + \frac{2}{x^{\frac{1}{3}}} + 1$, given that it passes through the point (1, 3).

(5 marks)

7 The fourth term of an arithmetic progression is 15. The fifth term is 19.
Find the sum of the first ten terms.

(4 marks)

8 a) Find the missing length a in the triangle.

(2 marks)

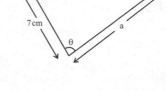

b) Find the angles θ and ϕ.

(3 marks)

9 a) Use the trapezium rule with 4 ordinates (3 strips) to find an approximate value for

$$\int_0^3 \sqrt{3 + x^2}\, dx.$$

Give your answer to 4 s.f.

(4 marks)

b) How could you improve your estimate?

(1 mark)

Section B (36 marks)

10

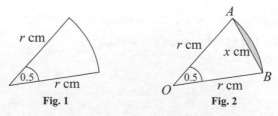

Fig. 1   Fig. 2

a) **Fig. 1** shows a sector of a circle of radius r cm and angle 0.5 radians.
The perimeter of the sector is equal to the area of the sector. Find r.

(6 marks)

b) **Fig. 2** shows a triangle OAB inscribed on the sector. OAB has sides of length
$OA = OB = r$ cm and $AB = x$ cm. Find:

(i) the length x,

(2 marks)

(ii) The area of the shaded region shown in **Fig. 2**.

(5 marks)

11 a) Sketch the graph of $y = \cos x$ for $0° \leq x \leq 360°$.

    (1 mark)

   b) Show that the equation $2 \sin^2 x = 1 + \cos x$ may be written as a quadratic in $\cos x$.

    (3 marks)

   c) Hence solve $2 \sin^2 x = 1 + \cos x$, giving all values of x such that $0° \leq x \leq 360°$.

    (4 marks)

   d) (i) Describe the geometrical transformation that maps the curve with equation $y = \cos x$ onto the curve with equation $y = \frac{1}{2}\cos x$.

    (2 marks)

       (ii) Sketch the graph of $y = \frac{1}{2}\cos x$.

    (1 mark)

12

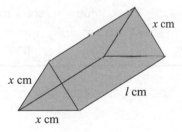

The diagram shows a solid triangular-prism. The two ends of the prism are equilateral triangles of side x cm and the length of the prism is l cm. The volume of the prism is $60\sqrt{3}$ cm³.

   a) Find l in terms of x.

    (3 marks)

   b) Hence show that the surface area, A cm², of the prism is given by $A = \frac{\sqrt{3}}{2}x^2 + \frac{720}{x}$.

    (2 marks)

   c) Find the value of x for which A is stationary, giving your answer to 3 significant figures.

    (2 marks)

   d) Show that this value of x is a minimum point.

    (3 marks)

   e) Hence find the minimum surface area of the prism.

    (2 marks)

Histograms

Histograms are glorified bar charts. The main difference is that you plot the <u>frequency density</u> rather than the frequency. Frequency density is easy to find — you just divide the <u>frequency</u> by the <u>width of the corresponding class</u>.

Using frequency density means it's a column's <u>area</u> (and <u>not</u> its height) that represents the <u>frequency</u>.

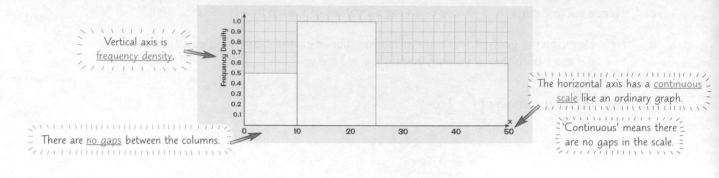

Vertical axis is <u>frequency density</u>.

The horizontal axis has a <u>continuous scale</u> like an ordinary graph.

There are <u>no gaps</u> between the columns.

'Continuous' means there are no gaps in the scale.

To Draw a **Histogram** it's best to Draw a **Table** First

Getting histograms right depends on finding the right <u>upper and lower boundaries</u> for each class.

EXAMPLE   Draw a histogram to represent the data below showing the masses of parcels (given to the nearest 100 g).

Mass of parcel (to nearest 100 g)	100 - 200	300 - 400	500 - 700	800 - 1100
Number of parcels	100	250	600	50

First draw a table showing the <u>upper and lower class boundaries</u>, plus the <u>frequency density</u>:

<u>Smallest</u> mass of parcel that will go <u>in that class</u>.

<u>Biggest</u> mass that will go <u>in that class</u>.

= ucb – lcb

Mass of parcel	Lower class boundary (lcb)	Upper class boundary (ucb)	Class width	Frequency	Frequency density = frequency ÷ class width
100 - 200	50	250	200	100	0.5
300 - 400	250	450	200	250	1.25
500 - 700	450	750	300	600	2
800 - 1100	750	1150	400	50	0.125

= 250 ÷ 200

Look — no gaps between a ucb and the next lcb.

= 1150 – 750

Now you can draw the histogram.

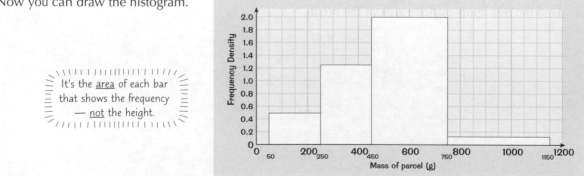

It's the <u>area</u> of each bar that shows the frequency — <u>not</u> the height.

Note: A class with a lower class boundary of 50 g and upper class boundary of 250 g can be written in different ways.

So you might see: "100 – 200 to nearest 100 g"
$50 \leq \text{mass} < 250$"
"50–", followed by "250–" for the next class and so on.

They all mean the same — just make sure you know how to spot the lower and upper class boundaries.

Stemplots and Vertical Line Charts

Here are two more ways of presenting data, although <u>vertical line charts</u> can only be used when the data is <u>discrete</u>.

Stem and Leaf Diagrams look nothing like stems or leaves

<u>Stem and leaf diagrams</u> (also called <u>stemplots</u>) are an easy way to represent your data.
They come in two flavours — plain and <u>back-to-back</u>.

 EXAMPLE   The lengths in metres of cars in a car park were measured to the nearest 10 cm.
Draw a stem and leaf diagram to show the following data: 2.9, 3.5, 4.0, 2.8, 4.1, 3.7, 3.1, 3.6, 3.8, 3.7

It's best to do a rough version first, and then put the 'leaves' in order afterwards.

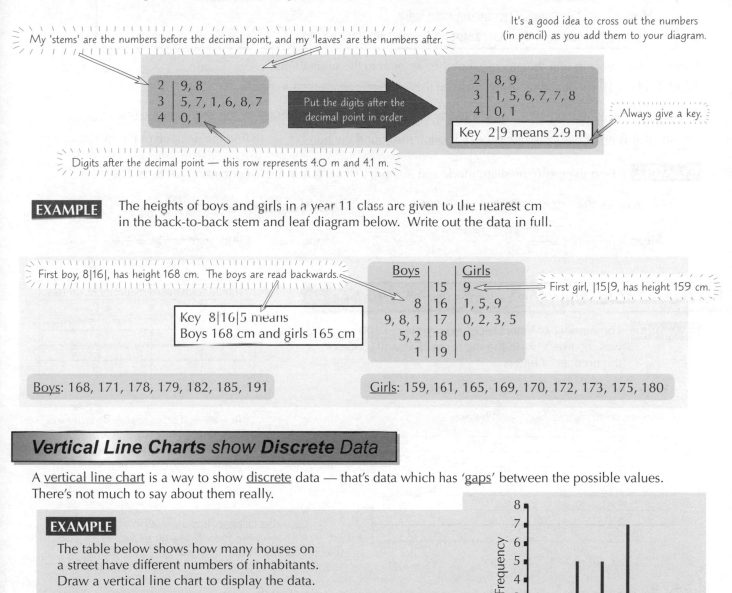

It's a good idea to cross out the numbers (in pencil) as you add them to your diagram.

My 'stems' are the numbers before the decimal point, and my 'leaves' are the numbers after.

```
2 | 9, 8
3 | 5, 7, 1, 6, 8, 7
4 | 0, 1
```

Put the digits after the decimal point in order

```
2 | 8, 9
3 | 1, 5, 6, 7, 7, 8
4 | 0, 1
Key  2|9 means 2.9 m
```

Always give a key.

Digits after the decimal point — this row represents 4.0 m and 4.1 m.

EXAMPLE   The heights of boys and girls in a year 11 class are given to the nearest cm
in the back-to-back stem and leaf diagram below. Write out the data in full.

First boy, 8|16|, has height 168 cm. The boys are read backwards.

Key 8|16|5 means
Boys 168 cm and girls 165 cm

First girl, |15|9, has height 159 cm.

Boys		Girls
	15	9
8	16	1, 5, 9
9, 8, 1	17	0, 2, 3, 5
5, 2	18	0
1	19	

<u>Boys:</u> 168, 171, 178, 179, 182, 185, 191

<u>Girls:</u> 159, 161, 165, 169, 170, 172, 173, 175, 180

Vertical Line Charts show Discrete Data

A <u>vertical line chart</u> is a way to show <u>discrete</u> data — that's data which has 'gaps' between the possible values.
There's not much to say about them really.

EXAMPLE

The table below shows how many houses on
a street have different numbers of inhabitants.
Draw a vertical line chart to display the data.

Number of inhabitants	1	2	3	4	5	6
Frequency	3	5	5	7	2	3

Your categories go along the horizontal axis.
Frequency goes up the vertical axis.

First things first: remember — there are lies, damned lies and statistics...

Histograms shouldn't cause too many problems — this is quite a friendly topic really. The main things to remember are to work out the <u>lower and upper boundaries</u> of each class <u>properly</u>, and then make sure you use <u>frequency density</u> (rather than just the frequency). Stemplots and vertical line charts — hah, they're easy, I do them in my sleep. Make sure you can too.

Location: Mean, Median, Mode and Midrange

The mean, median and mode are measures of location or central tendency (basically... where the centre of the data lies).

The Definitions are really GCSE stuff

You more than likely already know them. But if you don't, learn them now — you'll be needing them loads.

> **Mean** $= \overline{x} = \dfrac{\Sigma x}{n}$ or $\dfrac{\Sigma fx}{\Sigma f}$ The Σ (sigma) things just mean you add stuff up — so Σx means you add up all the values of x.
>
> where each x is a data value, f is the frequency of each x-value (the number of times it occurs), and n is the total number of data values.
>
> **Median** = middle data value when all the data values are placed in order of size.
>
> **Mode** = most frequently occurring data value.
>
> **Midrange** = mean of the maximum and minimum data values

There are two ways to find the median (but they amount to the same thing):

If $\frac{1}{2}(n+1)$ isn't a whole number, take the average of the terms either side.

Either: find the $\left(\dfrac{n+1}{2}\right)$th value in the ordered list. ←

Or: (i) if $\frac{n}{2}$ is a whole number (i.e. n is even), then the median is the average of this term and the one above.

   (ii) if $\frac{n}{2}$ is not a whole number (i.e. n is odd), just round the number up to find the position of the median.

EXAMPLE   Find the mean, median, mode and midrange of the following list of data: 2, 3, 6, 2, 5, 9, 3, 8, 7, 2

Put in order first: 2, 2, 2, 3, 3, 5, 6, 7, 8, 9   **Median** = average of 5th and 6th values = **4**

Mean $= \dfrac{2+2+2+3+3+5+6+7+8+9}{10} = \underline{\textbf{4.7}}$ **Mode = 2**   **Midrange** $= \dfrac{9+2}{2} = \underline{\textbf{5.5}}$

Use a Table when there are a lot of Numbers

EXAMPLE   The number of letters received one day in 100 houses was recorded. Find the mean, median and mode of the number of letters.

Number of letters	Number of houses
0	11
1	25
2	27
3	21
4	9
5	7

The first thing to do is make a table like this one:

Number of letters x	Number of houses f		fx
0	11	(11)	0
1	25	(36)	25
2	27	(63)	54
3	21		63
4	9		36
5	7		35
totals	100		213

Multiply x by f to get this column.

The number of letters received by each house is a **discrete** quantity (e.g. 3 letters). There isn't a **continuous** set of possible values between getting 3 and 4 letters (e.g. 3.45 letters).

Put the cumulative frequency (running total) in brackets — it's handy when you're finding the median. (But you can stop when you get past halfway.)

$\Sigma f = 100$ $\Sigma fx = 213$

(1) The mean is easy — just divide the total of the fx-column (sum of all the data values) by the total of the f-column (= n, the total number of data values).   **Mean** $= \dfrac{213}{100} = $ **2.13 letters**

(2) To find the position of the median, add 1 to the total frequency (= $\Sigma f = n$) and then divide by 2. Here the median is in position: $(100 + 1) \div 2 = \underline{50.5}$.

So the median is halfway between the 50th and 51st data values.

Using your running total of f, you can see that the data values in positions 37 to 63 are all 2s. This means the data values at positions 50 and 51 are both 2 — so   **Median = 2 letters**

(3) The highest frequency is for 2 letters — so   **Mode = 2 letters**

Location: Mean, Median, Mode and Midrange

If the data's Grouped you'll have to Estimate the Mean

There are no precise readings here — each reading's been put into one of these groups.

If the data's grouped, you can only estimate the mean and median, and identify a modal class.

EXAMPLE The height of a number of trees was recorded. The data collected is shown in this table:

Height of tree to nearest m	0 - 5	6 - 10	11 - 15	16 - 20
Number of trees	26	17	11	6

Find an estimate of the mean height of the trees, and state the modal class.

To estimate the mean, you assume that every reading in a class takes the mid-class value (which you find by adding the lower class boundary to the upper class boundary and dividing by 2). It's best to make another table...

Height of tree to nearest m	Mid-class value x	Number of trees f	fx
0 - 5	2.75	26 (26)	71.5
6 - 10	8	17 (43)	136
11 - 15	13	11	143
16 - 20	18	6	108
	Totals	60 ($= \Sigma f$)	458.5($= \Sigma fx$)

Lower class boundary (lcb) = O.
Upper class boundary (ucb) = 5.5.
So the mid-class value = (O + 5.5) ÷ 2 = 2.75.

Estimated mean $= \dfrac{458.5}{60} = 7.64$ **m**

The **modal class** is the class with the **highest frequency density**. In this example the modal class is **0 - 5 m**.

Linear Interpolation Means Assuming Values are Evenly Spread

When you have grouped data, you can only estimate the median. To do this, you use (linear) interpolation.

The median position in the above example is $(60 + 1) \div 2 = 30.5$, so the median is the 30.5th reading (halfway between the 30th and 31st). Your 'running total' tells you the median must be in the '6 - 10' class.

Now you have to assume that all the readings in this class are evenly spread.

There are 26 trees before class 6 - 10, so the 30.5th tree is the 4.5th value of this class.

Divide the class into 17 equally wide parts (as there are 17 readings) and assume there's a reading at the end of each part.

Width of class ⟶ $\frac{5}{17}$ $\frac{5}{17}$
Number of readings ⟶

5.5 (= lcb) $5.5 + (1 \times \frac{5}{17})$ $5.5 + (2 \times \frac{5}{17})$ 10.5 (= ucb)

Then you want the '4.5th reading' (which is '4.5 × width of 1 part' along).

So the **median** = lower class boundary + (4.5 × width of each 'part') $= 5.5 + \left[4.5 \times \frac{5}{17}\right] = 6.8$ **m** (to 1 d.p.)

Different Measures of Location are useful for Different Kinds of Data

These different averages are useful for different kinds of data.

Mean:
- The mean's a good average because you use **all** your data in working it out.
- But it can be heavily affected by **extreme values / outliers**.
- And it can only be used with **quantitative** data (i.e. numbers).

Median: The median is **not** affected by **extreme values**, so this is a good average to use when you have **outliers**.

See page 114 for more about outliers.

Mode:
- The mode can be used even with **non-numerical** data.
- But some data sets can have **more than one mode** (and if every value in a data set occurs just once, then the mode isn't very helpful at all).

Midrange: The midrange is heavily affected by **extreme values**, so this **isn't** a good average to use when you have **outliers**.

I can't deny it — these pages really are 'about average'...

If you have large amounts of grouped data ($n > 100$, say), it's usually okay to use the value in position $\frac{n}{2}$ (rather than $\frac{n+1}{2}$) as the median. With grouped data, you can only estimate the median anyway, and if you have a lot of data, that extra 'half a place' doesn't really make much difference. But if in any doubt, use the value in position $\frac{n+1}{2}$ — that'll always be okay.

Dispersion: Interquartile Range

'Dispersion' (or 'variation') means how spread out your data is. There are different ways to measure it.

The Range is a Measure of Dispersion...

The range is about the simplest measure of dispersion you could imagine.

Range = highest value – lowest value

But the range is heavily affected by extreme values, so it isn't really the most useful way to measure dispersion.

Quartiles divide the data into Four

You've seen how the median divides a data set into two halves. Well, the quartiles divide the data into four parts — with 25% of the data less than the lower quartile, and 75% of the data less than the upper quartile.

There are various ways you can find the quartiles, and they sometimes give different results. But if you use the method below, you'll be fine.

The median is also known as Q_2.

(1) To find the lower quartile (Q_1), first work out $\frac{n}{4}$.

   (i) if $\frac{n}{4}$ is a whole number, then the lower quartile is the average of this term and the one above.

   (ii) if $\frac{n}{4}$ is not a whole number, just round the number up to find the position of the lower quartile.

(2) To find the upper quartile (Q_3), first work out $\frac{3n}{4}$.

   (i) if $\frac{3n}{4}$ is a whole number, then the upper quartile is the average of this term and the one above.

   (ii) if $\frac{3n}{4}$ is not a whole number, just round the number up to find the position of the upper quartile.

EXAMPLE Find the median and quartiles of the following data: 2, 5, 3, 11, 6, 8, 3, 8, 1, 6, 2, 23, 9, 11, 18, 19, 22, 7.

First put the list in order: 1, 2, 2, 3, 3, 5, 6, 6, 7, 8, 8, 9, 11, 11, 18, 19, 22, 23

You need to find Q_1, Q_2 and Q_3, so work out $\frac{n}{4} = \frac{18}{4}$, $\frac{n}{2} = \frac{18}{2}$, and $\frac{3n}{4} = \frac{54}{4}$.

1) $\frac{n}{4}$ is not a whole number (= 4.5), so round up and take the 5th term: $Q_1 = 3$

2) $\frac{n}{2}$ is a whole number (= 9), so find the average of the 9th and 10th terms: $Q_2 = \frac{7+8}{2} = 7.5$

3) $\frac{3n}{4}$ is not a whole number (= 13.5), so round up and take the 14th term: $Q_3 = 11$

If your data is grouped, you might need to use interpolation to find the quartiles. See page 109 for more info.

The Interquartile Range is Another Measure of Dispersion

Interquartile range (IQR) = upper quartile (Q_3) – lower quartile (Q_1)

The IQR shows the range of the 'middle 50%' of the data.

EXAMPLE Find the interquartile range of the data in the previous example.

$Q_1 = 3$ and $Q_3 = 11$, so the interquartile range = $Q_3 - Q_1 = 11 - 3 = 8$

Percentiles divide the data into 100

Percentiles divide the data into 100 — the median is the 50th percentile and Q_1 is the 25th percentile, etc.

For example, the position of the 11th percentile (P_{11}) is $\frac{11}{100} \times$ total frequency.

You find interpercentile ranges by subtracting two percentiles, e.g. the middle 60% of the readings = $P_{80} - P_{20}$.

Cumulative Frequency Graphs

Cumulative frequency means 'running total'. Cumulative frequency graphs make medians and quartiles easy to find.

Use **Cumulative Frequency Graphs** to estimate the **Median** and **Quartiles**

EXAMPLE The ages of 200 students are shown. Draw a cumulative frequency graph and use it to estimate the median age, the interquartile range of ages, and how many students have already had their 18th birthday.

Age in completed years	11 - 12	13 - 14	15 - 16	17 - 18
Number of students	50	65	58	27

① First draw a table showing the upper class boundaries and the cumulative frequency (CF):

Age in completed years	Upper class boundary (ucb)	Number of students, f	Cumulative frequency (CF)
Under 11	11	0	0
11-12	13	50	50
13-14	15	65	115
15-16	17	58	173
17-18	19	27	200

The first reading in a cumulative frequency table must be zero — so add this extra row to show the number of students with age less than 11 is 0.

CF is the number of students with age less than the ucb — it's basically a running total.

The last number in the CF column should always be the total number of readings.

People say they're '18' right up until their 19th birthday — so the ucb of class 17-18 is 19.

Next draw the axes — cumulative frequency always goes on the vertical axis. Here, age goes on the other axis. Then plot the upper class boundaries against the cumulative frequencies, and join the points.

② To estimate the median from a graph, go to the median position on the vertical scale and read off the value from the horizontal axis.

Median position = $\frac{1}{2} \times 200 = 100$ so   Median = 14.5 years

Because there are so many data values, and because you can only estimate the median (since your data values are in groups), you can say that the median is in position $\frac{n}{2}$ instead of $\frac{n+1}{2}$. And you can use a similar approximation for the position of the quartiles.

Then you can estimate the quartiles in the same way. Find their positions first:

Q_1 position = $\frac{1}{4} \times 200 = 50$,
and so the lower quartile, Q_1 = 13 years

Q_3 position = $\frac{3}{4} \times 200 = 150$,
and so the upper quartile, Q_3 = 16.2 years

The interquartile range (IQR) = $Q_3 - Q_1$. It measures spread. The smaller it is the less spread the data is.

IQR = $Q_3 - Q_1$ = 16.2 – 13 = 3.2 years

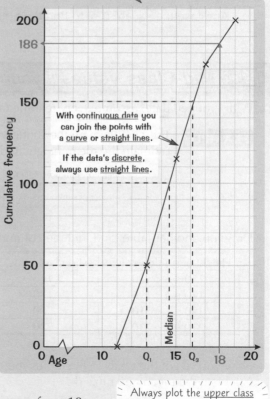

With continuous data you can join the points with a curve or straight lines.

If the data's discrete, always use straight lines.

Always plot the upper class boundary of each class.

③ To estimate how many students have not yet had their 18th birthday, go up from 18 on the horizontal axis, and read off the number of students 'younger' than 18 (= 186).

Then the number of students who are 'older' than 18 is just 200 – 186 = 14 (approximately).

I don't like those frequency tables — I've always wanted to live in a classless society...

Cumulative frequency sounds a bit scarier than running total — but if you remember they're the same thing, then that'll help. And remember to plot the points at the upper class boundary — this makes sense if you remember that a cumulative frequency graph shows how many data-values are less than the figure on the *x*-axis. The rest is more or less easyish.

Dispersion: Mean Square Deviation

"Mean square deviation" measures how spread out the values are from the mean.
The bigger the mean square deviation, the more spread out your readings.

The **Formulas** look pretty **Tricky**

Mean square deviation (m.s.d.) $= \dfrac{\sum(x - \overline{x})^2}{n} = \dfrac{S_{xx}}{n}$, where $S_{xx} = \sum(x - \overline{x})^2$

This formula is easier to use in the form: $\text{m.s.d.} = \dfrac{\sum x^2}{n} - \overline{x}^2$ or $\text{m.s.d.} = \dfrac{\sum fx^2}{\sum f} - \overline{x}^2$

The x-values are the data, $\overline{x}$ is the mean, f is the frequency of each x, and n (or $\sum f$) is the total number of values.

Root mean square deviation (r.m.s.d.) $= \sqrt{\text{Mean square deviation (m.s.d.)}}$

EXAMPLE Find the mean and root mean square deviation (r.m.s.d.) of the following numbers: 2, 3, 4, 4, 6, 11, 12

1) Find the total of the numbers first: $\sum x = 2 + 3 + 4 + 4 + 6 + 11 + 12 = 42$

2) Then the mean is easy: $\text{Mean} = \overline{x} = \dfrac{\sum x}{n} = \dfrac{42}{7} = 6$

3) Next find the sum of the squares: $\sum x^2 = 4 + 9 + 16 + 16 + 36 + 121 + 144 = 346$

4) Use this to find the m.s.d.: $\text{m.s.d.} = \dfrac{\sum x^2}{n} - \overline{x}^2 = \dfrac{346}{7} - 6^2 = \dfrac{346 - 252}{7} = \dfrac{94}{7} = 13.43$ (to 2 d.p.).

5) And take the square root to find the r.m.s.d.: $\text{r.m.s.d.} = \sqrt{\dfrac{94}{7}} = 3.66$ to 3 sig. fig.

Use **Mid-Class Values** if your data's **Grouped**

With grouped data, assume every reading takes the mid-class value. Then use the frequencies to find $\sum fx$ and $\sum fx^2$.

EXAMPLE The heights of all the sunflowers in a garden were measured and recorded in the table below. Estimate the mean height and the root mean square deviation (r.m.s.d.).

Height of sunflower, h (cm)	$150 \le h < 170$	$170 \le h < 190$	$190 \le h < 210$	$210 \le h < 230$
Number of sunflowers	5	10	12	3

Draw up another table, and include columns for the mid-class values x, as well as fx and fx^2:

Height of sunflower (cm)	Mid-class value, x	x^2	f	fx	fx^2
$150 \le h < 170$	160	25600	5	800	128000
$170 \le h < 190$	180	32400	10	1800	324000
$190 \le h < 210$	200	40000	12	2400	480000
$210 \le h < 230$	220	48400	3	660	145200
		Totals	30 ($= \Sigma f$)	5660 ($= \Sigma fx$)	1077200 ($= \Sigma fx^2$)

fx^2 means $f \times (x^2)$ — not $(fx)^2$.

Now you've got the totals in the table, you can calculate the mean and r.m.s.d.:

$\text{Mean} = \overline{x} = \dfrac{\sum fx}{\sum f} = \dfrac{5660}{30} = 189$ cm to 3 sig. fig.

$\text{m.s.d.} = \dfrac{\sum fx^2}{\sum f} - \overline{x}^2 = \dfrac{1\,077\,200}{30} - \left(\dfrac{5660}{30}\right)^2 = 312$ to 3 sig. fig.

$\text{r.m.s.d.} = \sqrt{\text{m.s.d.}} = 17.7$ cm to 3 sig. fig.

People who enjoy this stuff are mean, square deviants...

The formula for the mean square deviation looks pretty scary, what with the x^2's and $\overline{x}$'s floating about. But it comes down to 'the mean of the squares minus the square of the mean'. That's how I remember it anyway — and my memory's rubbish.

Dispersion: Variance and Standard Deviation

This page is fairly similar to the previous one, but there is one subtle difference.

You often need to use *Sample Data* to find out about a *Population*

1) In any statistical investigation, there'll be a <u>group</u> of people or items you want to <u>find out about</u>.
   This group is called the <u>population</u>, and could be: ➡
   - All the students in a maths class
   - All the penguins in Antarctica
   - All the puddings produced by a company in a year

2) The formulas on the previous page assume that
   you have measurements from a whole <u>population</u>.

3) But you won't always have data collected from <u>every</u> person or thing in the population.
   Very often, you'll have data collected from just a <u>sample</u> from the population instead.

Sample Variance — similar to m.s.d., but *Divide by (n – 1) instead of n*

1) When you have sample data, you <u>don't</u> calculate the mean square deviation and root mean square deviation.

2) Instead you calculate two very similar quantities called the <u>variance</u> (s^2) and the <u>standard deviation</u> (s).

$$\text{Sample variance } (s^2) = \frac{\sum(x - \bar{x})^2}{n - 1} = \frac{S_{xx}}{n - 1}, \text{ where } S_{xx} = \sum(x - \bar{x})^2$$

$$\text{Sample standard deviation } (s) = \sqrt{\text{sample variance}}$$

This is exactly the same as the formula for m.s.d., only there's 'n − 1' on the bottom instead of 'n'.

3) The above formulas can be a bit awkward to use.
   So it's actually easier to use the formula for m.s.d., and then multiply by $\frac{n}{n-1}$.

See p112 for more about S_{xx}.

$$\text{Sample variance } (s^2) = \frac{n}{n - 1}\left[\frac{\sum x^2}{n} - \left(\frac{\sum x}{n}\right)^2\right]$$

$$\text{Sample standard deviation } (s) = \sqrt{\text{sample variance}} = \sqrt{\frac{n}{n - 1}\left[\frac{\sum x^2}{n} - \left(\frac{\sum x}{n}\right)^2\right]}$$

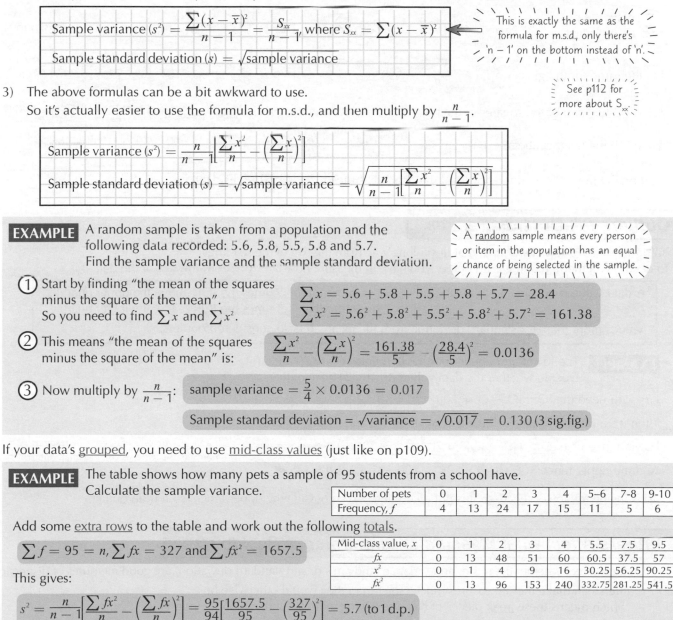

EXAMPLE A random sample is taken from a population and the
following data recorded: 5.6, 5.8, 5.5, 5.8 and 5.7.
Find the sample variance and the sample standard deviation.

A <u>random</u> sample means every person or item in the population has an equal chance of being selected in the sample.

① Start by finding "the mean of the squares minus the square of the mean".
   So you need to find $\sum x$ and $\sum x^2$.

$$\sum x = 5.6 + 5.8 + 5.5 + 5.8 + 5.7 = 28.4$$
$$\sum x^2 = 5.6^2 + 5.8^2 + 5.5^2 + 5.8^2 + 5.7^2 = 161.38$$

② This means "the mean of the squares minus the square of the mean" is:

$$\frac{\sum x^2}{n} - \left(\frac{\sum x}{n}\right)^2 = \frac{161.38}{5} - \left(\frac{28.4}{5}\right)^2 = 0.0136$$

③ Now multiply by $\frac{n}{n-1}$: $\quad$ sample variance $= \frac{5}{4} \times 0.0136 = 0.017$

$$\text{Sample standard deviation} = \sqrt{\text{variance}} = \sqrt{0.017} = 0.130 \,(3 \text{ sig.fig.})$$

If your data's <u>grouped</u>, you need to use <u>mid-class values</u> (just like on p109).

EXAMPLE The table shows how many pets a sample of 95 students from a school have.
Calculate the sample variance.

Number of pets	0	1	2	3	4	5–6	7-8	9-10
Frequency, f	4	13	24	17	15	11	5	6

Add some <u>extra rows</u> to the table and work out the following <u>totals</u>.

$$\sum f = 95 = n, \sum fx = 327 \text{ and } \sum fx^2 = 1657.5$$

This gives:

Mid-class value, x	0	1	2	3	4	5.5	7.5	9.5
fx	0	13	48	51	60	60.5	37.5	57
x^2	0	1	4	9	16	30.25	56.25	90.25
fx^2	0	13	96	153	240	332.75	281.25	541.5

$$s^2 = \frac{n}{n - 1}\left[\frac{\sum fx^2}{n} - \left(\frac{\sum fx}{n}\right)^2\right] = \frac{95}{94}\left[\frac{1657.5}{95} - \left(\frac{327}{95}\right)^2\right] = 5.7 \,(\text{to 1 d.p.})$$

It's the standard kind of deviants who enjoy this kind of thing...

A lot of calculators will work out the r.m.s.d. and the standard deviation for you (look out for functions marked σ_n and σ_{n-1}).
That <u>doesn't</u> mean you <u>don't</u> need to know how to use the formulas, though — so make sure you read this page carefully.

Dispersion and Outliers

Questions about **Mean Square Deviation** can look a bit **Weird**

They can ask questions using m.s.d. and variance in different ways. But you just need to use the same old formulas.

EXAMPLE The mean of 10 boys' heights is 180 cm, and the r.m.s.d. is 10 cm. The mean for 9 girls is 165 cm, and the r.m.s.d. is 8 cm. Find the mean and r.m.s.d. for this whole population of 19 girls and boys.

(1) Let the boys' heights be x and the girls' heights be y.

Write down the formula for the mean and put the numbers in for the boys: $\bar{x} = \dfrac{\sum x}{n} \Rightarrow 180 = \dfrac{\sum x}{10} \Rightarrow \sum x = 1800$

Do the same for the girls: $165 = \dfrac{\sum y}{9} \Rightarrow \sum y = 1485$

So the sum of the heights for the <u>boys and the girls</u> = $\sum x + \sum y = 1800 + 1485 = 3285$

And the <u>mean height</u> of the boys and the girls is: $\dfrac{3285}{19} = 172.9\,\text{cm}$

Round the fraction to 1 d.p. to give your answer. But if you need to use the mean in more calculations, use the <u>fraction</u> (or your <u>calculator's memory</u>) so you don't lose accuracy.

(2) Now the m.s.d. — boys first: $\text{m.s.d.} = \dfrac{\sum x^2}{n} - \bar{x}^2 \Rightarrow 10^2 = \dfrac{\sum x^2}{10} - 180^2 \Rightarrow \sum x^2 = 10 \times (100 + 32\,400) = 325\,000$

Do the same for the girls: $\text{m.s.d.} = \dfrac{\sum y^2}{n} - \bar{y}^2 \Rightarrow 8^2 = \dfrac{\sum y^2}{9} - 165^2 \Rightarrow \sum y^2 = 9 \times (64 + 27\,225) = 245\,601$

Okay, so the sum of the squares of the heights of the boys and the girls is: $\sum x^2 + \sum y^2 = 325\,000 + 245\,601 = 570\,601$

So for <u>all</u> the heights, the m.s.d. is: $\text{m.s.d.} = \dfrac{570\,601}{19} - \left(\dfrac{3285}{19}\right)^2 = 139.0\,\text{cm}^2$

Don't use the <u>rounded</u> mean (172.9) — you'll lose accuracy.

And finally the r.m.s.d. of the boys and the girls is: $\text{r.m.s.d.} = \sqrt{139.0} = 11.8\,\text{cm}$

Phew.

Outliers fall **Outside Fences**

An <u>outlier</u> is a <u>freak</u> piece of data that lies a long way from the rest of the readings.
To decide whether a reading is an outlier you have to measure how far away from the rest of the data it is.

A data value is considered to be an outlier if it is: more than <u>1.5 times the IQR above</u> the <u>upper quartile</u>
or more than <u>1.5 times the IQR below</u> the <u>lower quartile</u>.
Values <u>more than 2 × standard deviation from the mean</u> are also considered outliers.

EXAMPLE The lower and upper quartiles of a data set are 70 and 100. Decide whether the data values 30 and 210 are outliers.

First you need the IQR: $Q_3 - Q_1 = 100 - 70 = 30$

Then it's a piece of cake to find where your <u>fences</u> are.

Lower fence first: $Q_1 - (1.5 \times \text{IQR}) = 70 - (1.5 \times 30) = 25$

And the upper fence: $Q_3 + (1.5 \times \text{IQR}) = 100 + (1.5 \times 30) = 145$

25 and 145 are called <u>fences</u>. Any reading lying <u>outside</u> the fences is considered an <u>outlier</u>.

30 is <u>inside the lower fence</u>, so it is <u>not</u> an outlier. 210 is <u>outside</u> the upper fence, so it <u>is</u> an outlier.

Outliers Affect what Measure of **Dispersion** is Best to Use

1) Outliers affect whether the <u>m.s.d.</u> and <u>variance</u> (and r.m.s.d. and standard deviation) are good measures of <u>dispersion</u>.

2) Outliers can make these measures <u>much</u> larger than they would otherwise be
— which means these <u>freak</u> pieces of data are having more influence than they deserve.

3) If a data set contains outliers, then a better measure of dispersion is the <u>interquartile range</u>.

'Outlier' is the name I give to something that my theory can't explain...

Measures of <u>location</u> and <u>dispersion</u> are supposed to capture the essential characteristics of a data set in just one or two numbers. So don't choose a measure that's heavily affected by freaky, far-flung outliers — it won't be much good.

Coding

Linear Coding can make the Numbers much Easier

Linear coding means <u>adding</u> or <u>multiplying</u> every reading by numbers that will make them easier to work with.

Finding the mean of 1001, 1002 and 1006 looks hard(ish). But take 1000 off each number and finding the mean of what's left (1, 2 and 6) is much easier — it's <u>3</u>. So the mean of the original numbers must be <u>1003</u>. That's coding.

You usually change your original variable, x, to an easier one to work with, y (so here, if $x = 1001$, then $y = 1$).

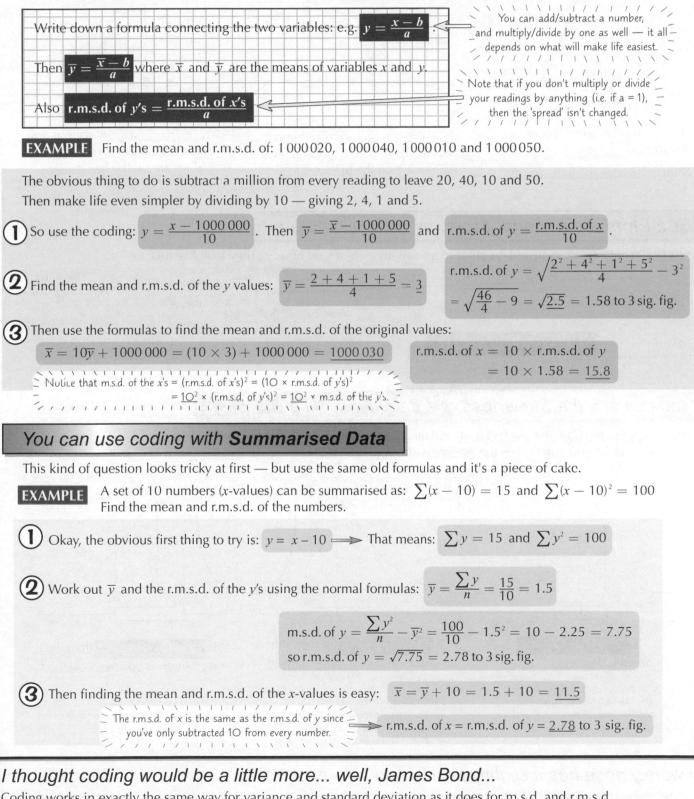

Write down a formula connecting the two variables: e.g. $y = \dfrac{x - b}{a}$.

Then $\overline{y} = \dfrac{\overline{x} - b}{a}$ where $\overline{x}$ and $\overline{y}$ are the means of variables x and y.

Also $\text{r.m.s.d. of } y\text{'s} = \dfrac{\text{r.m.s.d. of } x\text{'s}}{a}$

You can add/subtract a number, and multiply/divide by one as well — it all depends on what will make life easiest.

Note that if you don't multiply or divide your readings by anything (i.e. if a = 1), then the 'spread' isn't changed.

EXAMPLE Find the mean and r.m.s.d. of: 1 000 020, 1 000 040, 1 000 010 and 1 000 050.

The obvious thing to do is subtract a million from every reading to leave 20, 40, 10 and 50.
Then make life even simpler by dividing by 10 — giving 2, 4, 1 and 5.

① So use the coding: $y = \dfrac{x - 1000\,000}{10}$. Then $\overline{y} = \dfrac{\overline{x} - 1000\,000}{10}$ and $\text{r.m.s.d. of } y = \dfrac{\text{r.m.s.d. of } x}{10}$.

② Find the mean and r.m.s.d. of the y values: $\overline{y} = \dfrac{2 + 4 + 1 + 5}{4} = \underline{3}$

$\text{r.m.s.d. of } y = \sqrt{\dfrac{2^2 + 4^2 + 1^2 + 5^2}{4} - 3^2}$
$= \sqrt{\dfrac{46}{4} - 9} = \sqrt{2.5} = 1.58 \text{ to 3 sig. fig.}$

③ Then use the formulas to find the mean and r.m.s.d. of the original values:

$\overline{x} = 10\overline{y} + 1000\,000 = (10 \times 3) + 1000\,000 = \underline{1000\,030}$

$\text{r.m.s.d. of } x = 10 \times \text{r.m.s.d. of } y$
$= 10 \times 1.58 = \underline{15.8}$

Notice that m.s.d. of the x's = (r.m.s.d. of x's)^2 = (10 × r.m.s.d. of y's)^2
= 10^2 × (r.m.s.d. of y's)^2 = 10^2 × m.s.d. of the y's.

You can use coding with Summarised Data

This kind of question looks tricky at first — but use the same old formulas and it's a piece of cake.

EXAMPLE A set of 10 numbers (x-values) can be summarised as: $\sum(x - 10) = 15$ and $\sum(x - 10)^2 = 100$
Find the mean and r.m.s.d. of the numbers.

① Okay, the obvious first thing to try is: $y = x - 10 \Longrightarrow$ That means: $\sum y = 15$ and $\sum y^2 = 100$

② Work out $\overline{y}$ and the r.m.s.d. of the y's using the normal formulas: $\overline{y} = \dfrac{\sum y}{n} = \dfrac{15}{10} = 1.5$

$\text{m.s.d. of } y = \dfrac{\sum y^2}{n} - \overline{y}^2 = \dfrac{100}{10} - 1.5^2 = 10 - 2.25 = 7.75$
so r.m.s.d. of $y = \sqrt{7.75} = 2.78 \text{ to 3 sig. fig.}$

③ Then finding the mean and r.m.s.d. of the x-values is easy: $\overline{x} = \overline{y} + 10 = 1.5 + 10 = \underline{11.5}$

The r.m.s.d. of x is the same as the r.m.s.d. of y since you've only subtracted 10 from every number. → r.m.s.d. of x = r.m.s.d. of y = <u>2.78</u> to 3 sig. fig.

I thought coding would be a little more... well, James Bond...

Coding works in exactly the same way for variance and standard deviation as it does for m.s.d. and r.m.s.d.
So if you have some data and you use the linear coding formulas at the top of the page, then you find that:
(i) standard deviation of x's = a × standard deviation of y's, and (ii) variance of x's = a^2 × variance of y's. Couldn't be easier.

Skewness and Box Plots

So far you've seen that: (i) location/central tendency tells you where the centre of the data is, (ii) dispersion tells you how spread out the values are. Now it's time to find out about a third thing: (iii) skewness — how symmetrical the data is.

Skewness tells you whether your data is Symmetrical or Lopsided

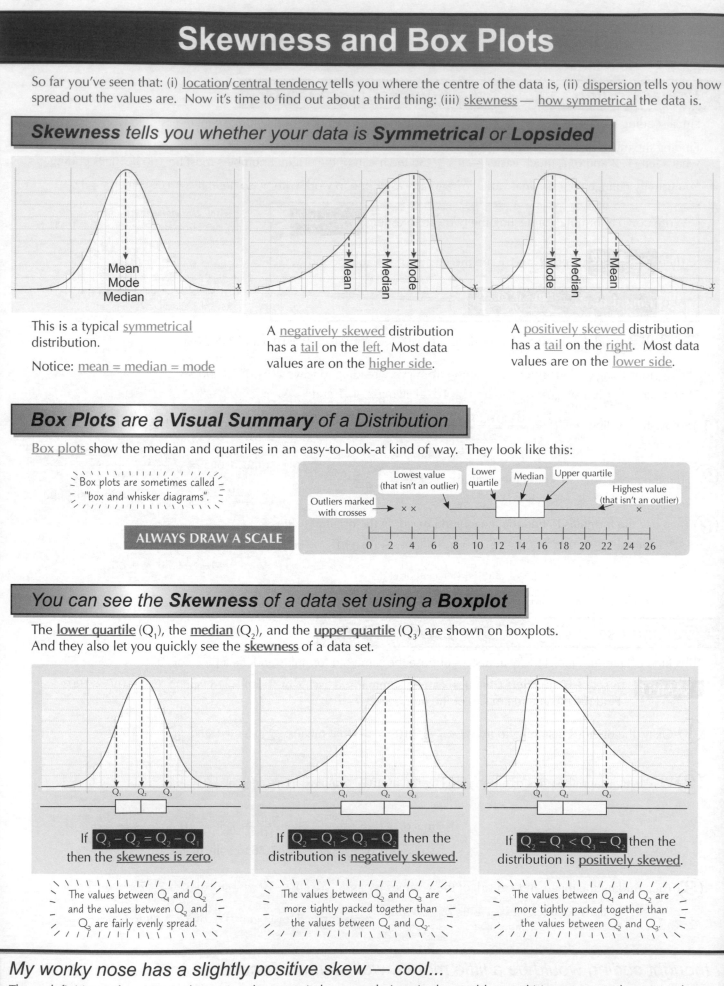

This is a typical symmetrical distribution.

Notice: mean = median = mode

A negatively skewed distribution has a tail on the left. Most data values are on the higher side.

A positively skewed distribution has a tail on the right. Most data values are on the lower side.

Box Plots are a Visual Summary of a Distribution

Box plots show the median and quartiles in an easy-to-look-at kind of way. They look like this:

Box plots are sometimes called "box and whisker diagrams".

ALWAYS DRAW A SCALE

Lowest value (that isn't an outlier)
Lower quartile
Median
Upper quartile
Highest value (that isn't an outlier)

Outliers marked with crosses

You can see the Skewness of a data set using a Boxplot

The lower quartile (Q_1), the median (Q_2), and the upper quartile (Q_3) are shown on boxplots. And they also let you quickly see the skewness of a data set.

If $Q_3 - Q_2 = Q_2 - Q_1$ then the skewness is zero.

If $Q_2 - Q_1 > Q_3 - Q_2$ then the distribution is negatively skewed.

If $Q_2 - Q_1 < Q_3 - Q_2$ then the distribution is positively skewed.

The values between Q_1 and Q_2 and the values between Q_2 and Q_3 are fairly evenly spread.

The values between Q_2 and Q_3 are more tightly packed together than the values between Q_1 and Q_2.

The values between Q_1 and Q_2 are more tightly packed together than the values between Q_2 and Q_3.

My wonky nose has a slightly positive skew — cool...

Those definitions of positive and negative skew aren't the most obvious in the world — and it's easy to get them mixed up. Remember that negative skew involves a tail on the left, which means that low values tend to be really low. Positive skew is the opposite — a tail on the right, and high readings tending to be really high.

Comparing Distributions

To compare data sets, you need to know how to use all the formulas and what the results tell you.

Use **Location**, **Dispersion** and **Skewness** to Compare Distributions

EXAMPLE This table summarises the marks obtained in Maths 'calculator' and 'non-calculator' papers. Compare the location, dispersion and skewness of the distributions.

Calculator Paper		Non-calculator paper
28	Minimum	12
78	Maximum	82
40	Lower quartile, Q_1	35
58	Median, Q_2	42
70	Upper quartile, Q_3	56
55	Mean	46.1
21.2	Standard deviation	17.8

Location: The mean, the median and the quartiles are all higher for the calculator paper. This means that scores were generally higher on the calculator paper.

Although the maximum mark on the non-calculator paper was higher than the maximum mark on the calculator paper, this doesn't say anything about the results generally.

Dispersion: The range for the calculator paper is $78 - 28 = 50$.
The range for the non-calculator paper is $82 - 12 = 70$.
The interquartile range (IQR) for the calculator paper is $Q_3 - Q_1 = 70 - 40 = 30$.
The interquartile range (IQR) for the non-calculator paper is $Q_3 - Q_1 = 56 - 35 = 21$.

The IQR and the standard deviation are both higher for the calculator paper, so it looks like the scores on the calculator paper are more spread out than for the non-calculator paper. Although the range is higher for the non-calculator paper, this might not be a reliable guide to the dispersion since the data may well contain outliers.

Skewness: The calculator paper marks are negatively skewed (since $Q_2 - Q_1 = 18$ is greater than $Q_3 - Q_2 = 12$). This means the higher marks were more tightly packed than the lower marks.
The non-calculator paper marks are positively skewed (since $Q_2 - Q_1 = 7$ is less than $Q_3 - Q_2 = 14$). This means the higher marks were more spread out than the lower marks.

EXAMPLE Compare the distributions represented by the box plots below.

Distribution 1:
Distribution 2:

0   20   40   60   80   100

Location: The median and the quartiles are higher for Distribution 1, showing that these data values are generally higher than for Distribution 2.

Dispersion: The interquartile range (IQR) and the range for Distribution 1 are higher, showing that the values are more varied for Distribution 1 than for Distribution 2.

Skewness: Distribution 1 is negatively skewed, showing that there is a tail on the left of this distribution, meaning the lower values are more spread out / the higher values are more tightly bunched.
Distribution 2 is positively skewed, showing that there is a tail on the right of this distribution, meaning the higher values are more spread out / the lower values are more tightly bunched.

That's the end of the Data section — hurrah for that...

On exam day, you could be asked to compare two distributions. Just work out any measures of location, dispersion and skewness you can. Then say which distribution has a higher value for each measure, and what it means — e.g. a higher variance means the values are more spread out, while a higher mean means the scores are generally higher. And so on.

S1 Section 1 — Practice Questions

It's important to make sure you know this stuff like the back of your hand — but unlike the back of your hand you won't have this book in the exam. So here are some practice questions to help you remember it all. We'll start off gently...

Warm-up Questions

1) Twenty phone calls were made by a householder one evening.
   The lengths of the calls (in minutes to the nearest minute)
   are recorded below. Draw a histogram of the data.

Length of call	0 - 2	3 - 5	6 - 8	9 - 15
Number of calls	10	6	3	1

2) The stem and leaf diagram on the right represents the lengths
   (in cm) of 15 bananas. Write down the original data as a list.

12	8
13	2, 5
14	3, 3, 6, 8
15	2, 9
16	1, 1, 2, 3
17	0, 2

   Key 12|8 means 12.8 cm

3) Calculate the mean, median, mode and midrange of the data in this table.
   Then draw a vertical line chart to illustrate the data.

x	0	1	2	3	4
f	5	4	4	2	1

4) The speeds of 60 cars travelling in a 40 mph speed limit area were measured to the nearest mph.
   The data is summarised in the table.
   Estimate the mean and the median speed of
   the 40 cars, and state the modal class.

Speed (mph)	30 - 34	35 - 39	40 - 44	45 - 50
Frequency	12	37	9	2

5) Find the median and quartiles of the data below, and draw a box and whisker diagram.
   Consider outliers to be any values less than $Q_1 - 1.5 \times (Q_3 - Q_1)$ or greater than $Q_3 + 1.5 \times (Q_3 - Q_1)$.
   Comment on any skewness.

   Amount of pocket money (in £) received per week by twenty 15-year-olds:
   10, 5, 20, 50, 5, 1, 6, 5, 15, 20, 5, 7, 5, 10, 12, 4, 8, 6, 7, 30.

6) Draw a cumulative frequency diagram of the data given in the table.
   Use your diagram to estimate the median and interquartile range.

Distance walked (km)	0 - 2	2 - 4	4 - 6	6 - 8
Number of walkers	10	5	3	2

7) Find the mean and root mean square deviation of the following numbers: 11, 12, 14, 17, 21, 23, 27.

8) The scores in an IQ test for a sample
   of 50 people are recorded in the table.
   Estimate the mean and the variance.

Score	100 - 106	107 - 113	114 - 120	121 - 127	128 - 134
Frequency	6	11	22	9	2

9) A data value is considered an outlier if it's more than 1.5 times the IQR above the upper quartile
   or more than 1.5 times the IQR below the lower quartile.
   If the lower and upper quartiles of a data set are 62 and 88, decide which of the following data
   are outliers: a) 121,   b) 134,   c) 29

10) For a set of data, $n = 100$, $\sum(x - 20) = 125$, and $\sum(x - 20)^2 = 221$.
    Find the mean and root mean square deviation of x.

S1 Section 1 — Practice Questions

Well wasn't that lovely. I bet you're now ready and raring to test yourself with some proper exam-style questions. Here are some I made earlier, lucky you.

Exam Questions

1   A group of 19 people played a game. The scores, x, that the people achieved are summarised by:
$$\sum(x - 30) = 228 \text{ and } \sum(x - 30)^2 = 3040$$

    a)   Calculate the mean and the root mean square deviation of the 19 scores.

(3 marks)

    b)   Show that $\sum x = 798$ and $\sum x^2 = 33\,820$.

(3 marks)

    c)   Another student played the game. Her score was 32.
       Find the new mean and root mean square deviation of all 20 scores.

(4 marks)

2   Two workers iron clothes. Each irons 10 items, and records the time it takes for each, to the nearest minute:

                 Worker A: 3 5 2 7 10 4 5 5 4 12
                 Worker B: 3 4 8 6 7 8 9 10 11 9

    a)   For worker A's times. Find:
       (i)   the median

(1 mark)

       (ii) the lower and upper quartiles

(2 marks)

    b)   On graph paper, draw two box plots representing the workers' times (i.e. one box plot for each worker). Both box plots should be drawn using the same scale.

(6 marks)

    c)   Make one statement comparing the two sets of data.

(1 mark)

    d)   Which worker would be better to employ? Give a reason for your answer.

(1 mark)

3   In a supermarket, samples of two types of chocolate drops were compared.
The weights, a grams, of 20 chocolate drops of brand A are summarised by:
$$\Sigma a = 60.3 \text{ g} \qquad \Sigma a^2 = 219 \text{ g}^2$$
The mean weight of 30 chocolate drops of brand B was 2.95 g, and the standard deviation was 1 g.

    a)   Find the mean weight of a brand A chocolate drop.

(1 mark)

    b)   Find the sample standard deviation of the brand A weights.

(3 marks)

    c)   Compare brands A and B.

(2 marks)

    d)   Find the sample standard deviation of the weight of all 50 chocolate drops.

(4 marks)

S1 Section 1 — Practice Questions

Despair not, valiant mathematician, for the end is nigh. Just a few more questions, then you can have a nap and a biscuit.

Exam Questions

4 The table shows the number of hits received by people at a paint ball party.

No. of Hits	12	13	14	15	16	17	18	19	20	21	22	23	24	25
Frequency	2	4	6	7	6	4	4	2	1	1	0	0	0	1

a) Find the median and mode number of hits.

(3 marks)

b) Find the interquartile range. Use your answer to show whether or not 25 is an outlier.

(3 marks)

c) Sketch a box plot of the distribution.
Comment on any skewness.

(2 marks)

d) How would the shape of the distribution be affected if the value of 25 was removed?

(1 mark)

5 The profits of 100 businesses are given in the table.

Profit, £x million.	Number of businesses
$4.5 \leqslant x < 5.0$	24
$5.0 \leqslant x < 5.5$	26
$5.5 \leqslant x < 6.0$	21
$6.0 \leqslant x < 6.5$	19
$6.5 \leqslant x < 8.0$	10

a) Represent the data in a histogram.

(3 marks)

b) Comment on the distribution of the profits of the businesses.

(2 marks)

6 The stem and leaf diagram shows the test marks for 30 male students and 16 female students.

```
        Male students         Female students
            8, 3, 3 | 4 |
   8, 7, 7, 7, 5, 3, 2 | 5 | 5, 6, 7
9, 7, 6, 6, 5, 5, 2, 2, 1, 1, 0 | 6 | 1, 2, 3, 3, 4, 5, 6, 7, 9
   9, 9, 8, 5, 4, 3, 1, 0, 0 | 7 | 2, 4, 8, 9
```

Key 5|6|2 means Male student test mark 65 and Female student test mark 62

a) Find the median test mark of the male students.

(1 mark)

b) Compare the distribution of the male and female marks.

(2 marks)

7 The histogram shows the nose-to-tail lengths of 50 lions in a game reserve.

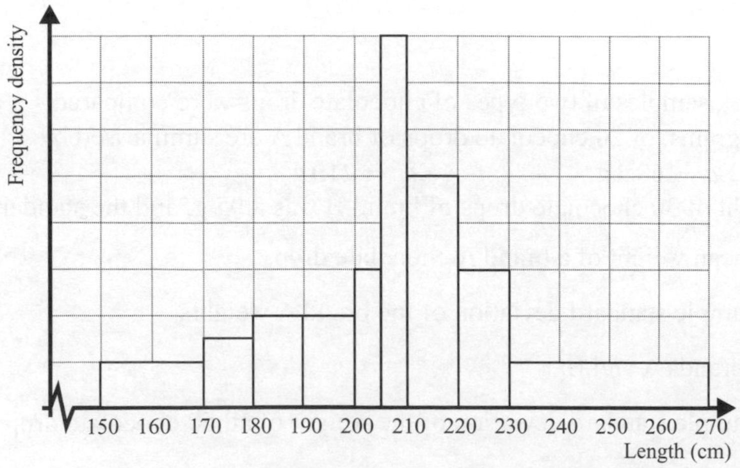

Use the histogram to find the number of lions who measured over 220 cm from nose to tail.

(5 marks)

Permutations and Combinations

<u>Choices</u>. That's what this page is all about. Bear that in mind when I tell you that you <u>must</u> read all this <u>very carefully</u>.

In a **Permutation**, the **Order Matters**

First of all, you need to know that a <u>permutation</u> is an arrangement of things where the <u>order matters</u>.
So AB and BA are <u>different permutations</u> of the letters A and B, for example.

> **EXAMPLE** How many 3-digit permutations using the numbers 0-9 are there, if each digit can only appear once?
>
> You have <u>10 choices</u> for the first digit, <u>9 choices</u> for the second digit, and <u>8 choices</u> for the third digit.
>
> So there are $10 \times 9 \times 8 = \underline{720}$ different permutations . This is just $\dfrac{10 \times 9 \times 8 \times 7 \times \ldots \times 1}{7 \times 6 \times \ldots \times 1} = \dfrac{10!}{7!} = \dfrac{10!}{(10-3)!}$.

> ### Permutations
>
> When choosing r objects from n, the number of possible <u>permutations</u> is: $\dfrac{n!}{(n-r)!}$

Always count the 'choices' you have at each point.

See p134 for more about 'n!'.

In a **Combination**, the **Order Doesn't Matter**

In a <u>combination</u>, the <u>order</u> of things <u>isn't important</u>. So AB and BA are actually the <u>same combination</u> of A and B.

> **EXAMPLE** How many 3-digit combinations using the numbers 0-9 are there, if each digit can only appear once?
>
> From the example above, there are 720 <u>permutations</u> with 3 digits. But think of the permutation 123 — this is the <u>same combination</u> as 321. In fact, it's the same combination as <u>any</u> rearrangement of the digits 1, 2 and 3 (and there are $3! = 3 \times 2 \times 1 = 6$ permutations of the digits 1, 2 and 3).
>
> So the number of <u>combinations</u> of 3 digits must be $720 \div 6 = \underline{120}$. This is $\dfrac{10!}{7!3!} = \dfrac{10!}{(10-3)! \times 3!}$.

> ### Combinations
>
> When choosing r objects from n, the number of possible <u>combinations</u> is: ${}^nC_r = \dbinom{n}{r} = \dfrac{n!}{(n-r)!r!}$
>
> ${}^nC_r$ is called a <u>binomial coefficient</u>.

Do **"Pick r from n"** questions using **Binomial Coefficients**

See p134 for more on binomial coefficients.

Questions on this kind of thing sometimes <u>look</u> a bit different — but they're often no more tricky.

> **EXAMPLE** A school is picking its team for a maths quiz. A team of 6 is chosen at random from a group of 10 volunteers. 4 of the volunteers are boys and 6 are girls.
> a) How many different teams could be chosen?
> b) How many different teams consisting of 3 boys and 3 girls could be chosen?
>
> a) This is a "How many ways to <u>pick r things from n things</u>?" type of question.
> More precisely, the question is: How many ways are there to pick 6 things from 10 things?
>
> This is just $\dbinom{10}{6} = \dfrac{10!}{(10-6)! \times 6!} = \dfrac{10!}{4! \times 6!} = \dfrac{3\,628\,800}{24 \times 720} = 210$ teams
>
> b) This time, you need to know <u>two</u> things: (i) how many ways there are to pick <u>3 boys</u> from <u>4 male volunteers</u>, and (ii) how many ways there are to pick <u>3 girls</u> from <u>6 female volunteers</u>.
>
> These are: (i) $\dbinom{4}{3} = \dfrac{4!}{(4-3)! \times 3!} = \dfrac{24}{1 \times 6} = 4$ and (ii) $\dbinom{6}{3} = \dfrac{6!}{(6-3)! \times 3!} = \dfrac{720}{6 \times 6} = 20$
>
> Since <u>any</u> group of 3 boys could be put together with <u>any</u> group of 3 girls, the total number of teams with 3 boys and 3 girls must be $4 \times 20 = 80$ teams .

In the Exam, you'll have no choice but to answer a question on this topic...

I'm afraid you must learn all this business about permutations and combinations. But, once you've done that, you can calculate how many tickets you'd need to buy to be certain of winning the lottery jackpot. Quite a few, I'm guessing.

Random Events and Venn Diagrams

Random events happen by chance. Probability is a measure of how likely they are. It can be a chancy business.

A Random Event has **Various Outcomes**

1) In a trial (or experiment) the things that can happen are called outcomes (so if I time how long it takes to eat my dinner, 63 seconds is a possible outcome).
2) Events are 'groups' of one or more outcomes (so an event might be 'it takes me less than a minute to eat my dinner every day one week').
3) When all outcomes are equally likely, you can work out the probability of an event by counting the outcomes:

$$P(\text{event}) = \frac{\text{Number of outcomes where event happens}}{\text{Total number of possible outcomes}}$$

EXAMPLE   Suppose I've got a bag with 15 balls in — 5 red, 6 blue and 4 green.

If I take a ball out without looking, then any ball is equally likely — there are 15 possible outcomes.
Of these 15 outcomes, 5 are red, 6 are blue and 4 are green. And so...

$$P(\text{red ball}) = \frac{5}{15} = \frac{1}{3} \qquad P(\text{blue ball}) = \frac{6}{15} = \frac{2}{5} \qquad P(\text{red or green ball}) = \frac{9}{15} = \frac{3}{5}$$

If I then do 90 trials (i.e. I pick a ball out 90 times, replacing the ball each time), then I would expect to pick:

a red ball $\frac{1}{3} \times 90 = 30$ times   a blue ball $\frac{2}{5} \times 90 = 36$ times   either a red or a green ball $\frac{3}{5} \times 90 = 54$ times

You can also use relative frequencies to assign probabilities — you use the results of trials you've already carried out.

$$P(\text{event}) = \frac{\text{Number of trials where event happened}}{\text{Total number of trials carried out}}$$

The **Sample Space** is the Set of **All Possible Outcomes**

Drawing the sample space (called S) helps you count the outcomes you're interested in.

EXAMPLE   The classic probability machine is a dice. If you roll it twice, you can record all the possible outcomes in a 6 × 6 table (a possible diagram of the sample space).

There are 36 outcomes in total. You can find probabilities by counting the ones you're interested in (and using the above formula). For example:

(i) The probability of an odd number and then a '1'. There are 3 outcomes that make up this event, so the probability is: $\frac{3}{36} = \frac{1}{12}$

(ii) The probability of the total being 7. There are 6 outcomes that correspond to this event, giving a probability of: $\frac{6}{36} = \frac{1}{6}$

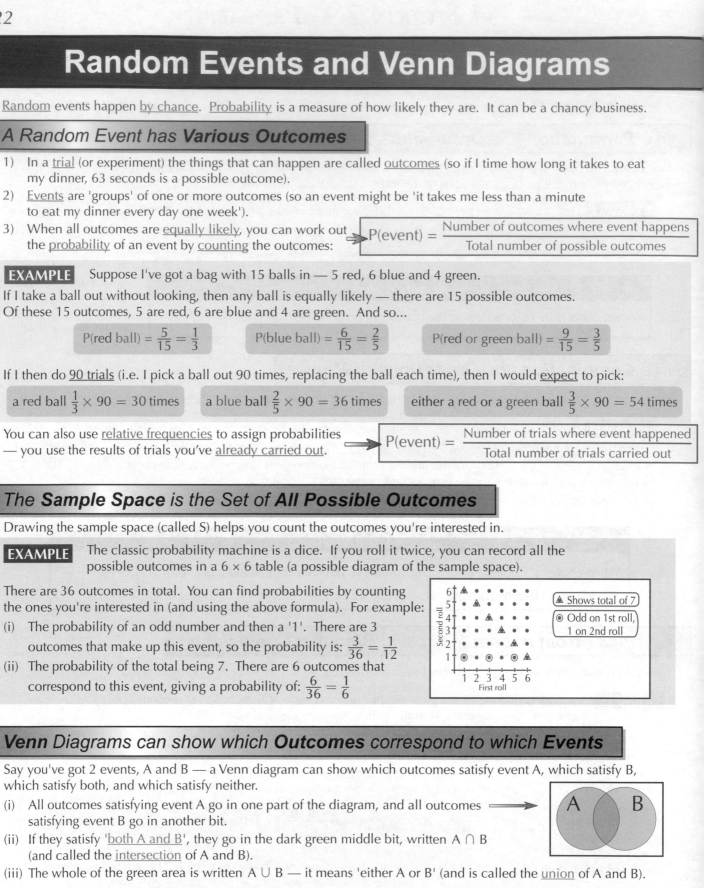

Venn Diagrams can show which **Outcomes** correspond to which **Events**

Say you've got 2 events, A and B — a Venn diagram can show which outcomes satisfy event A, which satisfy B, which satisfy both, and which satisfy neither.

(i) All outcomes satisfying event A go in one part of the diagram, and all outcomes satisfying event B go in another bit.
(ii) If they satisfy 'both A and B', they go in the dark green middle bit, written A ∩ B (and called the intersection of A and B).
(iii) The whole of the green area is written A ∪ B — it means 'either A or B' (and is called the union of A and B).

Again, you can work out probabilities of events by counting outcomes and using the formula above.
You can also get a nice formula linking P(A ∩ B) and P(A ∪ B).

$$P(A \cup B) = P(A) + P(B) - P(A \cap B)$$

If you just add up the outcomes in A and B, you end up counting A ∩ B twice — that's why you have to subtract it.

EXAMPLE   If you roll a dice, event A could be 'I get an even number', and B 'I get a number bigger than 4'. The Venn diagram would be:

$$P(A) = \frac{3}{6} = \frac{1}{2} \qquad P(B) = \frac{2}{6} = \frac{1}{3} \qquad P(A \cap B) = \frac{1}{6} \qquad P(A \cup B) = \frac{4}{6} = \frac{2}{3}$$

Here, I've just counted outcomes — but I could have used the formula.

Random Events and Venn Diagrams

EXAMPLE A survey was carried out to find what pets people like.

The probability they like dogs is 0.6. The probability they like cats is 0.5. The probability they like gerbils is 0.4. The probability they like dogs and cats is 0.4. The probability they like cats and gerbils is 0.1, and the probability they like gerbils and dogs is 0.2. Finally, the probability they like all three kinds of animal is 0.1. You can draw all this in a Venn diagram. (Here I've used C for 'likes cats', D for 'likes dogs' and G for 'likes gerbils'.)

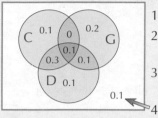

1) Stick in the middle one first — 'likes all 3 animals' (i.e. $C \cap D \cap G$).

2) Then do the 'likes 2 animals' probabilities by taking 0.1 from each of the given 'likes 2 animals' probabilities. (If they like 3 animals, they'll also be in the 'likes 2 animals' bits.)

3) Then do the 'likes 1 kind of animal' probabilities, by making sure the total probability in each circle adds up to the probability in the question.

4) Finally, subtract all the probabilities so far from 1 to find 'likes none of these animals'.

① From the Venn diagram, the probability that someone likes either dogs or cats is 0.7.

② The probability that someone likes gerbils but not dogs is 0.2.

③ You can work out the probability that a dog-lover <u>also</u> like cats by ignoring everything outside the 'dogs' circle.

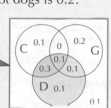

P(dog-lover also like cats)

$$= \frac{0.3 + 0.1}{0.3 + 0.1 + 0.1 + 0.1} = \frac{2}{3}$$

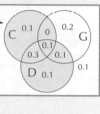

The **Complement** of 'Event A' is '**Not Event A**'

An event A will either happen or not happen. The event 'A doesn't happen' is called the <u>complement</u> of A (or <u>A'</u>). On a Venn diagram, it would look like this (because $A \cup A' = S$, the sample space): At least one of A and A' has to happen, so...

$$P(A) + P(A') = 1 \quad \text{or} \quad P(A') = 1 - P(A)$$

A' A S

EXAMPLE A teacher keeps socks loose in a box. One morning, he picks out a sock. He calculates that the probability of then picking out a matching sock is 0.56. What is the probability of him not picking a matching sock?

Call event A 'picks a matching sock'. Then A' is 'doesn't pick a matching sock'. Now A and A' are <u>complementary</u> events (and P(A) = 0.56), so $P(A) + P(A') = 1$, and therefore $P(A') = 1 - 0.56 = 0.44$

Mutually Exclusive Events Have **No Overlap**

If two events can't both happen at the same time (i.e. $P(A \cap B) = 0$) they're called <u>mutually exclusive</u> (or just '<u>exclusive</u>'). If A and B are exclusive, then the probability of A <u>or</u> B is: $P(A \cup B) = P(A) + P(B)$. ← Use the formula from page 122, but put $P(A \cap B) = 0$.
More generally,

For *n* <u>exclusive</u> events (i.e. only one of them can happen at a time):
$$P(A_1 \cup A_2 \cup ... \cup A_n) = P(A_1) + P(A_2) + ... + P(A_n)$$

EXAMPLE Find the probability that a card pulled at random from a standard pack of cards (no jokers) is <u>either</u> a picture card (a Jack, Queen or King) <u>or</u> the 7, 8 or 9 of clubs.

Call <u>event A</u> — 'I get a picture card', and <u>event B</u> — 'I get the 7, 8 or 9 of clubs'.
Events A and B are <u>mutually exclusive</u> — they can't both happen. Also, $P(A) = \frac{12}{52} = \frac{3}{13}$ and $P(B) = \frac{3}{52}$.
So the probability of either A or B is: $P(A \cup B) = P(A) + P(B) = \frac{12}{52} + \frac{3}{52} = \frac{15}{52}$

Two heads are better than one — though only half as likely using two coins...

I must admit — I kind of like these pages. This stuff isn't too hard, and it's really useful for answering loads of questions. And one other good thing is that Venn diagrams look, well, nice somehow. But more importantly, when you're filling one in, the thing to remember is that you usually need to 'start from the inside and work out'.

Tree Diagrams

Tree diagrams — they blossom from a tiny question-acorn into a beautiful tree of possibility. Inspiring _and_ useful.

Tree Diagrams Show Probabilities for **Two or More** Events

Each 'chunk' of a tree diagram is a trial, and each branch of that chunk is a possible outcome. Multiplying probabilities along the branches gives you the probability of a <u>series</u> of outcomes.

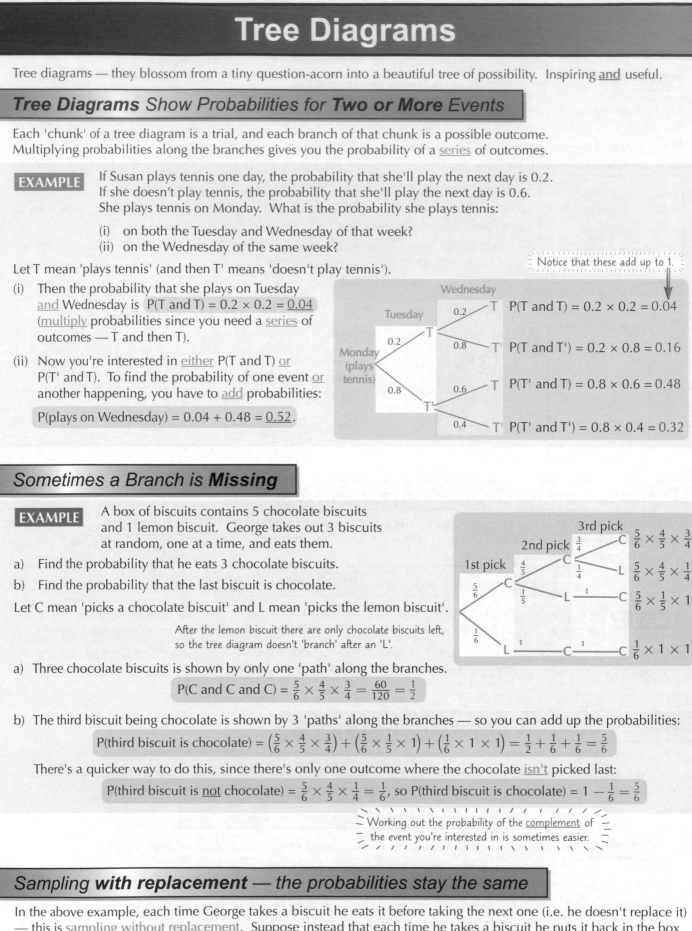

EXAMPLE   If Susan plays tennis one day, the probability that she'll play the next day is 0.2. If she doesn't play tennis, the probability that she'll play the next day is 0.6. She plays tennis on Monday. What is the probability she plays tennis:

  (i)   on both the Tuesday and Wednesday of that week?
  (ii) on the Wednesday of the same week?

Let T mean 'plays tennis' (and then T' means 'doesn't play tennis').

(i)   Then the probability that she plays on Tuesday <u>and</u> Wednesday is   P(T and T) = 0.2 × 0.2 = 0.04   (<u>multiply</u> probabilities since you need a <u>series</u> of outcomes — T and then T).

(ii) Now you're interested in <u>either</u> P(T and T) <u>or</u> P(T' and T). To find the probability of one event <u>or</u> another happening, you have to <u>add</u> probabilities:

    P(plays on Wednesday) = 0.04 + 0.48 = <u>0.52</u>.

Notice that these add up to 1.

P(T and T) = 0.2 × 0.2 = 0.04
P(T and T') = 0.2 × 0.8 = 0.16
P(T' and T) = 0.8 × 0.6 = 0.48
P(T' and T') = 0.8 × 0.4 = 0.32

Sometimes a Branch is **Missing**

EXAMPLE   A box of biscuits contains 5 chocolate biscuits and 1 lemon biscuit. George takes out 3 biscuits at random, one at a time, and eats them.

a)   Find the probability that he eats 3 chocolate biscuits.

b)   Find the probability that the last biscuit is chocolate.

Let C mean 'picks a chocolate biscuit' and L mean 'picks the lemon biscuit'.

After the lemon biscuit there are only chocolate biscuits left, so the tree diagram doesn't 'branch' after an 'L'.

a)   Three chocolate biscuits is shown by only one 'path' along the branches.

$$P(C \text{ and } C \text{ and } C) = \frac{5}{6} \times \frac{4}{5} \times \frac{3}{4} = \frac{60}{120} = \frac{1}{2}$$

b)   The third biscuit being chocolate is shown by 3 'paths' along the branches — so you can add up the probabilities:

$$P(\text{third biscuit is chocolate}) = \left(\frac{5}{6} \times \frac{4}{5} \times \frac{3}{4}\right) + \left(\frac{5}{6} \times \frac{1}{5} \times 1\right) + \left(\frac{1}{6} \times 1 \times 1\right) = \frac{1}{2} + \frac{1}{6} + \frac{1}{6} = \frac{5}{6}$$

There's a quicker way to do this, since there's only one outcome where the chocolate <u>isn't</u> picked last:

$$P(\text{third biscuit is } \underline{not} \text{ chocolate}) = \frac{5}{6} \times \frac{4}{5} \times \frac{1}{4} = \frac{1}{6}, \text{ so } P(\text{third biscuit is chocolate}) = 1 - \frac{1}{6} = \frac{5}{6}$$

Working out the probability of the <u>complement</u> of the event you're interested in is sometimes easier.

Sampling **with replacement** — the probabilities stay the same

In the above example, each time George takes a biscuit he eats it before taking the next one (i.e. he doesn't replace it) — this is <u>sampling without replacement</u>. Suppose instead that each time he takes a biscuit he puts it back in the box before taking the next one — this is <u>sampling with replacement</u>. All this means is that the probability of choosing a particular item <u>remains the same</u> for each pick.

    So part a) above becomes:

$$P(C \text{ and } C \text{ and } C) = \frac{5}{6} \times \frac{5}{6} \times \frac{5}{6} = \frac{125}{216} > \frac{1}{2}$$

So the probability that George picks 3 chocolate biscuits is slightly greater when sampling is done <u>with replacement</u>. This makes sense because now there are, on average, more chocolate biscuits available for his 2nd and 3rd picks, so he is more likely to choose one.

Conditional Probability

After the first set of branches, tree diagrams actually show <u>conditional probabilities</u>. Read on...

P(B|A) means *Probability of B*, given that *A has Already Happened*

Conditional probability means the probability of something, given that something else has already happened. For example, P(B|A) means the probability of B, given that A has already happened. Back to tree diagrams...

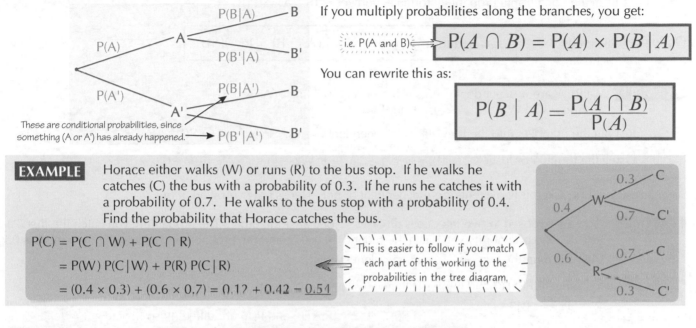

These are conditional probabilities, since something (A or A') has already happened. ⟶ P(B'|A')

If you multiply probabilities along the branches, you get:

i.e. P(A and B) ⟹ $$P(A \cap B) = P(A) \times P(B \mid A)$$

You can rewrite this as:

$$P(B \mid A) = \frac{P(A \cap B)}{P(A)}$$

EXAMPLE Horace either walks (W) or runs (R) to the bus stop. If he walks he catches (C) the bus with a probability of 0.3. If he runs he catches it with a probability of 0.7. He walks to the bus stop with a probability of 0.4. Find the probability that Horace catches the bus.

$$P(C) = P(C \cap W) + P(C \cap R)$$
$$= P(W)\,P(C \mid W) + P(R)\,P(C \mid R)$$
$$= (0.4 \times 0.3) + (0.6 \times 0.7) = 0.12 + 0.42 = \underline{0.54}$$

This is easier to follow if you match each part of this working to the probabilities in the tree diagram.

If *B is Conditional* on A then *A is Conditional* on B

If B depends on A then A depends on B — and it doesn't matter which event happens first.

EXAMPLE Horace turns up at school either late (L) or on time (L'). He is then either shouted at (S) or not (S'). The probability that he turns up late is 0.4. If he turns up late the probability that he is shouted at is 0.7. If he turns up on time the probability that he is shouted at is 0.2.

If you hear Horace being shouted at, what is the probability that he turned up late?

1) The probability you want is P(L|S).   Get this the right way round — he's <u>already</u> being shouted at.

2) Use the conditional probability formula: $P(L \mid S) = \dfrac{P(L \cap S)}{P(S)}$

3) The best way to find P(L ∩ S) and P(S) is with a tree diagram.

   Be careful with questions like this — the information in the question tells you what you need to know to draw the tree diagram with L (or L') considered first.

   But you need P(L|S) — where S is considered first. So don't just rush in.

   $$P(L \cap S) = 0.4 \times 0.7 = 0.28$$
   $$P(S) = P(L \cap S) + P(L' \cap S) = 0.28 + 0.12 = 0.40$$

   0.7 S   P(L ∩ S) = 0.4 × 0.7 = 0.28
   0.4 L
   0.3 S'

   0.2 S   P(L' ∩ S) = 0.6 × 0.2 = 0.12
   0.6 L'
   0.8 S'

4) Put these in your conditional probability formula to get:

   $$P(L \mid S) = \frac{0.28}{0.4} = 0.7$$

   These are all conditional probabilities — e.g. P(S' | L') = 0.8.

There's a *Formula* for Working this Out — but it's *Easier* to Use the *Tree Diagram*

This formula will be on the formula sheet in your exam.

$$P(A \mid B) = \frac{P(A \cap B)}{P(B)} = \frac{P(B \mid A)P(A)}{P(B \mid A)P(A) + P(B \mid A')P(A')}$$

This is basically the same working as with the tree diagram above.

Here, this gives:

$$P(L \mid S) = \frac{P(L \cap S)}{P(S)} = \frac{P(S \mid L)P(L)}{P(S \mid L)P(L) + P(S \mid L')P(L')} = \frac{0.7 \times 0.4}{(0.7 \times 0.4) + (0.2 \times 0.6)} = \frac{0.28}{0.4} = 0.7$$

Independent Events

Independent Events Have No Effect on Each Other

If the probability of B happening doesn't depend on whether or not A has happened, then A and B are <u>independent</u>.

If A and B are independent: P(B | A) = P(B).

If you put this in the conditional probability formula, you get: $P(B \mid A) = P(B) = \dfrac{P(A \cap B)}{P(A)}$

Or, to put that another way:

For independent events: P(A ∩ B) = P(A)P(B)

EXAMPLE   V and W are independent events, where P(V) = 0.2 and P(W) = 0.6.
    a) Find P(V ∩ W).   b) Find P(V ∪ W).

a)   Just put the numbers into the formula for independent events: P(V ∩ W) = P(V)P(W) = 0.2 × 0.6 = 0.12

b)   Using the formula on page 122: P(V ∪ W) = P(V) + P(W) − P(V ∩ W) = 0.2 + 0.6 − 0.12 = 0.68

Sometimes you'll be asked if two events are independent or not. Here's how you work it out...

EXAMPLE   You are exposed to two infectious diseases — one after the other. The probability you catch the first (A) is 0.25, the probability you catch the second (B) is 0.5, and the probability you catch both of them is 0.2. Are catching the two diseases independent events?

You need to compare P(A | B) and P(A) — if they're different, the events <u>aren't independent</u>.

$P(A \mid B) = \dfrac{P(A \cap B)}{P(B)} = \dfrac{0.2}{0.5} = 0.4$ P(A) = 0.25 P(A | B) and P(A) are different, so they're <u>not independent</u>.

Take Your Time with Tough Probability Questions

EXAMPLE   A and B are two events, with P(A) = 0.4, P(B | A) = 0.25, and P(A' ∩ B) = 0.2.
    a) Find: (i) P(A ∩ B), (ii) P(A'), (iii) P(B' | A), (iv) P(B | A'), (v) P(B), (vi) P(A | B).
    b) Say whether or not A and B are independent.

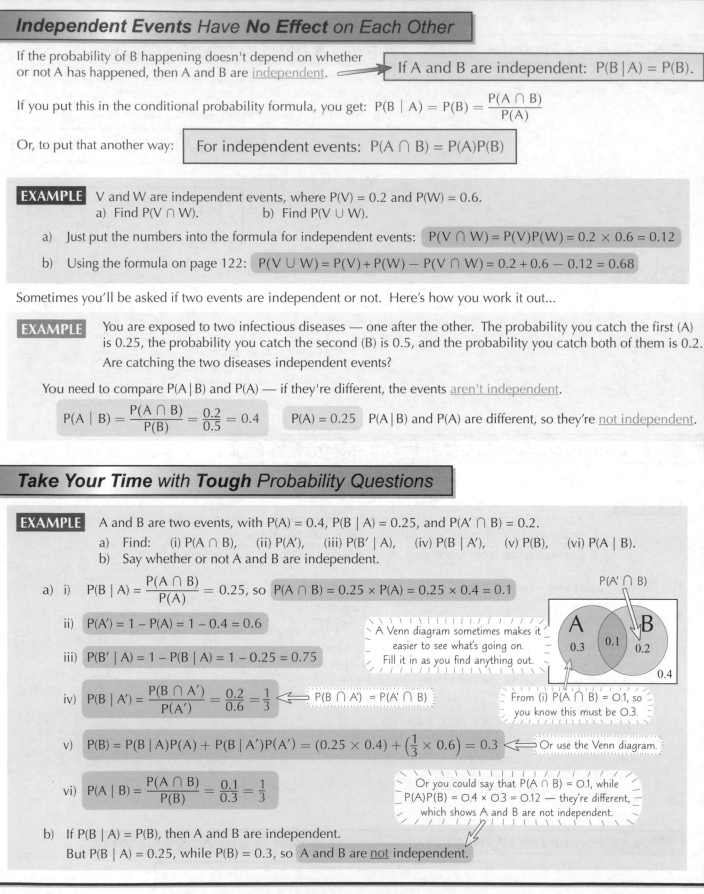

a) i) $P(B \mid A) = \dfrac{P(A \cap B)}{P(A)} = 0.25$, so P(A ∩ B) = 0.25 × P(A) = 0.25 × 0.4 = 0.1

ii) P(A') = 1 − P(A) = 1 − 0.4 = 0.6

iii) P(B' | A) = 1 − P(B | A) = 1 − 0.25 = 0.75

A Venn diagram sometimes makes it easier to see what's going on. Fill it in as you find anything out.

P(A' ∩ B)

iv) $P(B \mid A') = \dfrac{P(B \cap A')}{P(A')} = \dfrac{0.2}{0.6} = \dfrac{1}{3}$ ⟸ P(B ∩ A') = P(A' ∩ B)

From (i) P(A ∩ B) = 0.1, so you know this must be 0.3.

v) $P(B) = P(B \mid A)P(A) + P(B \mid A')P(A') = (0.25 \times 0.4) + \left(\dfrac{1}{3} \times 0.6\right) = 0.3$ ⟸ Or use the Venn diagram.

vi) $P(A \mid B) = \dfrac{P(A \cap B)}{P(B)} = \dfrac{0.1}{0.3} = \dfrac{1}{3}$

Or you could say that P(A ∩ B) = 0.1, while P(A)P(B) = 0.4 × 0.3 = 0.12 — they're different, which shows A and B are not independent.

b) If P(B | A) = P(B), then A and B are independent.
    But P(B | A) = 0.25, while P(B) = 0.3, so A and B are <u>not</u> independent.

Statisticians say: P(Having cake ∩ Eating it) = 0...

Probability questions can be tough. For tricky questions like the last one, try drawing a Venn diagram or a tree diagram, even if the question doesn't tell you to — they're really useful for getting your head round things and understanding what on earth is going on. And don't forget the tests for independent events — you're likely to get asked a question on those.

S1 Section 2 — Practice Questions

Gosh. A whole page of warm-up questions. By the time you've finished these, you'll be warmer than a wolf in woollen mittens. Oh, and you'll probably be <u>awesome at probability questions</u> too.

Warm-up Questions

1) There are two types of film showing at the local cinema: 5 Westerns and 7 romantic comedies.

   a) I am going to watch a total of 4 films today.
      How many different combinations of films could I choose?

   b) If I want to watch an equal number of the two types of film,
      how many combinations of 4 films are there?

2) A standard dice and a coin are thrown and the outcomes recorded.
   If a head is thrown, the score on the dice is doubled.
   If a tail is thrown, 4 is added to the score on the dice.

   a) Represent this by means of a sample space diagram.

   b) What is the probability that you score more than 5?

   c) If you throw a tail, what is the probability that you get an even score?

3) Arabella rolls two standard dice and adds the two results together.

   a) What is the probability that she scores a prime number?

   b) What is the probability that she scores a square number?

   c) What is the probability that she scores a number that is
      either a prime number or a square number?

4) Half the students in a sixth-form college eat sausages for dinner and 20% eat chips.
   10% of those who eat chips also eat sausages. By use of a Venn diagram or otherwise, find:

   a) the percentage of students who eat both chips and sausages,

   b) the percentage of students who eat chips but not sausages,

   c) the percentage of students who eat either chips or sausages but not both.

5) In a school orchestra (made up of pupils in either the upper or lower school),
   40% of the musicians are boys. Of the boys, 30% are in the upper school.
   Of the girls in the orchestra, 50% are in the upper school.

   a) Draw a tree diagram to show the various probabilities.

   b) Find the probability that a musician chosen at random is in the upper school.

6) Albert eats a limited choice of lunch. He eats either chicken or beef
   for his main course, and either chocolate pudding or ice cream for dessert.
   The probability that he eats chicken is 1/3, the probability that he eats
   ice cream given that he has chicken is 2/5, and the probability that he
   has ice cream given that he has beef is 3/4.

   a) Find the probability he has either chicken or ice cream — but not both.

   b) Find the probability that he eats ice cream.

   c) Find the probability that he had chicken given that you see him eating ice cream.

S1 Section 2 — Practice Questions

Boop. Boop. Boop. Exam simulation has begun. Repeat, exam simulation has begun. Please ensure your safety goggles are firmly attached. Emergency exits can be found on the right- and left-hand sides of the page.

Exam Questions

1   A soap company asked 120 people about the types of soap (from Brands A, B and C) they bought. Brand A was bought by 40 people, Brand B by 30 people and Brand C by 25. Both Brands A and B (and possibly C as well) were bought by 8 people, B and C (and maybe A) were bought by 10 people, and A and C (and maybe B) by 7 people. All three brands were bought by 3 people.

  a)   Represent this information in a Venn diagram.

(5 marks)

  b)   If a person is selected at random, find the probability that:

  (i)   they buy at least one of the soaps.

(2 marks)

  (ii)   they buy at least two of the soaps.

(2 marks)

  (iii)   they buy soap B, given that they buy only one type of soap.

(3 marks)

2   A jar contains counters of 3 different colours. There are 3 red counters, 4 white counters and 5 green counters. Two random counters are removed from the jar one at a time. Once removed, the colour of the counter is noted. The first counter is not replaced before the second one is drawn.

  a)   Draw a tree diagram to show the probabilities of the various outcomes.

(3 marks)

  b)   Find the probability that the second counter is green.

(2 marks)

  c)   Find the probability that both the counters are red.

(2 marks)

  d)   Find the probability that the two counters are not both the same colour.

(3 marks)

3   Event J and Event K are independent events, where $P(J) = 0.7$ and $P(K) = 0.1$.
  a)   Find:
  (i) $P(J \cap K)$,

(1 mark)

  (ii) $P(J \cup K)$.

(2 marks)

  b)   If L is the event that neither J or K occurs, find $P(L|K')$.

(3 marks)

4   For a particular biased dice, the event 'throw a 6' is called event B. $P(B) = 0.2$.
   This biased dice and a fair dice are rolled together. Find the probability that:

  a)   the biased dice doesn't show a 6,

(1 mark)

  b)   at least one of the dice shows a 6,

(2 marks)

  c)   exactly one of the dice shows a 6, given that at least one of them shows a 6.

(3 marks)

Probability Distributions

This stuff isn't hard — but it can seem a bit weird at times.

Getting your head round this **Basic Stuff** will help a bit

This first bit isn't particularly interesting. But understanding the difference between X and x (bear with me) might make the later stuff a bit less confusing. Might.

1) X (upper case) is just the <u>name</u> of a <u>random variable</u>. So X could be 'score on a dice' — it's <u>just a name</u>.

2) A <u>random variable</u> doesn't have a <u>fixed</u> value. Like with a dice score — the value on any 'roll' is all down to chance.

3) x (lower case) is a <u>particular value</u> that X can take. So for one roll of a dice, x could be 1, 2, 3, 4, 5 or 6.

4) <u>Discrete</u> random variables only have a <u>certain number</u> of possible values. Often these values are whole numbers, but they don't have to be. Usually there are only a few possible values (e.g. the possible scores with one roll of a dice).

5) A <u>probability distribution</u> is basically a list of the <u>possible values</u> of x, plus a way to find the <u>probability</u> for each one.

6) A <u>probability function</u> is a <u>formula</u> to generate the probabilities of different values of x, or a <u>table</u> listing them.

All the Probabilities **Add up to 1**

For a discrete random variable X:

$$\sum_{\text{all } x} P(X = x) = 1$$

This says that if you add up the probabilities of all the possible values of X, you get 1.

EXAMPLE   The random variable X has probability function $P(X = x) = kx$ for $x = 1, 2, 3$. Find the value of k.

So X has three possible values ($x = 1, 2$ and 3), and the probability of each is kx (where you need to find k).

It's easier to understand with a table:

x	1	2	3
$P(X = x)$	$k \times 1 = k$	$k \times 2 = 2k$	$k \times 3 = 3k$

Now just use the formula. 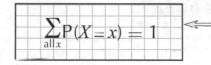 $\sum_{\text{all } x} P(X = x) = 1$ Here, this means: $k + 2k + 3k = 6k = 1$

i.e. $k = \dfrac{1}{6}$

Piece of cake.

EXAMPLE   The discrete random variable X has the probability distribution shown below.

x	0	1	2	3	4
$P(X = x)$	0.1	0.2	0.3	0.2	a

Find: (i) the value of a,   (ii) $P(X > 2)$ (iii) $P(2 \leq X < 4)$.

(i)   Use the formula $\sum_{\text{all } x} P(X = x) = 1$ again.

From the table: $0.1 + 0.2 + 0.3 + 0.2 + a = 1$
$0.8 + a = 1$
$\underline{a = 0.2}$

(ii) This is asking you to find the probability that 'X is greater than 2'.
So you need to add up the probabilities for $x = 3$ and $x = 4$.

$P(X > 2) = P(X = 3) + P(X = 4) = 0.2 + 0.2 = \underline{0.4}$

(iii) This is asking for the probability that 'X is greater than or equal to 2, but less than 4'.
Easy — just add up the probabilities again.

Careful with the inequality signs — you need to include $x = 2$ but not $x = 4$.

$P(2 \leq X < 4) = P(X = 2) + P(X = 3) = 0.3 + 0.2 = \underline{0.5}$

Probability Distributions

EXAMPLE An unbiased six-sided dice has faces marked 1, 1, 1, 2, 2, 3.
The dice is rolled twice. Let X be the random variable "sum of the two scores on the dice".
Show that $P(X = 4) = \frac{5}{18}$. Find the probability distribution of X.

① Make a table showing the 36 possible outcomes.
You can see from the table that 10 of these have the outcome $X = 4$

... so $\boxed{P(X = 4) = \frac{10}{36} = \frac{5}{18}}$

Score on roll 1

+	1	1	1	2	2	3
1	2	2	2	3	3	4
1	2	2	2	3	3	4
1	2	2	2	3	3	4
2	3	3	3	4	4	5
2	3	3	3	4	4	5
3	4	4	4	5	5	6

Score on roll 2

Don't forget to change the fractions into their simplest form.

② Use the table to work out the probabilities for the other outcomes and then fill in a table summarising the probability distribution. So...

... $\frac{9}{36}$ of the outcomes are a score of 2

... $\frac{12}{36}$ of the outcomes are a score of 3

... $\frac{4}{36}$ of the outcomes are a score of 5

... $\frac{1}{36}$ of the outcomes are a score of 6

x	2	3	4	5	6
$P(X = x)$	$\frac{1}{4}$	$\frac{1}{3}$	$\frac{5}{18}$	$\frac{1}{9}$	$\frac{1}{36}$

Do Complicated questions Bit by bit

EXAMPLE A game involves rolling two fair dice. If the sum of the scores is greater than 10 then the player wins 50p.
If the sum is between 8 and 10 (inclusive) then they win 20p. Otherwise they get nothing.
If X is the random variable "amount player wins", find the probability distribution of X.

There are 3 possible values for X (0, 20 and 50) and you need the probability of each.
To work these out, you need the probability of getting various totals on the dice.

① You need to know $P(8 \le \text{score} \le 10)$ — the probability that the score is between 8 and 10 inclusive (i.e. including 8 and 10) and $P(11 \le \text{score} \le 12)$ — the probability that the score is greater than 10.

This means working out: $P(\text{score} = 8)$, $P(\text{score} = 9)$, $P(\text{score} = 10)$, $P(\text{score} = 11)$ and $P(\text{score} = 12)$. Use a table...

②

Score on dice 1

+	1	2	3	4	5	6
1	2	3	4	5	6	7
2	3	4	5	6	7	8
3	4	5	6	7	8	9
4	5	6	7	8	9	10
5	6	7	8	9	10	11
6	7	8	9	10	11	12

Score on dice 2

There are 36 possible outcomes...

...5 of these have a total of 8 — so the probability of scoring 8 is $\frac{5}{36}$

...4 have a total of 9 — so the probability of scoring 9 is $\frac{4}{36}$,

...the probability of scoring 10 is $\frac{3}{36}$

...the probability of scoring 11 is $\frac{2}{36}$

...the probability of scoring 12 is $\frac{1}{36}$

③ To find the probabilities you need, you just add the right bits together:

$P(X = 20p) = P(8 \le \text{score} \le 10) = \frac{5}{36} + \frac{4}{36} + \frac{3}{36} = \frac{12}{36} = \frac{1}{3}$

$P(X = 50p) = P(11 \le \text{score} \le 12) = \frac{2}{36} + \frac{1}{36} = \frac{3}{36} = \frac{1}{12}$

To find $P(X = 0)$ just take the total of the two probabilities above from 1 (since $X = 0$ is the only other possibility).

$P(X = 0) = 1 - \left[\frac{12}{36} + \frac{3}{36}\right] = 1 - \frac{15}{36} = \frac{21}{36} = \frac{7}{12}$

④ Now just stick all this info in a table (and check that the probabilities all add up to 1):

x	0	20	50
$P(X = x)$	$\frac{7}{12}$	$\frac{1}{3}$	$\frac{1}{12}$

Useful quotes: All you need in life is ignorance and confidence, then success is sure*...

I said earlier that the 'counting the outcomes' approach was useful — well there you go. And if you remember how to do that, then you can work out a probability distribution. And if you can work out one of those, then you can often begin to unravel even fairly daunting-looking questions. But most of all, REMEMBER THAT ALL THE PROBABILITIES ADD UP TO 1.

* Mark Twain

Expected Values, Mean and Variance

This is all about the mean and variance of <u>random variables</u> — <u>not</u> a load of data. It's a tricky concept, but bear with it.

Discrete Random Variables have an 'Expected Value' or 'Mean'

You can work out the <u>expected value E(X)</u> (or 'mean', μ) for a discrete <u>random variable</u> X. E(X) is a kind of 'theoretical mean' — it's what you'd <u>expect</u> the mean of X to be if you took <u>loads</u> of readings. <u>In practice</u>, the mean of your results is unlikely to match the theoretical mean <u>exactly</u>, but it should be pretty near.

Remember, 'discrete' just means it can only take a certain number of values.

If the possible values of X are x_1, x_2, x_3,... then the expected value of X is:

$$\text{Mean } (\mu) = \text{Expected Value, } E(X) = \sum x_i P(X = x_i) = \sum x_i p_i$$

$p_i = P(X = x_i)$

EXAMPLE The probability distribution of X, the number of daughters in a family of 3 children, is shown in the table. Find the expected number of daughters.

x_i	0	1	2	3
p_i	$\frac{1}{8}$	$\frac{3}{8}$	$\frac{3}{8}$	$\frac{1}{8}$

$$\text{Mean} = \sum x_i p_i = \left[0 \times \frac{1}{8}\right] + \left[1 \times \frac{3}{8}\right] + \left[2 \times \frac{3}{8}\right] + \left[3 \times \frac{1}{8}\right] = 0 + \frac{3}{8} + \frac{6}{8} + \frac{3}{8} = \frac{12}{8} = 1.5$$

So the <u>expected</u> number of daughters is 1.5 — which sounds a bit weird. But all it means is that if you check a <u>large number</u> of 3-child families, the <u>mean</u> will be close to 1.5.

The Variance measures how Spread Out the distribution is

You can also find the <u>variance</u> of a random variable. It's the 'expected variance' of a <u>large number</u> of readings.

$$\text{Var}(X) = E(X - \mu)^2 = E(X^2) - \mu^2 = \sum x_i^2 p_i - \left[\sum x_i p_i\right]^2$$

This formula needs $E(X^2) = \sum x_i^2 p_i$ — take each possible value of x, square it, multiply it by its probability and then add up all the results.

The formula for variance can be written in lots of different ways. You might also see Var(X) = E(X²) − [E(X)]² = "the mean of the squares minus the square of the mean".

EXAMPLE Work out the variance for the '3 daughters' example above:

First work out E(X²): $E(X^2) = \sum x_i^2 p_i = \left[0^2 \times \frac{1}{8}\right] + \left[1^2 \times \frac{3}{8}\right] + \left[2^2 \times \frac{3}{8}\right] + \left[3^2 \times \frac{1}{8}\right]$

$$= 0 + \frac{3}{8} + \frac{12}{8} + \frac{9}{8} = \frac{24}{8} = 3$$

The <u>standard deviation</u> (s.d.) of a random variable is the <u>square root</u> of its variance: s.d. $= \sqrt{\text{Var}(X)}$

Now you take away the mean squared: $\text{Var}(X) = E(X^2) - \mu^2 = 3 - 1.5^2 = 3 - 2.25 = \underline{0.75}$

EXAMPLE X has the probability function $P(X = x) = k(x + 1)$ for x = 0, 1, 2, 3, 4. Find the mean and variance of X.

① First you need to find k — work out all the probabilities and make sure they add up to 1.

$P(X = 0) = k \times (0 + 1) = k$. Similarly, $P(X = 1) = 2k$, $P(X = 2) = 3k$, $P(X = 3) = 4k$, $P(X = 4) = 5k$.

So $k + 2k + 3k + 4k + 5k = 1$, i.e. 15k = 1, and so $k = \frac{1}{15}$

Now you can work out p_1, p_2, p_3... where $p_1 = P(X = 1)$ etc.

② Now use the formulas — find the mean E(X) first:

$$E(X) = \sum x_i p_i = \left[0 \times \frac{1}{15}\right] + \left[1 \times \frac{2}{15}\right] + \left[2 \times \frac{3}{15}\right] + \left[3 \times \frac{4}{15}\right] + \left[4 \times \frac{5}{15}\right] = \frac{40}{15} = \frac{8}{3}$$

For the variance you need E(X²):

$$E(X^2) = \sum x_i^2 p_i = \left[0^2 \times \frac{1}{15}\right] + \left[1^2 \times \frac{2}{15}\right] + \left[2^2 \times \frac{3}{15}\right] + \left[3^2 \times \frac{4}{15}\right] + \left[4^2 \times \frac{5}{15}\right] = \frac{130}{15} = \frac{26}{3}$$

And finally: $\text{Var}(X) = E(X^2) - [E(X)]^2 = \frac{26}{3} - \left[\frac{8}{3}\right]^2 = \frac{14}{9}$

S1 Section 3 — Practice Questions

Random variable, probability distribution, probability function...
a lot of <u>fancy-looking names</u> for things that are actually quite straightforward...ish. Have a go at
these to make sure you know who's who in the <u>glitzy world of discrete random variables</u>.

Warm-up Questions

1) The probability distribution of Y is shown below:

y	0	1	2	3
P($Y = y$)	0.5	k	k	$3k$

   a) Find the value of k.

   b) Find P($Y < 2$).

2) The probability distribution for the random variable W
   is given in the table.

w	0.2	0.3	0.4	0.5
P($W = w$)	0.2	0.2	0.3	0.3

   a) Find E(W).

   b) Find Var(W).

   c) Find P($W > 0.3$).

3) A discrete random variable X has the probability
   distribution shown in the table, where k is a constant.

x_i	1	2	3	4
p_i	$\frac{1}{6}$	$\frac{1}{2}$	k	$\frac{5}{24}$

   a) Find k.

   b) Find E(X).

   c) Show that Var(X) = $\frac{63}{64}$.

   d) Find P($X \leq 3$).

4) A discrete random variable X has the probability
   distribution shown in the table.

x_i	1	2	3	4	5	6
p_i	0.1	0.2	0.25	0.2	0.1	0.15

   a) Find E(X).

   b) Find Var(X).

   c) Find P($3 < X \leq 5$).

5) The number of points awarded to each contestant in a talent competition is given by
   the discrete random variable X with the following probability distribution:

x	0	1	2	3
P($X = x$)	0.4	0.3	0.2	0.1

   a) Find E(X).

   b) Show that Var(X) = 1.

6) A discrete random variable X has the probability function P($X = x$) = k,
   for x = 0, 1, 2,..., 9, where k is a constant.

   a) Find k.

   b) Calculate E(X).

   c) Calculate Var(X).

S1 Section 3 — Practice Questions

There's nothing I enjoy more than pretending I'm <u>in an exam</u>. An eerie silence, sweaty palms, having to be escorted to the toilet by a responsible adult... and all these <u>lovely maths questions</u> too. Just like the real thing.

Exam Questions

1   A discrete random variable X can only take values 0, 1, 2 and 3. Its probability distribution is shown.

x	0	1	2	3
$P(X = x)$	$2k$	$3k$	k	k

   a)   Find the value of k.

(1 mark)

   b)   Find $P(X > 2)$.

(1 mark)

2   A discrete random variable X has the probability function:
$P(X = x) = ax$ for $x = 1, 2, 3$, where a is a constant.

   a)   Show $a = \frac{1}{6}$.

(1 mark)

   b)   Find $E(X)$.

(2 marks)

   c)   If $Var(X) = \frac{5}{9}$ find $E(X^2)$.

(2 marks)

3   In a game a player tosses three fair coins.
If three heads occur then the player gets 20p; if two heads occur then the player gets 10p.
For any other outcome, the player gets nothing.

   a)   If X is the random variable 'amount received', tabulate the probability distribution of X.

(4 marks)

The player pays 10p to play one game.

   b)   Use the probability distribution to find the probability that the player wins
(i.e. gets more money than they pay to play) in one game.

(2 marks)

4   A discrete random variable X has the probability distribution shown in the table.

x	0	1	2	3
$P(X = x)$	0.4	0.3	a	b

   a)   Write down an expression for $a + b$.

(1 mark)

   b)   Given that $E(X) = 1.1$, show that $2a + 3b = 0.8$.

(2 marks)

   c)   Find a and b.

(2 marks)

   d)   Calculate $Var(X)$.

(3 marks)

Binomial Coefficients

This page is a bit of a gentle introduction to the section, to be honest, because it's basically about <u>counting things</u>.

n Different Objects can be Arranged in *n!* Different Ways...

There are $n!$ ("<u>n factorial</u>") ways of arranging <u>n different</u> objects, where <u>$n! = n \times (n-1) \times (n-2) \times \dots \times 3 \times 2 \times 1$</u>.

> **EXAMPLE**   a) In how many ways can 4 different ornaments be arranged on a shelf?
>   b) In how many ways can 8 different objects be arranged?

a)   You have <u>4 choices</u> for the first ornament, <u>3 choices</u> for the second ornament, <u>2 choices</u> for the third ornament, and <u>1 choice</u> for the last ornament. So there are $4! = 4 \times 3 \times 2 \times 1 = 24$ arrangements.

b)   There are $8! = 40\,320$ arrangements.

...but **Divide by *r!*** if *r* of These Objects are the **Same**

If r of your n objects are <u>identical</u>, then the total number of possible arrangements is <u>$n! \div r!$</u>.

> **EXAMPLE**   a) In how many different ways can 5 objects be arranged if 2 of those objects are identical?
>   b) In how many different ways can 7 objects be arranged if 4 of those objects are identical?

a)   Imagine those 2 identical objects were <u>different</u>. Then there would be $5! = 120$ possible arrangements. But because those 2 objects are actually <u>identical</u>, you can always <u>swap them round</u> without making a different arrangement. So there are really only $120 \div 2 = 60$ different ways to arrange the objects.

b)   There are $\dfrac{n!}{r!} = \dfrac{7!}{4!} = \dfrac{5040}{24} = 210$ different ways to arrange the objects.

Use **Binomial Coefficients** if There are **Only Two Types** of Object

> **Binomial Coefficients**
>
> $$\binom{n}{r} = {}^nC_r = \frac{n!}{r!(n-r)!}$$

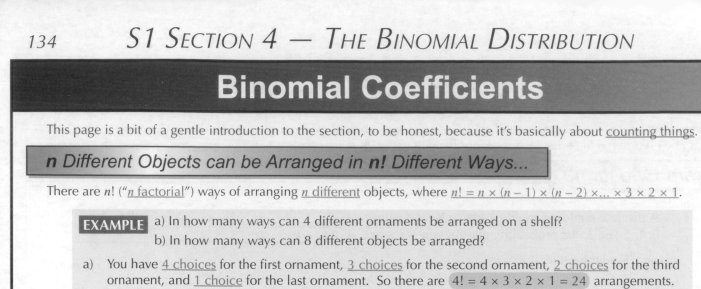

${}^nC_r$ and $\binom{n}{r}$ both mean $\dfrac{n!}{r!(n-r)!}$

> **EXAMPLE**   a)   In how many different ways can n objects of two types be arranged if r are of the first type?
>   b)   How many ways are there to select 11 players from a squad of 16?
>   c)   How many ways are there to pick 6 lottery numbers from 49?

a)   If the objects were all <u>different</u>, there would be $n!$ ways to arrange them. But r of the objects are of the same type and could be <u>swapped around</u>, so divide by $r!$. Since there are only <u>two types</u>, the other $(n-r)$ could also be <u>swapped around</u> — so divide by $(n-r)!$. This means there are $\dfrac{n!}{r!(n-r)!}$ arrangements.

b)   This is basically a 'number of different arrangements' problem. Imagine the 16 players are lined up — then you could 'pick' or 'not pick' players by giving each of them a sign marked with a tick or a cross. So just find the number of ways to arrange 11 ticks and 5 crosses — this is $\dbinom{16}{11} = \dfrac{16!}{11!5!} = 4368$.

c)   Again, numbers are either '<u>picked</u>' or '<u>unpicked</u>', so there are $\dbinom{49}{6} = \dfrac{49!}{6!43!} = 13\,983\,816$ possibilities.

You can use your fingers and toes for counting up to 5! ÷ 3!...

So there you go — hopefully it didn't seem too bad. But statistics (like maths generally) is one of those subjects where everything <u>builds</u> on what you've just learnt. So you need to make really sure you commit all this to memory, and (preferably) understand <u>why</u> it's true too — which is what the three <u>part a)</u>'s are about in the above examples.

The Binomial Probability Function

Being able to count the number of different arrangements of things is a big help when it comes to finding <u>probabilities</u>. This is because the <u>probability</u> of something depends on the number of different ways things <u>could</u> turn out.

Use **Binomial Coefficients** to Count Arrangements of 'Successes' and 'Failures'

You've seen already that if <u>P(something happens) = p</u>, then <u>P(that thing doesn't happen) = $1 - p$</u> (see p123). You'll need that fact now.

EXAMPLE I toss a fair coin 5 times. Find the probability of: a) 0 heads,   b) 1 head,   c) 2 heads.

First, note that each coin toss is <u>independent</u> of the others.
That means you can <u>multiply</u> individual probabilities together.

a) P(0 heads) = P(tails) × P(tails) × P(tails) × P(tails) × P(tails) = 0.5^5 = 0.03125

> P(tails) = P(heads) = 0.5.

P(1 head) =   P(heads) × P(tails) × P(tails) × P(tails) × P(tails)
+ P(tails) × P(heads) × P(tails) × P(tails) × P(tails)
+ P(tails) × P(tails) × P(heads) × P(tails) × P(tails)
+ P(tails) × P(tails) × P(tails) × P(heads) × P(tails)
+ P(tails) × P(tails) × P(tails) × P(tails) × P(heads)

> These are the $\binom{5}{1}$ = 5 ways to arrange 1 head and 4 tails.

So P(1 head) = $0.5 \times (0.5)^4 \times \binom{5}{1} = 0.03125 \times \frac{5!}{1!4!} = 0.15625$

> = P(heads) × [P(tails)]⁴
> × ways to arrange 1 head and 4 tails.

b) P(2 heads) = $[P(heads)]^2 \times [P(tails)]^3 \times$ ways to arrange 2 heads and 3 tails $= (0.5)^2 \times (0.5)^3 \times \binom{5}{2} = 0.3125$

The **Binomial Probability Function** gives P(r successes out of n trials)

The previous example really just shows why this thing in a box must be true.

> See p171 for more about binomial coefficients and 'picking r from n'.

Binomial Probability Function

$$P(r \text{ successes in } n \text{ trials}) = \binom{n}{r} \times [P(\text{success})]^r \times [P(\text{failure})]^{n-r}$$

> This is the <u>probability function</u> for a <u>binomial distribution</u> — see next page for more info.

EXAMPLE I roll a fair dice 5 times. Find the probability of rolling: a) 2 sixes, b) 3 sixes, c) 4 numbers less than 3.

Again, note that each roll of a dice is <u>independent</u> of the other rolls.

a) For this part, call "roll a 6" a success, and "roll anything other than a 6" a failure.

Then P(roll 2 sixes) = $\binom{5}{2} \times \left(\frac{1}{6}\right)^2 \times \left(\frac{5}{6}\right)^3 = \frac{5!}{2!3!} \times \frac{1}{36} \times \frac{125}{216} = 0.161$ (to 3 d.p.).

b) Again, call "roll a 6" a success, and "roll anything other than a 6" a failure.

Then P(roll 3 sixes) = $\binom{5}{3} \times \left(\frac{1}{6}\right)^3 \times \left(\frac{5}{6}\right)^2 = \frac{5!}{3!2!} \times \frac{1}{216} \times \frac{25}{36} = 0.032$ (to 3 d.p.).

> Notice how $\binom{5}{2} = \binom{5}{3}$.
> In fact, $\binom{n}{r} = \binom{n}{n-r}$.

c) This time, success means "roll a 1 or a 2", while failure is now "roll a 3, 4, 5 or 6".

Then P(roll 4 numbers less than 3) = $\binom{5}{4} \times \left(\frac{1}{3}\right)^4 \times \left(\frac{2}{3}\right) = \frac{5!}{4!1!} \times \frac{1}{81} \times \frac{2}{3} = 0.041$ (to 3 d.p.).

Let this formula for success go to your head — and then keep it there...

This page is all about finding the probabilities of <u>different numbers</u> of successes in n trials. Now then... if you carry out n trials, there are $n + 1$ possibilities for the number of successes (0, 1, 2, ..., n). This 'family' of possible results along with their probabilities is sounding suspiciously like a <u>probability distribution</u>. Oh rats... I've given away what's on the next page.

The Binomial Distribution

Remember the fun you had when you learnt all about random variables... well, happy days are here again. This page is about random variables following a binomial distribution (whose probability function you saw on p135).

There are 5 Conditions for a Binomial Distribution

Binomial Distribution: B(n, p)

A random variable X follows a Binomial Distribution as long as these 5 conditions are satisfied:

1) There is a fixed number (n) of trials.
2) Each trial involves either "success" or "failure".
3) All the trials are independent.
4) The probability of "success" (p) is the same in each trial.
5) The variable is the total number of successes in the n trials.

> Binomial random variables are discrete, since they only take values O, 1, 2... n.

n and p are the two parameters of the binomial distribution. (Or n is sometimes called the 'index'.)

In this case, $P(X = x) = \binom{n}{x} \times p^x \times (1 - p)^{n-x}$ for $x = 0, 1, 2,..., n$, and you can write $X \sim \mathbf{B(n, p)}$.

EXAMPLE: Which of the random variables described below would follow a binomial distribution? For those that do, state the distribution's parameters.

a) **The number of faulty items (T) produced in a factory per day, if the probability of each item being faulty is 0.01 and there are 10 000 items produced every day.**
Binomial — there's a fixed number (10 000) of trials with two possible results ('faulty' or 'not faulty'), a constant probability of 'success', and T is the total number of 'faulty' items. So (as long as faulty items occur independently) $T \sim B(10\ 000, 0.01)$.

b) **The number of red cards (R) drawn from a standard 52-card deck in 10 picks, not replacing the cards each time.**
Not binomial, since the probability of 'success' changes each time (as I'm not replacing the cards).

c) **The number of red cards (R) drawn from a standard 52-card deck in 10 picks, replacing the cards each time.**
Binomial — there's a fixed number (10) of independent trials with two possible results ('red' or 'black/not red'), a constant probability of success (I'm replacing the cards), and R is the number of red cards drawn. $R \sim B(10, 0.5)$.

d) **The number of times (T) I have to toss a coin before I get heads.**
Not binomial, since the number of trials isn't fixed.

e) **The number of left-handed people (L) in a sample of 500 randomly chosen people, if the fraction of left-handed people in the population as a whole is 0.13.**
Binomial — there's a fixed number (500) of independent trials with two possible results ('left-handed' or 'not left-handed'), a constant probability of success (0.13), and L is the number of left-handers. $L \sim B(500, 0.13)$.

EXAMPLE: When I toss a grape in the air and try to catch it in my mouth, my probability of success is always 0.8. The number of grapes I catch in 10 throws is described by the discrete random variable X.

a) How is X distributed? Name the type of distribution, and give the values of any parameters.
b) Find the probability of me catching at least 9 grapes.

a) There's a fixed number (10) of independent trials with two possible results ('catch' and 'not catch'), a constant probability of success (0.8), and X is the total number of catches. Therefore X follows a binomial distribution, $X \sim B(10, 0.8)$.

b) P(at least 9 catches)
$= P(9 \text{ catches}) + P(10 \text{ catches})$
$= \left\{ \binom{10}{9} \times 0.8^9 \times 0.2^1 \right\} + \left\{ \binom{10}{10} \times 0.8^{10} \times 0.2^0 \right\}$
$= 0.268435... + 0.107374... = 0.376$ (to 3 d.p.).

Binomial distributions come with 5 strings attached...

There's a big, boring box at the top of the page with a list of 5 conditions in — and you do need to know it, unfortunately. There's only one way to learn it — keep trying to write down the 5 conditions until you can do it in your sleep.

Using Binomial Tables

Your life is just about to be made a whole lot <u>easier</u>. So smile sweetly and admit that statistics isn't <u>all</u> bad.

Look up Probabilities in Binomial Tables

EXAMPLE I have an unfair coin. When I toss this coin, the probability of getting heads is 0.35.
Find the probability that it will land on heads fewer than 3 times when I toss it 12 times in total.

If the random variable X represents the number of heads I get in 12 tosses, then $X \sim \mathrm{B}(12, 0.35)$.
You need to find $P(X \leq 2)$.

① You <u>could</u> work this out 'manually'...

$$P(0\text{ heads}) + P(1\text{ head}) + P(2\text{ heads}) = \left\{\binom{12}{0} \times 0.35^0 \times 0.65^{12}\right\} + \left\{\binom{12}{1} \times 0.35^1 \times 0.65^{11}\right\} + \left\{\binom{12}{2} \times 0.35^2 \times 0.65^{10}\right\}$$

$$= 0.0057 + 0.0368 + 0.1088 = 0.1513$$

② But it's much quicker to use tables of the <u>binomial cumulative distribution function</u> (c.d.f.).
These show $P(X \leq x)$, for $X \sim \mathrm{B}(n, p)$.

- First find the table for the <u>correct values of n and p</u>. Then the table gives you a value for $P(X \leq x)$.
- Here: $n = 12$ and $p = 0.35$.

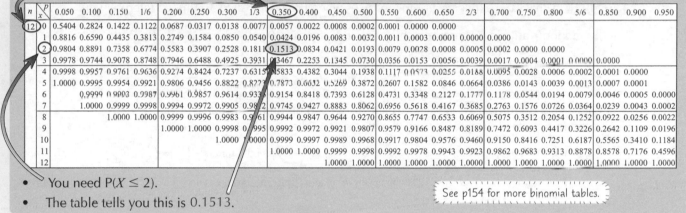

n	x	0.050	0.100	0.150	1/6	0.200	0.250	0.300	1/3	0.350	0.400	0.450	0.500	0.550	0.600	0.650	2/3	0.700	0.750	0.800	5/6	0.850	0.900	0.950
12	0	0.5404	0.2824	0.1422	0.1122	0.0687	0.0317	0.0138	0.0077	0.0057	0.0022	0.0008	0.0002	0.0001	0.0000	0.0000								
	1	0.8816	0.6590	0.4435	0.3813	0.2749	0.1584	0.0850	0.0540	0.0424	0.0196	0.0083	0.0032	0.0011	0.0003	0.0001	0.0000	0.0000						
	2	0.9804	0.8891	0.7358	0.6774	0.5583	0.3907	0.2528	0.1811	0.1513	0.0834	0.0421	0.0193	0.0079	0.0028	0.0008	0.0005	0.0002	0.0000	0.0000				
	3	0.9978	0.9744	0.9078	0.8748	0.7946	0.6488	0.4925	0.3931	0.3467	0.2253	0.1345	0.0730	0.0356	0.0153	0.0056	0.0039	0.0017	0.0004	0.0001	0.0000	0.0000		
	4	0.9998	0.9957	0.9761	0.9636	0.9274	0.8424	0.7237	0.6315	0.5833	0.4382	0.3044	0.1938	0.1117	0.0573	0.0255	0.0188	0.0095	0.0028	0.0006	0.0002	0.0001	0.0000	
	5	1.0000	0.9995	0.9954	0.9921	0.9806	0.9456	0.8822	0.8223	0.7873	0.6652	0.5269	0.3872	0.2607	0.1582	0.0846	0.0664	0.0386	0.0143	0.0039	0.0013	0.0007	0.0001	
	6		0.9999	0.9993	0.9987	0.9961	0.9857	0.9614	0.9333	0.9154	0.8418	0.7393	0.6128	0.4731	0.3348	0.2127	0.1777	0.1178	0.0544	0.0194	0.0079	0.0046	0.0005	0.0000
	7		1.0000	0.9999	0.9998	0.9994	0.9972	0.9905	0.9812	0.9745	0.9427	0.8883	0.8062	0.6956	0.5618	0.4167	0.3685	0.2763	0.1576	0.0726	0.0364	0.0239	0.0043	0.0002
	8			1.0000	1.0000	0.9999	0.9996	0.9983	0.9961	0.9944	0.9847	0.9644	0.9270	0.8655	0.7747	0.6533	0.6069	0.5075	0.3512	0.2054	0.1252	0.0922	0.0256	0.0022
	9					1.0000	1.0000	0.9998	0.9995	0.9992	0.9972	0.9921	0.9807	0.9579	0.9166	0.8487	0.8189	0.7472	0.6093	0.4417	0.3226	0.2642	0.1109	0.0196
	10							1.0000	1.0000	0.9999	0.9997	0.9989	0.9968	0.9917	0.9804	0.9576	0.9460	0.9150	0.8416	0.7251	0.6187	0.5565	0.3410	0.1184
	11									1.0000	1.0000	0.9999	0.9998	0.9992	0.9978	0.9943	0.9923	0.9862	0.9683	0.9313	0.8878	0.8578	0.7176	0.4596
	12											1.0000	1.0000	1.0000	1.0000	1.0000	1.0000	1.0000	1.0000	1.0000	1.0000	1.0000	1.0000	1.0000

- You need $P(X \leq 2)$.
- The table tells you this is 0.1513.

See p154 for more binomial tables.

Practise using those Binomial Tables

Binomial tables can be a bit <u>awkward</u>. Make sure you know how to find out what you want to know.

EXAMPLE I have a different unfair coin. When I toss this coin, the probability of getting tails is 0.6.
The random variable X represents the number of tails in 12 tosses, so $X \sim \mathrm{B}(12, 0.6)$.

If I toss this coin 12 times, use the table above to find the probability that:
- a) it will land on tails at least 9 times,
- b) it will land on heads exactly 9 times,
- c) it will land on heads at least 6 times,
- d) it will land on tails more than 3 but fewer than 6 times.

a) $P(X \geq 9) = 1 - P(X < 9) = 1 - P(X \leq 8) = 1 - 0.7747 = 0.2253$

⟵ 1) P(event happens) = 1 − P(event doesn't happen),
2) $P(X < 9) = P(X \leq 8)$, as X takes whole number values.

b) This means exactly <u>3 tails</u>.

  $P(X = 3) = P(X \leq 3) - P(X \leq 2) = 0.0153 - 0.0028 = 0.0125$

⟵ Use P(A or B) = P(A) + P(B) with the mutually exclusive events "$X \leq 2$" and "$X = 3$" to get $P(X \leq 3) = P(X \leq 2) + P(X = 3)$.
Or you can think of it as "subtracting $P(X \leq 2)$ from $P(X \leq 3)$ leaves just $P(X = 3)$".

c) At least 6 heads means <u>6 or fewer tails</u>. $P(X \leq 6) = 0.3348$

d) $P(3 < X < 6) = P(X \leq 5) - P(X \leq 3) = 0.1582 - 0.0153 = 0.1429$

Statistical tables are the original labour-saving device...

...as long as you know what you're doing. Careful, though — it's easy to trip yourself up. Basically, as long as you can find the right value of n and p in a table, you can use those tables to work out <u>anything</u> you might need. So hurrah for tables.

Mean and Variance of B(n, p)

You know from Section 3 what the <u>mean</u> (or <u>expected value</u>) and <u>variance</u> of a random variable are.
And you also know what the <u>binomial distribution</u> is. Put those things together, and you get this page.

For a Binomial Distribution: Mean = np

This formula will be in your formula booklet, but it's worth committing to memory anyway.

Mean of a Binomial Distribution

If $X \sim$ B(n, p), then:

Mean (or Expected Value) = μ = E(X) = np

> Greek letters (e.g. μ) often show something based purely on <u>theory</u> rather than <u>experimental results</u>.

Remember... the expected value is the value you'd expect the random variable to take <u>on average</u> if you took loads and loads of readings. It's a "<u>theoretical mean</u>" — the mean of experimental results is unlikely to match it <u>exactly</u>.

EXAMPLE If $X \sim$ B(20, 0.2), what is E(X)?

Just use the formula: E(X) = np = 20 × 0.2 = 4

EXAMPLE What's the expected number of sixes when I roll a fair dice 30 times? Interpret your answer.

If the random variable X represents the number of sixes in 30 rolls, then $X \sim$ B(30, $\frac{1}{6}$).

So the expected value of X is E(X) = 30 × $\frac{1}{6}$ = 5

If I were to repeatedly throw the dice 30 times, and find the <u>average</u> number of sixes in each set of 30 throws, then I would expect it to end up pretty close to 5.
And the more sets of 30 throws I did, the closer to 5 I'd expect the average to be.

Notice that the probability of getting <u>exactly</u> 5 sixes on my next set of 30 throws = $\binom{30}{5} \times \left(\frac{1}{6}\right)^5 \times \left(\frac{5}{6}\right)^{25}$ = 0.192
So I'm much more likely <u>not</u> to get exactly 5 sixes (= 1 − 0.192 = 0.808).
This is why it only makes sense to talk about the mean as a "<u>long-term average</u>", and <u>not</u> as "what I expect to happen next".

For a Binomial Distribution: Variance = npq

Variance of a Binomial Distribution

If $X \sim$ B(n, p), then:

Variance = Var(X) = σ^2 = $np(1-p)$ = npq
Standard Deviation = σ = $\sqrt{np(1-p)}$ = $\sqrt{npq}$

> For a binomial distribution, P(success) is usually called p, and P(failure) is sometimes called q (= $1 - p$).

EXAMPLE If $X \sim$ B(20, 0.2), what is Var(X)?

Just use the formula: Var(X) = $np(1-p)$ = 20 × 0.2 × 0.8 = 3.2

EXAMPLE If $X \sim$ B(18, $\frac{1}{3}$), find: a) P($X \leq \mu$), b) P($X \leq \mu - \sigma$), c) P($X \leq \mu - 2\sigma$)

E(X) = μ = 18 × $\frac{1}{3}$ = 6, and Var(X) = σ^2 = 18 × $\frac{1}{3}$ × (1 − $\frac{1}{3}$) = 4, which gives $\sigma = 2$.

So, using tables (for n = 18 and p = $\frac{1}{3}$):

a) P($X \leq \mu$) = P($X \leq 6$) = 0.6085

b) P($X \leq \mu - \sigma$) = P($X \leq 4$) = 0.2311

c) P($X \leq \mu - 2\sigma$) = P($X \leq 2$) = 0.0326

See page 154.

For B(n, p) — the variance is always less than the mean...

Nothing too fancy there really. A couple of easy-to-remember formulas, and some stuff about how to interpret these figures which you've seen before anyway. So learn the formulas, put the kettle on, and have a cup of tea while the going's good.

Binomial Distribution Problems

That's everything you need to know about binomial distributions (for now).
So it's time to put it all together and have a look at the kind of thing you might get asked in the exam.

EXAMPLE 1: Selling Double Glazing

A double-glazing salesman is handing out leaflets in a busy shopping centre. He knows that the probability of each passing person taking a leaflet is always 0.3. During a randomly chosen one-minute interval, 17 people passed him.
a)   Suggest a suitable model to describe the number of people (X) who take a leaflet.
b)   What is the probability that more than 10 people take a leaflet?
c)   How many people would the salesman expect to take a leaflet?
d)   Find the variance and standard deviation of X.

a)   During this one-minute interval, there's a fixed number (17) of independent trials with two possible results ("take a leaflet" and "do not take a leaflet"), a constant probability of success (0.3), and X is the total number of people taking leaflets. So $X \sim B(17, 0.3)$.

Use binomial tables for this — see p154.   *Or 5, to the nearest whole person.*

b) $P(X > 10) = 1 - P(X \leq 10) = 1 - 0.9968 = 0.0032$
c)   The number of people the salesman could expect to take a leaflet is $E(X) = np = 17 \times 0.3 = 5.1$
d)   Variance $= np(1 - p) = 17 \times 0.3 \times (1 - 0.3) = 3.57$ Standard deviation $= \sqrt{3.57} = 1.89$ (to 2 d.p.)

EXAMPLE 2: Multiple-Choice Guessing

A student has to take a 20-question multiple-choice exam, where each question has five possible answers, of which only one is correct. He believes he can pass the exam by guessing answers at random.
a)   How many questions could the student be expected to guess correctly?
b)   If the pass mark is 8:
   (i)   What is the probability that the student will pass the exam?
   (ii) How many times would you expect the student to pass if he were to take 50 of these multiple-choice exams?
c)   The examiner decides to set the pass mark so that it is at least 3 standard deviations above the expected number of correct guesses. What should the minimum pass mark be?

Let X be the number of correct guesses over the 20 questions. Then $X \sim B(20, 0.2)$.   *Define your random variable first, and say how it will be distributed.*
a) $E(X) = np = 20 \times 0.2 = 4$
b)   (i) $P(X \geq 8) = 1 - P(X < 8) = 1 - P(X \leq 7) = 1 - 0.9679 = 0.0321$
   (ii) Expected frequency = probability × number of trials = $0.0321 \times 50 = 1.605$.   *See page 122.*
       So you'd expect the student to pass approximately 1.6 times.   *Or 2 times, to the nearest whole number.*
c) $Var(X) = np(1 - p) = 20 \times 0.2 \times 0.8 = 3.2$ — so the standard deviation $= \sqrt{3.2} = 1.789$ (to 3 d.p.).
   So the pass mark needs to be at least $4 + (3 \times 1.789) \approx 9.4$ — i.e. the minimum pass mark should be 10.

EXAMPLE 3: An Unfair Coin

I am spinning a coin that I know is three times as likely to land on heads as it is on tails.
a)   What is the probability that it lands on tails for the first time on the third spin?
b)   What is the probability that in 10 spins, it lands on heads at least 7 times?

Careful... this doesn't need you to use one of the binomial formulas.

You know that P(heads) $= 3 \times$ P(tails), and that P(heads) + P(tails) $= 1$.
This means that P(heads) $= 0.75$ and P(tails) $= 0.25$.

a)   P(lands on tails for the first time on the third spin) $= 0.75 \times 0.75 \times 0.25 = 0.141$ (to 3 d.p.).

b)   If X represents the number of heads in 10 spins, then $X \sim B(10, 0.75)$.

   $P(X \geq 7) = 1 - P(X < 7) = 1 - P(X \leq 6) = 1 - 0.2241 = 0.7759$

Proof that you shouldn't send a monkey to take your multi-choice exams...

You can see now how useful a working knowledge of statistics is. Ever since you first started using CGP books, I've been banging on about how hard it is to pass an exam without revising. Well, now you can prove I was correct using a bit of knowledge and binomial tables. Yup... statistics can help out with some of those tricky situations you face in life.

S1 Section 4 — Practice Questions

Hopefully, everything you've just read will already be stuck in your brain. But if you need a bit of help to wedge it in place, then try these questions. Actually... I reckon you'd best try them anyway — a little suffering is good for the soul.

Warm-up Questions

1) In how many different orders can the following be arranged?

   a) 15 identical red balls, plus 6 other balls, all of different colours.

   b) 4 red counters, 4 blue counters, 4 yellow counters and 4 green counters.

2) a) What is the probability of the following?

   (i) Getting <u>exactly</u> 5 heads when you spin a fair coin 10 times.

   (ii) Getting <u>exactly</u> 9 heads when you spin a fair coin 10 times.

   b) I'm going to carry out 40 trials, where each trial involves tossing a fair coin 10 times. In how many of the trials would you expect me to get:

   (i) 5 heads?

   (ii) 9 heads?

3) Which of the following would follow a binomial distribution? Explain your answers.

   a) The number of prime numbers you throw in 30 throws of a standard dice.

   b) The number of people in a particular class at a school who get 'heads' when they flip a coin.

   c) The number of aces in a 7-card hand dealt from a standard deck of 52 cards.

   d) The number of shots I have to take before I score from the free-throw line in basketball.

4) What is the probability of the following?

   a) Getting <u>at least</u> 5 heads when you spin a fair coin 10 times.

   b) Getting <u>at least</u> 9 heads when you spin a fair coin 10 times.

5) If $X \sim B(14, 0.27)$, find:

   a) $P(X = 4)$ b) $P(X < 2)$ c) $P(5 < X \leq 8)$

6) If $X \sim B(18, 0.15)$ and $Y \sim B(15, 0.65)$ find:

   a) $P(X \leq 3)$ b) $P(X \leq 7)$

   c) $P(X \leq 15)$ d) $P(Y \leq 3)$

   e) $P(Y \leq 7)$ f) $P(Y \leq 15)$

7) Find the required probability for each of the following binomial distributions.

   a) $P(X \leq 15)$ if $X \sim B(20, 0.4)$ b) $P(X < 4)$ if $X \sim B(14, 0.15)$

   c) $P(X > 7)$ if $X \sim B(15, 0.45)$ d) $P(X \geq 4)$ if $X \sim B(9, 0.8)$

   e) $P(X = 10)$ if $X \sim B(20, 0.7)$ f) $P(X = 7)$ if $X \sim B(10, 0.75)$

8) Find the mean and variance of the following random variables.

   a) $X \sim B(20, 0.4)$ b) $X \sim B(40, 0.15)$

   c) $X \sim B(25, 0.45)$ d) $X \sim B(50, 0.8)$

   e) $X \sim B(30, 0.7)$ f) $X \sim B(45, 0.012)$

S1 Section 4 — Practice Questions

Right then... you're nearly at the end of the section, and with any luck your tail is up, the wind is in your sails and the going is good. But the real test of whether you're ready for the exam is some exam questions. And as luck would have it, there are some right here. So give them a go and test your mettle, see if you can walk the walk... and so on.

Exam Questions

1   a)   The random variable X follows the binomial distribution B(12, 0.6). Find:

         (i) $P(X < 8)$,

(2 marks)

         (ii) $P(X = 5)$,

(2 marks)

         (iii) $P(3 < X \leq 7)$.

(2 marks)

   b)   If $Y \sim$ B(21, 0.8), find:

         (i) $P(Y = 14)$,

(2 marks)

         (ii) $E(Y)$,

(1 mark)

         (iii) $Var(Y)$.

(1 mark)

2   The probability of an apple containing a maggot is 0.15.

   a)   Find the probability that in a random sample of 20 apples there are:

         (i)   fewer than 6 apples containing maggots,

(2 marks)

         (ii)   more than 2 apples containing maggots,

(2 marks)

         (iii)   exactly 7 apples containing maggots.

(2 marks)

   b)   These apples are sold in crates of 20. Ed buys 3 crates.

       Find the probability that more than 1 crate contains more than 2 apples with maggots.

(3 marks)

3   Simon tries to solve the crossword puzzle in his newspaper every day for two weeks.
He either succeeds in solving the puzzle, or he fails to solve it.

   a)   Simon believes that this situation can be modelled by a random variable following a binomial distribution.

         (i)   State two conditions needed for a binomial distribution to arise here.

(2 marks)

         (ii)   State which quantity would follow a binomial distribution (assuming the above conditions are satisfied).

(1 mark)

   b)   Simon believes a random variable X follows the distribution B(18, p).
If $P(X = 4) = P(X = 5)$, find p.

(5 marks)

Null and Alternative Hypotheses

Before tackling this section, it'd be a good idea to make sure you're happy with everything that went on in Section 4.

A **Hypothesis** is a **Statement** you want to **Test**

1) Hypothesis testing means checking whether a theory you have about a situation is consistent with observations.

2) Here, that's going to mean testing a claim about the value of a binomial parameter p. The basic idea is to use some data to test whether a suggested value for p is so wildly unlikely that it probably isn't true.

You need to know a few technical terms:

- **Null Hypothesis (H_0)** — a statement about the value of a population parameter. Your data may allow you to reject this hypothesis.
- **Alternative Hypothesis (H_1)** — a statement that describes the value of the population parameter if H_0 is rejected.
- **Test Statistic** — a statistic calculated from sample data which is used to decide whether or not to reject H_0.

3) For any hypothesis test, you need to write a null hypothesis (H_0) and an alternative hypothesis (H_1).

4) You often choose the null hypothesis to be something you actually think is false, and then see if your evidence 'disproves' it. (Hypothesis tests can only show that statements are false — they can't prove that things are true.)

> For the purposes of the test, you assume H_0 is true, and then see if your data allows you to reject it.

5) H_0 needs to give a specific value to the parameter, since all your calculations will be based on this value. H_1 describes how you think the value of the parameter differs from the value given by H_0 (e.g. is it 'bigger than', 'smaller than' or just 'different from' the value in H_0?).

6) In a test about a binomial parameter (p), the test statistic will be the 'number of successes in n trials'.

Here's an example...

EXAMPLE A 4-sided spinner has sides labelled A–D. Jemma thinks that the spinner is biased towards side A. She spins it 20 times and counts the number of times, Y, that she gets side A.

   a) Write down a suitable null hypothesis to test Jemma's theory.
   b) Write down a suitable alternative hypothesis.
   c) Describe the test statistic Jemma should use.

This is a test on a binomial parameter, p. The number of times that the spinner lands on side A in 20 spins will follow a binomial distribution, $B(20, p)$, and Jemma wants to test a theory about the value of p.

   a) If the spinner were unbiased, each side would have a probability of 0.25 of being spun. So use this value in H_0: $H_0: p = 0.25$

   > Jemma actually thinks this is untrue. She's going to see if her data will allow her to 'reject' it. H_0 always gives a specific value to p.

   b) If the spinner is biased towards side A, then p will be greater than 0.25. So: $H_1: p > 0.25$

   > This is what Jemma really thinks.

   c) The test statistic is Y, the number of times the spinner lands on side A.

   > Assuming H_0 is true, $Y \sim B(20, 0.25)$.

Hypothesis Tests can be **One-Tailed** or **Two-Tailed**

> The 'tailed' business is to do with the critical region used by the test — see next page.

1) In a one-tailed test, H_1 is specific about whether p is greater than or smaller than the value in H_0.

   E.g. $H_1: p > 0.25$ or $H_1: p < 0.25$.

2) In a two-tailed test, H_1 says only that p doesn't equal the value in H_0 — but doesn't specify whether it's bigger or smaller.

   E.g. $H_1: p \neq 0.25$.

3) Whether you use a one-tailed or a two-tailed test depends on: (i) what you want to find out about the parameter, and (ii) any suspicions you might already have about it.

In the example above, Jemma thinks the probability of getting side A is greater than 0.25, so she uses a one-tailed test. If she wanted to test for bias either towards or against side A, she could use a two-tailed test with $H_1: p \neq 0.25$.

A statistician's party game — pin two tails on the donkey...

Or should it be one? Anyway, a very important thing to remember is that the results of a hypothesis test are either 'reject H_0', or 'do not reject H_0'. Not rejecting H_0 means you haven't found enough evidence to disprove H_0, and **not** that you've proved it.

Significance Levels and Critical Regions

You use the value of your test statistic to decide whether or not to reject your null hypothesis. Poor little unloved H_0.

If your Data is *Significant*, Reject H_0

1) You would reject H_0 if the observed value of the test statistic is really unlikely under the null hypothesis.

2) The significance level (α) of a test determines how unlikely the value needs to be before H_0 is rejected. You'll be told what value to use for α — it'll often be $\alpha = 0.01$ (or 1%), $\alpha = 0.05$ (or 5%) or $\alpha = 0.1$ (or 10%).

3) The significance level also determines the strength of the evidence that the test has provided — the lower the value of α, the stronger the evidence you have for saying H_0 is false. And α is also the probability of incorrectly rejecting H_0 — i.e. of getting extreme data by chance when H_0 is true.

4) To decide whether your result is significant (and so whether you should reject H_0):
   - Define the distribution of the test statistic under the null hypothesis.
   - Calculate the probability of getting a value that's at least as extreme as the observed value from this distribution.
   - If the probability is less than or equal to the significance level, reject H_0 in favour of H_1.

> **EXAMPLE** Javed wants to test at the 5% level whether or not a coin is biased towards tails. He tosses the coin 10 times and records the number of tails, X. He gets 9 tails.
> a) Define suitable hypotheses for p, the probability of getting tails.
> b) State the condition under which Javed would reject H_0.
>
> a) $H_0: p = 0.5$ and $H_1: p > 0.5$.   *P(at least as extreme as 9) means 9 or more.*
>
> b) Under H_0, $X \sim B(10, 0.5)$. If $P(X \geq 9) \leq 0.05$, Javed would reject H_0.
>   *Distribution of X*   *Significance level*

The *Critical Region* is the *Set of Significant Values*

1) The critical region (CR) is the set of all values of the test statistic that would cause you to reject H_0. And the acceptance region is the set of values of the test statistic that would mean you do not reject H_0.

2) The critical region is chosen so that P(test statistic is in critical region) = α.

   Sometimes it's not possible to find a CR so that P(test statistic in CR) is exactly α. In this case, you'd choose the CR so that: P(test statistic in CR) is as near α as possible, but no greater than α.

3) One-tailed tests have a single CR, containing the highest or lowest values. For two-tailed tests, the region is split into two — half at the lower end and half at the upper end. Each half has a probability of $\frac{1}{2}\alpha$ (or as near as possible — but not greater than this value).

4) To test whether your result is significant, find the critical region and if it contains the observed value, reject H_0.

> **EXAMPLE**   Returning to the example above...
>
> The table below shows the probability distribution of X — the number of tails in 10 tosses, under H_0.
>
> | x | 0 | 1 | 2 | 3 | 4 | 5 | 6 | 7 | 8 | 9 | 10 |
> |---|---|---|---|---|---|---|---|---|---|---|---|
> | $P(X = x)$ | 0.001 | 0.010 | 0.044 | 0.117 | 0.205 | 0.246 | 0.205 | 0.117 | 0.044 | 0.010 | 0.001 |
>
> *This is B(10, 0.5).*
>
> Find the critical region for the test, at the 5% level.
>
> This is a one-tailed test with $H_1: p > 0.5$, so you're only interested in the upper end of the distribution.
>
> The critical region is the biggest possible set of 'high' values of X with a total probability of ≤ 0.05.
>
> - Try the set $X \geq 8$: $P(X \geq 8) = 0.044 + 0.010 + 0.001 = 0.055 > 0.05$
> - Try the set $X \geq 9$: $P(X \geq 9) = 0.010 + 0.001 = 0.011 < 0.05$
>
> So the critical region is $X \geq 9$.   *Justify your CR by writing down the probabilities.*
>
> *So values of 9 or 10 would cause you to reject $H_0: p = 0.5$. And the acceptance region is therefore $X < 9$.*
>
> *Careful here: $P(X = x)$ can be $\leq \alpha$ without X being in the CR. E.g. $P(X = 8) = 0.044$, but 8 isn't in the CR because $P(X \geq 8) > \alpha$.*

I repeat, X has entered the critical region — we have a significant situation...

Hope you've been following the last two pages closely. Basically, you need two hypotheses and the value of a test statistic calculated from sample data. By assuming H_0 is true, you can find the probabilities of the different values this statistic can take — if the observed value is unlikely enough, then reject H_0. Right, time to put all the different components together...

Hypothesis Tests and Binomial Distributions

OK, it's time to pick your best hypothesis-testing foot and put it firmly forward.
This is the full six-point step-by-step method...

Use a **Hypothesis Test** to **Find Out** about the **Population Parameter p**

Hypothesis tests for the binomial parameter p all follow the <u>same general method</u> — shown in the example below.

EXAMPLE:

In a past census of employees, 30% were in favour of a change to working hours. A later survey is carried out on a random sample of 20 employees, and 2 vote for a change to hours. The manager claims that there has been a decrease in the proportion of employees in favour of a change to working hours.

Stating your hypotheses clearly, test the manager's claim at the 5% level of significance.

1) Start by <u>identifying the population parameter</u> that you're going to test:

   Let p = proportion of employees in favour of change to hours.

   You assume there's been no change in the value of the parameter, so you can give it a value of 0.3. The alternative hypothesis states what the manager actually thinks.

2) Write <u>null and alternative hypotheses</u> for p.
   If you assume there's been no change in the proportion: $H_0: p = 0.3$

   The manager's interested in whether the proportion has decreased, so: $H_1: p < 0.3$

3) State the <u>test statistic</u> X — the number of 'successes', and its <u>distribution</u> under H_0.
   $X \sim B(n, p)$ where n is the number in the sample and p is the probability of 'success' under H_0.

   Let X = number of employees in sample who are in favour of change. Under H_0, $X \sim B(20, 0.3)$.

4) State the <u>significance level</u> of the test. Here it's 5%, so $\alpha = 0.05$.

   The distribution of the test statistic uses the value $p = 0.3$.

5) <u>Test for significance</u> by finding the <u>probability of a value for your test statistic at least as extreme as the observed value</u>. This is a one-tailed test and you're interested in the lower end of the distribution. So you want to find the probability of X taking a value less than or equal to 2.

   Using the binomial tables (see p154): $P(X \leq 2) = 0.0355$, and since $0.0355 < 0.05$, the result is significant.

6) Now write your <u>conclusion</u>. Remember, hypothesis testing is about disproving the null hypothesis, or not disproving it — i.e. <u>rejecting</u> H_0, or <u>not rejecting</u> it. So that's how you need to word your conclusion. And don't forget to answer the original question:

   There is evidence at the 5% level of significance to reject H_0 and to support the manager's claim that the proportion in favour of change has decreased.

   Always say "there is evidence to reject H_0", or "there is insufficient evidence to reject H_0". Never talk about "accepting H_0" or "rejecting H_1".

And if you're asked (or prefer) to find a <u>critical region</u>, your test would look the same except for step 5...

5) <u>Test for significance</u> by finding the <u>critical region</u> for a test at this level of significance.
   This is a one-tailed test and you're interested in the lower end of the distribution.
   The critical region is the biggest possible set of 'low' values of X with a total probability of ≤ 0.05.

   Using the binomial tables: Try $X \leq 2$: $P(X \leq 2) = 0.0355 < 0.05$. Now try $X \leq 3$: $P(X \leq 3) = 0.1071 > 0.05$. So, CR is $X \leq 2$. These results fall in the CR, so the result is significant.

My hypothesis is — this is very likely to come up in the exam...

There are different sorts of questions that might come up on hypothesis testing. But this is the basic method, so make sure you learn it inside out. Cover the page and outline the six steps. Then work through the example again yourself.

Hypothesis Tests and Binomial Distributions

A couple more examples here of the sorts of questions that might come up in the exam. Aren't I kind.

EXAMPLES:

Exam questions can look quite 'involved' and be a bit long-winded.
But at the heart of them all is just a hypothesis test.

EXAMPLE 1 — USING CRITICAL REGIONS

Records show that the proportion of trees in a wood that suffer from a particular leaf disease is 15%. Chloe thinks that recent weather conditions might have affected this proportion. She examines a random sample of 20 of the trees.

a) Using a 10% level of significance, find the critical region for a two-tailed test of Chloe's theory.

Chloe finds that 8 of the sampled trees have the leaf disease.

b) Comment on this finding in relation to your answer to part a) and Chloe's theory.

a) Let p = proportion of trees with the leaf disease.
$H_0: p = 0.15$ $H_1: p \neq 0.15$
Let X = number of sampled trees with the disease. Under H_0, $X \sim B(20, 0.15)$.
$\alpha = 0.1$, and since the test is two-tailed, the probability of X falling in each tail should be 0.05, at most.

This is a two-tailed test, so you're interested in both ends of the sampling distribution.
The lower tail is the biggest possible set of 'low' values of X with a total probability of ≤ 0.05.
The upper tail is the biggest possible set of 'high' values of X with a total probability of ≤ 0.05.

Using the tables:

Lower tail:
$P(X \leq 0) = 0.0388 < 0.05$
$P(X \leq 1) = 0.1756 > 0.05$
So, CR is $X = 0$ or $X \geq 7$.

Upper tail: Look up $P(X \leq x - 1)$ and subtract from 1.
$P(X \geq 6) = 1 - P(X \leq 5) = 1 - 0.9327 = 0.0673 > 0.05$
$P(X \geq 7) = 1 - P(X \leq 6) = 1 - 0.9781 = 0.0219 < 0.05$

b) The observed value of 8 is in the critical region. So there is evidence at the 10% level of significance to reject H_0 and to support Chloe's theory that there has been a change in the proportion of affected trees.

And if you can't use the tables for your value of p, you have to use the binomial probability function to work things out.

EXAMPLE 2 — WITHOUT USING TABLES

The proportion of pupils at a school who support the local football team is found to be $\frac{1}{8}$. Nigel attends a school nearby and claims that there is less support for the same local team at his school. In a random sample of 20 pupils from Nigel's school, 1 supports the local team. Use a 5% level of significance to test Nigel's claim.

Let p = proportion of pupils who support the local team.
$H_0: p = \frac{1}{8}$ $H_1: p < \frac{1}{8}$
Let X = number of sampled pupils supporting the team. Under H_0, $X \sim B(20, \frac{1}{8})$. $\alpha = 0.05$.

Now you need to find the probability of getting a value less than or equal to 1. The tables don't have values for $p = \frac{1}{8}$, so you need to work out the probabilities individually and add them up:

See p136 for binomial probabilities.
Here you need to use: $\binom{20}{x}(\frac{1}{8})^x(\frac{7}{8})^{20-x}$

$P(X \leq 1) = P(X = 0) + P(X = 1)$
$= (\frac{7}{8})^{20} + 20(\frac{1}{8})(\frac{7}{8})^{19} = 0.267$

$0.267 > 0.05$, so the result is not significant. There is insufficient evidence at the 5% level of significance to reject H_0 and to support Nigel's claim that there is less support for the team.

If your value of p isn't in the binomial tables, don't panic...

You won't find $p = 0.2438$ in the tables, or even $p = 0.24$, for that matter. But this isn't a problem as long as you know how to use the binomial formula. But the most important thing is not to panic when you first see a tricky-looking question.

S1 Section 5 — Practice Questions

This is <u>real</u> statistics now — the kind that's too tricky for most newspapers to report accurately.
But if you can answer these questions, then you'll probably be able to explain where they're going wrong.

Warm-up Questions

1) Salma thinks a coin might be biased. She wants to find out about p,
   the proportion of coin tosses that result in 'heads'.
   a) State whether she should use a one-tailed or two-tailed hypothesis test.
   b) Define suitable null and alternative hypotheses.

2) Suggest a suitable test statistic for a hypothesis test of a binomial parameter, p.

3) Carry out the following tests of the binomial parameter p.
   Let X represent the number of successes in a random sample of size 20:
   a) Test H_0: $p = 0.2$ against H_1: $p < 0.2$, at the 5% significance level, using $x = 2$.
   b) Test H_0: $p = 0.4$ against H_1: $p > 0.4$, at the 1% significance level, using $x = 15$.

4) Find the critical region for the following test where $X \sim B(10, p)$:
   Test H_0: $p = 0.3$ against H_1: $p < 0.3$, at the 5% significance level.

5) Let X represent the number of successes in a random sample of size 50.
   Test H_0: $p = 0.09$ against H_1: $p < 0.09$, at the 5% significance level, using $x = 1$.

Nearly done... just a couple of exam questions and you're home and dry. (Apart from the practice exams, obviously.)

Exam Questions

1   Over a long period of time, the chef at an Italian restaurant has found that there is a probability of
     0.2 that a customer ordering a dessert on a weekday evening will order tiramisu. He thinks that the
     proportion of customers ordering desserts on Saturday evenings who order tiramisu is greater than 0.2.

   a)   State the name of the probability distribution that would be used in a hypothesis test for the
         value of p, the proportion of Saturday evening dessert eaters ordering tiramisu.
         (1 mark)

     A random sample of 20 customers who ordered a dessert on a Saturday evening was taken.
     7 of these customers ordered tiramisu.

   b)   (i)   Stating your hypotheses clearly, test the chef's theory at the 5% level of significance.
         (ii)   Find the minimum number of tiramisu orders needed for the result to be significant.
         (7 marks)

2   The residents of a small village are being asked their views on a plan to build a wind farm nearby.
     Environmental campaigners claim that 30% of the residents are against the plan.
     A random sample of 18 residents is surveyed.

   a)   Using a 10% significance level, find the critical region for a two-tailed test of this claim.
         (5 marks)

     It's found that 3 of the sampled residents say they are against the plan.

   b)   Comment on this finding in relation to the environmental campaigners' claim.
         (2 marks)

General Certificate of Education
Advanced Subsidiary (AS) and Advanced Level

Statistics S1 — Practice Exam One

Time Allowed: 1 hour 30 min

Graphical calculators may be used for this exam.

Give any non-exact numerical answers to an appropriate degree of accuracy.

Statistical tables can be found on page 154.
Values used from these tables must be quoted in full.

There are 72 marks available for this paper.

Section A (36 marks)

1   A group of 10 friends play a round of mini golf.
     Their total score ($\sum x$) is 500 and $\sum x^2 = 25\ 622$.

   a)   Find the mean and the root mean square deviation for this data.

   (3 marks)

   b)   Another friend wants to incorporate his score of 50. Without further calculation and
        giving reasons, explain the effect of adding this score on:

        (i)   the mean,

   (2 marks)

        (ii) the root mean square deviation.

   (2 marks)

2   The events A and B are mutually exclusive.
     P(A) = 0.3 and P(B) = 0.4.

   a)   Write down $P(A \cap B)$.

   (1 mark)

   b)   Find $P(A \cup B)$.

   (2 marks)

   c)   Hence find the probability that neither event happens.

   (2 marks)

   d)   Write down $P(A \mid B)$. Explain your answer.

   (2 marks)

3   The probability distribution for the cash prizes, x pence, offered by a gambling machine is as follows:

x	0	10	20	50	100
$P(X = x)$	0.2	0.2	0.2	0.2	p

a)   Write down the value of p.

(1 mark)

b)   Find the probability that the next prize won on this machine is at least 20p.

(1 mark)

c)   Find E(X).

(2 marks)

d)   Find Var(X).

(2 marks)

e)   The owner of the machine charges 40p per game. Comment on this cost.

(2 marks)

4   A student has a standard pack of 52 cards, which contains 12 picture cards in total.

a)   She picks 3 cards at random from the pack, without replacing the selected cards before the next pick. The random variable X represents the number of picture cards picked.
Explain why X does not follow a binomial distribution.

(1 mark)

b)   The student then chooses 3 cards at random from the pack, but replaces each of the selected cards before the next pick. The random variable Y represents the number of picture cards picked.
Calculate:

     (i)   the probability that the student chooses exactly two picture cards,

(3 marks)

     (ii)   the mean of Y.

(1 mark)

c)   If the student carried out this same selection of 3 cards with replacement 50 times, how many times would you expect her to get exactly two picture cards?

(2 marks)

5   Jack runs 'beginners' judo classes. He estimates that one fifth of the people who attend his classes have done judo before. To test this, he plans to question a random sample of 20 of the people who attend his classes.

a)   Find the critical region for a two-tailed test of Jack's hypothesis at the 5% level of significance. *(5 marks)*

b)   Given that 7 of the sampled class members say they have done judo before, carry out the above test of Jack's hypothesis.

(2 marks)

Section B (36 marks)

6   Of 30 drivers interviewed, 9 have been involved in a car crash at some time.
    Of those who have been involved in a crash, 5 wear glasses. The probability of wearing glasses,
    given that the driver has not been involved in a crash, is $\frac{1}{3}$.

a)   Represent this information in a tree diagram,
     giving all probabilities as fractions in their simplest form.

(3 marks)

b)   What is the probability that a person chosen at random has not been involved in a crash?

(1 mark)

c)   What is the probability that a person chosen at random wears glasses?

(3 marks)

d)   What is the probability that a glasses wearer has been a crash victim?

(3 marks)

e)   Out of the original 30 drivers, 13 were 35 years of age or older.
     Four people are selected at random from this group of 30.

     Calculate the probability that only one of these people is less than 35 years of age.

(3 marks)

The 30 drivers were each asked if they had taken their car to the garage in the last 6 months,
and if so, what work was carried out. The Venn diagram below shows the numbers for each type of work.

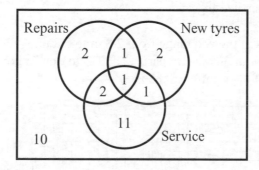

f)   Find the probability that a randomly selected driver's car:

(i)   Has not been taken to the garage in the last 6 months.

(1 mark)

(ii) Has had, at most, one type of work carried out in the last 6 months.

(2 marks)

(iii) Has had exactly two types of work carried out in the last 6 months.

(2 marks)

7 The heights of giraffes in a game reserve were measured.
   This data is summarised in the box plot below.

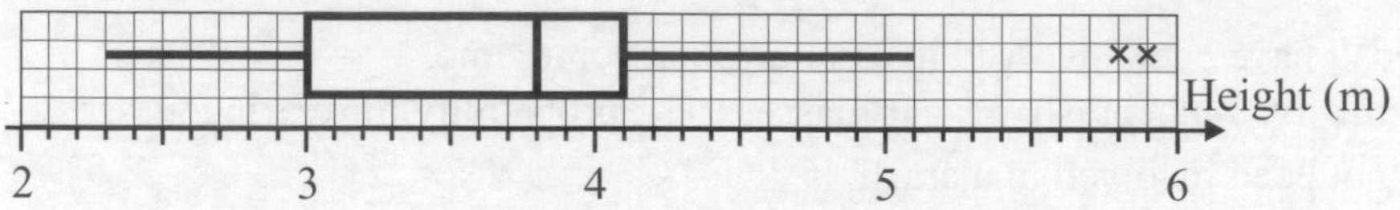

Height (m)

a) What height do only 25% of the giraffes exceed?

(1 mark)

b) Two heights are marked with crosses. Explain why these two heights are marked in this way.

(1 mark)

The heights of giraffes living in a zoo in the same country were also measured.
The table below shows the cumulative frequency distribution for these giraffes.

Height (x metres)	3	4	5	6
Cumulative Frequency	2	4	8	11

c) Use the table to calculate an estimate of the median height of these giraffes.

(3 marks)

d) Draw a cumulative frequency graph for the giraffes in the zoo.

(2 marks)

e) Use your cumulative frequency graph to estimate the lower and upper quartiles of the data.
    Then calculate the interquartile range.

(3 marks)

f) The heights of the giraffes in the zoo range from 2.8 m to 5.8 m.
    Use this information and your answers to parts c) and e) to draw a box plot
    representing the heights of the giraffes in the zoo.

(4 marks)

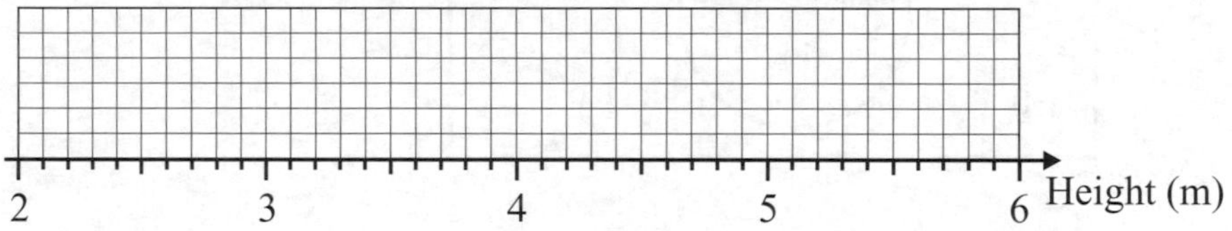

Height (m)

g) Compare the heights of the two groups of giraffes.

(4 marks)

General Certificate of Education
Advanced Subsidiary (AS) and Advanced Level

Statistics S1 — Practice Exam Two

Time Allowed: 1 hour 30 min

Graphical calculators may be used for this exam.

Give any non-exact numerical answers to an appropriate degree of accuracy.

Statistical tables can be found on page 154.
Values used from these tables must be quoted in full.

There are 72 marks available for this paper.

Section A (36 marks)

1   A survey to find the time taken to service a sample of 10 cars was carried out.
    The results are shown in the table below.

Number of days (x)	1	2	3	4	5	6	7	8
Frequency (f)	5	3	1	0	0	0	0	1

a)   Calculate:

   (i)   the sample mean,

(2 marks)

   (ii)   the sample standard deviation,

(2 marks)

   (iii) the median of this data.

(2 marks)

b)   Sam wants to use the range as a summary of the variation in the data.

   Do you consider this to be an appropriate measure to use? Give a reason for your answer.

(2 marks)

2   A choirmaster needs to choose 5 new people to join his choir. 6 women and 3 men audition for the places.

a)   How many different selections of 5 people are possible?

(2 marks)

b)   If the choirmaster selects the 5 new members at random,
     find the probability that he selects more women than men.

(5 marks)

3 The random variable X has the following probability distribution.

x	2	4	6	8	10
$P(X=x)$	0.1	0.2	p	q	0.2

The mean of the random variable X is 6.3.

a) (i) Write down two independent equations involving p and q.

(2 marks)

(ii) Solve your equations to find the values of p and q.

(3 marks)

b) Find $\text{Var}(X)$.

(3 marks)

4 A box of chocolates contains 20 chocolates, all of which are either hard or soft centred.
Some of the chocolates contain nuts. 13 chocolates have hard centres, of which 6 contain nuts.
There are 10 nutty chocolates in total.

a) Represent the data in a Venn diagram.

(2 marks)

b) A chocolate is selected at random. Find the probability of:
   (i) it having a soft centre.

(1 mark)

   (ii) it having a hard centre, given that it contains a nut.

(2 marks)

c) If 3 chocolates are selected at random without replacement, find the probability that
exactly one has a hard centre.

(3 marks)

5 An average of 10% of chocolate bars made by a particular manufacturer contain a 'golden ticket'.
A student buys 5 chocolate bars every week for 4 weeks.
The number of golden tickets he finds is represented by the random variable X.

Assuming that $X \sim B(20, 0.10)$, find:

a) $P(X > 1)$,

(2 marks)

b) $P(2 < X \leq 6)$

(3 marks)

Section B (36 marks)

6   The sales figures of a gift shop for a 12-week period are shown below.

Week	1	2	3	4	5	6	7	8	9	10	11	12
Sales (£'000s), x	5.5	4.2	5.8	9.1	3.8	4.6	6.4	6.2	4.9	5.9	6.0	4.1

(You may use $\Sigma x = 66.5$, and $\Sigma x^2 = 390.97$.)

a)   Find the mean and mean square deviation of the weekly sales.

(4 marks)

b)   Find the median and quartiles of the sales data.

(3 marks)

This 12-week period included Christmas. The shop's manager wants to exclude any outliers from his analysis of the data to get a more realistic idea of how the shop is performing.

c)   Use your answer to b) to identify any outliers in the data. Show your working.

(4 marks)

A different gift shop collects weekly sales figures for a whole year.
The table below shows in how many weeks sales fell into various categories.

Sales (£'000s)	$0 \leq y < 3$	$3 \leq y < 6$	$6 \leq y < 7$	$7 \leq y < 8$	$8 \leq y < 9$	$9 \leq y < 10$
Number of weeks, f	3	6	9	11	13	10

d)   Calculate an estimate of the mean weekly sales.

(2 marks)

e)   Draw a histogram to represent this data.

(4 marks)

f)   State the type of skewness shown by this distribution.

(1 mark)

7   Past records suggest that 45% of the members of a gym use the swimming pool.

a)   10 gym members are selected at random.
     Assuming that the proportion of members using the pool is unchanged, find:
     (i)   The probability that exactly 2 of them use the pool.

(3 marks)

     (ii) The probability that fewer than 5 of them use the pool.

(2 marks)

     (iii) The probability that at least 3 of them use the pool.

(3 marks)

     (iv) The expected number who use the pool.

(2 marks)

The gym's manager thinks that the popularity of the swimming pool has decreased over recent months.
She surveys a random sample of 16 of the gym members and finds that 3 of them use the pool.

b)   (i)   Write down suitable hypotheses for a test to determine if there is any evidence to suggest
           that the popularity of the pool has decreased. Justify your choice of alternative hypothesis.

(4 marks)

     (ii) Carry out the test at the 5% significance level.

(4 marks)

OCR (MEI) S1 — STATISTICAL TABLES

Cumulative binomial probabilities

The following tables show $P(X \le x) = \sum_{r=0}^{x} \binom{n}{r} \times p^r \times (1-p)^{n-r}$

n	x	p = 0.050	0.100	0.150	1/6	0.200	0.250	0.300	1/3	0.350	0.400	0.450	0.500	0.550	0.600	0.650	2/3	0.700	0.750	0.800	5/6	0.850	0.900	0.950
1	0	0.9500	0.9000	0.8500	0.8333	0.8000	0.7500	0.7000	0.6667	0.6500	0.6000	0.5500	0.5000	0.4500	0.4000	0.3500	0.3333	0.3000	0.2500	0.2000	0.1667	0.1500	0.1000	0.0500
	1	1.0000	1.0000	1.0000	1.0000	1.0000	1.0000	1.0000	1.0000	1.0000	1.0000	1.0000	1.0000	1.0000	1.0000	1.0000	1.0000	1.0000	1.0000	1.0000	1.0000	1.0000	1.0000	1.0000
2	0	0.9025	0.8100	0.7225	0.6944	0.6400	0.5625	0.4900	0.4444	0.4225	0.3600	0.3025	0.2500	0.2025	0.1600	0.1225	0.1111	0.0900	0.0625	0.0400	0.0278	0.0225	0.0100	0.0025
	1	0.9975	0.9900	0.9775	0.9722	0.9600	0.9375	0.9100	0.8889	0.8775	0.8400	0.7975	0.7500	0.6975	0.6400	0.5775	0.5556	0.5100	0.4375	0.3600	0.3056	0.2775	0.1900	0.0975
	2	1.0000	1.0000	1.0000	1.0000	1.0000	1.0000	1.0000	1.0000	1.0000	1.0000	1.0000	1.0000	1.0000	1.0000	1.0000	1.0000	1.0000	1.0000	1.0000	1.0000	1.0000	1.0000	1.0000
3	0	0.8574	0.7290	0.6141	0.5787	0.5120	0.4219	0.3430	0.2963	0.2746	0.2160	0.1664	0.1250	0.0911	0.0640	0.0429	0.0370	0.0270	0.0156	0.0080	0.0046	0.0034	0.0010	0.0001
	1	0.9928	0.9720	0.9393	0.9259	0.8960	0.8438	0.7840	0.7407	0.7183	0.6480	0.5748	0.5000	0.4253	0.3520	0.2818	0.2593	0.2160	0.1563	0.1040	0.0741	0.0608	0.0280	0.0073
	2	0.9999	0.9990	0.9966	0.9954	0.9920	0.9844	0.9730	0.9630	0.9571	0.9360	0.9089	0.8750	0.8336	0.7840	0.7254	0.7037	0.6570	0.5781	0.4880	0.4213	0.3859	0.2710	0.1426
	3	1.0000	1.0000	1.0000	1.0000	1.0000	1.0000	1.0000	1.0000	1.0000	1.0000	1.0000	1.0000	1.0000	1.0000	1.0000	1.0000	1.0000	1.0000	1.0000	1.0000	1.0000	1.0000	1.0000
4	0	0.8145	0.6561	0.5220	0.4823	0.4096	0.3164	0.2401	0.1975	0.1785	0.1296	0.0915	0.0625	0.0410	0.0256	0.0150	0.0123	0.0081	0.0039	0.0016	0.0008	0.0005	0.0001	0.0000
	1	0.9860	0.9477	0.8905	0.8681	0.8192	0.7383	0.6517	0.5926	0.5630	0.4752	0.3910	0.3125	0.2415	0.1792	0.1265	0.1111	0.0837	0.0508	0.0272	0.0162	0.0120	0.0037	0.0005
	2	0.9995	0.9963	0.9880	0.9838	0.9728	0.9492	0.9163	0.8889	0.8735	0.8208	0.7585	0.6875	0.6090	0.5248	0.4370	0.4074	0.3483	0.2617	0.1808	0.1319	0.1095	0.0523	0.0140
	3	1.0000	0.9999	0.9995	0.9992	0.9984	0.9961	0.9919	0.9877	0.9850	0.9744	0.9590	0.9375	0.9085	0.8704	0.8215	0.8025	0.7599	0.6836	0.5904	0.5177	0.4780	0.3439	0.1855
	4	1.0000	1.0000	1.0000	1.0000	1.0000	1.0000	1.0000	1.0000	1.0000	1.0000	1.0000	1.0000	1.0000	1.0000	1.0000	1.0000	1.0000	1.0000	1.0000	1.0000	1.0000	1.0000	1.0000
5	0	0.7738	0.5905	0.4437	0.4019	0.3277	0.2373	0.1681	0.1317	0.1160	0.0778	0.0503	0.0313	0.0185	0.0102	0.0053	0.0041	0.0024	0.0010	0.0003	0.0001	0.0001	0.0000	0.0000
	1	0.9774	0.9185	0.8352	0.8038	0.7373	0.6328	0.5282	0.4609	0.4284	0.3370	0.2562	0.1875	0.1312	0.0870	0.0540	0.0453	0.0308	0.0156	0.0067	0.0033	0.0022	0.0005	0.0000
	2	0.9988	0.9914	0.9734	0.9645	0.9421	0.8965	0.8369	0.7901	0.7648	0.6826	0.5931	0.5000	0.4069	0.3174	0.2352	0.2099	0.1631	0.1035	0.0579	0.0355	0.0266	0.0086	0.0012
	3	1.0000	0.9995	0.9978	0.9967	0.9933	0.9844	0.9692	0.9547	0.9460	0.9130	0.8688	0.8125	0.7438	0.6630	0.5716	0.5391	0.4718	0.3672	0.2627	0.1962	0.1648	0.0815	0.0226
	4	1.0000	0.9999	0.9999	0.9999	0.9997	0.9990	0.9976	0.9959	0.9947	0.9898	0.9815	0.9688	0.9497	0.9222	0.8840	0.8683	0.8319	0.7627	0.6723	0.5981	0.5563	0.4095	0.2262
	5	1.0000	1.0000	1.0000	1.0000	1.0000	1.0000	1.0000	1.0000	1.0000	1.0000	1.0000	1.0000	1.0000	1.0000	1.0000	1.0000	1.0000	1.0000	1.0000	1.0000	1.0000	1.0000	1.0000
6	0	0.7351	0.5314	0.3771	0.3349	0.2621	0.1780	0.1176	0.0878	0.0754	0.0467	0.0277	0.0156	0.0083	0.0041	0.0018	0.0014	0.0007	0.0002	0.0001	0.0000	0.0000	0.0000	0.0000
	1	0.9672	0.8857	0.7765	0.7368	0.6554	0.5339	0.4202	0.3512	0.3191	0.2333	0.1636	0.1094	0.0692	0.0410	0.0223	0.0178	0.0109	0.0046	0.0016	0.0007	0.0004	0.0001	0.0000
	2	0.9978	0.9842	0.9527	0.9377	0.9011	0.8306	0.7443	0.6804	0.6471	0.5443	0.4415	0.3438	0.2553	0.1792	0.1174	0.1001	0.0705	0.0376	0.0170	0.0087	0.0059	0.0013	0.0001
	3	0.9999	0.9987	0.9941	0.9913	0.9830	0.9624	0.9295	0.8999	0.8826	0.8208	0.7447	0.6563	0.5585	0.4557	0.3529	0.3196	0.2557	0.1694	0.0989	0.0623	0.0473	0.0159	0.0022
	4	1.0000	0.9999	0.9996	0.9993	0.9984	0.9954	0.9891	0.9822	0.9777	0.9590	0.9308	0.8906	0.8364	0.7667	0.6809	0.6488	0.5798	0.4661	0.3446	0.2632	0.2235	0.1143	0.0328
	5	1.0000	1.0000	1.0000	0.9999	0.9999	0.9998	0.9993	0.9986	0.9982	0.9959	0.9917	0.9844	0.9723	0.9533	0.9246	0.9122	0.8824	0.8220	0.7379	0.6651	0.6229	0.4686	0.2649
	6	1.0000	1.0000	1.0000	1.0000	1.0000	1.0000	1.0000	1.0000	1.0000	1.0000	1.0000	1.0000	1.0000	1.0000	1.0000	1.0000	1.0000	1.0000	1.0000	1.0000	1.0000	1.0000	1.0000
7	0	0.6983	0.4783	0.3206	0.2791	0.2097	0.1335	0.0824	0.0585	0.0490	0.0280	0.0152	0.0078	0.0037	0.0016	0.0006	0.0005	0.0002	0.0001	0.0000	0.0000	0.0000	0.0000	0.0000
	1	0.9556	0.8503	0.7166	0.6698	0.5767	0.4449	0.3294	0.2634	0.2338	0.1586	0.1024	0.0625	0.0357	0.0188	0.0090	0.0069	0.0038	0.0013	0.0004	0.0001	0.0001	0.0000	0.0000
	2	0.9962	0.9743	0.9262	0.9042	0.8520	0.7564	0.6471	0.5706	0.5323	0.4199	0.3164	0.2266	0.1529	0.0963	0.0556	0.0453	0.0288	0.0129	0.0047	0.0020	0.0012	0.0002	0.0000
	3	0.9998	0.9973	0.9879	0.9824	0.9667	0.9294	0.8740	0.8267	0.8002	0.7102	0.6083	0.5000	0.3917	0.2898	0.1998	0.1733	0.1260	0.0706	0.0333	0.0176	0.0121	0.0027	0.0002
	4	1.0000	0.9998	0.9988	0.9980	0.9953	0.9871	0.9712	0.9547	0.9444	0.9037	0.8471	0.7734	0.6836	0.5801	0.4677	0.4294	0.3529	0.2436	0.1480	0.0958	0.0738	0.0257	0.0038
	5	1.0000	1.0000	0.9999	0.9999	0.9996	0.9987	0.9962	0.9931	0.9910	0.9812	0.9643	0.9375	0.8976	0.8414	0.7662	0.7366	0.6706	0.5551	0.4233	0.3302	0.2834	0.1497	0.0444
	6	1.0000	1.0000	1.0000	1.0000	0.9999	0.9999	0.9998	0.9995	0.9994	0.9984	0.9963	0.9922	0.9848	0.9720	0.9510	0.9415	0.9176	0.8665	0.7903	0.7209	0.6794	0.5217	0.3017
	7	1.0000	1.0000	1.0000	1.0000	1.0000	1.0000	1.0000	1.0000	1.0000	1.0000	1.0000	1.0000	1.0000	1.0000	1.0000	1.0000	1.0000	1.0000	1.0000	1.0000	1.0000	1.0000	1.0000

OCR (MEI) S1 — STATISTICAL TABLES

Cumulative binomial probabilities (continued)

n = 8

x	0.050	0.100	0.150	1/6	0.200	0.250	0.300	1/3	0.350	0.400	0.450	0.500	0.550	0.600	0.650	2/3	0.700	0.750	0.800	5/6	0.850	0.900	0.950
0	0.6634	0.4305	0.2725	0.2326	0.1678	0.1001	0.0576	0.0390	0.0319	0.0168	0.0084	0.0039	0.0017	0.0007	0.0002	0.0002	0.0001	0.0000	0.0000	0.0000	0.0000	0.0000	0.0000
1	0.9428	0.8131	0.6572	0.6047	0.5033	0.3671	0.2553	0.1951	0.1691	0.1064	0.0632	0.0352	0.0181	0.0085	0.0036	0.0026	0.0013	0.0004	0.0001	0.0000	0.0000	0.0000	0.0000
2	0.9942	0.9619	0.8948	0.8652	0.7969	0.6785	0.5518	0.4682	0.4278	0.3154	0.2201	0.1445	0.0885	0.0498	0.0253	0.0197	0.0113	0.0042	0.0012	0.0004	0.0002	0.0000	0.0000
3	0.9996	0.9950	0.9786	0.9693	0.9437	0.8862	0.8059	0.7414	0.7064	0.5941	0.4770	0.3633	0.2604	0.1737	0.1061	0.0879	0.0580	0.0273	0.0104	0.0046	0.0029	0.0004	0.0000
4	1.0000	0.9996	0.9971	0.9954	0.9896	0.9727	0.9420	0.9121	0.8939	0.8263	0.7396	0.6367	0.5230	0.4059	0.2936	0.2586	0.1941	0.1138	0.0563	0.0307	0.0214	0.0050	0.0004
5	1.0000	1.0000	0.9998	0.9995	0.9988	0.9958	0.9887	0.9803	0.9747	0.9502	0.9115	0.8555	0.7799	0.6846	0.5722	0.5318	0.4482	0.3215	0.2031	0.1348	0.1052	0.0381	0.0058
6	1.0000	1.0000	1.0000	1.0000	0.9999	0.9996	0.9987	0.9974	0.9964	0.9915	0.9819	0.9648	0.9368	0.8936	0.8309	0.8049	0.7447	0.6329	0.4967	0.3953	0.3428	0.1869	0.0572
7	1.0000	1.0000	1.0000	1.0000	1.0000	1.0000	0.9999	0.9998	0.9998	0.9993	0.9983	0.9961	0.9916	0.9832	0.9681	0.9610	0.9424	0.8999	0.8322	0.7674	0.7275	0.5695	0.3366
8	1.0000	1.0000	1.0000	1.0000	1.0000	1.0000	1.0000	1.0000	1.0000	1.0000	1.0000	1.0000	1.0000	1.0000	1.0000	1.0000	1.0000	1.0000	1.0000	1.0000	1.0000	1.0000	1.0000

n = 9

x	0.050	0.100	0.150	1/6	0.200	0.250	0.300	1/3	0.350	0.400	0.450	0.500	0.550	0.600	0.650	2/3	0.700	0.750	0.800	5/6	0.850	0.900	0.950
0	0.6302	0.3874	0.2316	0.1938	0.1342	0.0751	0.0404	0.0260	0.0207	0.0101	0.0046	0.0020	0.0008	0.0003	0.0001	0.0001	0.0000	0.0000	0.0000	0.0000	0.0000	0.0000	0.0000
1	0.9288	0.7748	0.5995	0.5427	0.4362	0.3003	0.1960	0.1431	0.1211	0.0705	0.0385	0.0195	0.0091	0.0038	0.0014	0.0010	0.0004	0.0001	0.0000	0.0000	0.0000	0.0000	0.0000
2	0.9916	0.9470	0.8591	0.8217	0.7382	0.6007	0.4628	0.3772	0.3373	0.2318	0.1495	0.0898	0.0498	0.0250	0.0112	0.0083	0.0043	0.0013	0.0003	0.0001	0.0000	0.0000	0.0000
3	0.9994	0.9917	0.9661	0.9520	0.9144	0.8343	0.7297	0.6503	0.6089	0.4826	0.3614	0.2539	0.1658	0.0994	0.0536	0.0424	0.0253	0.0100	0.0031	0.0011	0.0006	0.0001	0.0000
4	1.0000	0.9991	0.9944	0.9910	0.9804	0.9511	0.9012	0.8552	0.8283	0.7334	0.6214	0.5000	0.3786	0.2666	0.1717	0.1448	0.0988	0.0489	0.0196	0.0090	0.0056	0.0009	0.0000
5	1.0000	0.9999	0.9994	0.9989	0.9969	0.9900	0.9747	0.9576	0.9464	0.9006	0.8342	0.7461	0.6386	0.5174	0.3911	0.3497	0.2703	0.1657	0.0856	0.0480	0.0339	0.0083	0.0006
6	1.0000	1.0000	1.0000	0.9999	0.9997	0.9987	0.9957	0.9917	0.9888	0.9750	0.9502	0.9102	0.8505	0.7682	0.6627	0.6228	0.5372	0.3993	0.2618	0.1783	0.1409	0.0530	0.0084
7	1.0000	1.0000	1.0000	1.0000	1.0000	0.9999	0.9996	0.9990	0.9986	0.9962	0.9909	0.9805	0.9615	0.9295	0.8789	0.8569	0.8040	0.6997	0.5638	0.4573	0.4005	0.2252	0.0712
8	1.0000	1.0000	1.0000	1.0000	1.0000	1.0000	1.0000	0.9999	0.9999	0.9997	0.9992	0.9980	0.9954	0.9899	0.9793	0.9740	0.9596	0.9249	0.8658	0.8062	0.7684	0.6126	0.3698
9	1.0000	1.0000	1.0000	1.0000	1.0000	1.0000	1.0000	1.0000	1.0000	1.0000	1.0000	1.0000	1.0000	1.0000	1.0000	1.0000	1.0000	1.0000	1.0000	1.0000	1.0000	1.0000	1.0000

n = 10

x	0.050	0.100	0.150	1/6	0.200	0.250	0.300	1/3	0.350	0.400	0.450	0.500	0.550	0.600	0.650	2/3	0.700	0.750	0.800	5/6	0.850	0.900	0.950
0	0.5987	0.3487	0.1969	0.1615	0.1074	0.0563	0.0282	0.0173	0.0135	0.0060	0.0025	0.0010	0.0003	0.0001	0.0000	0.0000	0.0000	0.0000	0.0000	0.0000	0.0000	0.0000	0.0000
1	0.9139	0.7361	0.5443	0.4845	0.3758	0.2440	0.1493	0.1040	0.0860	0.0464	0.0233	0.0107	0.0045	0.0017	0.0005	0.0004	0.0001	0.0000	0.0000	0.0000	0.0000	0.0000	0.0000
2	0.9885	0.9298	0.8202	0.7752	0.6778	0.5256	0.3828	0.2991	0.2616	0.1673	0.0996	0.0547	0.0274	0.0123	0.0048	0.0034	0.0016	0.0004	0.0001	0.0000	0.0000	0.0000	0.0000
3	0.9990	0.9872	0.9500	0.9303	0.8791	0.7759	0.6496	0.5593	0.5138	0.3823	0.2660	0.1719	0.1020	0.0548	0.0260	0.0197	0.0106	0.0035	0.0009	0.0003	0.0001	0.0000	0.0000
4	0.9999	0.9984	0.9901	0.9845	0.9672	0.9219	0.8497	0.7869	0.7515	0.6331	0.5044	0.3770	0.2616	0.1662	0.0949	0.0766	0.0473	0.0197	0.0064	0.0024	0.0014	0.0001	0.0000
5	1.0000	0.9999	0.9986	0.9976	0.9936	0.9803	0.9527	0.9234	0.9051	0.8338	0.7384	0.6230	0.4956	0.3669	0.2485	0.2131	0.1503	0.0781	0.0328	0.0155	0.0099	0.0016	0.0001
6	1.0000	1.0000	0.9999	0.9997	0.9991	0.9965	0.9894	0.9803	0.9740	0.9452	0.8980	0.8281	0.7340	0.6177	0.4862	0.4407	0.3504	0.2241	0.1209	0.0697	0.0500	0.0128	0.0010
7	1.0000	1.0000	1.0000	1.0000	0.9999	0.9996	0.9984	0.9966	0.9952	0.9877	0.9726	0.9453	0.9004	0.8327	0.7384	0.7009	0.6172	0.4744	0.3222	0.2248	0.1798	0.0702	0.0115
8	1.0000	1.0000	1.0000	1.0000	1.0000	1.0000	0.9999	0.9996	0.9995	0.9983	0.9955	0.9893	0.9767	0.9536	0.9140	0.8960	0.8507	0.7560	0.6242	0.5155	0.4557	0.2639	0.0861
9	1.0000	1.0000	1.0000	1.0000	1.0000	1.0000	1.0000	1.0000	1.0000	0.9999	0.9997	0.9990	0.9975	0.9940	0.9865	0.9827	0.9718	0.9437	0.8926	0.8385	0.8031	0.6513	0.4013
10	1.0000	1.0000	1.0000	1.0000	1.0000	1.0000	1.0000	1.0000	1.0000	1.0000	1.0000	1.0000	1.0000	1.0000	1.0000	1.0000	1.0000	1.0000	1.0000	1.0000	1.0000	1.0000	1.0000

n = 11

x	0.050	0.100	0.150	1/6	0.200	0.250	0.300	1/3	0.350	0.400	0.450	0.500	0.550	0.600	0.650	2/3	0.700	0.750	0.800	5/6	0.850	0.900	0.950
0	0.5688	0.3138	0.1673	0.1346	0.0859	0.0422	0.0198	0.0116	0.0088	0.0036	0.0014	0.0005	0.0002	0.0000	0.0000	0.0000	0.0000	0.0000	0.0000	0.0000	0.0000	0.0000	0.0000
1	0.8981	0.6974	0.4922	0.4307	0.3221	0.1971	0.1130	0.0751	0.0606	0.0302	0.0139	0.0059	0.0022	0.0007	0.0002	0.0001	0.0001	0.0000	0.0000	0.0000	0.0000	0.0000	0.0000
2	0.9848	0.9104	0.7788	0.7268	0.6174	0.4552	0.3127	0.2341	0.2001	0.1189	0.0652	0.0327	0.0148	0.0059	0.0020	0.0014	0.0006	0.0001	0.0000	0.0000	0.0000	0.0000	0.0000
3	0.9984	0.9815	0.9306	0.9044	0.8389	0.7133	0.5696	0.4726	0.4256	0.2963	0.1911	0.1133	0.0610	0.0293	0.0122	0.0088	0.0043	0.0012	0.0002	0.0001	0.0000	0.0000	0.0000
4	0.9999	0.9972	0.9841	0.9755	0.9496	0.8854	0.7897	0.7110	0.6683	0.5328	0.3971	0.2744	0.1738	0.0994	0.0501	0.0386	0.0216	0.0076	0.0020	0.0006	0.0003	0.0000	0.0000
5	1.0000	0.9997	0.9973	0.9954	0.9883	0.9657	0.9218	0.8779	0.8513	0.7535	0.6331	0.5000	0.3669	0.2465	0.1487	0.1221	0.0782	0.0343	0.0117	0.0046	0.0027	0.0003	0.0000
6	1.0000	1.0000	0.9997	0.9994	0.9980	0.9924	0.9784	0.9614	0.9499	0.9006	0.8262	0.7256	0.6029	0.4672	0.3317	0.2890	0.2103	0.1146	0.0504	0.0245	0.0159	0.0028	0.0001
7	1.0000	1.0000	1.0000	0.9999	0.9998	0.9988	0.9957	0.9912	0.9878	0.9707	0.9390	0.8867	0.8089	0.7037	0.5744	0.5274	0.4304	0.2867	0.1611	0.0956	0.0694	0.0185	0.0016
8	1.0000	1.0000	1.0000	1.0000	1.0000	0.9999	0.9994	0.9986	0.9980	0.9941	0.9852	0.9673	0.9348	0.8811	0.7999	0.7659	0.6873	0.5448	0.3826	0.2732	0.2212	0.0896	0.0152
9	1.0000	1.0000	1.0000	1.0000	1.0000	1.0000	1.0000	0.9999	0.9998	0.9993	0.9978	0.9941	0.9861	0.9698	0.9394	0.9249	0.8870	0.8029	0.6779	0.5693	0.5078	0.3026	0.1019
10	1.0000	1.0000	1.0000	1.0000	1.0000	1.0000	1.0000	1.0000	1.0000	1.0000	0.9998	0.9995	0.9986	0.9964	0.9902	0.9884	0.9802	0.9578	0.9141	0.8654	0.8327	0.6862	0.4312
11	1.0000	1.0000	1.0000	1.0000	1.0000	1.0000	1.0000	1.0000	1.0000	1.0000	1.0000	1.0000	1.0000	1.0000	1.0000	1.0000	1.0000	1.0000	1.0000	1.0000	1.0000	1.0000	1.0000

Cumulative binomial probabilities (continued)

n	x	0.050	0.100	0.150	1/6	0.200	0.250	0.300	1/3	0.350	0.400	0.450	0.500	0.550	0.600	0.650	2/3	0.700	0.750	0.800	5/6	0.850	0.900	0.950
12	0	0.5404	0.2824	0.1422	0.1122	0.0687	0.0317	0.0138	0.0077	0.0057	0.0022	0.0008	0.0002	0.0001	0.0000	0.0000	0.0000	0.0000						
	1	0.8816	0.6590	0.4435	0.3813	0.2749	0.1584	0.0850	0.0540	0.0424	0.0196	0.0083	0.0032	0.0011	0.0003	0.0001	0.0000	0.0000						
	2	0.9804	0.8891	0.7358	0.6774	0.5583	0.3907	0.2528	0.1811	0.1513	0.0834	0.0421	0.0193	0.0079	0.0028	0.0008	0.0005	0.0002	0.0000					
	3	0.9978	0.9744	0.9078	0.8748	0.7946	0.6488	0.4925	0.3931	0.3467	0.2253	0.1345	0.0730	0.0356	0.0153	0.0056	0.0039	0.0017	0.0004	0.0001	0.0000			
	4	0.9998	0.9957	0.9761	0.9636	0.9274	0.8424	0.7237	0.6315	0.5833	0.4382	0.3044	0.1938	0.1117	0.0573	0.0255	0.0188	0.0095	0.0028	0.0006	0.0002	0.0001	0.0000	
	5	1.0000	0.9995	0.9954	0.9921	0.9806	0.9456	0.8822	0.8223	0.7873	0.6652	0.5269	0.3872	0.2607	0.1582	0.0846	0.0664	0.0386	0.0143	0.0039	0.0013	0.0007	0.0001	
	6		0.9999	0.9993	0.9987	0.9961	0.9857	0.9614	0.9336	0.9154	0.8418	0.7393	0.6128	0.4731	0.3348	0.2127	0.1777	0.1178	0.0544	0.0194	0.0079	0.0046	0.0005	0.0000
	7		1.0000	0.9999	0.9998	0.9994	0.9972	0.9905	0.9812	0.9745	0.9427	0.8883	0.8062	0.6956	0.5618	0.4167	0.3685	0.2763	0.1576	0.0726	0.0364	0.0239	0.0043	0.0002
	8			1.0000	1.0000	0.9999	0.9996	0.9983	0.9961	0.9944	0.9847	0.9644	0.9270	0.8655	0.7747	0.6533	0.6069	0.5075	0.3512	0.2054	0.1252	0.0922	0.0256	0.0022
	9					1.0000	1.0000	0.9998	0.9995	0.9992	0.9972	0.9921	0.9807	0.9579	0.9166	0.8487	0.8189	0.7472	0.6093	0.4417	0.3226	0.2642	0.1109	0.0196
	10							1.0000	1.0000	0.9999	0.9997	0.9989	0.9968	0.9917	0.9804	0.9576	0.9460	0.9150	0.8416	0.7251	0.6187	0.5565	0.3410	0.1184
	11									1.0000	1.0000	0.9999	0.9998	0.9992	0.9978	0.9943	0.9923	0.9862	0.9683	0.9313	0.8878	0.8578	0.7176	0.4596
	12											1.0000	1.0000	1.0000	1.0000	1.0000	1.0000	1.0000	1.0000	1.0000	1.0000	1.0000	1.0000	1.0000
13	0	0.5133	0.2542	0.1209	0.0935	0.0550	0.0238	0.0097	0.0051	0.0037	0.0013	0.0004	0.0001	0.0000	0.0000	0.0000	0.0000	0.0000						
	1	0.8646	0.6213	0.3983	0.3365	0.2336	0.1267	0.0637	0.0385	0.0296	0.0126	0.0049	0.0017	0.0005	0.0001	0.0000	0.0000	0.0000						
	2	0.9755	0.8661	0.6920	0.6281	0.5017	0.3326	0.2025	0.1387	0.1132	0.0579	0.0269	0.0112	0.0041	0.0013	0.0003	0.0002	0.0001	0.0000					
	3	0.9969	0.9658	0.8820	0.8419	0.7473	0.5843	0.4206	0.3224	0.2783	0.1686	0.0929	0.0461	0.0203	0.0078	0.0025	0.0016	0.0007	0.0001	0.0000				
	4	0.9997	0.9935	0.9658	0.9488	0.9009	0.7940	0.6543	0.5520	0.5005	0.3530	0.2279	0.1334	0.0698	0.0321	0.0126	0.0088	0.0040	0.0010	0.0002	0.0000	0.0000		
	5	1.0000	0.9991	0.9925	0.9873	0.9700	0.9198	0.8346	0.7587	0.7159	0.5744	0.4268	0.2905	0.1788	0.0977	0.0462	0.0347	0.0182	0.0056	0.0012	0.0003	0.0002	0.0000	
	6		0.9999	0.9987	0.9976	0.9930	0.9757	0.9376	0.8965	0.8705	0.7712	0.6437	0.5000	0.3563	0.2288	0.1295	0.1035	0.0624	0.0243	0.0070	0.0024	0.0013	0.0001	0.0000
	7		1.0000	0.9998	0.9997	0.9988	0.9944	0.9818	0.9653	0.9538	0.9023	0.8212	0.7095	0.5732	0.4256	0.2841	0.2413	0.1654	0.0802	0.0300	0.0127	0.0075	0.0009	0.0000
	8			1.0000	1.0000	0.9998	0.9990	0.9960	0.9912	0.9874	0.9679	0.9302	0.8666	0.7721	0.6470	0.4995	0.4480	0.3457	0.2060	0.0991	0.0512	0.0342	0.0065	0.0003
	9					1.0000	0.9999	0.9993	0.9984	0.9975	0.9922	0.9797	0.9539	0.9071	0.8314	0.7217	0.6776	0.5794	0.4157	0.2527	0.1581	0.1180	0.0342	0.0031
	10						1.0000	0.9999	0.9998	0.9997	0.9987	0.9959	0.9888	0.9731	0.9421	0.8868	0.8613	0.7975	0.6674	0.4983	0.3719	0.3080	0.1339	0.0245
	11							1.0000	1.0000	1.0000	0.9999	0.9995	0.9983	0.9951	0.9874	0.9704	0.9615	0.9363	0.8733	0.7664	0.6635	0.6017	0.3787	0.1354
	12										1.0000	1.0000	0.9999	0.9996	0.9987	0.9963	0.9949	0.9903	0.9762	0.9450	0.9065	0.8791	0.7458	0.4867
	13												1.0000	1.0000	1.0000	1.0000	1.0000	1.0000	1.0000	1.0000	1.0000	1.0000	1.0000	1.0000
14	0	0.4877	0.2288	0.1028	0.0779	0.0440	0.0178	0.0068	0.0034	0.0024	0.0008	0.0002	0.0001	0.0000	0.0000	0.0000	0.0000							
	1	0.8470	0.5846	0.3567	0.2960	0.1979	0.1010	0.0475	0.0274	0.0205	0.0081	0.0029	0.0009	0.0003	0.0001	0.0000	0.0000							
	2	0.9699	0.8416	0.6479	0.5795	0.4481	0.2811	0.1608	0.1053	0.0839	0.0398	0.0170	0.0065	0.0022	0.0006	0.0001	0.0001	0.0000						
	3	0.9958	0.9559	0.8535	0.8063	0.6982	0.5213	0.3552	0.2612	0.2205	0.1243	0.0632	0.0287	0.0114	0.0039	0.0011	0.0007	0.0002	0.0000					
	4	0.9996	0.9908	0.9533	0.9310	0.8702	0.7415	0.5842	0.4755	0.4227	0.2793	0.1672	0.0898	0.0426	0.0175	0.0060	0.0040	0.0017	0.0003	0.0000				
	5	1.0000	0.9985	0.9885	0.9809	0.9561	0.8883	0.7805	0.6898	0.6405	0.4859	0.3373	0.2120	0.1189	0.0583	0.0243	0.0174	0.0083	0.0022	0.0004	0.0001	0.0000		
	6		0.9998	0.9978	0.9959	0.9884	0.9617	0.9067	0.8505	0.8164	0.6925	0.5461	0.3953	0.2586	0.1501	0.0753	0.0576	0.0315	0.0103	0.0024	0.0007	0.0003	0.0000	
	7		1.0000	0.9997	0.9993	0.9976	0.9897	0.9685	0.9424	0.9247	0.8499	0.7414	0.6047	0.4539	0.3075	0.1836	0.1495	0.0933	0.0383	0.0116	0.0041	0.0022	0.0002	0.0000
	8			1.0000	0.9999	0.9996	0.9978	0.9917	0.9826	0.9757	0.9417	0.8811	0.7880	0.6627	0.5141	0.3595	0.3102	0.2195	0.1117	0.0439	0.0191	0.0115	0.0015	0.0000
	9				1.0000	1.0000	0.9997	0.9983	0.9960	0.9940	0.9825	0.9574	0.9102	0.8328	0.7207	0.5773	0.5245	0.4158	0.2585	0.1298	0.0690	0.0467	0.0092	0.0004
	10						1.0000	0.9998	0.9993	0.9989	0.9961	0.9886	0.9713	0.9368	0.8757	0.7795	0.7388	0.6448	0.4787	0.3018	0.1937	0.1465	0.0441	0.0042
	11							1.0000	0.9999	0.9999	0.9994	0.9978	0.9935	0.9830	0.9602	0.9161	0.8947	0.8392	0.7189	0.5519	0.4205	0.3521	0.1584	0.0301
	12								1.0000	1.0000	0.9999	0.9997	0.9991	0.9971	0.9919	0.9795	0.9726	0.9525	0.8990	0.8021	0.7040	0.6433	0.4154	0.1530
	13										1.0000	1.0000	0.9999	0.9998	0.9992	0.9976	0.9966	0.9932	0.9822	0.9560	0.9221	0.8972	0.7712	0.5123
	14												1.0000	1.0000	1.0000	1.0000	1.0000	1.0000	1.0000	1.0000	1.0000	1.0000	1.0000	1.0000

OCR (MEI) S1 — STATISTICAL TABLES

Cumulative binomial probabilities (continued)

Cumulative binomial probabilities, with p across the top:

n	x	0.050	0.100	0.150	1/6	0.200	0.250	0.300	1/3	0.350	0.400	0.450	0.500	0.550	0.600	0.650	2/3	0.700	0.750	0.800	5/6	0.850	0.900	0.950
15	0	0.4633	0.2059	0.0874	0.0649	0.0352	0.0134	0.0047	0.0023	0.0016	0.0005	0.0001	0.0000	0.0000										
	1	0.8290	0.5490	0.3186	0.2595	0.1671	0.0802	0.0353	0.0194	0.0142	0.0052	0.0017	0.0005	0.0001	0.0000	0.0000								
	2	0.9638	0.8159	0.6042	0.5322	0.3980	0.2361	0.1268	0.0794	0.0617	0.0271	0.0107	0.0037	0.0011	0.0003	0.0001	0.0000	0.0000						
	3	0.9945	0.9444	0.8227	0.7685	0.6482	0.4613	0.2969	0.2092	0.1727	0.0905	0.0424	0.0176	0.0063	0.0019	0.0005	0.0003	0.0001	0.0000					
	4	0.9994	0.9873	0.9383	0.9102	0.8358	0.6865	0.5155	0.4041	0.3519	0.2173	0.1204	0.0592	0.0255	0.0093	0.0028	0.0018	0.0007	0.0001	0.0000				
	5	0.9999	0.9978	0.9832	0.9726	0.9389	0.8516	0.7216	0.6184	0.5643	0.4032	0.2608	0.1509	0.0769	0.0338	0.0124	0.0085	0.0037	0.0008	0.0001	0.0000	0.0000		
	6	1.0000	0.9997	0.9964	0.9934	0.9819	0.9434	0.8689	0.7970	0.7548	0.6098	0.4522	0.3036	0.1818	0.0950	0.0422	0.0308	0.0152	0.0042	0.0008	0.0002	0.0001		
	7		1.0000	0.9994	0.9987	0.9958	0.9827	0.9500	0.9118	0.8868	0.7869	0.6535	0.5000	0.3465	0.2131	0.1132	0.0882	0.0500	0.0173	0.0042	0.0013	0.0006	0.0000	
	8			0.9999	0.9998	0.9992	0.9958	0.9848	0.9692	0.9578	0.9050	0.8182	0.6964	0.5478	0.3902	0.2452	0.2030	0.1311	0.0566	0.0181	0.0066	0.0036	0.0003	0.0000
	9			1.0000	1.0000	0.9999	0.9992	0.9963	0.9915	0.9876	0.9662	0.9231	0.8491	0.7392	0.5968	0.4357	0.3816	0.2784	0.1484	0.0611	0.0274	0.0168	0.0022	0.0001
	10					1.0000	0.9999	0.9993	0.9982	0.9972	0.9907	0.9745	0.9408	0.8796	0.7827	0.6481	0.5959	0.4845	0.3135	0.1642	0.0898	0.0617	0.0127	0.0006
	11						1.0000	0.9999	0.9997	0.9995	0.9981	0.9937	0.9824	0.9576	0.9095	0.8273	0.7908	0.7031	0.5387	0.3518	0.2315	0.1773	0.0556	0.0055
	12							1.0000	1.0000	0.9999	0.9997	0.9989	0.9963	0.9893	0.9729	0.9383	0.9206	0.8732	0.7639	0.6020	0.4678	0.3958	0.1841	0.0362
	13									1.0000	1.0000	0.9999	0.9995	0.9983	0.9948	0.9858	0.9806	0.9647	0.9198	0.8329	0.7404	0.6814	0.4510	0.1710
	14											1.0000	1.0000	0.9999	0.9995	0.9984	0.9977	0.9953	0.9866	0.9648	0.9351	0.9126	0.7941	0.5367
	15													1.0000	1.0000	1.0000	1.0000	1.0000	1.0000	1.0000	1.0000	1.0000	1.0000	1.0000
16	0	0.4401	0.1853	0.0743	0.0541	0.0281	0.0100	0.0033	0.0015	0.0010	0.0003	0.0001	0.0000											
	1	0.8108	0.5147	0.2839	0.2272	0.1407	0.0635	0.0261	0.0137	0.0098	0.0033	0.0010	0.0003	0.0001	0.0000									
	2	0.9571	0.7892	0.5614	0.4868	0.3518	0.1971	0.0994	0.0594	0.0451	0.0183	0.0066	0.0021	0.0006	0.0001	0.0000	0.0000							
	3	0.9930	0.9316	0.7899	0.7291	0.5981	0.4050	0.2459	0.1659	0.1339	0.0651	0.0281	0.0106	0.0035	0.0009	0.0002	0.0001	0.0000						
	4	0.9991	0.9830	0.9209	0.8866	0.7982	0.6302	0.4499	0.3391	0.2892	0.1666	0.0853	0.0384	0.0149	0.0049	0.0013	0.0008	0.0003	0.0000					
	5	0.9999	0.9967	0.9765	0.9622	0.9183	0.8103	0.6598	0.5469	0.4900	0.3288	0.1976	0.1051	0.0486	0.0191	0.0062	0.0040	0.0016	0.0003	0.0000				
	6	1.0000	0.9995	0.9944	0.9899	0.9733	0.9204	0.8247	0.7374	0.6881	0.5272	0.3660	0.2272	0.1241	0.0583	0.0229	0.0159	0.0071	0.0016	0.0002	0.0000	0.0000		
	7		0.9999	0.9989	0.9979	0.9930	0.9729	0.9256	0.8735	0.8406	0.7161	0.5629	0.4018	0.2559	0.1423	0.0671	0.0500	0.0257	0.0075	0.0015	0.0004	0.0002	0.0000	
	8		1.0000	0.9998	0.9996	0.9985	0.9925	0.9743	0.9500	0.9329	0.8577	0.7441	0.5982	0.4371	0.2839	0.1594	0.1265	0.0744	0.0271	0.0070	0.0021	0.0011	0.0001	
	9			1.0000	1.0000	0.9998	0.9984	0.9929	0.9841	0.9771	0.9417	0.8759	0.7728	0.6340	0.4728	0.3119	0.2626	0.1753	0.0796	0.0267	0.0101	0.0056	0.0005	0.0000
	10					1.0000	0.9997	0.9984	0.9960	0.9938	0.9809	0.9514	0.8949	0.8024	0.6712	0.5100	0.4531	0.3402	0.1897	0.0817	0.0378	0.0235	0.0033	0.0001
	11						1.0000	0.9997	0.9992	0.9987	0.9951	0.9851	0.9616	0.9147	0.8334	0.7108	0.6609	0.5501	0.3698	0.2018	0.1134	0.0791	0.0170	0.0009
	12							1.0000	0.9999	0.9998	0.9991	0.9965	0.9894	0.9719	0.9349	0.8661	0.8341	0.7541	0.5950	0.4019	0.2709	0.2101	0.0684	0.0070
	13								1.0000	1.0000	0.9999	0.9994	0.9979	0.9934	0.9817	0.9549	0.9406	0.9006	0.8029	0.6482	0.5132	0.4386	0.2108	0.0429
	14										1.0000	0.9999	0.9997	0.9990	0.9967	0.9902	0.9863	0.9739	0.9365	0.8593	0.7728	0.7161	0.4853	0.1892
	15											1.0000	1.0000	0.9999	0.9997	0.9990	0.9985	0.9967	0.9900	0.9719	0.9459	0.9257	0.8147	0.5599
	16													1.0000	1.0000	1.0000	1.0000	1.0000	1.0000	1.0000	1.0000	1.0000	1.0000	1.0000

Cumulative binomial probabilities (continued)

n		*p* 0.050	0.100	0.150	1/6	0.200	0.250	0.300	1/3	0.350	0.400	0.450	0.500	0.550	0.600	0.650	2/3	0.700	0.750	0.800	5/6	0.850	0.900	0.950
17	0	0.4181	0.1668	0.0631	0.0451	0.0225	0.0075	0.0023	0.0010	0.0007	0.0002	0.0000	0.0000											
	1	0.7922	0.4818	0.2525	0.1983	0.1182	0.0501	0.0193	0.0096	0.0067	0.0021	0.0006	0.0001	0.0000	0.0000									
	2	0.9497	0.7618	0.5198	0.4435	0.3096	0.1637	0.0774	0.0442	0.0327	0.0123	0.0041	0.0012	0.0003	0.0001	0.0000								
	3	0.9912	0.9174	0.7556	0.6887	0.5489	0.3530	0.2019	0.1304	0.1028	0.0464	0.0184	0.0064	0.0019	0.0005	0.0001	0.0000	0.0000						
	4	0.9988	0.9779	0.9013	0.8604	0.7582	0.5739	0.3887	0.2814	0.2348	0.1260	0.0596	0.0245	0.0086	0.0025	0.0006	0.0003	0.0001	0.0000					
	5	0.9999	0.9953	0.9681	0.9496	0.8943	0.7653	0.5968	0.4777	0.4197	0.2639	0.1471	0.0717	0.0301	0.0106	0.0030	0.0019	0.0007	0.0001	0.0000				
	6	1.0000	0.9992	0.9917	0.9853	0.9623	0.8929	0.7752	0.6739	0.6188	0.4478	0.2902	0.1662	0.0826	0.0348	0.0120	0.0080	0.0032	0.0006	0.0001	0.0000			
	7		0.9999	0.9983	0.9965	0.9891	0.9598	0.8954	0.8281	0.7872	0.6405	0.4743	0.3145	0.1834	0.0919	0.0383	0.0273	0.0127	0.0031	0.0005	0.0001	0.0000		
	8		1.0000	0.9997	0.9993	0.9974	0.9876	0.9597	0.9245	0.9006	0.8011	0.6626	0.5000	0.3374	0.1989	0.0994	0.0755	0.0403	0.0124	0.0026	0.0007	0.0003	0.0000	
	9			1.0000	0.9999	0.9995	0.9969	0.9873	0.9727	0.9617	0.9081	0.8166	0.6855	0.5257	0.3595	0.2128	0.1719	0.1046	0.0402	0.0109	0.0035	0.0017	0.0001	
	10				1.0000	0.9999	0.9994	0.9968	0.9920	0.9880	0.9652	0.9174	0.8338	0.7098	0.5522	0.3812	0.3261	0.2248	0.1071	0.0377	0.0147	0.0083	0.0008	0.0000
	11					1.0000	0.9999	0.9993	0.9981	0.9970	0.9894	0.9699	0.9283	0.8529	0.7361	0.5803	0.5223	0.4032	0.2347	0.1057	0.0504	0.0319	0.0047	0.0001
	12						1.0000	0.9999	0.9997	0.9994	0.9975	0.9914	0.9755	0.9404	0.8740	0.7652	0.7186	0.6113	0.4261	0.2418	0.1396	0.0987	0.0221	0.0012
	13							1.0000	1.0000	0.9999	0.9995	0.9981	0.9936	0.9816	0.9536	0.8972	0.8696	0.7981	0.6470	0.4511	0.3113	0.2444	0.0826	0.0088
	14									1.0000	0.9999	0.9997	0.9988	0.9959	0.9877	0.9673	0.9558	0.9226	0.8363	0.6904	0.5565	0.4802	0.2382	0.0503
	15										1.0000	1.0000	0.9999	0.9994	0.9979	0.9933	0.9904	0.9807	0.9499	0.8818	0.8017	0.7475	0.5182	0.2078
	16												1.0000	1.0000	0.9998	0.9993	0.9990	0.9977	0.9925	0.9775	0.9549	0.9369	0.8332	0.5819
	17														1.0000	1.0000	1.0000	1.0000	1.0000	1.0000	1.0000	1.0000	1.0000	1.0000
18	0	0.3972	0.1501	0.0536	0.0376	0.0180	0.0056	0.0016	0.0007	0.0004	0.0001	0.0000	0.0000											
	1	0.7735	0.4503	0.2241	0.1728	0.0991	0.0395	0.0142	0.0068	0.0046	0.0013	0.0003	0.0001	0.0000										
	2	0.9419	0.7338	0.4797	0.4027	0.2713	0.1353	0.0600	0.0326	0.0236	0.0082	0.0025	0.0007	0.0001	0.0000									
	3	0.9891	0.9018	0.7202	0.6479	0.5010	0.3057	0.1646	0.1017	0.0783	0.0328	0.0120	0.0038	0.0010	0.0002	0.0000	0.0000							
	4	0.9985	0.9718	0.8794	0.8318	0.7164	0.5187	0.3327	0.2311	0.1886	0.0942	0.0411	0.0154	0.0049	0.0013	0.0003	0.0001	0.0000						
	5	0.9998	0.9936	0.9581	0.9347	0.8671	0.7175	0.5344	0.4122	0.3550	0.2088	0.1077	0.0481	0.0183	0.0058	0.0014	0.0009	0.0003	0.0000					
	6	1.0000	0.9988	0.9882	0.9794	0.9487	0.8610	0.7217	0.6085	0.5491	0.3743	0.2258	0.1189	0.0537	0.0203	0.0062	0.0039	0.0014	0.0002	0.0000				
	7		0.9998	0.9973	0.9947	0.9837	0.9431	0.8593	0.7767	0.7283	0.5634	0.3915	0.2403	0.1280	0.0576	0.0212	0.0144	0.0061	0.0012	0.0002	0.0000	0.0000		
	8		1.0000	0.9995	0.9989	0.9957	0.9807	0.9404	0.8924	0.8609	0.7368	0.5778	0.4073	0.2527	0.1347	0.0597	0.0433	0.0210	0.0054	0.0009	0.0002	0.0001		
	9			0.9999	0.9998	0.9991	0.9946	0.9790	0.9567	0.9403	0.8653	0.7473	0.5927	0.4222	0.2632	0.1391	0.1076	0.0596	0.0193	0.0043	0.0011	0.0005	0.0000	
	10			1.0000	1.0000	0.9998	0.9988	0.9939	0.9856	0.9788	0.9424	0.8720	0.7597	0.6085	0.4366	0.2717	0.2233	0.1407	0.0569	0.0163	0.0053	0.0027	0.0002	
	11					1.0000	0.9998	0.9986	0.9961	0.9938	0.9797	0.9463	0.8811	0.7742	0.6257	0.4509	0.3915	0.2783	0.1390	0.0513	0.0206	0.0118	0.0012	0.0000
	12						1.0000	0.9997	0.9991	0.9986	0.9942	0.9817	0.9519	0.8923	0.7912	0.6450	0.5878	0.4656	0.2825	0.1329	0.0653	0.0419	0.0064	0.0002
	13							1.0000	0.9999	0.9997	0.9987	0.9951	0.9846	0.9589	0.9058	0.8114	0.7689	0.6673	0.4813	0.2836	0.1682	0.1206	0.0282	0.0015
	14								1.0000	1.0000	0.9998	0.9990	0.9962	0.9880	0.9672	0.9217	0.8983	0.8354	0.6943	0.4990	0.3521	0.2798	0.0982	0.0109
	15										1.0000	0.9999	0.9993	0.9975	0.9918	0.9764	0.9674	0.9400	0.8647	0.7287	0.5973	0.5203	0.2662	0.0581
	16											1.0000	0.9999	0.9997	0.9987	0.9954	0.9932	0.9858	0.9605	0.9009	0.8272	0.7759	0.5497	0.2265
	17												1.0000	1.0000	0.9999	0.9996	0.9993	0.9984	0.9944	0.9820	0.9624	0.9464	0.8499	0.6028
	18														1.0000	1.0000	1.0000	1.0000	1.0000	1.0000	1.0000	1.0000	1.0000	1.0000

Cumulative binomial probabilities (continued)

Cumulative binomial probabilities $P(X \le x)$, where the top row gives the value of p.

n = 19

x	0.050	0.100	0.150	1/6	0.200	0.250	0.300	1/3	0.350	0.400	0.450	0.500	0.550	0.600	0.650	2/3	0.700	0.750	0.800	5/6	0.850	0.900	0.950
0	0.3774	0.1351	0.0456	0.0313	0.0144	0.0042	0.0011	0.0005	0.0003	0.0001	0.0000												
1	0.7547	0.4203	0.1985	0.1502	0.0829	0.0310	0.0104	0.0047	0.0031	0.0008	0.0002	0.0000											
2	0.9335	0.7054	0.4413	0.3643	0.2369	0.1113	0.0462	0.0240	0.0170	0.0055	0.0015	0.0004	0.0001	0.0000									
3	0.9868	0.8850	0.6841	0.6070	0.4551	0.2631	0.1332	0.0787	0.0591	0.0230	0.0077	0.0022	0.0005	0.0001	0.0000	0.0000							
4	0.9980	0.9648	0.8556	0.8011	0.6733	0.4654	0.2822	0.1879	0.1500	0.0696	0.0280	0.0096	0.0028	0.0006	0.0001	0.0001	0.0000						
5	0.9998	0.9914	0.9463	0.9176	0.8369	0.6678	0.4739	0.3519	0.2968	0.1629	0.0777	0.0318	0.0109	0.0031	0.0007	0.0004	0.0001	0.0000					
6	1.0000	0.9983	0.9837	0.9719	0.9324	0.8251	0.6655	0.5431	0.4812	0.3081	0.1727	0.0835	0.0342	0.0116	0.0031	0.0019	0.0006	0.0001					
7		0.9997	0.9959	0.9921	0.9767	0.9225	0.8180	0.7207	0.6656	0.4878	0.3169	0.1796	0.0871	0.0352	0.0114	0.0074	0.0028	0.0005	0.0000	0.0000			
8		1.0000	0.9992	0.9982	0.9933	0.9713	0.9161	0.8538	0.8145	0.6675	0.4940	0.3238	0.1841	0.0885	0.0347	0.0241	0.0105	0.0023	0.0003	0.0001	0.0000		
9			0.9999	0.9996	0.9984	0.9911	0.9674	0.9352	0.9125	0.8139	0.6710	0.5000	0.3290	0.1861	0.0875	0.0648	0.0326	0.0089	0.0016	0.0004	0.0001		
10			1.0000	0.9999	0.9997	0.9977	0.9895	0.9759	0.9653	0.9115	0.8159	0.6762	0.5060	0.3325	0.1855	0.1462	0.0839	0.0287	0.0067	0.0018	0.0008	0.0000	
11				1.0000	1.0000	0.9995	0.9972	0.9926	0.9886	0.9648	0.9129	0.8204	0.6831	0.5122	0.3344	0.2793	0.1820	0.0775	0.0233	0.0079	0.0041	0.0003	
12						0.9999	0.9994	0.9981	0.9969	0.9884	0.9658	0.9165	0.8273	0.6919	0.5188	0.4569	0.3345	0.1749	0.0676	0.0281	0.0163	0.0017	
13						1.0000	0.9999	0.9996	0.9993	0.9969	0.9891	0.9682	0.9223	0.8371	0.7032	0.6481	0.5261	0.3322	0.1631	0.0824	0.0537	0.0086	0.0002
14							1.0000	0.9999	0.9999	0.9994	0.9972	0.9904	0.9720	0.9304	0.8500	0.8121	0.7178	0.5346	0.3267	0.1989	0.1444	0.0352	0.0020
15								1.0000	1.0000	0.9999	0.9995	0.9978	0.9923	0.9770	0.9409	0.9213	0.8668	0.7369	0.5449	0.3930	0.3159	0.1150	0.0132
16										1.0000	0.9999	0.9996	0.9985	0.9945	0.9830	0.9760	0.9538	0.8887	0.7631	0.6357	0.5587	0.2946	0.0665
17											1.0000	1.0000	0.9998	0.9992	0.9969	0.9953	0.9896	0.9690	0.9171	0.8498	0.8015	0.5797	0.2453
18													1.0000	0.9999	0.9997	0.9995	0.9989	0.9958	0.9856	0.9687	0.9544	0.8649	0.6226
19														1.0000	1.0000	1.0000	1.0000	1.0000	1.0000	1.0000	1.0000	1.0000	1.0000

n = 20

x	0.050	0.100	0.150	1/6	0.200	0.250	0.300	1/3	0.350	0.400	0.450	0.500	0.550	0.600	0.650	2/3	0.700	0.750	0.800	5/6	0.850	0.900	0.950
0	0.3585	0.1216	0.0388	0.0261	0.0115	0.0032	0.0008	0.0003	0.0002	0.0000	0.0000												
1	0.7358	0.3917	0.1756	0.1304	0.0692	0.0243	0.0076	0.0033	0.0021	0.0005	0.0001	0.0000											
2	0.9245	0.6769	0.4049	0.3287	0.2061	0.0913	0.0355	0.0176	0.0121	0.0036	0.0009	0.0002	0.0000										
3	0.9841	0.8670	0.6477	0.5665	0.4114	0.2252	0.1071	0.0604	0.0444	0.0160	0.0049	0.0013	0.0003	0.0000									
4	0.9974	0.9568	0.8298	0.7687	0.6296	0.4148	0.2375	0.1515	0.1182	0.0510	0.0189	0.0059	0.0015	0.0003	0.0000	0.0000							
5	0.9997	0.9887	0.9327	0.8982	0.8042	0.6172	0.4164	0.2972	0.2454	0.1256	0.0553	0.0207	0.0064	0.0016	0.0003	0.0002	0.0000						
6	1.0000	0.9976	0.9781	0.9629	0.9133	0.7858	0.6080	0.4793	0.4166	0.2500	0.1299	0.0577	0.0214	0.0065	0.0015	0.0009	0.0003						
7		0.9996	0.9941	0.9887	0.9679	0.8982	0.7723	0.6615	0.6010	0.4159	0.2520	0.1316	0.0580	0.0210	0.0060	0.0037	0.0013	0.0002	0.0000				
8		0.9999	0.9987	0.9972	0.9900	0.9591	0.8867	0.8095	0.7624	0.5956	0.4143	0.2517	0.1308	0.0565	0.0196	0.0130	0.0051	0.0009	0.0001	0.0000			
9		1.0000	0.9998	0.9994	0.9974	0.9861	0.9520	0.9081	0.8782	0.7553	0.5914	0.4119	0.2493	0.1275	0.0532	0.0376	0.0171	0.0039	0.0006	0.0001	0.0000		
10			1.0000	0.9999	0.9994	0.9961	0.9829	0.9624	0.9468	0.8725	0.7507	0.5881	0.4086	0.2447	0.1218	0.0919	0.0480	0.0139	0.0026	0.0006	0.0002	0.0000	
11				1.0000	0.9999	0.9991	0.9949	0.9870	0.9804	0.9435	0.8692	0.7483	0.5857	0.4044	0.2376	0.1905	0.1133	0.0409	0.0100	0.0028	0.0013	0.0001	
12					1.0000	0.9998	0.9987	0.9963	0.9940	0.9790	0.9420	0.8684	0.7480	0.5841	0.3990	0.3385	0.2277	0.1018	0.0321	0.0113	0.0059	0.0004	
13						1.0000	0.9997	0.9991	0.9985	0.9935	0.9786	0.9423	0.8701	0.7500	0.5834	0.5207	0.3920	0.2142	0.0867	0.0371	0.0219	0.0024	0.0000
14							1.0000	0.9998	0.9997	0.9984	0.9936	0.9793	0.9447	0.8744	0.7546	0.7028	0.5836	0.3828	0.1958	0.1018	0.0673	0.0113	0.0003
15								1.0000	1.0000	0.9997	0.9985	0.9941	0.9811	0.9490	0.8818	0.8485	0.7625	0.5852	0.3704	0.2313	0.1702	0.0432	0.0026
16										1.0000	0.9997	0.9987	0.9951	0.9840	0.9556	0.9396	0.8929	0.7748	0.5886	0.4335	0.3523	0.1330	0.0159
17											1.0000	0.9998	0.9991	0.9964	0.9879	0.9824	0.9645	0.9087	0.7939	0.6713	0.5951	0.3231	0.0755
18												1.0000	0.9999	0.9995	0.9979	0.9967	0.9924	0.9757	0.9308	0.8696	0.8244	0.6083	0.2642
19													1.0000	1.0000	0.9998	0.9997	0.9992	0.9968	0.9885	0.9739	0.9612	0.8784	0.6415
20															1.0000	1.0000	1.0000	1.0000	1.0000	1.0000	1.0000	1.0000	1.0000

Vectors

'Vector' might sound like a really dull Bond villain, but... well, it's not. Vectors have both size (or <u>magnitude</u>) and <u>direction</u>. If a measurement just has size but not direction, it's called a <u>scalar</u>.   - So, Vector, you expect me to talk?
   - No, Mr Bond, I expect you to die! Ak ak ak!

Vectors have Magnitude and Direction — Scalars only have Magnitude

<u>Vectors</u>: velocity, displacement, acceleration, force. E.g: a train heading due east at 16 ms⁻¹.

<u>Scalars</u>: speed, distance. E.g. a car travelling at 4 ms⁻¹.

A really important thing to remember is that an object's speed and velocity <u>aren't always the same</u>:

EXAMPLE   A runner sprints 100 m along a track at a speed of 8 ms⁻¹ and then she jogs back 50 m at 4 ms⁻¹.

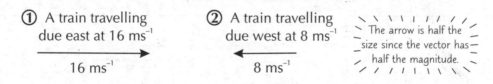

Average <u>Speed</u>

Speed = Distance ÷ Time

The runner takes (100 ÷ 8) + (50 ÷ 4) = 25 s to travel **150 m**.

So the average speed is 150 ÷ 25 = 6 ms⁻¹

Average <u>Velocity</u>

Velocity = Change in displacement ÷ Time

In total, the runner ends up **50 m** away from her start point and it takes 25 s.

So the average velocity is 50 ÷ 25 = 2 ms⁻¹ in the direction of the sprint.

She jogged back 50 m after she jogged forward 100 m.

The Length of the Arrow shows the Magnitude of a Vector

You can draw vectors as arrows where the <u>length</u> shows the <u>magnitude</u>:

① A train travelling due east at 16 ms⁻¹

    16 ms⁻¹

② A train travelling due west at 8 ms⁻¹

    8 ms⁻¹

The arrow is half the size since the vector has half the magnitude.

You can add vectors together by drawing the arrows <u>nose to tail</u>.
The single vector that goes from the start to the end of the vectors is called the <u>resultant</u> vector.

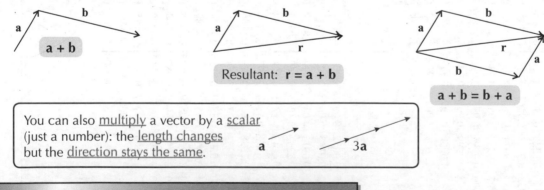

a + b

Resultant: **r = a + b**

a + b = b + a

You can also <u>multiply</u> a vector by a <u>scalar</u> (just a number): the <u>length changes</u> but the <u>direction stays the same</u>.

   a   **3a**

Vectors can be described using i + j Units

You can <u>describe</u> vectors using the <u>unit vectors</u> **i** + **j**. They're called unit vectors because they each have a <u>magnitude of 1</u> and a <u>direction</u>. **i** is in the direction of the <u>x-axis</u> (horizontal or east), and **j** is in the direction of the <u>y-axis</u> (vertical or north).

E.g. $\overrightarrow{AB}$ = 5**i** + 4**j** :

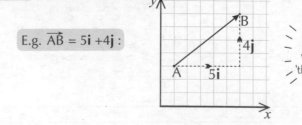

$\overrightarrow{AB}$ is just another way of writing a vector — it means 'the displacement of B from A'.

Vectors

Position Vectors Describe Where a Point Lies

You can use a vector to describe the <u>position of a point</u>, in relation to the <u>origin, O</u>.

The <u>position vector</u> of point <u>A</u> is $\overrightarrow{OA}$. It's usually called <u>vector **a**</u>.

The <u>position vector</u> of point <u>B</u> is $\overrightarrow{OB}$. It's usually called <u>vector **b**</u>.

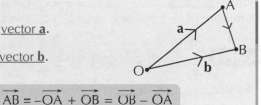

You can write other vectors in terms of position vectors: $\overrightarrow{AB} = -\overrightarrow{OA} + \overrightarrow{OB} = \overrightarrow{OB} - \overrightarrow{OA}$
$$= -\mathbf{a} + \mathbf{b} = \mathbf{b} - \mathbf{a}$$

Then there are Column Vectors

1) If writing **i**'s and **j**'s gets a bit much for your wrists, you can use <u>column vectors</u> instead. ⟶ $x\mathbf{i} + y\mathbf{j} = \begin{pmatrix} x \\ y \end{pmatrix}$

2) <u>Calculating</u> with them is a breeze. Just add or subtract the <u>top row</u>, then add or subtract the <u>bottom row</u> separately.

$$\mathbf{a} = 5\mathbf{i} + 7\mathbf{j} = \begin{pmatrix} 5 \\ 7 \end{pmatrix} \quad \mathbf{b} = 4\mathbf{i} + \mathbf{j} = \begin{pmatrix} 4 \\ 1 \end{pmatrix}$$
$$\overrightarrow{AB} = \mathbf{b} - \mathbf{a} = \begin{pmatrix} 4 \\ 1 \end{pmatrix} - \begin{pmatrix} 5 \\ 7 \end{pmatrix} = \begin{pmatrix} -1 \\ -6 \end{pmatrix}$$

3) When you're <u>multiplying</u> a column vector by a <u>scalar</u>, you multiply <u>each number</u> in the column vector by the scalar.

$$2\mathbf{b} - 3\mathbf{a} = 2\begin{pmatrix} 4 \\ 1 \end{pmatrix} - 3\begin{pmatrix} 5 \\ 7 \end{pmatrix} = \begin{pmatrix} 8 \\ 2 \end{pmatrix} - \begin{pmatrix} 15 \\ 21 \end{pmatrix} = \begin{pmatrix} -7 \\ -19 \end{pmatrix}$$

You Can Have Vectors in Three Dimensions Too

1) Imagine that the x- and y-axes lie <u>flat</u> on the page. Then imagine a <u>third axis</u> sticking <u>straight through</u> the page at right angles to it — this is the <u>z-axis</u>.

2) The points in three dimensions are given <u>(x, y, z) coordinates</u>.

3) When you're talking vectors, **k** is the <u>unit vector</u> in the direction of the <u>z-axis</u>.

4) You can write three-dimensional vectors as <u>column vectors</u> like this: $x\mathbf{i} + y\mathbf{j} + z\mathbf{k} = \begin{pmatrix} x \\ y \\ z \end{pmatrix}$

5) So the <u>position vector</u> of <u>point Q</u> is: $2\mathbf{i} + 5\mathbf{j} + 4\mathbf{k} = \begin{pmatrix} 2 \\ 5 \\ 4 \end{pmatrix}$

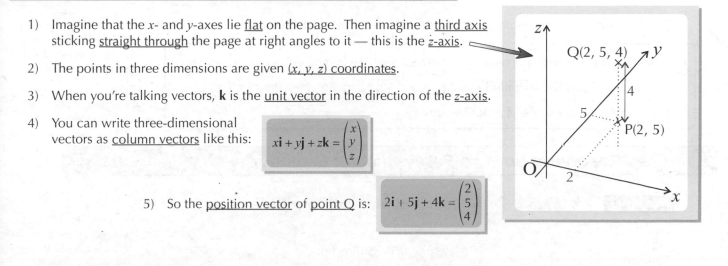

I've got B + Q units in my kitchen...

Three dimensions doesn't really make things much more difficult — it just gives you an extra number to calculate with.
You add, subtract and multiply 3D column vectors in the <u>same way</u> as 2D ones — you just have three rows to deal with.

Vectors

Resolving means writing a vector as **Component Vectors**

Splitting a vector up like this means you can work things out with <u>one component at a time</u>.
When <u>adding</u> vectors to get a <u>resultant vector</u>, it's easier to <u>add</u> the <u>horizontal</u> and <u>vertical</u>
components <u>separately</u>. So you <u>split</u> the vector into components first — this is <u>resolving</u>.
If the vectors are in **i** + **j** notation <u>already</u>, you don't need to split them up — just add the **i** and **j**'s:

EXAMPLE $\overrightarrow{AB} = 3\mathbf{i} + 2\mathbf{j}$ and $\overrightarrow{BC} = 5\mathbf{i} - 3\mathbf{j}$. Work out $\overrightarrow{AC}$.

Add the horizontal and vertical components <u>separately</u>.

$\overrightarrow{AC} = \overrightarrow{AB} + \overrightarrow{BC} = (3\mathbf{i} + 2\mathbf{j}) + (5\mathbf{i} - 3\mathbf{j}) = 8\mathbf{i} - \mathbf{j}$

Use **Trig** and **Pythagoras** to **Change** a vector into **Component Form**

EXAMPLE   The speed of a ball is 5 ms⁻¹ at an angle of 30° to the horizontal.
Find the horizontal and vertical components of the ball's velocity, **v**.

First, draw a diagram
and make a
right-angle triangle:

Using trigonometry, we can find x and y:

$\cos 30° = \dfrac{x}{5}$ so $x = 5\cos30°$

$\sin 30° = \dfrac{y}{5}$ so $y = 5\sin30°$

So $\mathbf{v} = (5\cos30°\mathbf{i} + 5\sin30°\mathbf{j})$ ms⁻¹

EXAMPLE   The acceleration of a body is given by the vector $\mathbf{a} = 6\mathbf{i} - 2\mathbf{j}$.
Find the magnitude and direction of the acceleration.

Start with a diagram again. Remember, the y-component "–2" means "down 2".

Using Pythagoras' theorem, you can
work out the magnitude of **a**:

$a^2 = 6^2 + (-2)^2 = 40$

so $a = \sqrt{40} = 6.32$ (to 3 s.f.)

Use trigonometry to
work out the angle:

$\tan\theta = \dfrac{2}{6}$ so $\tan\theta = \tan^{-1}\left(\dfrac{2}{6}\right) = 18.4°$

So vector **a** has magnitude 6.32 and direction 18.4° below the horizontal.

In general, a vector **r** with magnitude r and direction θ can be written as $r\cos\theta\mathbf{i} + r\sin\theta\mathbf{j}$

The vector $\mathbf{r} = x\mathbf{i} + y\mathbf{j}$ has magnitude $r = |\mathbf{r}| = \sqrt{x^2 + y^2}$ and direction $\theta = \tan^{-1}\left(\dfrac{y}{x}\right)$

In three dimensions, $\mathbf{r} = x\mathbf{i} + y\mathbf{j} + z\mathbf{k}$ has magnitude $r = |\mathbf{r}| = \sqrt{x^2 + y^2 + z^2}$.

*The angle θ is usually
measured between the
vector and the horizontal.*

*The magnitude of a vector
a is denoted |a| or a.*

You can **Resolve** in any two **Perpendicular Directions** — not just x and y

EXAMPLE   Find the resultant of the forces shown in the diagram.

Resolving in ⬉ direction: 3 N – 3 N = 0

Resolving in ⬈ direction: 5 N – 2 N = 3 N

*The two forces of 3 N are
acting in opposite directions,
so you take one away from the
other — balancing them out.*

So the resultant force is 3 N in the direction of the 5 N force.

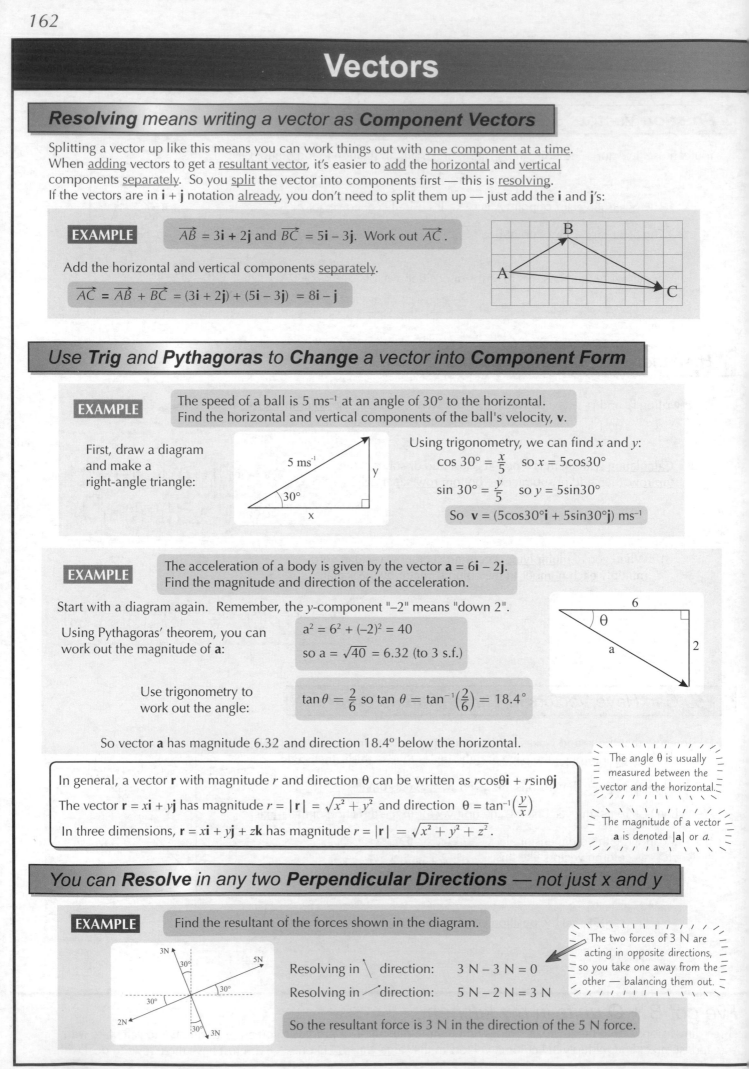

Vectors

Vectors are much more than just a pretty face (or arrow). Once you deal with all the waffle in the question, all sorts of problems involving <u>displacement</u>, <u>velocity</u>, <u>acceleration</u> and <u>forces</u> can be solved using vectors.

Draw a Diagram if there are Lots of Vectors floating around

In fact, draw a diagram when there are only a <u>couple</u> of vectors. But it's <u>vital</u> when there are lots of the little beggars.

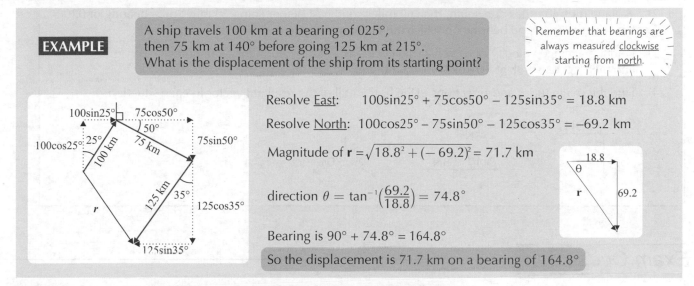

EXAMPLE

A ship travels 100 km at a bearing of 025°, then 75 km at 140° before going 125 km at 215°. What is the displacement of the ship from its starting point?

Remember that bearings are always measured <u>clockwise</u> starting from <u>north</u>.

Resolve <u>East</u>: $100\sin25° + 75\cos50° - 125\sin35° = 18.8$ km

Resolve <u>North</u>: $100\cos25° - 75\sin50° - 125\cos35° = -69.2$ km

Magnitude of $\mathbf{r} = \sqrt{18.8^2 + (-69.2)^2} = 71.7$ km

direction $\theta = \tan^{-1}\left(\frac{69.2}{18.8}\right) = 74.8°$

Bearing is $90° + 74.8° = 164.8°$

So the displacement is 71.7 km on a bearing of 164.8°

The Direction part of a vector is Really Important

...and that means that you've got to make sure your <u>diagram</u> is <u>spot on</u>. These two problems look similar, and the final answers are pretty similar too. But <u>look closely</u> at the diagrams and you will see they are a bit <u>different</u>.

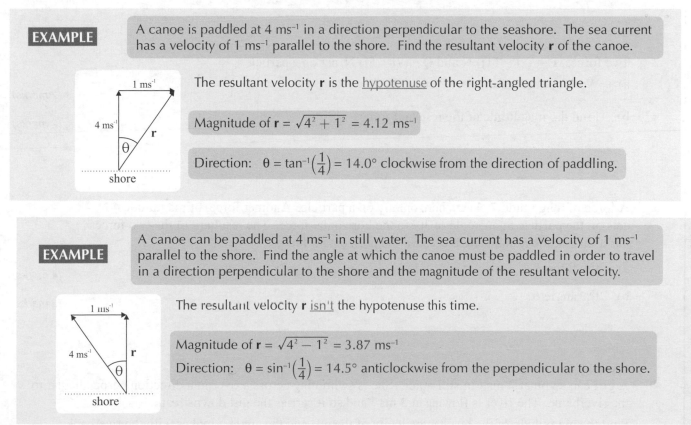

EXAMPLE

A canoe is paddled at 4 ms⁻¹ in a direction perpendicular to the seashore. The sea current has a velocity of 1 ms⁻¹ parallel to the shore. Find the resultant velocity $\mathbf{r}$ of the canoe.

The resultant velocity $\mathbf{r}$ is the <u>hypotenuse</u> of the right-angled triangle.

Magnitude of $\mathbf{r} = \sqrt{4^2 + 1^2} = 4.12$ ms⁻¹

Direction: $\theta = \tan^{-1}\left(\frac{1}{4}\right) = 14.0°$ clockwise from the direction of paddling.

EXAMPLE

A canoe can be paddled at 4 ms⁻¹ in still water. The sea current has a velocity of 1 ms⁻¹ parallel to the shore. Find the angle at which the canoe must be paddled in order to travel in a direction perpendicular to the shore and the magnitude of the resultant velocity.

The resultant velocity $\mathbf{r}$ <u>isn't</u> the hypotenuse this time.

Magnitude of $\mathbf{r} = \sqrt{4^2 - 1^2} = 3.87$ ms⁻¹

Direction: $\theta = \sin^{-1}\left(\frac{1}{4}\right) = 14.5°$ anticlockwise from the perpendicular to the shore.

Bet you can't say 'perpendicular' 10 times fast...

Next time you're baffled by vectors, just start <u>resolving</u> and Bob's your mother's brother.

M1 Section 1 — Practice Questions

Quite a nice little introduction to Mechanics, don't you think? You're going to be using vectors all the way through M1, so you need to make sure you're super cool with them.

Warm-up Questions

1) Find $\mathbf{a} + 2\mathbf{b} - 3\mathbf{c}$ where $\mathbf{a} = 3\mathbf{i} + 7\mathbf{j}$; $\mathbf{b} = -2\mathbf{i} + 2\mathbf{j}$; $\mathbf{c} = \mathbf{i} - 3\mathbf{j}$.

2) A plane flies 40 miles due south, then 60 miles southeast before going 70 miles on a bearing of 020°. Find the distance and bearing on which the plane must fly to return to its starting point.

3) Find the average velocity of a cyclist who cycles at 15 kmh⁻¹ north for 15 minutes and then cycles south at 10 kmh⁻¹ for 45 minutes.

4) Find the magnitudes and directions to the horizontal of the resultant vector in each situation.

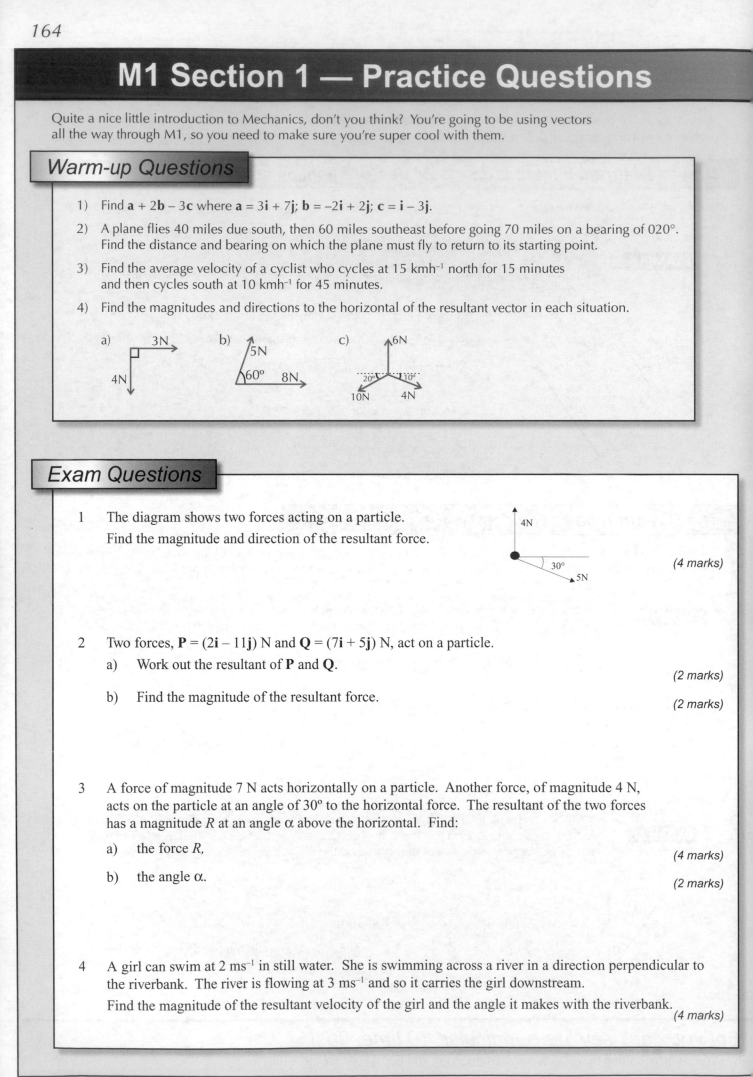

Exam Questions

1   The diagram shows two forces acting on a particle.
     Find the magnitude and direction of the resultant force.

     (4 marks)

2   Two forces, $\mathbf{P} = (2\mathbf{i} - 11\mathbf{j})$ N and $\mathbf{Q} = (7\mathbf{i} + 5\mathbf{j})$ N, act on a particle.
     a)   Work out the resultant of $\mathbf{P}$ and $\mathbf{Q}$.

     (2 marks)

     b)   Find the magnitude of the resultant force.

     (2 marks)

3   A force of magnitude 7 N acts horizontally on a particle. Another force, of magnitude 4 N, acts on the particle at an angle of 30° to the horizontal force. The resultant of the two forces has a magnitude R at an angle α above the horizontal. Find:

     a)   the force R,

     (4 marks)

     b)   the angle α.

     (2 marks)

4   A girl can swim at 2 ms⁻¹ in still water. She is swimming across a river in a direction perpendicular to the riverbank. The river is flowing at 3 ms⁻¹ and so it carries the girl downstream.
     Find the magnitude of the resultant velocity of the girl and the angle it makes with the riverbank.

     (4 marks)

Constant Acceleration Equations

Welcome to the technicolour world of Kinematics. Fashions may change, but there will <u>always</u> be M1 questions that involve objects travelling in a <u>straight line</u>. It's just a case of picking the right equations to solve the problem.

There are **Five Constant Acceleration Equations**

Examiners call these "<u>uvast</u>" questions (pronounced ewe-vast, like a large sheep) because of the five variables involved:

u = <u>initial velocity</u> (or <u>speed</u>) in ms⁻¹

v = <u>final velocity</u> (or <u>speed</u>) in ms⁻¹

a = <u>acceleration</u> in ms⁻²

s = <u>displacement</u> in m

t = <u>time</u> that passes in s (seconds)

The acceleration must be <u>constant</u>. <u>Displacement</u> is the distance between the start and end points of motion. It's not always the same as the <u>total distance</u> travelled.

The constant acceleration equations are:

$$v = u + at$$

$$s = ut + \tfrac{1}{2}at^2$$

$$s = \tfrac{1}{2}(u + v)t$$

$$v^2 = u^2 + 2as$$

$$s = vt - \tfrac{1}{2}at^2$$

Speed and distance are <u>scalar</u> quantities. Acceleration, velocity and displacement are <u>vector</u> quantities. See p. 160.

None of those equations are in the formula book, so you're going to have to <u>learn them</u>. Questions will usually give you <u>three variables</u> — your job is to choose the equation that will find you the missing <u>fourth variable</u>.

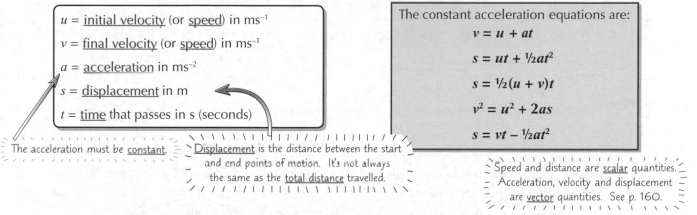

EXAMPLE

A jet ski travels in a straight line along a river. It passes under two bridges 200 m apart and is observed to be travelling at 5 ms⁻¹ under the first bridge and at 9 ms⁻¹ under the second bridge. Calculate its acceleration (assuming it is constant).

List the variables ("<u>uvast</u>"):

$u = 5$

$v = 9$ You have to work out a.

$a = a$

$s = 200$ You're not told about the time taken.

$t = t$

Choose the equation with u, v, s and a in it: $v^2 = u^2 + 2as$

<u>Substitute</u> values: $9^2 = 5^2 + (2 \times a \times 200)$

<u>Simplify</u>: $81 = 25 + 400a$

<u>Rearrange</u>: $400a = 81 - 25 = 56$

Then <u>solve</u>: $a = \dfrac{56}{400} = 0.14\,\text{ms}^{-2}$

Check you're using the right <u>units</u> — m, s, ms⁻¹ and ms⁻².

*Motion under Gravity just means taking **a = g**...*

Don't be put off by questions involving objects <u>moving freely under gravity</u> — they're just telling you the <u>acceleration is g</u>.

Use the value of g given on the front of the paper or in the question. If you don't, you risk losing a mark because your answer won't match the examiners' answer.

EXAMPLE

A pebble is dropped into a well 18 m deep and moves freely under gravity until it hits the bottom. Calculate the time it takes to reach the bottom. (Take g = 9.8 ms⁻².)

First, list the variables:

$u = 0$ Because the pebble was <u>dropped</u>, not thrown.

$v = v$

$a = 9.8$ $a = g = 9.8$ ms⁻², because it's falling freely.

$s = 18$

$t = t$

You need the equation with u, a, s and t in it: $s = ut + \tfrac{1}{2}at^2$

Substitute values: $18 = (0 \times t) + (\tfrac{1}{2} \times 9.8 \times t^2)$

Simplify: $18 = 4.9t^2$

Rearrange to give t^2: $t^2 = \dfrac{18}{4.9} = 3.67...$

Solve by square-rooting: $t = \sqrt{3.67...} = 1.92$ s

Watch out for tricky questions like this — at first it <u>looks like</u> they've only given you <u>one variable</u>. You have to spot that the pebble was <u>dropped</u> (so it started with no velocity) and that it's <u>moving freely under gravity</u>.

Constant Acceleration Equations

...or a = –g

EXAMPLE A ball is projected vertically upwards at 3 ms⁻¹ from a point 1.5 m above the ground.
How long does it take to reach its maximum height?
How fast will the ball be travelling when it hits the ground? (Take g = 9.8 ms⁻².)

First, list the variables, taking up as
the positive direction:

$u = 3$

When projected objects reach the top of their motion, they stop momentarily.

$v = 0$

$a = -9.8$

Because g always acts downwards and up was taken as positive, a is negative.

$s = s$

$t = ?$

s is negative as the ground is below the point of projection.

Use the equation with u, v, a and t in it: $v = u + at$

Substitute values: $0 = 3 + (-9.8 \times t)$

Simplify: $0 = 3 - 9.8t$

Rearrange and solve to find t: $t = \dfrac{3}{9.8} = 0.306$ s

To find the speed of the ball when it hits the ground consider the complete path of the ball.
$s = -1.5$ as it's the <u>displacement</u> from the ball's original position, not total distance travelled.

Using $v^2 = u^2 + 2as$ where $u = 3$, $v = ?$, $a = -9.8$, $s = -1.5$:
$v^2 = u^2 + 2as = 3^2 + 2(-9.8 \times -1.5) = 38.4$, so $v = \sqrt{38.4} = 6.20$ ms⁻¹ (to 3 s.f.)

Sometimes there's More Than One Object Moving at the Same Time

For these questions, t is often the same (or connected as in this example) because time ticks along for both objects at the same rate. The distance travelled might also be connected.

EXAMPLE A car, A, travelling along a straight road at a constant 30 ms⁻¹ passes point R at $t = 0$.
Exactly 2 seconds later, a second car, B, travelling at 25 ms⁻¹, moves in the same direction
from point R. Car B accelerates at a constant 2 ms⁻². Show that the two cars are level
when $t^2 - 9t - 46 = 0$, where t is the time taken by car A.

For each car, there are different "uvast" equations, so you write separate lists and separate equations.

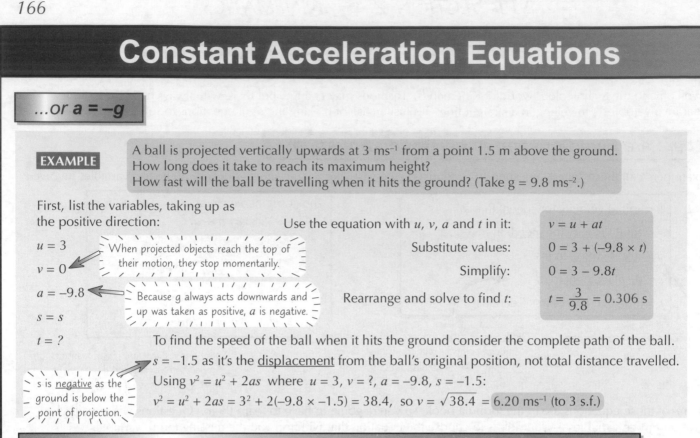

CAR A

Constant speed so $a_A = 0$

$u_A = 30$ $\quad v_A = 30$

$a_A = 0$ $\quad s_A = s$

$t_A = t$

CAR B

s is the same for both cars because they're level.

B starts moving 2 seconds after A passes point R.

$u_B = 25$ $\quad v_B = v$

$a_B = 2$ $\quad s_B = s$

$t_B = (t - 2)$

The two cars are level, so choose
an equation with s in it:

$$s = ut + \tfrac{1}{2}at^2$$

Substitute values: $s = 30t + (\tfrac{1}{2} \times 0 \times t^2)$

Simplify: $\mathbf{s = 30t}$

Use the same equation for car B: $s = ut + \tfrac{1}{2}at^2$

Substitute values: $s = 25(t - 2) + (\tfrac{1}{2} \times 2 \times (t - 2)^2)$

Simplify: $s = 25t - 50 + (t - 2)(t - 2)$

$s = 25t - 50 + (t^2 - 4t + 4)$

$\mathbf{s = t^2 + 21t - 46}$

The distance travelled by both cars is equal,
so put the expressions for s equal to each other:

$30t = t^2 + 21t - 46$

$t^2 - 9t - 46 = 0$

That's the result you were asked to find.

Constant acceleration questions involve <u>modelling assumptions</u> (simplifications to real life so you can use the equations):

1) <u>The object is a particle</u> — this just means it's very small and so isn't affected by air resistance as cars or stones would be in real life.

2) <u>Acceleration is constant</u> — without it, the equations couldn't be used.

As Socrates once said, "The unexamined life is not worth living"... *but what did he know...*

Make sure you: 1) Make a list of the uvast variables EVERY time you get one of these questions.

2) Look out for "hidden" values — e.g. "particle initially at rest…" means $u = 0$.

3) Choose and solve the equation that goes with the variables you've got.

Motion Graphs

You can use <u>displacement-time</u> (*x/t*), <u>velocity-time</u> (*v/t*) and <u>acceleration-time</u> (*a/t*) graphs to represent all sorts of motion.

Displacement-time Graphs: Height = Displacement and Gradient = Velocity

The <u>steeper</u> the line, the <u>greater</u> the velocity. A <u>horizontal</u> line has a <u>zero gradient</u>, so that means the object isn't moving.

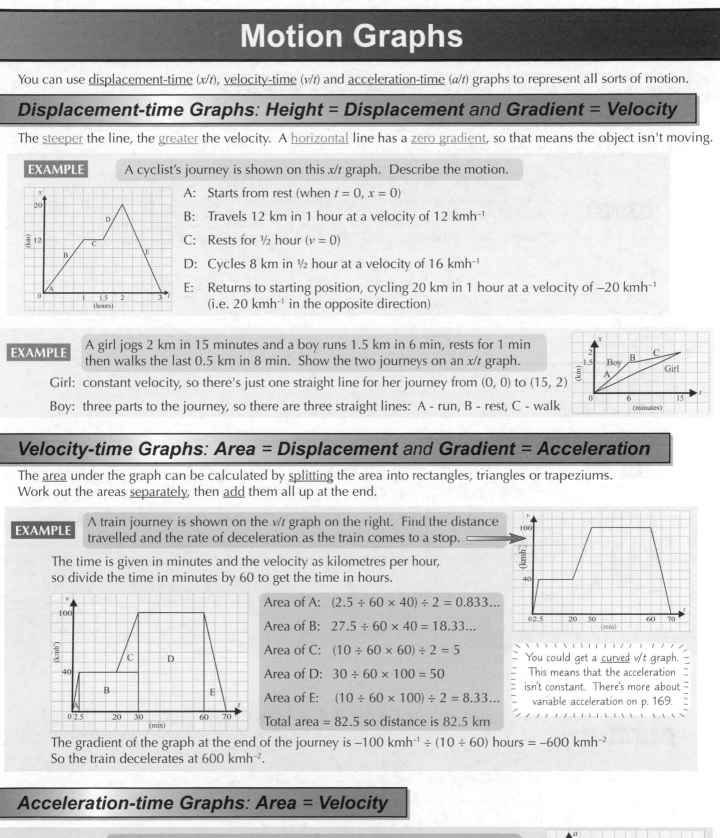

EXAMPLE   A cyclist's journey is shown on this *x/t* graph. Describe the motion.

A: Starts from rest (when $t = 0$, $x = 0$)

B: Travels 12 km in 1 hour at a velocity of 12 kmh⁻¹

C: Rests for ½ hour ($v = 0$)

D: Cycles 8 km in ½ hour at a velocity of 16 kmh⁻¹

E: Returns to starting position, cycling 20 km in 1 hour at a velocity of –20 kmh⁻¹ (i.e. 20 kmh⁻¹ in the opposite direction)

EXAMPLE   A girl jogs 2 km in 15 minutes and a boy runs 1.5 km in 6 min, rests for 1 min then walks the last 0.5 km in 8 min. Show the two journeys on an *x/t* graph.

Girl: constant velocity, so there's just one straight line for her journey from (0, 0) to (15, 2)

Boy: three parts to the journey, so there are three straight lines: A - run, B - rest, C - walk

Velocity-time Graphs: Area = Displacement and Gradient = Acceleration

The <u>area</u> under the graph can be calculated by <u>splitting</u> the area into rectangles, triangles or trapeziums. Work out the areas <u>separately</u>, then <u>add</u> them all up at the end.

EXAMPLE   A train journey is shown on the *v/t* graph on the right. Find the distance travelled and the rate of deceleration as the train comes to a stop.

The time is given in minutes and the velocity as kilometres per hour, so divide the time in minutes by 60 to get the time in hours.

Area of A: $(2.5 \div 60 \times 40) \div 2 = 0.833...$

Area of B: $27.5 \div 60 \times 40 = 18.33...$

Area of C: $(10 \div 60 \times 60) \div 2 = 5$

Area of D: $30 \div 60 \times 100 = 50$

Area of E: $(10 \div 60 \times 100) \div 2 = 8.33...$

Total area = 82.5 so distance is 82.5 km

You could get a <u>curved</u> v/t graph. This means that the acceleration isn't constant. There's more about variable acceleration on p. 169.

The gradient of the graph at the end of the journey is –100 kmh⁻¹ ÷ (10 ÷ 60) hours = –600 kmh⁻²
So the train decelerates at 600 kmh⁻².

Acceleration-time Graphs: Area = Velocity

EXAMPLE   The acceleration of a parachutist who jumps from a plane is modelled by the *a/t* graph on the right. Describe the motion of the parachutist and find her velocity when she is no longer accelerating.

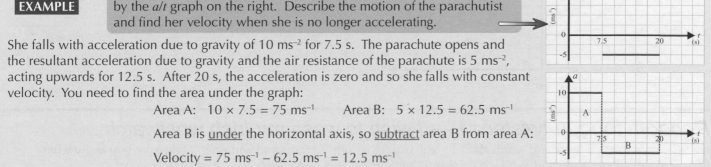

She falls with acceleration due to gravity of 10 ms⁻² for 7.5 s. The parachute opens and the resultant acceleration due to gravity and the air resistance of the parachute is 5 ms⁻², acting upwards for 12.5 s. After 20 s, the acceleration is zero and so she falls with constant velocity. You need to find the area under the graph:

Area A: 10 × 7.5 = 75 ms⁻¹   Area B: 5 × 12.5 = 62.5 ms⁻¹

Area B is <u>under</u> the horizontal axis, so <u>subtract</u> area B from area A:

Velocity = 75 ms⁻¹ – 62.5 ms⁻¹ = 12.5 ms⁻¹

Motion Graphs

Graphs can be used to Solve Complicated Problems

You might get a <u>speed-time</u> graph instead of a velocity-time graph — they're pretty much the same, except speeds are always positive, whereas you <u>can</u> have negative velocities.

As well as working out distance, velocity and acceleration from graphs, you can also solve more complicated problems. These might involve working out information <u>not shown directly on the graph</u>.

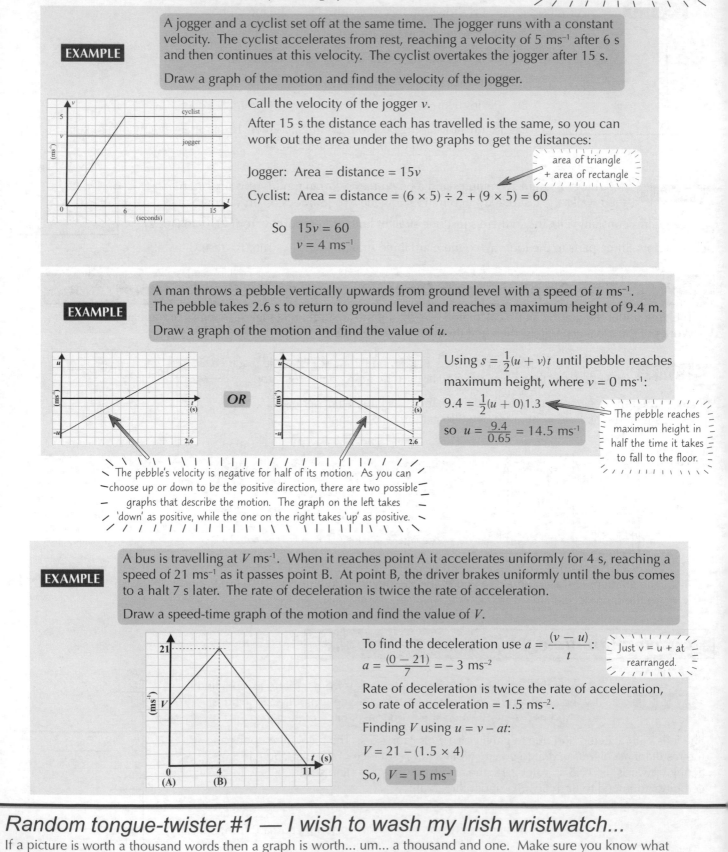

EXAMPLE

A jogger and a cyclist set off at the same time. The jogger runs with a constant velocity. The cyclist accelerates from rest, reaching a velocity of 5 ms^{-1} after 6 s and then continues at this velocity. The cyclist overtakes the jogger after 15 s.

Draw a graph of the motion and find the velocity of the jogger.

Call the velocity of the jogger v.

After 15 s the distance each has travelled is the same, so you can work out the area under the two graphs to get the distances:

area of triangle + area of rectangle

Jogger: Area = distance = $15v$

Cyclist: Area = distance = $(6 \times 5) \div 2 + (9 \times 5) = 60$

So $15v = 60$
$v = 4$ ms^{-1}

EXAMPLE

A man throws a pebble vertically upwards from ground level with a speed of u ms^{-1}. The pebble takes 2.6 s to return to ground level and reaches a maximum height of 9.4 m.

Draw a graph of the motion and find the value of u.

OR

Using $s = \frac{1}{2}(u + v)t$ until pebble reaches maximum height, where $v = 0$ ms^{-1}:

$9.4 = \frac{1}{2}(u + 0)1.3$

so $u = \frac{9.4}{0.65} = 14.5$ ms^{-1}

The pebble reaches maximum height in half the time it takes to fall to the floor.

The pebble's velocity is negative for half of its motion. As you can choose up or down to be the positive direction, there are two possible graphs that describe the motion. The graph on the left takes 'down' as positive, while the one on the right takes 'up' as positive.

EXAMPLE

A bus is travelling at V ms^{-1}. When it reaches point A it accelerates uniformly for 4 s, reaching a speed of 21 ms^{-1} as it passes point B. At point B, the driver brakes uniformly until the bus comes to a halt 7 s later. The rate of deceleration is twice the rate of acceleration.

Draw a speed-time graph of the motion and find the value of V.

To find the deceleration use $a = \frac{(v - u)}{t}$:

$a = \frac{(0 - 21)}{7} = -3$ ms^{-2}

Just $v = u + at$ rearranged.

Rate of deceleration is twice the rate of acceleration, so rate of acceleration = 1.5 ms^{-2}.

Finding V using $u = v - at$:

$V = 21 - (1.5 \times 4)$

So, $V = 15$ ms^{-1}

Random tongue-twister #1 — I wish to wash my Irish wristwatch...

If a picture is worth a thousand words then a graph is worth... um... a thousand and one. Make sure you know what type of graph you're using and learn what the gradient and the area under each type of graph tells you.

Displacement, Velocity and Acceleration

The "uvast" equations are all well and good when you've got a particle with constant acceleration. But when the acceleration of a particle varies with time, you need a few new tricks up your sleeve...

Differentiate to find Velocity and Acceleration from Displacement...

If you've got a particle moving in a straight line with acceleration that varies with time, you need to use calculus to find equations to describe the motion. (See p. 81 and p. 91 for a reminder about calculus.)

1) To find an equation for velocity, differentiate the equation for displacement with respect to time.

2) To find an equation for acceleration, differentiate the equation for velocity with respect to time. (Or differentiate the equation for displacement with respect to time twice.)

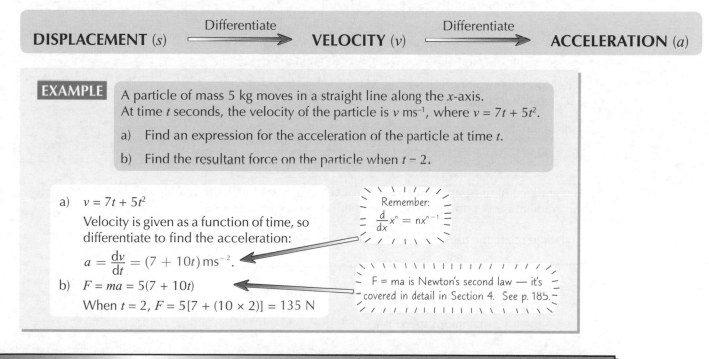

DISPLACEMENT (s) $\xrightarrow{\text{Differentiate}}$ **VELOCITY** (v) $\xrightarrow{\text{Differentiate}}$ **ACCELERATION** (a)

EXAMPLE

A particle of mass 5 kg moves in a straight line along the x-axis. At time t seconds, the velocity of the particle is v ms^{-1}, where $v = 7t + 5t^2$.

a) Find an expression for the acceleration of the particle at time t.

b) Find the resultant force on the particle when $t = 2$.

a) $v = 7t + 5t^2$

Velocity is given as a function of time, so differentiate to find the acceleration:

$a = \dfrac{dv}{dt} = (7 + 10t)\,\text{ms}^{-2}$.

Remember:
$\dfrac{d}{dx}x^n = nx^{n-1}$

b) $F = ma = 5(7 + 10t)$

When $t = 2$, $F = 5[7 + (10 \times 2)] = 135$ N

F = ma is Newton's second law — it's covered in detail in Section 4. See p. 185.

...and Integrate to find Velocity and Displacement from Acceleration

It's pretty similar if you're trying to go "back the other way", except you integrate rather than differentiate:

1) To find an equation for velocity, integrate the equation for acceleration with respect to time.

2) To find an equation for displacement, integrate the equation for velocity with respect to time.

DISPLACEMENT (s) $\xleftarrow[\text{Integrate}]{}$ **VELOCITY** (v) $\xleftarrow[\text{Integrate}]{}$ **ACCELERATION** (a)

EXAMPLE

A particle P sets off from O and moves in a straight line along the x-axis so that at time t seconds, its velocity is v ms^{-1}, where $v = 12 - t^2$, measured in the direction of x increasing. At $t = 0$, $s = 0$. Find the time taken for P to return to O.

Velocity is given as a function of t, so:

Don't forget the constant. Most questions will give you some info so you can find it.

$s = \int v\,dt = 12t - \dfrac{t^3}{3} + C$.

When $t = 0$, $s = 0$, so $0 = 12(0) - \dfrac{0^3}{3} + C \Rightarrow C = 0$.

Remember:
$\int x^n\,dx = \dfrac{x^{n+1}}{n+1} + c$

P is at O when $s = 0$, i.e. when: $12t - \dfrac{t^3}{3} = 0 \Rightarrow t(36 - t^2) = 0$

i.e. when $t = 0$, 6 or -6. So time taken for P to return to O is 6 seconds.

This can't be an answer, as you can't have a negative time.

Displacement, Velocity and Acceleration

Sometimes the Velocity is Defined only for a Particular Time Period

If you're trying to find the displacement of an object for a <u>certain interval</u> of t then you can integrate the velocity using <u>definite integrals</u>. No faffing about with constants — hooray.

EXAMPLE

The graph shows the motion of a wind-up toy moving in a straight line. The velocity of the toy in the interval $0 \leq t \leq 7$ is given by $v = -t^2 + 6t$.

a) How can you tell that the toy's acceleration is not constant for $0 \leq t \leq 7$?

b) (i) Find an expression for the toy's acceleration at time t.
   (ii) Show that the toy reaches its maximum speed in the interval $0 \leq t \leq 7$ at $t = 3$, and find the speed.

c) Find the two times in the interval $0 \leq t \leq 7$ when the toy is stationary.

d) Find the toy's displacement from the origin after 7 seconds.

e) Find the total distance the toy travels during the first 7 seconds.

a) The gradient of the graph gives the toy's acceleration. As the graph is a curve, the gradient is not constant, and so neither is the toy's acceleration.

b) (i) Differentiate the toy's velocity to find the acceleration: $a = \dfrac{dv}{dt} = -2t + 6$.

   (ii) The toy's speed is at a maximum when acceleration is equal to zero:
   i.e. when $a = -2t + 6 = 0 \Rightarrow t = 3$.
   Putting $t = 3$ back into the equation for v gives $v = -(3)^2 + 6(3) = 9$.
   So the toy's maximum speed is $v_{max} = 9$ ms^{-1}, and this occurs at time $t = 3$.

c) The toy is stationary when $v = 0$, i.e. when $-t^2 + 6t = t(-t + 6) = 0$
   So, the toy is stationary when $t = 0$ s and $t = 6$ s. ◄

> You can tell this by looking at the graph — these are the values where the graph crosses the t-axis. But it's always best to double-check using algebra.

d) Integrate the velocity to find an expression for the toy's displacement:

$$s = \int v\, dt = \int_0^7 (-t^2 + 6t)\, dt = \left[-\frac{t^3}{3} + 3t^2 \right]_0^7$$

> The limits 0 and 7 are used to find the displacement after 7 seconds.

$$= \left[-\frac{7^3}{3} + 3(7)^2 \right] - \left[-\frac{0^3}{3} + 3(0)^2 \right] = \left(32\tfrac{2}{3} - 0 \right) = 32\tfrac{2}{3} \text{ m}$$

e) From the graph and part c), you know that the toy moves with positive velocity until $t = 6$, and then begins to move back in the opposite direction.
So, first find the displacement of the toy at $t = 6$: ◄

> This will be the <u>maximum positive displacement</u> of the toy in the interval $0 \leq t \leq 7$.

$$s = \int_0^6 (-t^2 + 6t)\, dt = \left[-\frac{t^3}{3} + 3t^2 \right]_0^6 = \left[-\frac{6^3}{3} + 3(6)^2 \right] - 0 = \mathbf{36 \text{ m}}$$

From part d), you know the displacement of the toy at $t = 7$, so:

Total distance travelled $= 36 + \left(36 - 32\tfrac{2}{3} \right) = 36 + 3\tfrac{1}{3} = 39\tfrac{1}{3}$ m.

> This is how far the toy has moved in the opposite direction between $t = 6$ and $t = 7$.

CGP driving tips #1 — differentiate velocity from displacement...

Calculus? In Mechanics? What fresh horror is this? Actually, it's really not that bad at all. Just make sure you know when to differentiate and when to integrate and then bang in the numbers you're given in the question to get the answer. Sorted.

Describing Motion Using Vectors

I can tell that you're loving this section so far, but I know what you're thinking: "That's all fair enough mate, but what about when a particle is moving in two dimensions?" Well, you know I can't ignore a question like that, so get ready — it's time to break out those **i** + **j** vectors...

For particles travelling at *Constant Velocity*, s = vt

Flick back to page 160 to refresh your memory on what **i** + **j** vectors are all about.

If a particle is travelling at a constant velocity, v, then its displacement, s, after time, t, can be found by $s = vt$. This is handy for questions involving <u>position vectors</u> — these are vectors which describe the position of something relative to an origin.

EXAMPLE

At $t = 0$ a particle has position vector $(6\mathbf{i} + 8\mathbf{j})$ m relative to a fixed origin O. The particle is travelling at constant velocity $(2\mathbf{i} - 6\mathbf{j})$ ms^{-1}. Find its position vector at $t = 4$ s.

First find its displacement using $\mathbf{s} = \mathbf{v}t$: $\mathbf{s} = 4(2\mathbf{i} - 6\mathbf{j}) = (8\mathbf{i} - 24\mathbf{j})$ m

Then add this to its original position vector:

$(6\mathbf{i} + 8\mathbf{j}) + (8\mathbf{i} - 24\mathbf{j}) = (14\mathbf{i} - 16\mathbf{j})$ m

This "**i** and **j**" notation shows the two perpendicular components of a particle's displacement, velocity or acceleration separately.

You might need to use the *Constant Acceleration Equations*

If a particle is accelerating, you'll need to use the constant acceleration equations.

EXAMPLE

Find the velocity and speed of a particle after 3 s if its initial velocity is $(6\mathbf{i} + 4\mathbf{j})$ ms^{-1} and acceleration is $(0.3\mathbf{i} + 0.5\mathbf{j})$ ms^{-2}.

Using $\mathbf{v} = \mathbf{u} + \mathbf{a}t$: $\mathbf{v} = (6\mathbf{i} + 4\mathbf{j}) + 3(0.3\mathbf{i} + 0.5\mathbf{j}) = (6\mathbf{i} + 4\mathbf{j}) + (0.9\mathbf{i} + 1.5\mathbf{j}) = (6.9\mathbf{i} + 5.5\mathbf{j})$ ms^{-1}

Speed = magnitude of $\mathbf{v} = \sqrt{6.9^2 + 5.5^2} = 8.82$ ms^{-1}

EXAMPLE

At $t = 0$, a particle, P, has position vector $(3\mathbf{i} + \mathbf{j})$ m relative to a fixed origin, and velocity $(2\mathbf{i} - 5\mathbf{j})$ ms^{-1}, where **i** and **j** are the horizontal and vertical unit vectors respectively.

(i) Given that P accelerates at a rate of $(-2\mathbf{i} + \mathbf{j})$ ms^{-2}, find its position vector at $t = 6$ s.

(ii) Find the average velocity of the particle during this time.

(iii) Find the velocity of the particle and the value of t when it is travelling parallel to **i**.

(i) Use $\mathbf{s} = \mathbf{u}t + \frac{1}{2}\mathbf{a}t^2$:

$\mathbf{s} = 6(2\mathbf{i} - 5\mathbf{j}) + \frac{1}{2}(6^2)(-2\mathbf{i} + \mathbf{j}) = (12\mathbf{i} - 30\mathbf{j}) + (-36\mathbf{i} + 18\mathbf{j}) = (-24\mathbf{i} - 12\mathbf{j})$ m

New position vector $= (3\mathbf{i} + \mathbf{j}) + (-24\mathbf{i} - 12\mathbf{j}) = (-21\mathbf{i} - 11\mathbf{j})$ m

(ii) Use $\mathbf{v} = \frac{\mathbf{s}}{t}$ where **s** is the difference between the final and initial position vectors (calculated in part i)): $\mathbf{v}_{average} = \dfrac{(-24\mathbf{i} - 12\mathbf{j})}{6} = (-4\mathbf{i} - 2\mathbf{j})$ ms^{-1}.

(iii) Consider the horizontal and vertical components of motion separately:

Vertically:
When the particle is travelling parallel to **i**, the component of its velocity in the direction of **j** is zero. So:

$u_v = -5$, $v_v = 0$, $a_v = 1$
$v_v = u_v + a_v t \Rightarrow 0 = -5 + t \Rightarrow t = 5$

u_v, v_v and a_v are the vertical components of **u**, **v** and **a** respectively.

Horizontally:
$u_h = 2$, $a_h = -2$, $t = 5$.
$v_h = u_h + a_h t$
$\Rightarrow v_h = 2 + (-2 \times 5) = -8$

v_h is non-zero, so you know the particle is definitely moving.

So the velocity of the particle when it's travelling parallel to **i** is $-8\mathbf{i}$ ms^{-1}, and this occurs at time $t = 5$ s.

Describing Motion Using Vectors

Now that you've mastered two dimensional motion with constant acceleration, it's time to take it to the next level — two dimensional motion with variable acceleration. How exciting.

Differentiate and Integrate with Vector Notation for Motion on a Plane

1) When you've got a particle moving in two dimensions (i.e. in a plane), you can describe its position, velocity and acceleration using the unit vectors **i** and **j**. But then you knew that already. Yawn.

2) The relationship between displacement (position), velocity and acceleration from page 169 still applies to particles moving on a plane:

$$\textbf{POSITION (r)} \quad \xrightarrow{\text{Differentiate}} \quad \textbf{VELOCITY (v)} \quad \xrightarrow{\text{Differentiate}} \quad \textbf{ACCELERATION (a)}$$
$$\xleftarrow[\text{Integrate}]{} \qquad\qquad \xleftarrow[\text{Integrate}]{}$$

3) This means that you'll have to differentiate and integrate vectors written in **i** and **j** notation. Luckily, doing this is as easy as squeezing lemons — all you have to do is differentiate/integrate each component of the vector separately:

So, if $\mathbf{r} = x\mathbf{i} + y\mathbf{j}$ is a position vector, then:

velocity, $\mathbf{v} = \dfrac{d\mathbf{r}}{dt} = \dfrac{dx}{dt}\mathbf{i} + \dfrac{dy}{dt}\mathbf{j}$

> The shorthand for $\frac{dr}{dt}$ is $\dot{\mathbf{r}}$ (the single dot means differentiate r once with respect to time)...

and acceleration, $\mathbf{a} = \dfrac{d\mathbf{v}}{dt} = \dfrac{d^2\mathbf{r}}{dt^2} = \dfrac{d^2x}{dt^2}\mathbf{i} + \dfrac{d^2y}{dt^2}\mathbf{j}$.

> ...and the shorthand for $\frac{d^2r}{dt^2}$ is $\ddot{\mathbf{r}}$ (the double dots mean differentiate r twice with respect to time).

It's a similar thing for integration:

If $\mathbf{v} = w\mathbf{i} + z\mathbf{j}$ is a velocity vector, then position, $\mathbf{r} = \displaystyle\int \mathbf{v}\, dt = \int (w\mathbf{i} + z\mathbf{j})\, dt = \left[\int w\, dt\right]\mathbf{i} + \left[\int z\, dt\right]\mathbf{j}$

Unfortunately, there's no snazzy shorthand for integration. Ahh well, easy come, easy go.

EXAMPLE:

A particle is moving on a horizontal plane so that at time t it has velocity $\mathbf{v}$ ms^{-1}, where
$$\mathbf{v} = (8 + 2t)\mathbf{i} + (t^3 - 6t)\mathbf{j}$$
At $t = 2$, the particle has a position vector of $(10\mathbf{i} + 3\mathbf{j})$ m with respect to a fixed origin O.

a) Find the acceleration of the particle at time t.

b) Show that the position of the particle relative to O when $t = 4$ is $\mathbf{r} = 38\mathbf{i} + 27\mathbf{j}$.

a) $\mathbf{a} = \dot{\mathbf{v}} = \dfrac{d\mathbf{v}}{dt}$

> Yep, that really is all there is to it.

$= 2\mathbf{i} + (3t^2 - 6)\mathbf{j}$

b) $\mathbf{r} = \displaystyle\int \mathbf{v}\, dt$

> You still need a constant of integration, but it will be a vector with **i** and **j** components.

$= (8t + t^2)\mathbf{i} + \left(\dfrac{t^4}{4} - 3t^2\right)\mathbf{j} + \mathbf{C}$

When $t = 2$, $\mathbf{r} = (10\mathbf{i} + 3\mathbf{j})$, so use this info to find the vector $\mathbf{C}$:

$10\mathbf{i} + 3\mathbf{j} = 20\mathbf{i} - 8\mathbf{j} + \mathbf{C}$

$\Rightarrow \mathbf{C} = (10 - 20)\mathbf{i} + (3 - -8)\mathbf{j} = -10\mathbf{i} + 11\mathbf{j}$

> Collect **i** and **j** terms and add/subtract to simplify.

So, $\mathbf{r} = (8t + t^2 - 10)\mathbf{i} + \left(\dfrac{t^4}{4} - 3t^2 + 11\right)\mathbf{j}$.

When $t = 4$, $\mathbf{r} = (32 + 16 - 10)\mathbf{i} + (64 - 48 + 11)\mathbf{j} = 38\mathbf{i} + 27\mathbf{j}$ — as required.

Describing Motion Using Vectors

Use *F* = *ma* to find the Force acting on a particle

In the exam you may be asked to find the force acting on a particle in one of these vector questions. To do this, you'll need to use Newton's Second Law, $F = ma$, or $\mathbf{F} = m\mathbf{a}$ in vector notation. Newton's Laws are covered on p. 185.

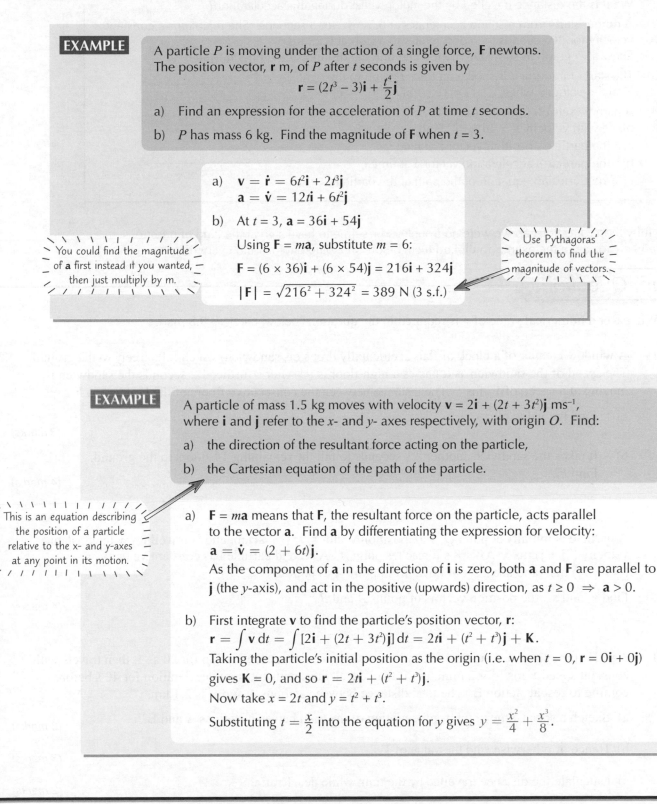

EXAMPLE

A particle P is moving under the action of a single force, $\mathbf{F}$ newtons. The position vector, $\mathbf{r}$ m, of P after t seconds is given by
$$\mathbf{r} = (2t^3 - 3)\mathbf{i} + \frac{t^4}{2}\mathbf{j}$$
a) Find an expression for the acceleration of P at time t seconds.

b) P has mass 6 kg. Find the magnitude of $\mathbf{F}$ when $t = 3$.

a) $\mathbf{v} = \dot{\mathbf{r}} = 6t^2\mathbf{i} + 2t^3\mathbf{j}$
    $\mathbf{a} = \dot{\mathbf{v}} = 12t\mathbf{i} + 6t^2\mathbf{j}$

b) At $t = 3$, $\mathbf{a} = 36\mathbf{i} + 54\mathbf{j}$

    Using $\mathbf{F} = m\mathbf{a}$, substitute $m = 6$:

    $\mathbf{F} = (6 \times 36)\mathbf{i} + (6 \times 54)\mathbf{j} = 216\mathbf{i} + 324\mathbf{j}$

    $|\mathbf{F}| = \sqrt{216^2 + 324^2} = 389$ N (3 s.f.)

You could find the magnitude of **a** first instead if you wanted, then just multiply by m.

Use Pythagoras' theorem to find the magnitude of vectors.

EXAMPLE

A particle of mass 1.5 kg moves with velocity $\mathbf{v} = 2\mathbf{i} + (2t + 3t^2)\mathbf{j}$ ms^{-1}, where $\mathbf{i}$ and $\mathbf{j}$ refer to the x- and y- axes respectively, with origin O. Find:

a) the direction of the resultant force acting on the particle,

b) the Cartesian equation of the path of the particle.

This is an equation describing the position of a particle relative to the x- and y-axes at any point in its motion.

a) $\mathbf{F} = m\mathbf{a}$ means that $\mathbf{F}$, the resultant force on the particle, acts parallel to the vector $\mathbf{a}$. Find $\mathbf{a}$ by differentiating the expression for velocity:
    $\mathbf{a} = \dot{\mathbf{v}} = (2 + 6t)\mathbf{j}$.
    As the component of $\mathbf{a}$ in the direction of $\mathbf{i}$ is zero, both $\mathbf{a}$ and $\mathbf{F}$ are parallel to $\mathbf{j}$ (the y-axis), and act in the positive (upwards) direction, as $t \geq 0 \Rightarrow \mathbf{a} > 0$.

b) First integrate $\mathbf{v}$ to find the particle's position vector, $\mathbf{r}$:
    $\mathbf{r} = \int \mathbf{v}\, dt = \int [2\mathbf{i} + (2t + 3t^2)\mathbf{j}]\, dt = 2t\mathbf{i} + (t^2 + t^3)\mathbf{j} + \mathbf{K}$.
    Taking the particle's initial position as the origin (i.e. when $t = 0$, $\mathbf{r} = 0\mathbf{i} + 0\mathbf{j}$)
    gives $\mathbf{K} = 0$, and so $\mathbf{r} = 2t\mathbf{i} + (t^2 + t^3)\mathbf{j}$.
    Now take $x = 2t$ and $y = t^2 + t^3$.

    Substituting $t = \frac{x}{2}$ into the equation for y gives $y = \frac{x^2}{4} + \frac{x^3}{8}$.

Motion in two dimensions — it's plane simple...

Just remember to differentiate and integrate by treating each component separately, and pretty soon you'll be able to differentiate velocity vectors in 11-dimensional hyperspace. Just think how cool that'll look at the next sci-fi convention.

M1 Section 2 — Practice Questions

Time for another lot of questions. A bit of advice — don't panic, take it step by step, and above all ~~don't get hurt~~ keep practising until it's second nature.

Warm-up Questions

1) A motorcyclist accelerates uniformly from 3 ms⁻¹ to 9 ms⁻¹ in 2 seconds.
   What is the distance travelled by the motorcyclist during this acceleration?

2) A runner starts from rest and accelerates at 0.5 ms⁻² for 5 seconds. She maintains a constant velocity for 20 seconds then decelerates to a stop at 0.25 ms⁻².
   Draw a v/t graph to show the motion and find the distance the runner travelled.

3) The start of a journey is shown on the a/t graph to the right.
   Find the velocity when: a) $t = 3$ b) $t = 5$ c) $t = 6$

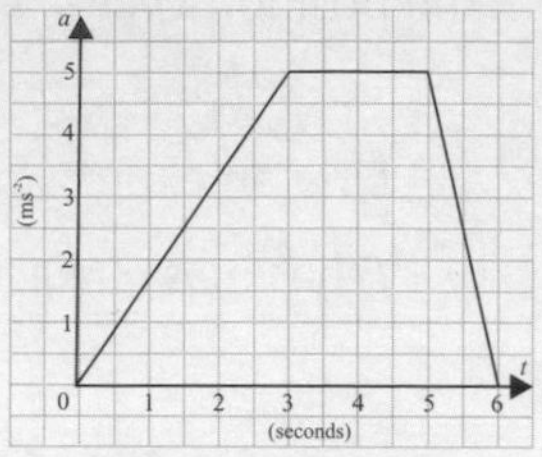

4) A particle sets off from the origin at $t = 0$ and moves in a plane with velocity $\mathbf{v} = 4t\mathbf{i} + t^3\mathbf{j}$. Find:
   a) the particle's position vector $\mathbf{r}$ at time t,
   b) the particle's acceleration vector $\mathbf{a}$ at time t,
   c) the Cartesian equation of the path of the particle.

Hopefully those questions above were no trouble, so it's time to have a go at the kind of questions you're likely to see in the exam. You'll find them below, in a different font and everything...

Exam Questions

Whenever a numerical value of g is required in the questions below, take $g = 9.8$ ms⁻².

1   A window cleaner of a block of flats accidentally drops his sandwich, which falls freely to the ground. The speed of the sandwich as it passes a high floor is u. After a further 1.2 seconds the sandwich is moving at a speed of 17 ms⁻¹. The distance between the consecutive floors of the building is h.

   a)   Find the value of u.

   (3 marks)

   b)   It takes the sandwich another 2.1 seconds to fall the remaining 14 floors to the ground.
        Find h.

   (4 marks)

2   A particle is initially at point Q, with position vector $\mathbf{s}_Q = (\mathbf{i} + 2\mathbf{j})$ m, and is travelling with constant velocity $(3\mathbf{i} + \mathbf{j})$ ms⁻¹. After 8 s it reaches point A. A second particle has constant velocity $(-4\mathbf{i} + 2\mathbf{j})$ ms⁻¹ and takes 5 s to travel from point A to point B.

   Find $\mathbf{s}_A$ and $\mathbf{s}_B$, the position vectors of points A and B.

   (4 marks)

3   A train starts from rest at station A and travels with constant acceleration for 20 s. It then travels with constant speed V ms⁻¹ for 2 minutes. It then decelerates with constant deceleration for 40 s before coming to rest at station B. The total distance between stations A and B is 2.1 km.

   a) Sketch a speed-time graph for the motion of the train between stations A and B.

   (3 marks)

   b) Hence or otherwise find the value of V.

   (3 marks)

   c) Calculate the distance travelled by the train while decelerating.

   (2 marks)

   d) Sketch an acceleration-time graph for this motion.

   (3 marks)

M1 Section 2 — Practice Questions

4   A particle sets off from the origin, O, at time $t = 0$ and moves in a straight line along the x-axis. At time t seconds, the velocity of the particle is given by $v = 9t - 3t^2$ ms^{-1} for $0 \leq t \leq 4$ and $v = -12$ ms^{-1} for $t > 4$. Find:

    a)   the time when the acceleration is zero in the interval $0 \leqslant t \leqslant 4$,

                   (2 marks)

    b)   the displacement of the particle from O at $t = 4$,

                   (3 marks)

    c)   the time when the particle returns to O for $t > 4$.

                   (3 marks)

5   A rocket is projected vertically upwards from a point 8 m above the ground at a speed of u ms^{-1} and travels freely under gravity. The rocket hits the ground at 20 ms^{-1}. Find:

    a)   the value of u,

                   (3 marks)

    b)   how long it takes to hit the ground.

                   (3 marks)

6   A particle P of mass 4 kg is moving in a horizontal plane under the action of a single force $\mathbf{F}$ newtons. After t seconds, P has position vector:

$$\mathbf{r} = (2t^3 - 7t^2 + 12)\mathbf{i} + (3t^2 - 4t^3 - 7)\mathbf{j} \text{ m}$$

    where the unit vectors $\mathbf{i}$ and $\mathbf{j}$ are in the directions of east and north respectively. Find:

    a)   an expression for the velocity of P after t seconds,

                   (2 marks)

    b)   the speed of P when $t = \frac{1}{2}$, and the direction of motion of P at this time,

                   (3 marks)

    c)   the acceleration of P at $t = 2$,

                   (3 marks)

    d)   the force, $\mathbf{F}$, acting on the particle at $t = 2$.

                   (2 marks)

7   At $t = 0$, a particle P is at position vector $(\mathbf{i} + 5\mathbf{j})$ m, relative to a fixed origin. P is moving with a constant velocity of $(7\mathbf{i} - 3\mathbf{j})$ ms^{-1}. After 4 s the velocity of P changes to $(a\mathbf{i} + b\mathbf{j})$ ms^{-1}. After a further 3.5 seconds P reaches position vector $(15\mathbf{i})$ m. Find:

    a)   the speed of P at $t = 0$

                   (2 marks)

    b)   the bearing of P at $t = 0$

                   (3 marks)

    c)   the values of a and b.

                   (4 marks)

8   The following graph models the velocity of a car pulling away from a set of traffic lights. The car's velocity from time $t = 0$ s to $t = 3$ s is given by $v = 6t - t^2$ ms^{-1}.

    a)   Write down an expression for the car's acceleration during the first 3 seconds of travel.

                   (1 mark)

    b)   Find the distance the car moves during this time.

                   (3 marks)

Forces and Modelling

Force questions come up all the time in M1, so you need to understand what each type of force is.
Then you can use that information to create a model to work from.

> Hint: 'modelling' in maths doesn't have anything
> to do with plastic aeroplane kits... or catwalks.

Types *of forces*

WEIGHT (*W*)

Due to the particle's mass, <u>m</u>, and the force of gravity, g: $W = mg$ — weight always acts <u>downwards</u>.

$W = mg$

THE NORMAL REACTION (*R* OR *N*)

The reaction from a surface. Reaction is always at <u>90° to the surface</u>.

R

W

TENSION (*T*)

Force in a taut rope, wire or string.

T

W

FRICTION (*F*)

Due to the <u>roughness</u> between a body and a surface. Always acts <u>against</u> motion, or likely motion.

Moving to
the right...

R

F

W

...so friction
acts to the left.

THRUST

<u>Force in a rod</u> (e.g. the pole of an open umbrella).

Talk *the Talk*

Maths questions in M1 use a lot of words that you already know, but here they're used
to mean something very <u>precise</u>. Learn these definitions so you don't get caught out:

<u>Particle</u>	the body is a point so its dimensions don't matter	<u>Rigid</u>	the body does not bend
<u>Light</u>	the body has no mass	<u>Thin</u>	the body has no thickness
<u>Static</u>	not moving	<u>Equilibrium</u>	nothing's moving
<u>Rough</u>	the surface will oppose motion with friction / drag	<u>Plane</u>	a flat surface
<u>Beam or Rod</u>	a long, thin, straight body (e.g. a broom handle)	<u>Inextensible</u>	the body can't be stretched
<u>Uniform</u>	the mass is evenly spread out throughout the body	<u>Smooth</u>	the surface doesn't have friction / drag opposing motion
<u>Non-uniform</u>	the mass is unevenly spread out		

Mathematical Modelling

You'll have to make lots of assumptions in M1. Doing this is called
'<u>modelling</u>', and you do it to make a sticky real-life situation <u>simpler</u>.

EXAMPLE   The ice hockey player

<u>You might have to assume:</u>

- no friction between the skates and the ice
- no drag (air resistance)
- the skater generates a constant forward force S
- the skater is very small (a point mass)
- there is only one point of contact with the ice
- the weight acts downwards

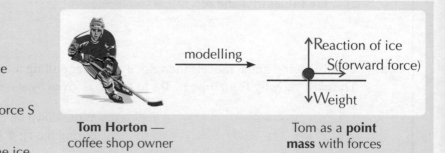

modelling

Reaction of ice

S (forward force)

Weight

Tom Horton —
coffee shop owner

Tom as a **point
mass** with forces

> The simplified model you end up with can
> then be used as your vector diagram.

Forces and Modelling

Modelling is a *Cycle*

Having created a model you can later <u>improve</u> it by making more (or fewer) <u>assumptions</u>.
Solve the problem using the initial assumptions, <u>compare</u> it to real life, <u>evaluate</u> the model and then
use that information to <u>change</u> the assumptions. Then keep going until you're <u>satisfied</u> with the model.

Always start by drawing a *Simple Diagram* of the *Model*

Here are a couple of old chestnuts that often turn up in M1 exams in one form or another.

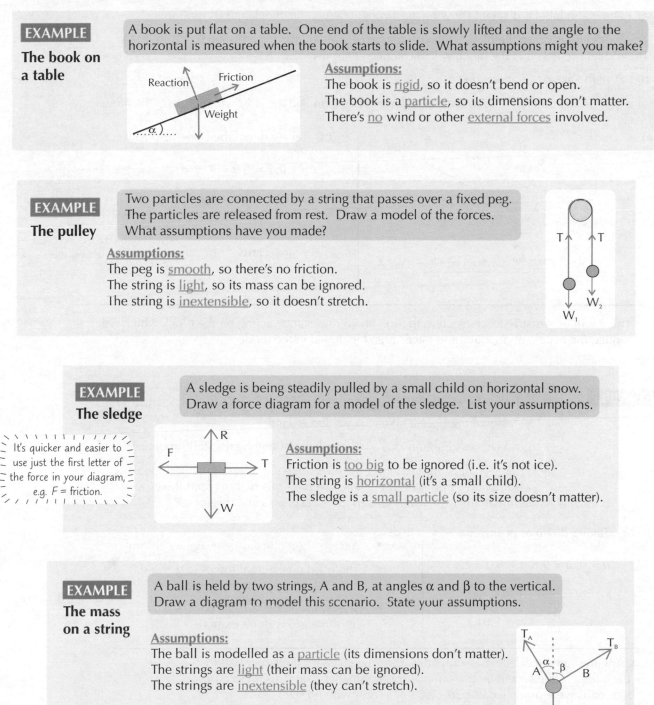

EXAMPLE

The book on a table

A book is put flat on a table. One end of the table is slowly lifted and the angle to the horizontal is measured when the book starts to slide. What assumptions might you make?

Reaction   Friction
Weight
α

Assumptions:
The book is <u>rigid</u>, so it doesn't bend or open.
The book is a <u>particle</u>, so its dimensions don't matter.
There's <u>no</u> wind or other <u>external forces</u> involved.

EXAMPLE

The pulley

Two particles are connected by a string that passes over a fixed peg. The particles are released from rest. Draw a model of the forces. What assumptions have you made?

T   T
W_1 W_2

Assumptions:
The peg is <u>smooth</u>, so there's no friction.
The string is <u>light</u>, so its mass can be ignored.
The string is <u>inextensible</u>, so it doesn't stretch.

EXAMPLE

The sledge

A sledge is being steadily pulled by a small child on horizontal snow. Draw a force diagram for a model of the sledge. List your assumptions.

It's quicker and easier to use just the first letter of the force in your diagram, e.g. F = friction.

R
F   T
W

Assumptions:
Friction is <u>too big</u> to be ignored (i.e. it's not ice).
The string is <u>horizontal</u> (it's a small child).
The sledge is a <u>small particle</u> (so its size doesn't matter).

EXAMPLE

The mass on a string

A ball is held by two strings, A and B, at angles α and β to the vertical. Draw a diagram to model this scenario. State your assumptions.

T_A T_B
α   β
A   B
W

Assumptions:
The ball is modelled as a <u>particle</u> (its dimensions don't matter).
The strings are <u>light</u> (their mass can be ignored).
The strings are <u>inextensible</u> (they can't stretch).

Forces and Modelling

Now for some proper examples — yeah baby.

You Might be asked to **Comment** on your **Model**

EXAMPLE

A wooden block of mass m kg is held at rest on a plane inclined at an angle of 30° to the horizontal. The block is then released from rest, and slides down the plane. A model of this situation makes the assumption that the only forces acting on the block are its <u>weight</u> and the <u>normal reaction</u> to the plane, N.

a)   Draw and label a diagram showing the forces acting on the block and its motion.

The block slides down the plane with constant acceleration, moving a distance of 8 m in 4 s. The model predicts that the block will accelerate at 4.9 ms^{-2}.

b)   Find the actual acceleration of the block.

c)   Explain the difference between the actual acceleration and the value predicted by the model.

a)

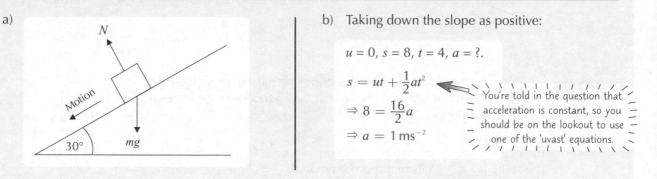

b)   Taking down the slope as positive:

$$u = 0, s = 8, t = 4, a = ?.$$

$$s = ut + \frac{1}{2}at^2$$

$$\Rightarrow 8 = \frac{16}{2}a$$

$$\Rightarrow a = 1 \text{ ms}^{-2}$$

You're told in the question that acceleration is constant, so you should be on the lookout to use one of the 'uvast' equations.

c)   There will be resistive forces such as friction and air resistance acting on the block which will reduce the acceleration, but these forces aren't included in the model.

EXAMPLE

a)   A ball is dropped from a height of 5 m above the ground.

   (i)   How long does it take to reach the ground?

   (ii) What assumptions have you made in modelling the ball's motion?

b)   A larger ball is dropped from the same height. Using the same modelling assumptions, how would the time taken for this ball to reach the ground compare to your answer to part a) (i)? Explain your answer.

a)   (i)   Taking down as positive:

$$u = 0, a = 9.8, s = 5, t = ?$$

$$s = ut + \frac{1}{2}at^2 \Rightarrow 5 = \frac{9.8}{2}t^2$$

$$t^2 = \frac{10}{9.8} \Rightarrow t = 1.01 \text{ s}$$

(ii)

• Acceleration due to gravity, g, is constant.

• There are no external forces (e.g. wind, air resistance) acting on the particle,

• The ball is modelled as a particle (its dimensions don't matter).

You can <u>always</u> assume this in M1, thank goodness.

b)   Using the same modelling assumptions, the time taken for the larger ball to reach the ground would be the same as for the smaller ball. This is because both balls were modelled as particles, i.e. a mass with no size.

I used to be a model when I was younger, but then I fell apart...

Make sure you're completely familiar with the different forces and all the jargon that gets bandied about in mechanics. Keep your models as simple as possible — that will make answering the questions as simple as possible too.

Forces are Vectors

Forces have direction and magnitude, which makes them vectors — this means that all the stuff you learnt about vectors you'll need here. To help you out, we've given you some more vector examples all about forces...

Forces have **Components**

Take a look back at Section 1 for a reminder about vectors.

You've done a fair amount of trigonometry already, so this should be as straightforward as watching dry paint.

EXAMPLE A particle is acted on by a force of 15 N at 30º above the horizontal. Find the horizontal and vertical components of the force.

A bit of trigonometry is all that's required:

Force = 15cos30°**i** + 15sin30°**j**

$= (13.0\,\mathbf{i} + 7.5\,\mathbf{j})$ N

(i.e. 13 N to the right and 7.5 N upwards)

Add Forces Nose to Tail to get the Resultant

The important bit when you're drawing a diagram to find the resultant is to make sure the arrows are the right way round. Repeat after me: nose to tail, nose to tail, nose to tail.

EXAMPLE A second horizontal force of 20 N to the right is also applied to the particle in the example above. Find the resultant of these forces.

You need to put the arrows nose to tail:

The 15 N force has been split into horizontal and vertical components.

Using Pythagoras and trigonometry:

$R = \sqrt{32.99^2 + 7.5^2} = 33.8$ N

$\alpha = \tan^{-1}\left(\dfrac{7.5}{32.99}\right) = 12.8°$ above the horizontal

EXAMPLE Find the magnitude and direction of the resultant of the forces shown acting on the particle.

The 20 N force has been split into horizontal and vertical components.

Hint: you could also use the cosine rule here to get R.

$R = \sqrt{(12 - 20\cos 60°)^2 + (20\sin 60°)^2} = 17.4$ N

$\theta = \tan^{-1}\left(\dfrac{20\sin 60°}{12 - 20\cos 60°}\right) = 83.4°$ to the vertical

If a particle is released it will move in the direction of the resultant.

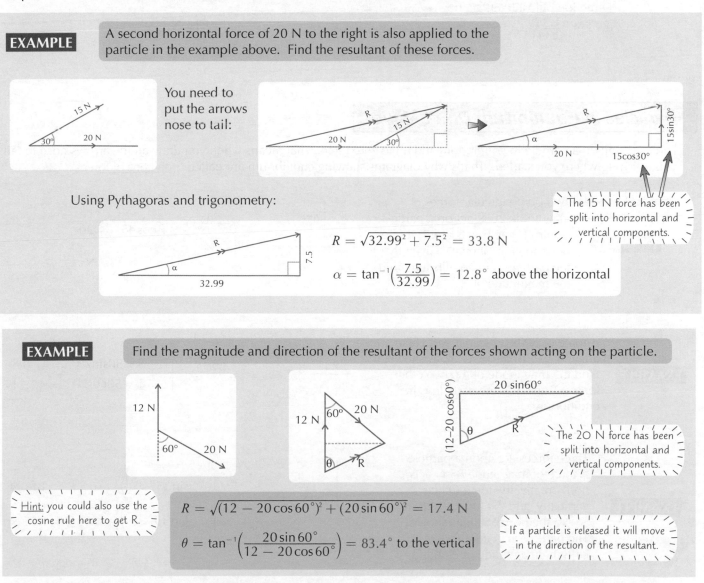

Forces are Vectors

Resolving *more than Two Forces*

A question could involve <u>more than two forces</u>. You still work it out the <u>same</u> though — <u>resolve, resolve, resolve</u>...

EXAMPLE

Three forces of magnitudes 9 N, 12 N and 13 N act on a particle P in the directions shown in the diagram.
Find the magnitude and direction of the resultant of the three forces.

One of the forces is already aligned with the y-axis, so it makes sense to start by resolving the other forces relative to this.

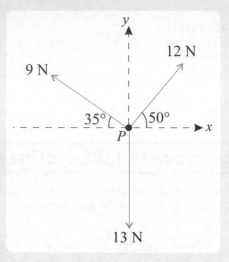

Along the y-axis:
Sum of components = $9\sin35° + 12\sin50° - 13$
= **1.355 N** (4 s.f.)

Along the x-axis:
Sum of components = $12\cos50° - 9\cos35°$
= **0.3411 N** (4 s.f.)

Magnitude of resultant = $\sqrt{1.355^2 + 0.3411^2}$
    = 1.40 N (3 s.f.)

Direction of resultant:
$\theta = \tan^{-1}\dfrac{1.355}{0.3411} = 75.9°$ above the positive x-axis.

Particles in *Equilibrium Don't Move*

Forces acting on a particle in <u>equilibrium</u> add up to zero force. That means when you draw all the arrows nose to tail, you finish up where you started. That's why diagrams showing equilibrium are called '<u>polygons of forces</u>'.

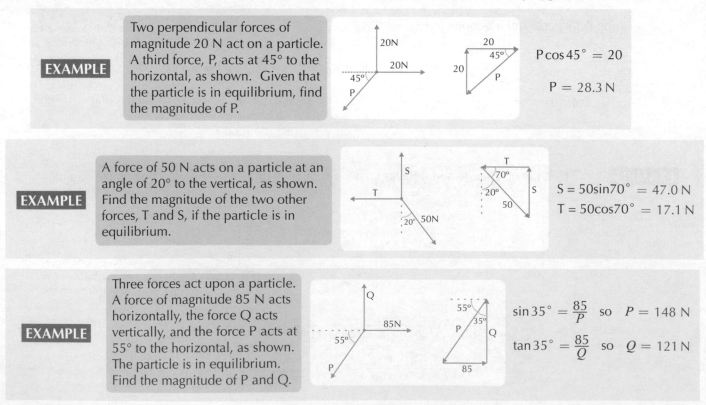

EXAMPLE

Two perpendicular forces of magnitude 20 N act on a particle. A third force, P, acts at 45° to the horizontal, as shown. Given that the particle is in equilibrium, find the magnitude of P.

$P\cos45° = 20$

$P = 28.3\,\text{N}$

EXAMPLE

A force of 50 N acts on a particle at an angle of 20° to the vertical, as shown. Find the magnitude of the two other forces, T and S, if the particle is in equilibrium.

$S = 50\sin70° = 47.0\,\text{N}$

$T = 50\cos70° = 17.1\,\text{N}$

EXAMPLE

Three forces act upon a particle. A force of magnitude 85 N acts horizontally, the force Q acts vertically, and the force P acts at 55° to the horizontal, as shown. The particle is in equilibrium. Find the magnitude of P and Q.

$\sin35° = \dfrac{85}{P}$ so $P = 148\,\text{N}$

$\tan35° = \dfrac{85}{Q}$ so $Q = 121\,\text{N}$

Forces are Vectors

An *Inclined Plane* is a *Sloping Surface*

EXAMPLE
A particle of mass 0.1 kg is held at rest on a rough plane inclined at 20° to the horizontal by a friction force acting up the plane. Find the magnitude of this friction force and the normal reaction. ($g = 9.8$ ms⁻².)

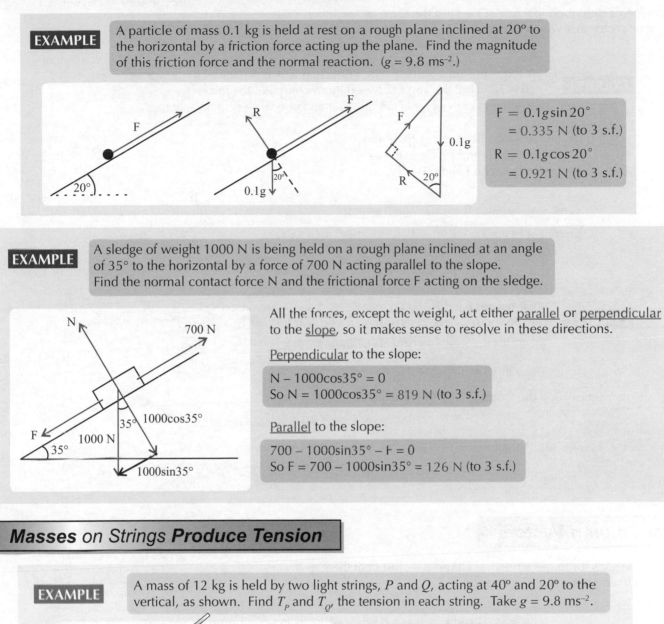

$$F = 0.1g\sin 20°$$
$$= 0.335 \text{ N (to 3 s.f.)}$$
$$R = 0.1g\cos 20°$$
$$= 0.921 \text{ N (to 3 s.f.)}$$

EXAMPLE
A sledge of weight 1000 N is being held on a rough plane inclined at an angle of 35° to the horizontal by a force of 700 N acting parallel to the slope. Find the normal contact force N and the frictional force F acting on the sledge.

All the forces, except the weight, act either <u>parallel</u> or <u>perpendicular</u> to the <u>slope</u>, so it makes sense to resolve in these directions.

<u>Perpendicular</u> to the slope:

$N - 1000\cos 35° = 0$
So $N = 1000\cos 35° = 819$ N (to 3 s.f.)

<u>Parallel</u> to the slope:

$700 - 1000\sin 35° - F = 0$
So $F = 700 - 1000\sin 35° = 126$ N (to 3 s.f.)

Masses on Strings *Produce Tension*

EXAMPLE
A mass of 12 kg is held by two light strings, P and Q, acting at 40° and 20° to the vertical, as shown. Find T_P and T_Q, the tension in each string. Take $g = 9.8$ ms⁻².

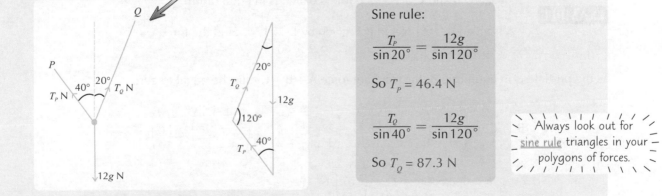

Sine rule:

$$\frac{T_P}{\sin 20°} = \frac{12g}{\sin 120°}$$

So $T_P = 46.4$ N

$$\frac{T_Q}{\sin 40°} = \frac{12g}{\sin 120°}$$

So $T_Q = 87.3$ N

Always look out for <u>sine rule</u> triangles in your polygons of forces.

Cliché #27 — *"The more things change, the more they stay the same"...*

As it makes their lives easier, examiners always stick the <u>same</u> kinds of questions into M1 exams. So, no need to panic — just keep practising the questions and then there'll be no surprises when it comes to the exam. Simple.

Forces are Vectors

Forces can be described using i + j Vectors...

Check out page 160 for a refresher course on i + j vectors.

Treat forces described in terms of **i** + **j** just the same as any other force or vector that you deal with in M1.

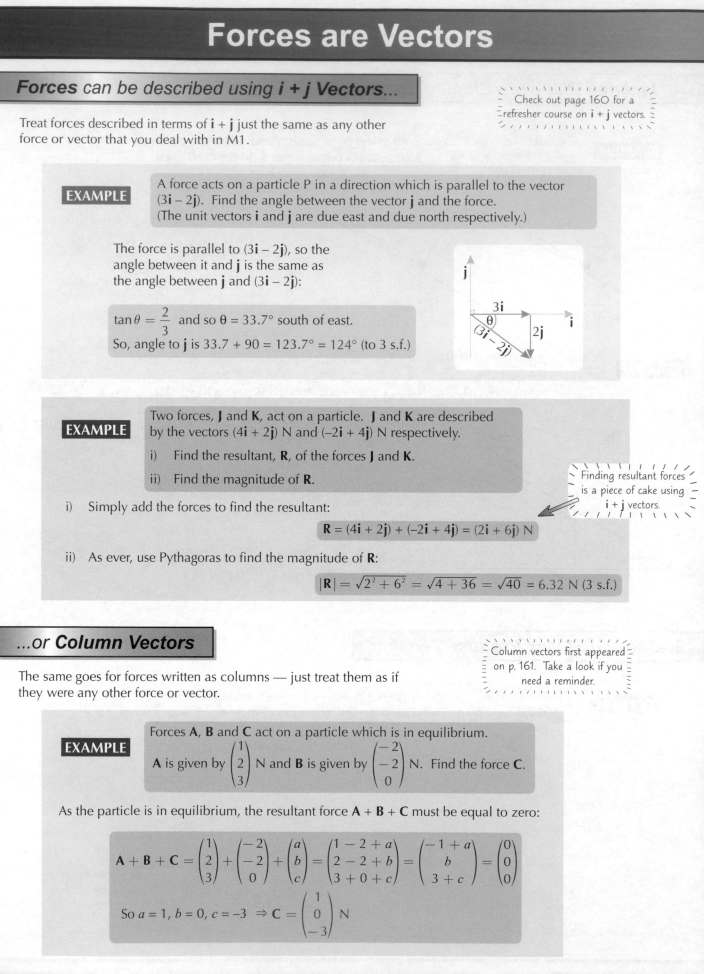

EXAMPLE

A force acts on a particle P in a direction which is parallel to the vector (3**i** – 2**j**). Find the angle between the vector **j** and the force. (The unit vectors **i** and **j** are due east and due north respectively.)

The force is parallel to (3**i** – 2**j**), so the angle between it and **j** is the same as the angle between **j** and (3**i** – 2**j**):

$\tan\theta = \dfrac{2}{3}$ and so $\theta = 33.7°$ south of east.

So, angle to **j** is $33.7 + 90 = 123.7° = 124°$ (to 3 s.f.)

EXAMPLE

Two forces, **J** and **K**, act on a particle. **J** and **K** are described by the vectors (4**i** + 2**j**) N and (–2**i** + 4**j**) N respectively.

i)   Find the resultant, **R**, of the forces **J** and **K**.

ii) Find the magnitude of **R**.

Finding resultant forces is a piece of cake using i + j vectors.

i)   Simply add the forces to find the resultant:

$$R = (4\mathbf{i} + 2\mathbf{j}) + (-2\mathbf{i} + 4\mathbf{j}) = (2\mathbf{i} + 6\mathbf{j}) \text{ N}$$

ii) As ever, use Pythagoras to find the magnitude of **R**:

$$|\mathbf{R}| = \sqrt{2^2 + 6^2} = \sqrt{4 + 36} = \sqrt{40} = 6.32 \text{ N (3 s.f.)}$$

...or Column Vectors

Column vectors first appeared on p. 161. Take a look if you need a reminder.

The same goes for forces written as columns — just treat them as if they were any other force or vector.

EXAMPLE

Forces **A**, **B** and **C** act on a particle which is in equilibrium.

A is given by $\begin{pmatrix} 1 \\ 2 \\ 3 \end{pmatrix}$ N and **B** is given by $\begin{pmatrix} -2 \\ -2 \\ 0 \end{pmatrix}$ N. Find the force **C**.

As the particle is in equilibrium, the resultant force **A** + **B** + **C** must be equal to zero:

$$\mathbf{A} + \mathbf{B} + \mathbf{C} = \begin{pmatrix} 1 \\ 2 \\ 3 \end{pmatrix} + \begin{pmatrix} -2 \\ -2 \\ 0 \end{pmatrix} + \begin{pmatrix} a \\ b \\ c \end{pmatrix} = \begin{pmatrix} 1-2+a \\ 2-2+b \\ 3+0+c \end{pmatrix} = \begin{pmatrix} -1+a \\ b \\ 3+c \end{pmatrix} = \begin{pmatrix} 0 \\ 0 \\ 0 \end{pmatrix}$$

So $a = 1$, $b = 0$, $c = -3$ $\Rightarrow$ $\mathbf{C} = \begin{pmatrix} 1 \\ 0 \\ -3 \end{pmatrix}$ N

An eye for an i, a tooth for a j...

Taking M1 exams might feel like punishment, unless you revise that is — then it'll feel like an invigorating walk in the park.

M1 Section 3 — Practice Questions

Time to resolve the force applied to your revision along the question axis... That didn't sound as good as I hoped.
Still, at least you can distract yourself from my terrible sense of humour with these excellent practice questions.

Warm-up Questions

Whenever a numerical value of g is required in the questions below, take $g = 9.8$ ms^{-2}.

1) The following items are dropped from a height of 2 m onto a cushion:

   a) a full 330 ml drinks can   b) an empty drinks can   c) a table tennis ball

   The time each takes to fall is measured.
   Draw a model of each situation and list any assumptions which you've made.

2) A car is travelling at 25 mph along a straight level road.
   Draw a model of the situation and list any assumptions which you've made.

3) A mass of m kg is suspended by two light wires A and B, with
   angles 60° and 30° to the vertical respectively, as shown.
   The tension in A is 20 N. Find:

   a)   the tension in wire B,

   b)   the value of m.

4) A particle, Q, of mass m kg, is in equilibrium on a smooth plane
    which makes an angle of 60° to the vertical. This is achieved by
    an attached string S, with tension 70 N, angled at 10° to the plane,
    as shown. Draw a force diagram and find both the mass of Q and
    the reaction on it from the surface.

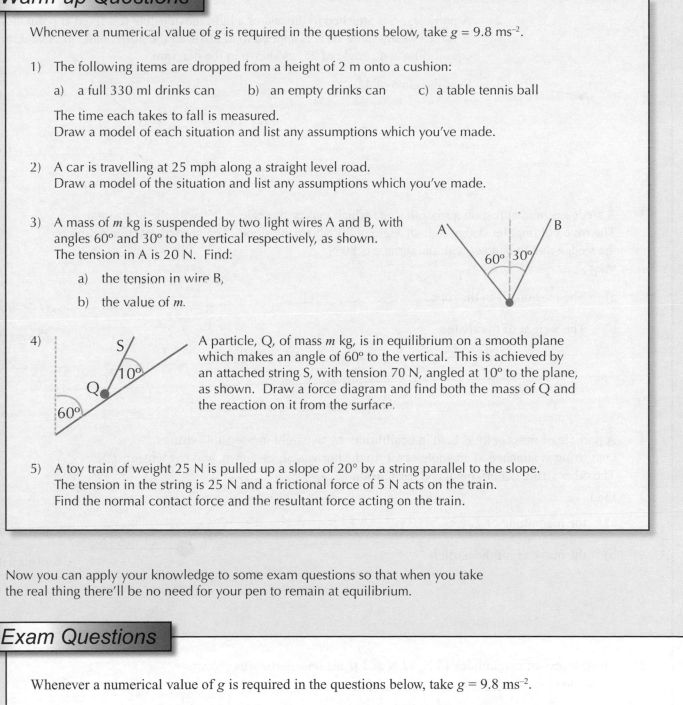

5) A toy train of weight 25 N is pulled up a slope of 20° by a string parallel to the slope.
   The tension in the string is 25 N and a frictional force of 5 N acts on the train.
   Find the normal contact force and the resultant force acting on the train.

Now you can apply your knowledge to some exam questions so that when you take
the real thing there'll be no need for your pen to remain at equilibrium.

Exam Questions

Whenever a numerical value of g is required in the questions below, take $g = 9.8$ ms^{-2}.

1   A box of mass 39 kg is at rest on a rough horizontal surface. The box is pushed with a
     force of 140 N from an angle of 20° above the horizontal. The box remains stationary.

   a)   Draw a diagram to show the four forces acting on the box.

   (2 marks)

   b)   Calculate the magnitude of the normal reaction force and the frictional force on the box.

   (4 marks)

M1 Section 3 — Practice Questions

Another page of questions to practise on here, so keep on truckin' (remembering that "truckin'" is a vector quantity with both magnitude *and* direction). The normal reaction to that joke is a sigh... on with the questions.

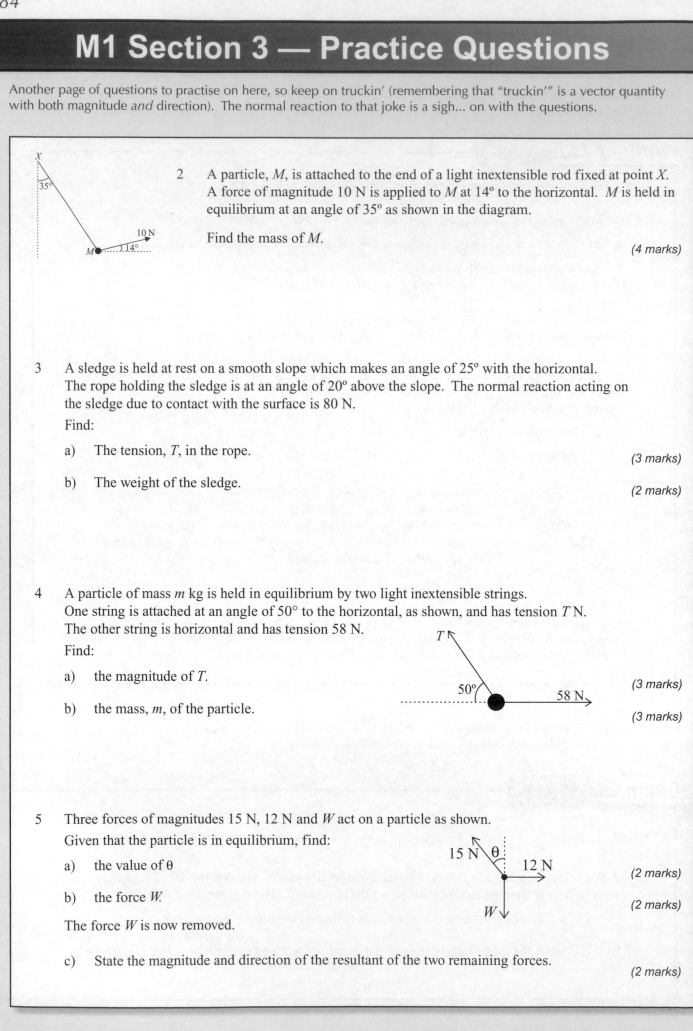

2   A particle, *M*, is attached to the end of a light inextensible rod fixed at point *X*. A force of magnitude 10 N is applied to *M* at 14° to the horizontal. *M* is held in equilibrium at an angle of 35° as shown in the diagram.

Find the mass of *M*.

(4 marks)

3   A sledge is held at rest on a smooth slope which makes an angle of 25° with the horizontal. The rope holding the sledge is at an angle of 20° above the slope. The normal reaction acting on the sledge due to contact with the surface is 80 N.

Find:

a)   The tension, *T*, in the rope.

(3 marks)

b)   The weight of the sledge.

(2 marks)

4   A particle of mass *m* kg is held in equilibrium by two light inextensible strings. One string is attached at an angle of 50° to the horizontal, as shown, and has tension *T* N. The other string is horizontal and has tension 58 N.

Find:

a)   the magnitude of *T*.

(3 marks)

b)   the mass, *m*, of the particle.

(3 marks)

5   Three forces of magnitudes 15 N, 12 N and *W* act on a particle as shown. Given that the particle is in equilibrium, find:

a)   the value of θ

(2 marks)

b)   the force *W*.

(2 marks)

The force *W* is now removed.

c)   State the magnitude and direction of the resultant of the two remaining forces.

(2 marks)

Newton's Laws

That clever chap Isaac Newton established 3 laws involving motion. You need to know __all__ of them.

Newton's Laws of Motion

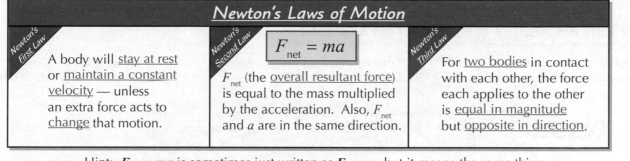

Newton's First Law
A body will stay at rest or maintain a constant velocity — unless an extra force acts to change that motion.

Newton's Second Law
$$F_{net} = ma$$
F_{net} (the overall resultant force) is equal to the mass multiplied by the acceleration. Also, F_{net} and a are in the same direction.

Newton's Third Law
For two bodies in contact with each other, the force each applies to the other is equal in magnitude but opposite in direction.

Hint: $F_{net} = ma$ is sometimes just written as $F = ma$, but it means the same thing.

F = ma equations are sometimes known as 'equations of motion'.

Resolve Forces in Perpendicular Directions

EXAMPLE A mass of 4 kg at rest on a smooth horizontal plane is acted on by a horizontal force of 5 N. Find the acceleration of the mass and the normal reaction from the plane. Take $g = 9.8$ ms^{-2}.

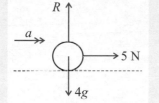

Resolve horizontally:
$F_{net} = ma$
$5 = 4a$
$a = 1.25$ ms^{-2} in the direction of the horizontal force

Always write $F_{net} = ma$ first.

Resolve vertically:
$F_{net} = ma$, so $R - 4g = 4 \times 0$
$R = 4g = 39.2$ N

EXAMPLE A particle of weight 30 N is being accelerated across a smooth horizontal plane by a force of 6 N acting at an angle of 25° to the horizontal, as shown. Given that the particle starts from rest, find:

    a) its speed after 4 seconds   b) the magnitude of the normal reaction with the plane.

a) Resolve horizontally:
$F_{net} = ma$
$6\cos25° = \dfrac{30}{g}a$ so $a = 1.776...$ ms^{-2}
$v = u + at$
$v = 0 + 1.776... \times 4 = 7.11$ ms^{-1} (to 3 s.f.)

b) Resolve vertically:
$F_{net} = ma$
$R + 6\sin25° - 30 = \dfrac{30}{g} \times 0$
So $R = 30 - 6\sin25° = 27.5$ N (to 3 s.f.)

For inclined plane questions, it's much easier to resolve forces parallel and perpendicular to the plane's surface.

EXAMPLE A mass of 600 g is propelled up the line of greatest slope of a smooth plane inclined at 30° to the horizontal. If its velocity is 3 ms^{-1} after the propelling force has stopped, find the distance it travels before coming to rest and the magnitude of the normal reaction. Use $g = 9.8$ ms^{-2}.

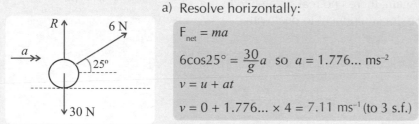

Resolve parallel to plane:
$F_{net} = ma$
$-0.6g\sin30° = 0.6a$
$a = -4.9$ ms^{-2}
$v^2 = u^2 + 2as$
$0 = 3^2 + 2(-4.9)s$
So $s = 0.918$ m (3 s.f.)

Taking up the plane as +ve.

Resolve perpendicular to plane:
$F_{net} = ma$
$R - 0.6g\cos30° = 0.6 \times 0$
So $R = 5.09$ N (3 s.f.)

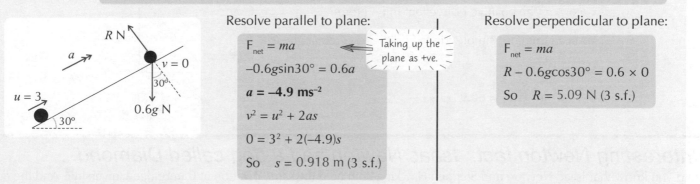

Newton's Laws

$F_{net} = ma$ is so flippin' awesome, you can even use it in two and three dimensions. How about that?

You can also apply **F = ma** to **i + j** Vectors...

Just when you thought you'd seen the last of those pesky **i + j** vectors, here they are popping up again. Don't worry though — there's nothing too difficult, it's very similar to the stuff you were doing on the previous page.

EXAMPLE A particle of mass m kg is acted on by two forces, $(6\mathbf{i} - \mathbf{j})$ N and $(2\mathbf{i} + 4\mathbf{j})$ N, resulting in an acceleration of magnitude 9 ms^{-2}. Find the value of m.

Resultant force, $\mathbf{R} = (6\mathbf{i} - \mathbf{j}) + (2\mathbf{i} + 4\mathbf{j}) = (8\mathbf{i} + 3\mathbf{j})$ N

Magnitude of **R**, $|\mathbf{R}| = \sqrt{8^2 + 3^2} = \sqrt{73} = 8.544$ N

*See p. 160 for a reminder about **i + j** vectors.*

Using $F = ma$: $8.544 = 9m$

$$\Rightarrow m = \frac{8.544}{9} = 0.949 \text{ kg (3 s.f.)}$$

The force of $(2\mathbf{i} + 4\mathbf{j})$ N ceases to be applied to the particle. Calculate the magnitude of the new acceleration.

The only force now acting on the particle is the $(6\mathbf{i} - \mathbf{j})$ N force.

This has magnitude $\sqrt{6^2 + (-1)^2} = \sqrt{37} = 6.083$ N.

So the new acceleration is given by: $a = \frac{F}{m} = \frac{6.083}{0.9493} = 6.41$ ms^{-2} (3 s.f.)

...and **Column Vectors**

Column vectors were covered on p. 161.

These questions are really common in exams. Again, there's no real difference to the stuff on the previous page — you just have <u>one extra component</u> to deal with.

EXAMPLE A force **F** accelerates a particle of mass 3 kg at a rate of $\binom{5}{9}$ ms^{-2}.

Find:

a)   **F**,

b)   the angle, θ, that **F** makes with the direction $\binom{1}{0}$.

a)   Use **F** = $m\mathbf{a}$:

$\mathbf{F} = 3\binom{5}{9} = \binom{15}{27}$ N.   *Yep, it really is as easy as that.*

b)   Think of the direction $\binom{1}{0}$ as the direction of the increasing x-axis, or 'the positive **i**-direction' in **i + j** form.

You can then use simple trig to find the required angle, θ:

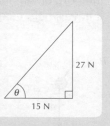

$\tan\theta = \frac{27}{15} = 1.8$

$\Rightarrow \theta = \tan^{-1}(1.8) = 60.9°$ (3 s.f.)

Interesting Newton fact: Isaac Newton had a dog called Diamond...

Did you know that Isaac Newton and Stephen Hawking both held the same position at Cambridge University? And the dog fact about Newton is true — don't ask me how I know such things, just bask in my amazing knowledge of all things trivial.

Connected Particles

Like Laurel goes with Hardy and Posh goes with Becks, some particles are destined to be together...

Connected Particles act like One Mass

Particles connected together have the <u>same speeds</u> and <u>magnitudes of acceleration</u> as each other, as long as the connection <u>holds</u>. So train carriages moving together have the same acceleration.

EXAMPLE

A 30 tonne locomotive engine is pulling a single 10 tonne carriage as shown. They are accelerating at 0.3 ms⁻² due to the force P generated by the engine. It's assumed that there are no forces resistant to motion. Find P and the tension in the coupling.

Here's the pretty picture:

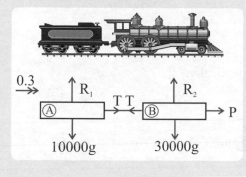

For A: $F_{net} = ma$

$\qquad T = 10\,000 \times 0.3$

$\qquad T = 3000$ N

If you weren't asked for the tension in the coupling, you could just consider the whole train as one object of mass 40 tonnes and use F = ma to find P.

For B: $F_{net} = ma$

$\qquad P - T = 30\,000 \times 0.3$

$\qquad P = 12\,000$ N

<u>Tensions</u> in connections act 'inwards', <u>away</u> from the particles. <u>Thrusts</u> (compressions) act 'outwards', <u>towards</u> the particles.

Pulleys (and 'Pegs') are always Smooth

In M1 questions, you can always assume that the <u>tension</u> in a string will be the <u>same</u> either side of a <u>smooth pulley</u>.

EXAMPLE

Masses of 3 kg and 5 kg are connected by an inextensible string and hang vertically either side of a smooth pulley. They are released from rest. Find their acceleration and the time it takes for each to move 40 cm. State any assumptions made in your model. Take $g = 9.8$ ms⁻².

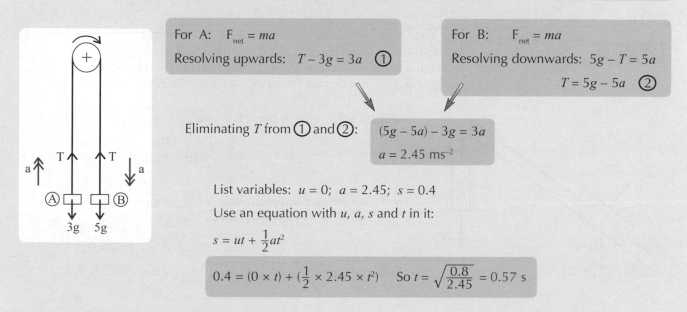

For A: $F_{net} = ma$
Resolving upwards: $T - 3g = 3a$ ①

For B: $F_{net} = ma$
Resolving downwards: $5g - T = 5a$
$\qquad\qquad\qquad\qquad\qquad T = 5g - 5a$ ②

Eliminating T from ① and ②: $(5g - 5a) - 3g = 3a$
$\qquad\qquad\qquad\qquad\qquad\qquad a = 2.45$ ms⁻²

List variables: $u = 0$; $a = 2.45$; $s = 0.4$

Use an equation with u, a, s and t in it:

$s = ut + \frac{1}{2}at^2$

$0.4 = (0 \times t) + (\frac{1}{2} \times 2.45 \times t^2)$ So $t = \sqrt{\dfrac{0.8}{2.45}} = 0.57$ s

Assumptions: The 3 kg mass does not hit the pulley; the 5 kg mass does not hit the ground; there's no air resistance; the string is 'light' so has zero mass; the string doesn't break; the pulley is fixed.

Connected Particles

Use F = ma in the Direction Each Particle Moves

Some connected particle systems can look a bit complex on first glance. There's no need to panic though, just keep doing what you're doing — consider each particle <u>separately</u> and everything will turn out <u>just fine</u>.

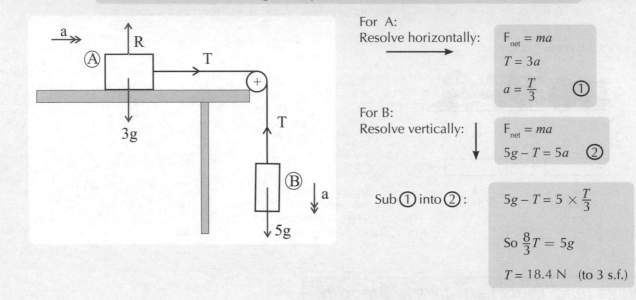

EXAMPLE

A mass of 3 kg is placed on a smooth horizontal table. A light inextensible string connects it over a smooth peg to a 5 kg mass which hangs vertically as shown. Find the tension in the string if the system is released from rest. Take $g = 9.8$ ms^{-2}.

For A:
Resolve horizontally:

$F_{net} = ma$

$T = 3a$

$a = \dfrac{T}{3}$ ①

For B:
Resolve vertically:

$F_{net} = ma$

$5g - T = 5a$ ②

Sub ① into ②:

$5g - T = 5 \times \dfrac{T}{3}$

So $\dfrac{8}{3}T = 5g$

$T = 18.4$ N (to 3 s.f.)

Rough Inclined Plane questions need Really Good force diagrams

You know the routine... resolve forces <u>parallel</u> and <u>perpendicular</u> to the plane... yawn.
Oh — and remember that friction always acts to <u>oppose</u> motion.

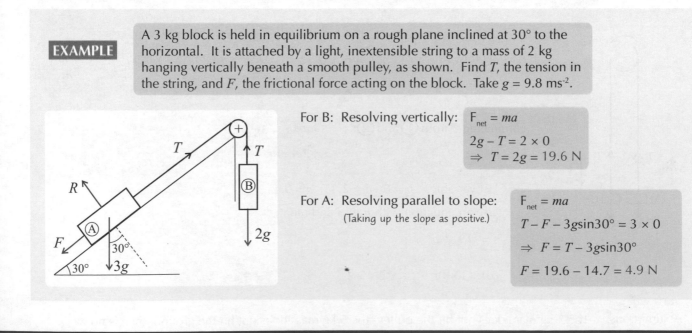

EXAMPLE

A 3 kg block is held in equilibrium on a rough plane inclined at 30° to the horizontal. It is attached by a light, inextensible string to a mass of 2 kg hanging vertically beneath a smooth pulley, as shown. Find T, the tension in the string, and F, the frictional force acting on the block. Take $g = 9.8$ ms^{-2}.

For B: Resolving vertically:

$F_{net} = ma$

$2g - T = 2 \times 0$

$\Rightarrow T = 2g = 19.6$ N

For A: Resolving parallel to slope:
(Taking up the slope as positive.)

$F_{net} = ma$

$T - F - 3g\sin30° = 3 \times 0$

$\Rightarrow F = T - 3g\sin30°$

$F = 19.6 - 14.7 = 4.9$ N

Useful if you're hanging over a Batman-style killer crocodile pit...

It makes things a lot easier when you know that connected particles act like one mass, and that in M1 pulleys can always be treated as smooth. Those examiners occasionally do try to make your life easier, honestly.

M1 Section 4 — Practice Questions

Find the frictional force between a student's pen and a sheet of paper. Model the student and the pen as connected particles... or else you could just answer the questions below, which would be a better use of your time.

Warm-up Questions

Whenever a numerical value of g is required in the questions below, take $g = 9.8$ ms^2.

1) A horizontal force of 2 N acts on a 1.5 kg particle initially at rest on a smooth horizontal plane. Find the speed of the particle 3 seconds later.

2) Two forces act on a particle of mass 8 kg which is initially at rest on a smooth horizontal plane. The two forces are $(24\mathbf{i} + 18\mathbf{j})$ N and $(6\mathbf{i} + 22\mathbf{j})$ N (with $\mathbf{i}$ and $\mathbf{j}$ being perpendicular unit vectors in the plane). Find the magnitude and direction of the resulting acceleration of the particle and the displacement of the particle after 3 seconds.

3) A force of $\begin{pmatrix} 6 \\ 4 \\ 2 \end{pmatrix}$ N acts on a particle of mass 2 kg. Give the acceleration of the particle as a vector.

4) A 2 tonne tractor experiences a resistance force of 1000 N whilst driving along a straight horizontal road. If the tractor engine provides a forward force of 1500 N and it's pulling a 1 tonne trailer, find the resistance force acting on the trailer, and the tension in the coupling between the tractor and trailer, if they are moving with constant speed.

5) Two particles are connected by a light inextensible string, and hang in a vertical plane either side of a smooth pulley. When released from rest the particles accelerate at 1.2 ms^{-2}. If the heavier mass is 4 kg, find the weight of the other.

6) Two particles of mass 3 kg and 4 kg are connected by a light, inextensible string passing over a smooth pulley as shown. The 3 kg mass is on a smooth slope angled at 40° to the horizontal. Find the acceleration of the system if released from rest, and find the tension in the string. What force acting on the 3 kg mass parallel to the plane would be needed to maintain equilibrium?

Right, now you've done the warm-up questions, it's time to dive head-first into these exam questions. May the ma be with you...

Exam Questions

Whenever a numerical value of g is required in the questions below, take $g = 9.8$ ms^{-2}.

1   A car of mass 1500 kg is pulling a caravan of mass 500 kg. They experience resistance forces totalling 1000 N and 200 N respectively. The forward force generated by the car's engine is 2500 N. The coupling between the two does not break.

   a)   Find the acceleration of the car and caravan.

(3 marks)

   b)   Find the tension in the coupling.

(2 marks)

2   Two forces, $(x\mathbf{i} + y\mathbf{j})$ N and $(5\mathbf{i} + \mathbf{j})$ N, act on a particle P of mass 2.5 kg. The resultant of the two forces is $(8\mathbf{i} - 3\mathbf{j})$ N. Find:

   a)   the values of x and y,

(2 marks)

   b)   the acceleration of P.

(3 marks)

M1 Section 4 — Practice Questions

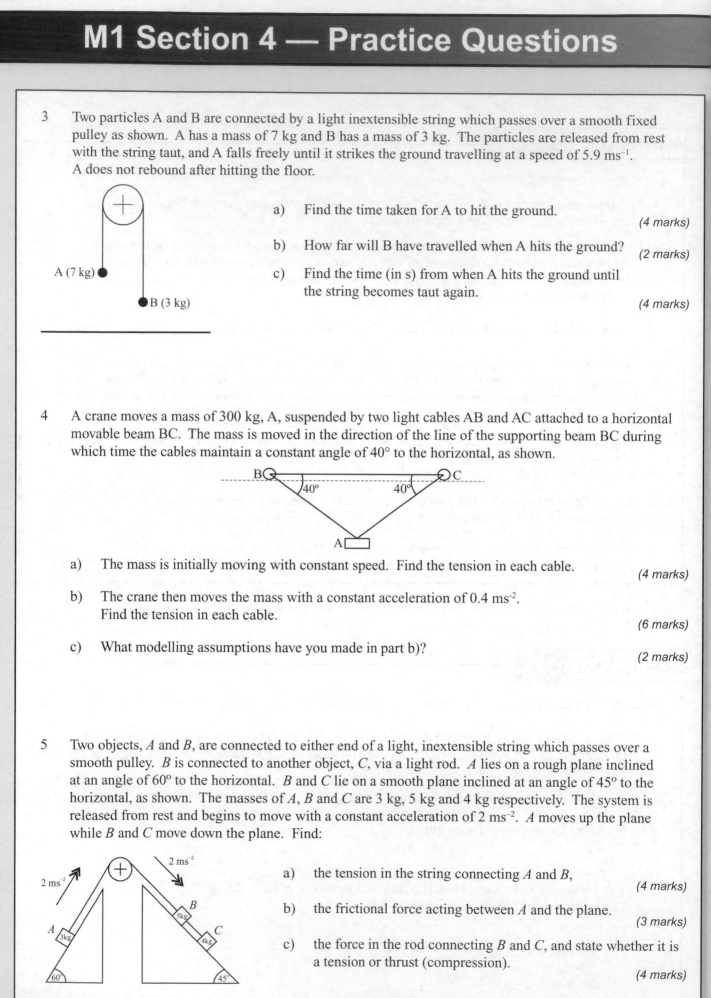

3   Two particles A and B are connected by a light inextensible string which passes over a smooth fixed pulley as shown. A has a mass of 7 kg and B has a mass of 3 kg. The particles are released from rest with the string taut, and A falls freely until it strikes the ground travelling at a speed of 5.9 ms⁻¹. A does not rebound after hitting the floor.

A (7 kg)

B (3 kg)

a)   Find the time taken for A to hit the ground.

(4 marks)

b)   How far will B have travelled when A hits the ground?

(2 marks)

c)   Find the time (in s) from when A hits the ground until the string becomes taut again.

(4 marks)

4   A crane moves a mass of 300 kg, A, suspended by two light cables AB and AC attached to a horizontal movable beam BC. The mass is moved in the direction of the line of the supporting beam BC during which time the cables maintain a constant angle of 40° to the horizontal, as shown.

B   40°   40°   C

A

a)   The mass is initially moving with constant speed. Find the tension in each cable.

(4 marks)

b)   The crane then moves the mass with a constant acceleration of 0.4 ms⁻².
Find the tension in each cable.

(6 marks)

c)   What modelling assumptions have you made in part b)?

(2 marks)

5   Two objects, *A* and *B*, are connected to either end of a light, inextensible string which passes over a smooth pulley. *B* is connected to another object, *C*, via a light rod. *A* lies on a rough plane inclined at an angle of 60° to the horizontal. *B* and *C* lie on a smooth plane inclined at an angle of 45° to the horizontal, as shown. The masses of *A*, *B* and *C* are 3 kg, 5 kg and 4 kg respectively. The system is released from rest and begins to move with a constant acceleration of 2 ms⁻². *A* moves up the plane while *B* and *C* move down the plane. Find:

2 ms⁻²

2 ms⁻²

B
5kg

A
3kg

C
4kg

60°   45°

a)   the tension in the string connecting *A* and *B*,

(4 marks)

b)   the frictional force acting between *A* and the plane.

(3 marks)

c)   the force in the rod connecting *B* and *C*, and state whether it is a tension or thrust (compression).

(4 marks)

Projectiles

A 'projectile' is just any old object that's been lobbed through the air. When you're doing projectile questions you'll have to model the motion of particles in two dimensions whilst ignoring air resistance.

Split *Velocity of Projection* into *Two Components*

A particle projected with a speed u at an angle α to the horizontal has two components of initial velocity — one horizontal (parallel to the x-axis) and one vertical (parallel to the y-axis). These are called x and y components, and they make projectile questions dead easy to deal with:

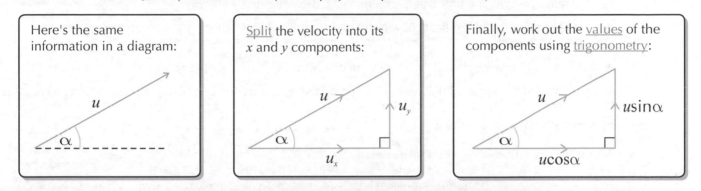

Here's the same information in a diagram:

Split the velocity into its x and y components:

Finally, work out the values of the components using trigonometry:

Split the Motion into *Horizontal* and *Vertical* Components too

Split everything you know about the motion into horizontal and vertical components too. Then you can deal with them separately using the 'uvast' equations. The only thing that's the same in both directions is time — so this connects the two directions. Remember that the only acceleration is due to gravity — so horizontal acceleration is zero.

EXAMPLE A stone is thrown horizontally with speed 10 ms⁻¹ from a height of 2 m above the horizontal ground. Find the time taken for the stone to hit the ground and the horizontal distance travelled before impact. Find also the stone's velocity after 0.5 s.

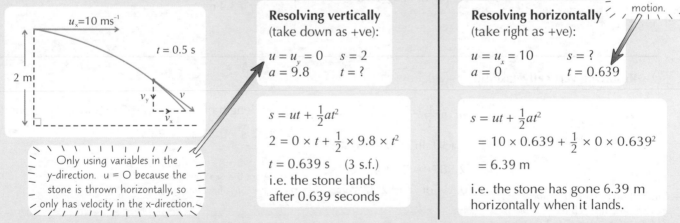

> The same as for the vertical motion.

Resolving vertically (take down as +ve):

$u = u_y = 0$ $s = 2$
$a = 9.8$ $t = ?$

$s = ut + \frac{1}{2}at^2$

$2 = 0 \times t + \frac{1}{2} \times 9.8 \times t^2$

$t = 0.639$ s   (3 s.f.)
i.e. the stone lands after 0.639 seconds

Resolving horizontally (take right as +ve):

$u = u_x = 10$ $s = ?$
$a = 0$ $t = 0.639$

$s = ut + \frac{1}{2}at^2$

$= 10 \times 0.639 + \frac{1}{2} \times 0 \times 0.639^2$

$= 6.39$ m

i.e. the stone has gone 6.39 m horizontally when it lands.

> Only using variables in the y-direction. $u = 0$ because the stone is thrown horizontally, so only has velocity in the x-direction.

Now find the velocity after 0.5 s — again, keep the vertical and horizontal bits separate.

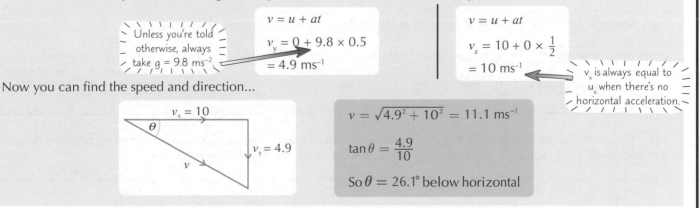

> Unless you're told otherwise, always take $g = 9.8$ ms⁻².

$v = u + at$

$v_y = 0 + 9.8 \times 0.5$

$= 4.9$ ms⁻¹

$v = u + at$

$v_x = 10 + 0 \times \frac{1}{2}$

$= 10$ ms⁻¹

> v_x is always equal to u_x when there's no horizontal acceleration.

Now you can find the speed and direction...

$v = \sqrt{4.9^2 + 10^2} = 11.1$ ms⁻¹

$\tan\theta = \dfrac{4.9}{10}$

So $\theta = 26.1°$ below horizontal

Projectiles

EXAMPLE A cricket ball is projected with a speed of 30 ms⁻¹ at an angle of 25° to the horizontal.
Assume the ground is horizontal and the ball is struck from a point 1.5 m above the ground. Find:

a) the maximum height the ball reaches (h),

b) the horizontal distance travelled by the ball before it hits the ground (r),

c) the length of time the ball is at least 5 m above the ground.

d) the magnitude of the vertical component of the ball's velocity when its speed is 29 ms⁻¹.

A heavier ball is projected with the same velocity under the same conditions.

e) How would the range of the heavier ball predicted by this model compare with your answer to part b)?

---

a) **Resolving vertically** (take up as +ve):

$u = 30\sin 25°$ $v = 0$

$a = -9.8$ $s = ?$

The ball will momentarily stop moving vertically when it reaches its maximum height.

$v^2 = u^2 + 2as$

$0 = (30\sin 25°)^2 + 2(-9.8 \times s)$

$s = 8.20\,\text{m}$

$h = 8.20\,\text{m} + 1.5\,\text{m} = 9.70\,\text{m}$

Don't forget to add the height from which the ball is hit.

---

b) **Resolving vertically** (take up as +ve):

$s = -1.5$

$a = -9.8$

$u = 30\sin 25°$

$t = ?$

Using the quadratic formula you get two answers, but time can't be negative, so forget about this answer.

$s = ut + \frac{1}{2}at^2$

$-1.5 = (30\sin 25°)t - \frac{1}{2}(9.8)t^2$

$t^2 - 2.587t - 0.306 = 0$

$t = -0.11$ or $t = \mathbf{2.70\,s}$

Resolving horizontally (take right as +ve)

$s = r$ $u = 30\cos 25°$

$t = 2.70$ $a = 0$

$s = ut + \frac{1}{2}at^2$

$r = 30\cos 25° \times 2.70 + \frac{1}{2} \times 0 \times 2.70^2$

$= 73.4\,\text{m}$

---

c) **Resolving vertically** (take up as +ve):

$s = 3.5$

$a = -9.8$

$u = 30\sin 25°$

$t = ?$

The ball is hit from 1.5 m above ground, so 5 m − 1.5 m = 3.5 m

$s = ut + \frac{1}{2}at^2$

$3.5 = (30\sin 25°)t - \frac{1}{2}(9.8)t^2$

$t^2 - 2.587t + 0.714 = 0$

$t = 0.31$ or $t = 2.27\,s$

These are the two times when the ball is 5 m above the ground.

So, length of time at least 5 m above the ground:

$2.27\,\text{s} - 0.31\,\text{s} = 1.96\,\text{s}$

---

d) Speed, $v = \sqrt{v_x^2 + v_y^2}$. v_x is always 30cos25°, as there is no acceleration horizontally, so:

$29 = \sqrt{(30\cos 25°)^2 + v_y^2} \Rightarrow v_y^2 = 29^2 - (30\cos 25°)^2 = 101.75$.

So, magnitude of $v_y = 10.1\,\text{ms}^{-1}$ (3 s.f.).

Remember, v_x is the horizontal component and v_y the vertical component of the ball's velocity.

---

e) This model would predict the range of the heavier ball as exactly the same as the answer to b), because the mass does not feature in any of the equations used to model the flight of the ball.

Projectiles

Just one last example of projectile motion. But boy is it a beauty...

EXAMPLE

A golf ball is struck from a point A on a horizontal plane. When the ball has moved a horizontal distance x, its height above the plane is y. The ball is modelled as a particle projected with initial speed u ms^{-1} at an angle α.

a) Show that $y = x\tan\alpha - \dfrac{gx^2}{2u^2\cos^2\alpha}$, where g is acceleration due to gravity.

The ball just passes over the top of a 10 m tall tree, which is 45 m away. Given that $\alpha = 45°$,

b) find the speed of the ball as it passes over the tree.

a) Displacement, acceleration and initial velocity are the only variables in the formula, so use these. Also use time, because that's the variable which connects the two components of motion. The formula includes motion in both directions (x and y), so form two equations and substitute one into the other:

Resolving horizontally (taking right as +ve):

$u_x = u\cos\alpha \qquad a = 0$
$s = x \qquad\qquad t = t$

When you're using these variables, this is the obvious equation to use.

Using $s = ut + \frac{1}{2}at^2$:

$x = u\cos\alpha \times t$

Rearrange to make t the subject:

$t = \dfrac{x}{u\cos\alpha}$ — call this **equation 1**

t doesn't appear in the final formula, so by making it the subject you can eliminate it.

Resolving vertically (taking up as +ve):

$u_y = u\sin\alpha \qquad a = -g$
$s = y \qquad\qquad t = t$

It would be a massive pain to make t the subject here, so do it with the other equation.

Using $s = ut + \frac{1}{2}at^2$:

$y = (u\sin\alpha \times t) - \frac{1}{2}gt^2$ — call this **equation 2**

t is the same horizontally and vertically, so you can <u>substitute</u> **equation 1** into **equation 2** and eliminate t:

$$y = u\sin\alpha \times \frac{x}{u\cos\alpha} - \frac{1}{2}g\left(\frac{x}{u\cos\alpha}\right)^2 = x\frac{\sin\alpha}{\cos\alpha} - \frac{1}{2}g\left(\frac{x^2}{u^2\cos^2\alpha}\right)$$

$\dfrac{\sin\theta}{\cos\theta} = \tan\theta$ $= x\tan\alpha - \dfrac{gx^2}{2u^2\cos^2\alpha}$ — as required.

b) Using the result from a), and substituting $x = 45$, $y = 10$ and $\alpha = 45°$:

$10 = 45\tan45° - \dfrac{9.8 \times 45^2}{2u^2 \times \cos^2 45°} = 45 - \dfrac{19\,845}{u^2}$

If you need to round part way through a calculation, then round to <u>more</u> s.f. than your final answer will be rounded to. A better idea is not to round at all and use your calculator's memory.

Rearrange to find the speed of projection, u:

$35u^2 = 19\,845 \Rightarrow u = \mathbf{23.81\,ms^{-1}}$

Now resolve to find the components of the ball's velocity as it passes over the tree:

Resolving horizontally (taking right as +ve):

$v_x = u_x = 23.81\cos45° = \mathbf{16.84\ ms^{-1}}$

Remember — with projectiles there's no horizontal acceleration, so v_x always equals u_x.

Resolving vertically (taking up as +ve):

$u_y = 23.81\sin45° \qquad a = -g$
$s = 10 \qquad\qquad v_y = ?$

Using $v^2 = u^2 + 2as$:

$v_y^2 = 283.46 - 2 \times 9.8 \times 10 = \mathbf{87.46}$

Don't bother finding the square root, as you need v_y^2 in the next step. Sneaky.

Now you can find the speed: $v = \sqrt{v_x^2 + v_y^2} = 19.3\,ms^{-1}$ (3 s.f.)

Projectiles — they're all about throwing up. Or across. Or slightly down...

The main thing to remember here is that <u>horizontal acceleration is zero</u> — great news because it makes half the calculations as easy as a log-falling beginner's class. Oh — and remember to keep track of which directions are positive and negative.

M1 Section 5 — Practice Questions

Well, if you've been revising M1 in order, that's your lot. Have a butcher's at these warm-up questions, then it's onwards and upwards, projectile style.

Warm-up Questions

Whenever a numerical value of g is required in the questions below, take $g = 9.8$ ms^{-2}.

1) A particle is projected with initial velocity u ms^{-1} at an angle α to the horizontal. What is the initial velocity of the particle in the direction parallel to the horizontal in terms of u and α?

2) A rifle fires a bullet horizontally at 120 ms^{-1}. The target is hit at a horizontal distance of 60 m from the end of the rifle. Find how far the target is vertically below the end of the rifle.

3) A golf ball takes 4 seconds to land after being hit with a golf club from a point on the horizontal ground. If it leaves the club with a speed of 22 ms^{-1}, at an angle of α to the horizontal, find α.

4) A particle is projected with velocity 20 ms^{-1} at an angle of 20° above the horizontal. The particle lands at the level of projection 30 seconds later. Find the minimum speed of the particle during its flight.

And it's the final furlong — one last dash to the finish.

Exam Questions

Whenever a numerical value of g is required in the questions below, take $g = 9.8$ ms^{-2}.

1 A stationary football is kicked with a speed of 20 ms^{-1}, at an angle of 30° to the horizontal, towards a goal 30 m away. The crossbar is 2.5 m above the level ground. Assuming the path of the ball is not impeded, determine whether the ball passes above or below the crossbar. What assumptions does your model make?

(6 marks)

2

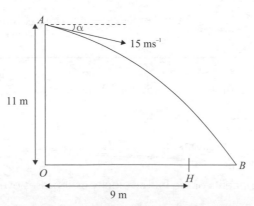

A stone is thrown from point A on the edge of a cliff, towards a point H, which is on horizontal ground. The point O is on the ground, 11 m vertically below the point of projection. The stone is thrown with speed 15 ms^{-1} at an angle α below the horizontal, where $\tan\alpha = \frac{3}{4}$.

The horizontal distance from O to H is 9 m.

The stone misses the point H and hits the ground at point B, as shown above. Find:

a) the time taken by the stone to reach the ground,

(5 marks)

b) the horizontal distance the stone misses H by,

(3 marks)

c) the speed of the stone when it lands at B,

(5 marks)

d) the angle between the direction of motion and the horizontal as the ball lands at B.

(2 marks)

General Certificate of Education
Advanced Subsidiary (AS) and Advanced Level

Mechanics M1 — Practice Exam One

Time Allowed: 1 hour 30 min

Graphical calculators may be used for this exam.

Whenever a numerical value of g is required, take g = 9.8 ms⁻².

Give any non-exact numerical answers to an appropriate degree of accuracy.

There are 72 marks available for this paper.

(handwritten annotations)
15ms⁻¹ →   40ms⁻¹ →   26ms⁻¹ →
A   B   C
t=4   a = -2·8

Section A (36 marks)

1   A motorcyclist is travelling at 15 ms⁻¹. As he passes point A on a straight section of road, he accelerates uniformly for 4 s until he passes point B at 40 ms⁻¹. He then immediately decelerates at 2.8 ms⁻² so that when he passes point C he is travelling at 26 ms⁻¹.
Find:

   (handwritten working)
   v=u+at
   40=15+4a
   25=4a
   25/4 = a
   a=6·25 ✓

   26=40+2·8t
   -14=-2·8t
   t=5s ✓

   v²=u²+2as
   26²=15²+2(11/9)s

   a)   his acceleration between A and B,   *(2 marks)*

   b)   the time to travel from B to C,   *(2 marks)*

   (handwritten working)
   v²=u²+2as
   26²=15²+2·
   S=
   u=15
   v=26   26=15+9a
   u=   11=9a   ∴ s=1
   t=9   11/9 =a

   c)   the distance from A to C.   *(3 marks)*

2   A particle P sets off from the origin at $t = 0$ and starts to move along the x-axis in the direction of increasing x. After t seconds, P has velocity v ms⁻¹, where $v = 11t - 2t^2$ for $0 \leq t \leq 5$ and $v = -175 + 56t - 4t^2$ for $t > 5$.
Find:

   a)   the displacement of P from the origin at $t = 5$,   *(4 marks)*

   b)   the maximum velocity of P for $t > 5$.   *(4 marks)*

   (handwritten annotations)
   F = √13
   F₁
   3
   2
   2
   F₂   t

3   A particle of mass 0.5 kg moves under the action of two forces, $\mathbf{F}_1$ and $\mathbf{F}_2$, where $\mathbf{F}_1 = (3\mathbf{i} + 2\mathbf{j})$ N and $\mathbf{F}_2 = (2\mathbf{i} - \mathbf{j})$ N.

   a)   Find, in degrees correct to one decimal place, the angle which the resultant force makes with the unit vector $\mathbf{i}$.   *(3 marks)*

   b)   Find, correct to three significant figures, the magnitude of the acceleration of the particle.   *(4 marks)*

4   A car of mass 1600 kg is towing a boat of mass 3000 kg along a straight, horizontal road. The car experiences a resistive force of magnitude 400 N and the boat experiences a constant resistive force of magnitude R N. A driving force of magnitude 4300 N acts on the car. The vehicles accelerate at 0.8 ms^{-2}.

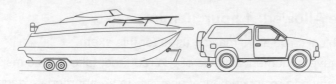

Assuming that the tow bar connecting the car to the boat is horizontal, find:

a)   the tension, T, in the tow bar,

(3 marks)

b)   the resistance force, R, acting on the boat.

(3 marks)

5   A block of mass 5 kg is held at rest on a rough inclined plane by a light, inextensible string. The angle between the plane and the horizontal is 30°, the tension in the string is T N, and the frictional force acting on the block is 12 N. The string is parallel to the slope, and the block is on the point of moving up the slope.

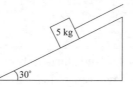

a)   Find the reaction force of the plane on the block.

(2 marks)

b)   Find the value of T.

(2 marks)

The string holding the block is cut and the block begins to move down the slope.

c)   Calculate the resultant force, F_{net}, acting on the block parallel to the slope.

(2 marks)

d)   Hence find the block's acceleration down the slope.

(2 marks)

Section B (36 marks)

6   A frog jumps off a rock of height 0.5 m with initial velocity U at an angle α° above the horizontal. The frog lands on horizontal ground at point P, as shown.

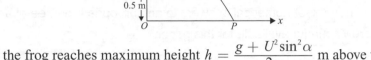

a)   Show that the frog reaches maximum height $h = \dfrac{g + U^2\sin^2\alpha}{2g}$ m above the ground, where g is the acceleration due to gravity.

(4 marks)

b)   Find an expression for the time, t, it takes the frog to reach this height, in terms of U, g and α.

(3 marks)

c)   Show that V, the speed of the frog when it lands at P, is $V = \sqrt{U^2 + g}$ ms^{-1}.

(5 marks)

d)   You are now given that $\alpha = 45^\circ$. Show that the equation of the frog's trajectory is

$$y = \frac{1}{2} + x - \frac{gx^2}{U^2},$$

referred to the coordinate axes shown in the diagram.

(4 marks)

You are also given that the horizontal range of the frog's jump is 0.5 m.

e)   Using your answer to part d), or otherwise, find U, the frog's initial velocity.

(3 marks)

7   A particle A of mass 3 kg is placed on a rough plane inclined at an angle of $\tan^{-1}\frac{3}{4}$ to the horizontal and is attached by a light, inextensible string to a second particle B of mass 4 kg. The string passes over a smooth pulley at the top of the inclined plane so that particle B hangs freely. When the system is released, particle B moves downwards vertically with an acceleration of 1.4 ms^{-2} and A moves up the plane.

a)   Draw a diagram showing clearly *all* the forces acting on the particles.

(1 mark)

b)   State what information in the question tells you that:

   (i)   the tension is the same throughout the string,

(1 mark)

   (ii)   the magnitudes of the accelerations of A and B are the same.

(1 mark)

Find:

c)   the normal reaction between particle A and the plane, to 2 decimal places,

(2 marks)

d)   the tension in the string,

(2 marks)

e)   the frictional force acting on particle A.

(3 marks)

Two seconds after the particles are released, the string breaks. A then continues up the plane until it comes instantaneously to rest. At no point does A reach the pulley. Find:

f)   how far particle B moves from the start of the motion until the string breaks,

(2 marks)

g)   how far particle A moves from the instant the string breaks until it comes to rest.

(5 marks)

General Certificate of Education
Advanced Subsidiary (AS) and Advanced Level

Mechanics M1 — Practice Exam Two

Time Allowed: 1 hour 30 min

Graphical calculators may be used for this exam.

Whenever a numerical value of g is required, take g = 9.8 ms^{-2}.

Give any non-exact numerical answers to an appropriate degree of accuracy.

There are 72 marks available for this paper.

Section A (36 marks)

1   Three forces act at a point, O, as shown below.

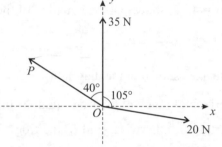

a)   Given that there is no net force in the direction of the x-axis, find P.

(2 marks)

b)   Find the magnitude and direction of the resultant force, R.

(3 marks)

2   A rocket with mass 1 400 000 kg is launched vertically upwards by engines providing a force of 34 000 000 N.

a)   Calculate the expected acceleration of the rocket, assuming that the only other force acting on the rocket is its weight.

(2 marks)

b)   The actual acceleration is measured at 12 ms^{-2}.
      Find the magnitude of the total resistive force, R, acting on the rocket.

(2 marks)

c)   Find the time taken for the rocket to reach a height of 20 km. Give your answer to the nearest second.

(2 marks)

d)   State one modelling assumption you have made.

(1 mark)

3   A painting is hung on a wall by two light, inextensible strings. The painting hangs in equilibrium, with the strings making angles of 30° with the horizontal, as shown.

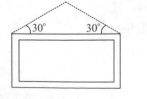

a)   Show that the tension in the two strings is equal.

(2 marks)

b)   Given that the tension in each string has magnitude 49 N, find the mass of the painting.

(3 marks)

4

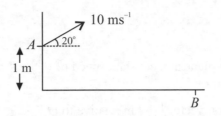

A stone is thrown from *A*, at a height of 1 m above the ground. The stone's initial velocity is 10 ms⁻¹ at an angle of 20° above the horizontal. The stone lands on the horizontal ground at *B*. Find:

a)   the maximum height the stone reaches during its flight,

(3 marks)

b)   the time it takes the stone to travel from *A* to *B*.

(4 marks)

5   A roller coaster moves from rest along a track with constant acceleration. Its motion is modelled as follows:

• The roller coaster takes 2 s to reach a speed of 6 ms⁻¹.
• It then travels at a constant speed for 15 s.
• The roller coaster decelerates to rest in 1 s as it reaches the top of the hill.
• It then waits for 5 s before accelerating down a vertical slope for 4 s, reaching a maximum speed of 30 ms⁻¹.

a)   Draw a speed-time graph representing the motion of the roller coaster.

(2 marks)

b)   Find the greatest acceleration experienced by the roller coaster.

(3 marks)

c)   What is the total distance travelled by the roller coaster?

(3 marks)

6

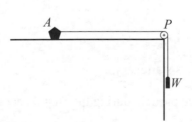

A particle, *A*, is attached to a weight, *W*, by a light inextensible string which passes over a smooth pulley, *P*, as shown. When the system is released from rest, with the string taut, *A* and *W* experience an acceleration of magnitude 4 ms⁻². *A* moves across a rough horizontal plane and *W* falls vertically.
A and *W* have masses of 0.2 kg and 0.3 kg respectively.

a)   Find the frictional force, *F*, between *A* and the horizontal plane.

(3 marks)

b)   How did you use the information that the pulley is smooth?

(1 mark)

Section B (36 marks)

7   A mouse is travelling on a horizontal plane at a constant speed of $\begin{pmatrix} 3 \\ 4 \end{pmatrix}$ ms^{-1}.
At time $t = 0$ s, the mouse is at a point O.

It heads for a mouse hole with position vector $\begin{pmatrix} 9 \\ 12 \end{pmatrix}$ m relative to O.

a)   Calculate the time it takes the mouse to reach the hole.

(3 marks)

Also at time t = 0 s, a cat of mass 3 kg is at rest with position vector $\begin{pmatrix} -3 \\ 3 \end{pmatrix}$ m relative to O.
The cat sees the mouse and immediately runs towards the hole to intercept it.

b)   The mouse continues to move with the same constant velocity, and the cat moves with constant
acceleration, **a**, and catches the mouse just as it reaches the hole. Find **a**.

(4 marks)

c)   Find the angle that the cat's acceleration makes with the unit vector $\begin{pmatrix} 1 \\ 0 \end{pmatrix}$.

(2 marks)

d)   The cat runs with a horizontal forward force of $\begin{pmatrix} 28 \\ 12 \end{pmatrix}$ N. Find the magnitude of the total resistive
force acting on the cat.

(4 marks)

After catching the mouse, the cat carries it outside. The cat passes through O with velocity
$\begin{pmatrix} -5 \\ -4 \end{pmatrix}$ ms^{-1} and acceleration $\begin{pmatrix} -2 \\ 1 \end{pmatrix}$ ms^{-2}.

e)   Assuming that the cat's acceleration remains constant, find the position vector of the cat relative
to O when it is travelling parallel to the unit vector $\begin{pmatrix} 1 \\ 0 \end{pmatrix}$.

(6 marks)

8   The displacement, x m, of a particle from a fixed point O at time t s is $x = t^4 - 4t^3 - 8t^2 + 1$, where $t \geq 0$.
Find:

a)   the particle's displacement at time $t = 2$ s,

(1 mark)

b)   the particle's velocity at time $t = 1$ s,

(3 marks)

c)   the time(s) at which the particle is stationary,

(4 marks)

d)   the total distance travelled by the particle during the first 5 seconds of motion,

(4 marks)

e)   the time at which the particle's acceleration is zero.

(5 marks)

Algorithms

Welcome to the wonderful world of Decision Maths. And what a good decision it was too. This page is on algorithms, which aren't as scary as they sound. You've probably come across algorithms before, though you might not know it.

Algorithms are sets of Instructions

An <u>algorithm</u> is just a fancy mathematical name for a <u>set of instructions</u> for <u>solving</u> a problem. You come across lots of algorithms in everyday life — <u>recipes</u>, <u>directions</u> and <u>assembly instructions</u> are all examples of algorithms.

1) Algorithms start with an <u>input</u> (e.g. in a recipe, the input is the raw ingredients). You carry out the algorithm on the input, following the instructions <u>in order</u>.

Anyone should be able to follow an algorithm — not just the person who wrote it.

2) Algorithms have an <u>end result</u> — something that you <u>achieve</u> by carrying out the algorithm (e.g. a cake). An algorithm is said to be <u>correct</u> if it achieves its end result.

3) Algorithms will <u>stop</u> when you've reached a <u>solution</u>, or produced your <u>finished product</u> — they're <u>finite</u>. They <u>must</u> have a <u>stopping condition</u> — an <u>instruction</u> that tells you to stop when you've reached a certain point.

4) Algorithms are often written so that <u>computers</u> could follow the instructions. <u>Computer programming</u> is an important application of Decision Maths.

In Maths, the End Result is the Solution

Most mathematical algorithms are general — they work for a range of different inputs.

Algorithms can be used to solve <u>mathematical problems</u> too.

1) The <u>input</u> in a mathematical algorithm is the <u>number</u> (or numbers) you start with. Your <u>end result</u> (<u>output</u>) is the <u>final number</u> you end up with — this'll be the <u>solution</u> to the original problem.

2) Any number you put in will have a <u>unique</u> output — you won't get different sets of solutions for the same input.

3) It's a good idea to <u>write down</u> the numbers each instruction produces in a <u>table</u> — sometimes the algorithm will <u>tell you</u> when to do this. This table is called a <u>trace table</u>.

The Russian Peasant algorithm Multiplies two numbers

The Russian Peasant algorithm is a well-known algorithm that multiplies two numbers together. And I've no idea what Russian peasants have to do with it.

1) Write down the two numbers that you are multiplying in a table. Call them x and y.

2) Divide x by 2 and write down the result underneath x, ignoring any halves. ◄ *E.g. if $x = 11$, when you divide it by 2 you write down 5, not 5.5.*

3) Multiply y by 2 and write down the result underneath y.

4) Repeat steps 2) - 3) for the numbers in the new row. Keep going until the number in the x-column is 1. *This is an example of a stopping condition.*

5) Work down your table and cross out every row that has an even value for x.

6) Add up the remaining numbers in the y-column (i.e. the ones that haven't been crossed out). This is the solution xy.

EXAMPLE
Multiply 37 and 43.

x	y
37	43
~~18~~	~~86~~
9	172
~~4~~	~~344~~
~~2~~	~~688~~
1	1376
Total	1591

37 ÷ 2 = 18.5, so write down 18.

The x-values in these rows are even, so cross them out.

This is the end result — 37 × 43 = 1591.

EXAMPLE
Multiply 21 and 52.

x	y
21	52
~~10~~	~~104~~
5	208
~~2~~	~~416~~
1	832
Total	1092

This is the end result — 21 × 52 = 1092.

Feel the beat of the rithm of the night...

For your homework tonight, I would like you to make me a cake please. My favourite's carrot cake with cream cheese icing.

Algorithms

There's a bit more background stuff you need to know about algorithms — it's the mathsiest bit in this section, so enjoy it while you can. Then it's onto pseudo-code, when you get to be a pseudo-computer.

The **Order** of an algorithm tells you how **Fast** it is

It's useful to know how long an algorithm takes to run — that way you can compare two algorithms and decide which is better.

1) The size of an algorithm is the number of inputs you have — so for an algorithm like the bubble sort (see p.204), the size is how many numbers you have in your list. The size of an algorithm is usually written as n.

2) How long an algorithm takes to run is measured by its efficiency — this will be a function of n (e.g. $n^2 - n$). The time it takes depends on how many operations the algorithm involves — if there are lots of operations, it'll take longer. The efficiency gives you the worst case scenario (i.e. the maximum number of times you'll need to run the algorithm or carry out a particular operation for n inputs).

3) The order (or complexity) of an algorithm is a way of comparing how efficient algorithms are.

4) You work out the order by looking at the highest power of n in the function:
   - If the highest power is 1, e.g. $5n + 2$, the algorithm is of linear order (you'd write it as $O(n)$ or order 1).
   - If the highest power is 2, e.g. $5n^2 + 6n$, the algorithm is of quadratic order (you'd write $O(n^2)$ or order 2).
   - If the highest power is 3, e.g. $n^3 + 2n^2 + 3n$, the algorithm is of cubic order (you'd write $O(n^3)$ or order 3).

5) The order tells you how the time changes as the size (n) increases. If n is doubled, a linear order algorithm will take about twice as long, a quadratic order algorithm will take about $2^2 = 4$ times as long and a cubic order algorithm will take about $2^3 = 8$ times as long.

> **EXAMPLE** A computer uses a quadratic algorithm. It takes 1.8 seconds to carry out the algorithm on a set of 50 numbers. Estimate how long it will take when there are 250 numbers.
>
> In this example, $n = 50$. $250 = 5 \times 50$, so you have to multiply the time by $5^2 = 25$ as the algorithm is quadratic. So when there are 250 numbers, it will take $1.8 \times 25 = 45$ seconds to carry out the algorithm.

Some algorithms are written in **Pseudo-Code**

1) Algorithms can be written in lots of different ways — e.g. a set of written instructions, a flow chart (see next page), computer programming language or pseudo-code.

2) Pseudo-code is a bit like computer programming language, but less formal — it's written for a person, not a computer. It won't be written in full sentences though — just a set of brief instructions.

3) In the exam, you need to be able to follow an algorithm written in pseudo-code, but you won't have to write your own. You might have conditions like IF and THEN ← *There's an example of this in the questions on p.210 — make sure you can follow it.* — you only do the THEN instruction if the IF bit's true.

> **EXAMPLE** This is the pseudo-code for an algorithm that outputs the first 10 triangle numbers:
>
> STEP 1: Input X = 1 and Y = 2
> STEP 2: Print X
> STEP 3: Let X = X + Y
> STEP 4: Let Y = Y + 1
> STEP 5: If Y < 12, then return to STEP 2. If Y = 12, then stop.
>
> *You start off with X = 1 and Y = 2, so you print 1, then X becomes 1 + 2 = 3 and Y becomes 3. 3 < 12, so you go back to step 2. This time, print 3, then X becomes 3 + 3 = 6 and Y becomes 4. You carry on like this until Y = 12.*
>
> Following this algorithm gives 1, 3, 6, 10, 15, 21, 28, 36, 45, 55.

4) Algorithms are pretty easy to alter — all you have to do is change one of the steps. You can do this on flow charts too, or on written instructions.

I'll have fish and chips twice please...

Say you had a cubic algorithm that was faster than a speeding bullet. Then if you doubled the size of the problem, it would take $2^3 = 8$ times as long. Which means that it would now be faster than a high-speed train, but not as fast as a bullet — good if you're trying to rescue someone tied to the train tracks, less good if you're trying to rescue someone from a bullet.

Flow Charts

Right, now you know all the background stuff, it's time to have some fun. Well, I say fun, but really it's just putting algorithms into flow charts and stuff like that.

Algorithms can be written as **Flow Charts**

Instead of giving instructions in <u>words</u> (like in the Russian Peasant example on p.201), some algorithms are written as <u>flow charts</u>. There are three different types of <u>boxes</u> which are used for different things:

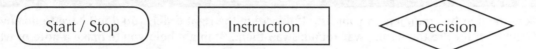

Start / Stop   Instruction   Decision

The boxes are connected with <u>arrows</u> to guide you through the flow chart. 'Decision' boxes will ask a question, and for each one you have a <u>choice</u> of arrows, one arrow for '<u>yes</u>' and one for '<u>no</u>', which will take you to another box. Sometimes flow charts will include a loop which takes you back to an earlier stage in the chart. Loops are a way of <u>repeating steps</u> until the algorithm is <u>finished</u>.

Put the **Results** from the flow chart into a **Trace Table**

It can sometimes be a bit tricky keeping track of the <u>results</u> of a flow chart, especially if you have to go round a <u>loop</u> lots of times. It's a good idea to put your results into a <u>trace table</u> — it's much easier to see the <u>solutions</u> that way.

EXAMPLE

This flow chart works out the factors of a number, a.

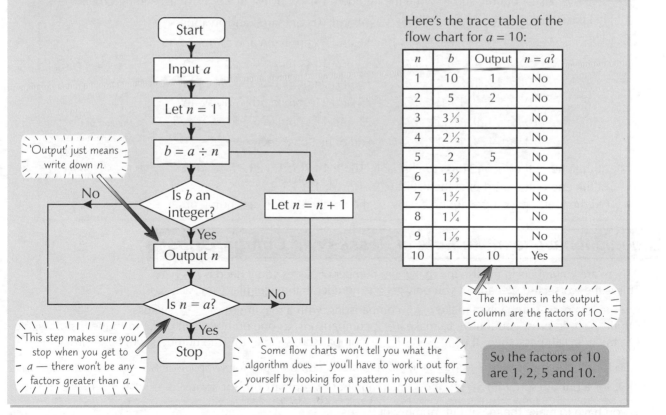

Here's the trace table of the flow chart for $a = 10$:

n	b	Output	$n = a$?
1	10	1	No
2	5	2	No
3	$3\frac{1}{3}$		No
4	$2\frac{1}{2}$		No
5	2	5	No
6	$1\frac{2}{3}$		No
7	$1\frac{3}{7}$		No
8	$1\frac{1}{4}$		No
9	$1\frac{1}{9}$		No
10	1	10	Yes

The numbers in the output column are the factors of 10.

So the factors of 10 are 1, 2, 5 and 10.

'Output' just means write down n.

This step makes sure you stop when you get to a — there won't be any factors greater than a.

Some flow charts won't tell you what the algorithm does — you'll have to work it out for yourself by looking for a pattern in your results.

Things seem to be flowing nicely...

Don't worry — you won't be expected to write algorithms in your exam, but you need to be able to use them. Some algorithms can look a bit confusing if there are lots of steps and decisions, but if you work through them slowly step by step they aren't too bad. Have a go at the one on this page for some different values of a — try $a = 12$, 17 and 18.

Sorting

You've probably been able to sort things into alphabetical or numerical order since you were knee-high to a hamster, but in D1 you need to be able to sort things using an algorithm. You don't have to memorise these sorting algorithms, but make sure you know how to use them so you don't get confused in the exam.

A **Bubble Sort** compares **Pairs** of numbers

The bubble sort is an algorithm that sorts numbers (or letters). It's pretty easy to do, but it can be a bit fiddly, so take care.

The Bubble Sort

1) Look at the <u>first two numbers</u> in your list. If they're in the right order, you don't have to do anything with them. If they're the wrong way round, <u>swap</u> them. It might help you to <u>make a note</u> of which numbers you swap each time.

2) Move on to the <u>next</u> pair of numbers (the first will be one of the two you've just compared) and <u>repeat step 1</u>. Keep going through the list until you get to the <u>last two numbers</u>. This set of comparisons is called a <u>pass</u>.

3) When you've finished the first pass, go back to the beginning of the list and <u>start again</u>. You won't have to compare the <u>last pair</u> of numbers, as the last number is now <u>in place</u>. Each pass has <u>one less comparison</u> than the one before it. When there are <u>no swaps</u> in a pass, the list is in <u>order</u>.

If there are n numbers in your list, there will be $n-1$ comparisons in the first pass.

Stop when there are **No More Swaps**

It's called the bubble sort because the highest numbers <u>rise</u> to the end of the list like <u>bubbles</u> (apparently). It'll all be a lot easier once you've been through an example...

> **EXAMPLE** Use a bubble sort to write the numbers 14, 10, 6, 15, 9, 21, 17 in ascending order.
>
> First pass:
> | | |
> |---|---|
> | <u>14, 10</u>, 6, 15, 9, 21, 17 | 14 and 10 compared and swapped |
> | 10, <u>14, 6</u>, 15, 9, 21, 17 | 14 and 6 compared and swapped |
> | 10, 6, <u>14, 15</u>, 9, 21, 17 | 14 and 15 compared — no swap |
> | 10, 6, 14, <u>15, 9</u>, 21, 17 | 15 and 9 compared and swapped |
> | 10, 6, 14, 9, <u>15, 21</u>, 17 | 15 and 21 compared — no swap |
> | 10, 6, 14, 9, 15, <u>21, 17</u> | 21 and 17 compared and swapped |
> | 10, 6, 14, 9, 15, 17, 21 | End of first pass. |
>
> *At the end of the first pass, the highest number has moved to the end of the list.*
>
> At the end of the second pass the list is: 6, 10, 9, 14, 15, 17, 21.
> At the end of the third pass the list is: 6, 9, 10, 14, 15, 17, 21.
> On the fourth pass there are no swaps, so the numbers are in <u>ascending order</u>.

You might have to make **Lots** of **Passes** and **Comparisons**

1) If there are <u>n</u> numbers in the list, the <u>maximum</u> number of <u>passes</u> you'll need is <u>$n-1$</u>. This is the worst case scenario (if you only get <u>one</u> number in the <u>right place</u> on each pass).

2) On the <u>first</u> pass, you have to make <u>$n-1$</u> comparisons, with a <u>maximum</u> of <u>$n-1$</u> swaps. On the <u>second</u> pass, you'll have to make <u>$n-2$</u> comparisons, as one number is in place from the first pass, etc. On the <u>$(n-1)$th</u> pass, there'll be <u>$n-(n-1)=1$</u> comparison, so after this the numbers will be in order.

> So for a bubble sort with <u>7 numbers</u>, max. number of comparisons (or swaps) is $6+5+4+3+2+1=21$
> Or for a bubble sort with <u>50 numbers</u>, max. number of comparisons (or swaps) is $\frac{1}{2} \times 49 \times 50 = 1225$

3) If you have to make the <u>maximum</u> number of <u>swaps</u>, it means that the original list was in <u>reverse order</u>.

4) You can also use the algorithm to put numbers in <u>descending</u> order — on each comparison, just put the <u>higher</u> number <u>first</u> instead.

For big lists, use the formula $S_k = \frac{1}{2}k(k+1)$ for the sum of the <u>first k whole numbers</u> (though if $n = 50$, you want the sum of the first 49 numbers).

Double, double, toil and trouble, fire burn and cauldron bubble...

The efficiency of the bubble sort algorithm is the maximum number of comparisons you might have to make. It's given by the function $\frac{1}{2}(n-1)n = \frac{1}{2}n^2 - \frac{1}{2}n$, so the bubble sort is a quadratic order algorithm — see p.202 for more about order.

Sorting

The bubble sort can get a bit boring after a while — sometimes when you swap one pair of numbers, you know that you're going to have to make another swap on the next pass. Fortunately the shuttle sort finds a way around that.

The **Shuttle Sort** is an **Improved** version of the **Bubble Sort**

The main <u>problem</u> with the bubble sort is that you have to make a lot of <u>comparisons</u>. The <u>shuttle sort</u> is a bit more <u>efficient</u>, as it <u>reduces</u> the overall number of comparisons needed.

The Shuttle Sort

1) Look at the <u>first two numbers</u> in your list. If they're in the right order, leave them as they are. If they're the wrong way round, <u>swap</u> them. This is your <u>first pass</u>.

2) Move on to the <u>next</u> pair of numbers (the first will be one of the two you've just compared) and <u>repeat step 1</u>.

3) If you made a <u>swap</u> on the <u>second comparison</u>, compare the number you've <u>just swapped</u> to the <u>first number</u> in the list. If they're the wrong way round, <u>swap</u> them. This is your <u>second pass</u>.

4) Now move on to the <u>next pair</u> of numbers (the <u>third</u> and <u>fourth</u> in the list) and compare them. If you make a <u>swap</u>, compare the number you've just <u>swapped</u> to the number <u>before</u> it, and swap if you need to. Keep working <u>backwards</u> until either you get to a number it can't be swapped with or you reach the <u>beginning</u> of the list. This is another <u>pass</u> completed.

5) <u>Continue</u> through the list, <u>repeating step 4</u> until you get to the last number in the list. Each time, <u>compare backwards</u> until you can't swap the number anymore.

A pass in a shuttle sort is different to a pass in a bubble sort.

The shuttle sort usually needs <u>fewer comparisons</u> than the bubble sort — though you'll have to make the <u>same number</u> of <u>swaps</u>. After the <u>first</u> pass, the first <u>2</u> numbers will be in the right places. After the <u>second</u> pass, the first <u>three</u> numbers will be in the right places <u>and so on</u>. For a list of <u>*n*</u> numbers, you'll need to make <u>*n* – 1</u> passes to get the list in order.

The **Shuttle Sort** will have the **Same Number** of **Swaps** as the **Bubble Sort**

Even though you'll have to make the <u>same number</u> of <u>swaps</u> as you would using the bubble sort, you'll make <u>fewer comparisons</u> — this means the shuttle sort's more <u>efficient</u>.

EXAMPLE Use a shuttle sort to write the numbers 14, 10, 6, 15, 9, 21, 17 in ascending order.

This is the same set of numbers used in the bubble sort example on the previous page.

First pass:	<u>14, 10</u>, 6, 15, 9, 21, 17	14 and 10 compared and swapped
Second pass:	10, <u>14, 6</u>, 15, 9, 21, 17	14 and 6 compared and swapped
	<u>10, 6</u>, 14, 15, 9, 21, 17	10 and 6 compared and swapped
Third pass:	6, 10, <u>14, 15</u>, 9, 21, 17	14 and 15 compared — no swap
Fourth pass:	6, 10, 14, <u>15, 9</u>, 21, 17	15 and 9 compared and swapped
	6, 10, <u>14, 9</u>, 15, 21, 17	14 and 9 compared and swapped
	6, <u>10, 9</u>, 14, 15, 21, 17	10 and 9 compared and swapped
	<u>6, 9</u>, 10, 14, 15, 21, 17	6 and 9 compared — no swap
Fifth pass:	6, 9, 10, 14, <u>15, 21</u>, 17	15 and 21 compared — no swap
Sixth pass:	6, 9, 10, 14, 15, <u>21, 17</u>	21 and 17 compared and swapped
	6, 9, 10, 14, <u>15, 17</u>, 21	15 and 17 compared — no swap
	6, 9, 10, 14, 15, 17, 21	End of shuttle sort.

The shuttle sort is also a quadratic algorithm.

There are 7 numbers, so you have to make 7 – 1 = 6 passes. It was much quicker than the bubble sort — there were only 11 comparisons (instead of 18). You still needed to make 7 swaps though.

Not quite as exciting as a space shuttle — more exciting than a shuttlecock...

The shuttle sort is trickier than a bubble sort, but it's more efficient. Make sure you don't get them mixed up — or even worse, combine the two. Attempting to do a buttle sort in the exam might make the examiners laugh, but it won't get you any marks. Again, you don't have to memorise this algorithm, but make sure you can use it.

Sorting

Here are the last two sorting methods — one's called the quick sort, and with a name like that, you'd hope it was pretty damn quick. I'd rank its speed as midway between a sloth and a fighter pigeon (and those pigeons can be rather fast). The other's an insertion sort. It's the least fancy sort in the whole book.

A **Quick Sort** breaks the list into **Smaller Lists**

The quick sort algorithm works by choosing a pivot which breaks down the list into two smaller lists, which are then broken down in the same way until the numbers are in order.

The Quick Sort

1) **Choose a pivot. Move any numbers that are less than the pivot to a new list on the left of it and the numbers that are greater to a new list on the right. Don't change the order of the numbers though.**

2) **Repeat step 1) for each of the smaller lists you've just made. You'll need to choose new pivots for the new lists.**

Sometimes the smaller lists will only have one number in them — you don't need to do anything with these as they're already in order.

3) **When every number has been chosen as a pivot, you can stop, as the list is in order.**

The pivot can be any number in the list — it's usually easiest to use the first number though.

Keep track of the **Pivots** you use

It's a good idea to circle or underline the pivots you're using at each step of the quick sort — it helps you keep track of where you're up to. In the example below, the numbers are written in grey when they're in the correct place.

EXAMPLE Sort the numbers 54, 36, 29, 56, 45, 39, 32, 27 into ascending order using a quick sort.

Use the first item in the list as the pivot. So the pivot is 54.

Now make new lists by moving numbers < 54 to the left, and numbers > 54 to the right. Don't reorder the numbers, just write them down in the order they appear in the original list on the correct side of the pivot.

These are all the numbers < 54 (in the same order as in the original list). → 36, 29, 45, 39, 32, 27, $\underline{54}$, 56 ← *This is the only number > 54.*
  l_1 l_2

The list has been divided into smaller lists, l_1 and l_2. l_2 only has one item in it, so 56 is in the correct place (it's a pivot in a list of its own). Use the first number in l_1 (36) as the new pivot. Rearranging around the new pivot gives:

29, 32, 27, $\underline{36}$, 45, 39, 54, 56 ← *54 and 56 are in the right place now.*
  l_3 l_4

This time, both lists have more than one item so there are two new pivots: 29 from list l_3 and 45 from list l_4. Rearranging again using the new pivots gives:

27, $\underline{29}$, 32, 36, 39, $\underline{45}$, 54, 56
 l_5 l_6 l_7

The lists l_5, l_6 and l_7 only have one item in them, so all the numbers are in the correct place — the list is now in order.

An **Insertion Sort** orders as it goes

The insertion sort is dead easy — all you have to do is take each number from the list in turn and insert it into the right place, using the first number in the list as a starting point. So for the list 7, 3, 12, 2, 10, you'd start with 7, then put 3 to the left as it's less than 7 and then 12 on the right. Then 2 goes on the left of 3 and 10 goes between 7 and 12.

Start with 7...   ...insert 3...   ...insert 12...   ...insert 2...   ...insert 10.
   7   →   3, 7   →   3, 7, 12   →   2, 3, 7, 12   →   2, 3, 7, 10, 12

The order is 2, 3, 7, 10, 12. Piece of cake.

Quick — let's get out of here...

Of course, you may be thinking that it would be much easier to sort them just by looking at them, but the point of all of these sorting algorithms is that you could program them into a computer and sort huge lists of numbers really quickly.

Packing

Packing to go on holiday can be a pain. You've got so much to fit in your suitcase, and there's always the risk of your shampoo leaking. Well, you'll be pleased to know that there are a couple of algorithms that are about packing (admittedly not holiday packing, but I'm sure you could adjust them to make them work).

These algorithms are called Bin Packing Algorithms

1) In <u>bin packing problems</u>, you have a set of items that you need to fit into the <u>minimum</u> number of <u>bins</u>.

2) One of the most common examples is fitting <u>boxes</u> of <u>different heights</u> on top of each other into <u>bins</u> of a <u>given height</u>. You need to arrange the boxes to use the <u>fewest bins possible</u>.

3) Other examples include things like cutting specified <u>lengths of wood</u> from <u>planks</u> of a fixed length (you want to <u>minimise</u> the number of planks used), or loading items of different <u>weights</u> into <u>lorries</u> that have a <u>maximum weight capacity</u> (again, you want to use the <u>smallest</u> number of lorries possible).

4) An <u>optimal solution</u> is one that uses the <u>least possible number of bins</u>. There's often more than one possible optimal solution.

Because the optimal solution has the least possible no. of bins, it also has the least <u>wasted space</u>.

You can Work Out the Minimum Possible Number of Bins you'll need

1) To work out the minimum possible number of bins you'll need, you <u>add up</u> the height / weights etc. of the items, and <u>divide</u> the total by the <u>capacity</u> of the bins. For the wooden planks example above, you'd add up the <u>lengths</u> of the different pieces of wood and divide by the <u>length</u> of the <u>planks</u> (the planks are all the same length).

2) Always <u>round up</u> your answer — if you get, say, 2.25, you'd need a <u>minimum</u> of <u>3 bins</u> (you wouldn't fit the items in 2 bins).

3) It doesn't mean you can definitely fit the items into this number of bins — you need <u>at least</u> this many. But if your solution <u>does match</u> this number, you know it's definitely <u>optimal</u>.

EXAMPLE Five boxes of heights 20 cm, 43 cm, 35 cm, 29 cm and 38 cm are to be packed into bins of height 60 cm.

Total height of boxes:
20 + 43 + 35 + 29 + 38 = 165 cm

165 ÷ 60 = 2.75, so you need at <u>least 3 bins</u>.

The First-Fit algorithm puts the items in the First Bin they'll go in

The first-fit algorithm is <u>quick</u> and <u>easy</u>, but it probably <u>won't</u> give you an <u>optimal solution</u>. Here's how it works:

1) Take the <u>first item</u> in the list and put it in the <u>first bin</u>.

2) Move on to the next item, and put it in the <u>first bin</u> it'll <u>fit</u> into. It might fit in the first bin, or you might have to move on to <u>another bin</u>.

3) Repeat step 2) until <u>all</u> the items are in a bin. For each item, try the <u>first bin</u> before you move on to the next.

EXAMPLE The ad breaks in a TV programme can be no longer than 150 seconds. Use the first-fit algorithm to sort the adverts into the breaks, saying how many breaks are needed and how much time is wasted.

A: 90 s   B: 75 s   C: 30 s   D: 65 s   E: 120 s   F: 45 s   G: 60 s

Ad break 1:	A: 90 s, C: 30 s	space left: ~~60 s~~ 30 s
Ad break 2:	B: 75 s, D: 65 s	space left: ~~75 s~~ 10 s
Ad break 3:	E: 120 s	space left: 30 s
Ad break 4:	F: 45 s, G: 60 s	space left: ~~105 s~~ 45 s

B won't fit in break 1, as there's only 60 s left after A, so it goes in break 2. However, C < 60 s, so it fits in break 1.

So the adverts can be fitted into 4 ad breaks, with 30 + 10 + 30 + 45 = 115 s wasted.

Some Solutions Won't be very Practical

1) Exam questions might ask you to comment on <u>how practical</u> different solutions are. It'll depend on their <u>contexts</u>.

2) E.g. if a group of five people are sharing camping equipment between their rucksacks, it won't be very fair if four people have full rucksacks and the fifth has an almost empty rucksack. It'd be better to spread the load <u>evenly</u>.

I've bin packing my suitcase for my holiday...

Sorry, sorry, that was terrible. Try not to confuse first-fit with first-past-the-post — one's a bin packing algorithm, the other's a voting system. If you get them mixed up, you might end up trying to see how many politicians you can fit in a box. Hmm...

Packing

If you decide to carry out your own bin packing problem with bits of wood, do be careful with the saw. Maths is a lot harder if you don't have all 10 fingers.

The **First-Fit Decreasing** algorithm needs the items in **Descending Order**

1) The <u>first-fit decreasing</u> algorithm is very <u>similar</u> to the <u>first-fit</u> algorithm except you need to put the items in <u>descending order</u> first.

2) You can do this by using one of the <u>sorting algorithms</u> on pages 204-206 (or just by sight if it's a small list).

3) Once you've got your ordered list, you just carry out the <u>first-fit algorithm</u> from the previous page.

4) The first-fit decreasing algorithm usually gives you a <u>better solution</u> than the first-fit algorithm, but it still might <u>not</u> be <u>optimal</u>.

> **EXAMPLE** Ribbon comes in rolls of length 5 m. For the lengths of ribbon given below, use the first-fit decreasing algorithm to work out how the lengths can be cut from the rolls. You should also say how many rolls are needed and how much ribbon is wasted. All lengths are in metres.
>
> 2.5   1.9   2.9   3.1   2.7   2.2   1.8   2.0
>
> First, put the lengths in decreasing order. The new list is:
>
> 3.1   2.9   2.7   2.5   2.2   2.0   1.9   1.8
>
> Now use the first-fit algorithm to sort the lengths into rolls:
>
> Roll 1:   3.1, 1.9   length left: ~~1.9~~ 0
>
> Roll 2:   2.9, 2.0   length left: ~~2.1~~ 0.1
>
> Roll 3:   2.7, 2.2   length left: ~~2.3~~ 0.1
>
> Roll 4:   2.5, 1.8   length left: ~~2.5~~ 0.7
>
> The ribbon can be cut from 4 rolls, with 0 + 0.1 + 0.1 + 0.7 = 0.9 m wasted.
>
> *If you solved this problem using the first-fit algorithm, you'd use 5 rolls and waste 5.9 m of ribbon.*

The **Full-Bin** packing algorithm usually wastes the **Least Space**

The <u>full-bin packing algorithm</u> needs a bit more <u>work</u> than the other two, but it's more likely to produce an <u>optimal solution</u>. However, it can be quite <u>hard</u> to do if you've got a lot of items.

1) In the full-bin algorithm, first you need to <u>look</u> at the items and find items that will <u>add up</u> to give a <u>full bin</u>. You just have to do this <u>by eye</u>, so it can get a bit tricky.

2) Once you've <u>filled</u> as many bins as you can, you use the <u>first-fit algorithm</u> (see previous page) to put the rest of the items in the <u>remaining spaces</u> in the bins.

> **EXAMPLE** Boxes of the same length and width need to be packed in bins of height 2.5 m. Use the full-bin packing algorithm to pack the boxes, and say how many bins are used, how much space is wasted and whether the solution is optimal. The heights of the boxes (in metres) are:
>
> 0.7   1.1   1.2   2.3   0.8   1.4   0.9   1.0   2.5
>
> Just by looking at the heights, you can see that 0.7 + 0.8 + 1.0 = 2.5, 1.1 + 1.4 = 2.5 and 2.5 = 2.5, so you can fill 3 bins straight away. Then use the first-fit algorithm to pack the remaining boxes.
>
> Bin 1:   0.7, 0.8, 1.0   space left: 0
>
> Bin 2:   1.1, 1.4   space left: 0
>
> Bin 3:   2.5   space left: 0
>
> Bin 4:   1.2, 0.9   space left: ~~1.3~~ 0.4
>
> Bin 5:   2.3   space left: 0.2
>
> The boxes can be packed into 5 bins, with 0.4 + 0.2 = 0.6 m wasted space.
>
> Using the method on the previous page, the lower bound for this problem is 11.9 ÷ 2.5 = 4.76 = 5 bins. As this solution uses 5 bins, it is optimal. Also, the amount of space wasted is less than one bin.

Don't forget to pack your pyjamas...

So, the first-fit algorithm is the quickest but doesn't give the best solution, the first-fit decreasing algorithm needs a little more work but usually gives a better solution, and the full-bin algorithm is a bit harder but is more likely to give an optimal solution.

D1 Section 1 — Practice Questions

That's the <u>first section of D1</u> done and dusted — and I don't think it was that bad. Once you get your head round the fact that 'algorithm' is just a fancy word for 'set of instructions', you're over the first hurdle. Time now for a few <u>questions</u> to check you know your stuff. Here are some <u>straightforward ones</u> to start off with.

Warm-up Questions

1) For each of the following sets of instructions, identify the <u>input</u> and <u>output</u>.
   a) a recipe for vegetable soup,
   b) directions from Leicester Square to the Albert Hall,
   c) flat-pack instructions for building a TV cabinet.

2) Use the <u>Russian Peasant algorithm</u> to multiply 17 and 56.

3) What are diamond-shaped boxes in <u>flow diagrams</u> used for?

4) Use the <u>flow chart on p.203</u> to work out the factors of 16.

5) Use a <u>bubble sort</u> to write the numbers 72, 57, 64, 54, 68, 71 in ascending order. <u>How many passes</u> do you need to make?

> You don't need to memorise the sorting algorithms (bubble sort, shuttle sort, quick sort and insertion sort), so you can check back to the page for the steps.

6) If you had to put a list of 10 numbers in order using a bubble sort, what is the <u>maximum number</u> of <u>comparisons</u> you'd need to make?

7) An algorithm has order $O(n^2)$. If it takes 0.4s to apply the algorithm to a set of 20 numbers, approximately how long will it take on a set of 60 numbers?

8) Use a shuttle sort to write the numbers 21, 11, 23, 19, 28, 26 in ascending order.

9) Sort the numbers 101, 98, 79, 113, 87, 108, 84 into ascending order using an insertion sort.

10) Sort the numbers 0.8, 1.2, 0.7, 0.5, 0.4, 1.0, 0.1 into <u>ascending order</u> using a <u>quick sort</u>. Write down the <u>pivots</u> you use at each step.

11) Six items of weights 5 kg, 11 kg, 8 kg, 9 kg, 12 kg, 7 kg need to be packed into boxes that can hold a <u>maximum weight of 15 kg</u>.
    a) Pack the items into the boxes using the <u>first-fit algorithm</u>.
    b) Pack the items into the boxes using the <u>first-fit decreasing algorithm</u>.
    c) Pack the items into the boxes using the <u>full-bin packing algorithm</u>.
    For each part, say how many boxes are needed and how much space is wasted.

> You need to know the packing algorithms though — so make sure you can do Q11 without checking back.

If those warm-up questions have left you <u>hungry for more</u>, here are some tasty exam-style questions for you to <u>sink your teeth</u> into. They'll need a bit more work than the warm-up questions, but it'll be <u>worth it</u>, I promise.

Exam Questions

1   77   83   96   105   78   89   112   80   98   94

   a) Use a quick sort to arrange the list of numbers above into ascending order.
      You must clearly show the pivots you use at each stage.

      (5 marks)

   b) A list of six numbers is to be sorted into ascending order using a bubble sort.
      (i) Which number(s) will definitely be in the correct position after the first pass?

      (1 mark)

      (ii) Write down the maximum number of passes and the maximum number of swaps needed to sort a list of six numbers into ascending order.

      (2 marks)

D1 Section 1 — Practice Questions

If you thought I'd leave you hanging with just one <u>exam question</u>, you're very much mistaken.
I'd <u>never</u> be that mean to you — and to prove it, here's another page full of <u>beautiful exam questions</u>.

Exam Questions

2   Consider the following algorithm:

Step 1:   Input A, B with $A < B$
Step 2:   Input $N = 1$
Step 3:   Calculate $C = A \div N$
Step 4:   Calculate $D = B \div N$
Step 5:   If both C and D are integers, output N
Step 6:   If $N = A$, then stop. Otherwise let $N = N + 1$ and go back to Step 3.

a)   Carry out the algorithm with $A = 8$ and $B = 12$. Record your results.

(3 marks)

b)   (i)   What does this algorithm produce?

(1 mark)

(ii)   Using your answer to part (i) or otherwise, write down the output that would be
produced if you applied the algorithm to $A = 19$ and $B = 25$, and explain your answer.
You do not need to carry out the algorithm again.

(2 marks)

3   Mark   Adam   Dan   James   Stella   Helen   Robert

Use an insertion sort to list the above names in alphabetical order.

(2 marks)

4   A joiner has planks of wood that are 3 m long. He needs to cut pieces of wood from the planks in the
following lengths:
      1.2 m   2.3 m   0.6 m   0.8 m   1.5 m   1.0 m   0.9 m   2.5 m

a)   Use the first-fit bin packing algorithm to fit the lengths of wood onto the planks.
State how many planks are needed and how much wood is wasted.

(3 marks)

b)   (i)   Use the full-bin packing algorithm to fit the lengths of wood onto the planks.
Again, state how many planks are needed and how much wood is wasted.

(3 marks)

(ii)   Can you be sure this number of planks is optimal? Explain your answer.

(2 marks)

c)   The joiner knows that the first-fit decreasing algorithm is quadratic.
A computer takes 2.1 s to carry out the algorithm on a set of 30 numbers.
Estimate how long it will take for 120 numbers.

(2 marks)

5   a)   Rearrange the following set of numbers into ascending order using a shuttle sort.
              1.3   0.8   1.8   0.5   1.2   0.2   0.9
State how many passes you made.

(5 marks)

b)   How many comparisons and swaps were made on the first pass?

(1 mark)

Graphs

You probably reckon you're an old pro at graphs. But the graphs coming up are rather different. For a start, there's not a scrap of squared paper in sight. Fret not — soon they'll be as innocuous to you as a bar chart.

Graphs have **Points** Connected by **Lines**

Here's the definition of a graph:

> A **graph** is made up of **points** (called **vertices** or **nodes**)
> joined by **lines** (called **edges** or **arcs**).

Graphs can be used to <u>model</u> or <u>solve</u> real-life problems. Here are a few examples:

Use Graphs to show **Connections** in **Geographical Problems**

In this graph, the vertices represent towns and the edges represent roads.

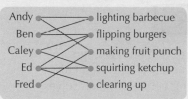

The graph doesn't show where the towns are in relation to each other — just how they are linked by roads.

The Bridges of Königsberg is a really famous example. The city of Königsberg was set on both sides of a river, and on two islands. Seven bridges connected different parts of the city.

The problem was to find a route that crossed each bridge exactly once and ended up back at the starting point. As only the connections between the different parts of the city were important, the problem could be simplified using a graph.

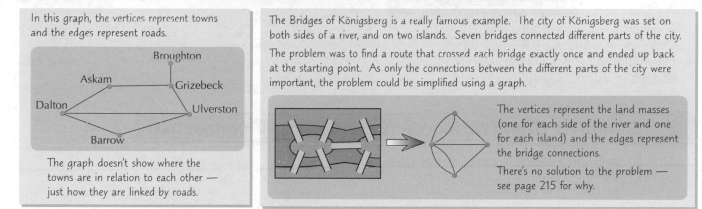

The vertices represent the land masses (one for each side of the river and one for each island) and the edges represent the bridge connections.

There's no solution to the problem — see page 215 for why.

Use **Bipartite Graphs to** Model **Matching Problems**

<u>Bipartite graphs</u> have <u>two sets</u> of vertices. An <u>edge</u> only ever joins a vertex <u>in one set</u> to a vertex in the <u>other set</u>. You can <u>never</u> connect two vertices in the <u>same set</u> together.

This graph shows the jobs a group of students would prefer to do at the end-of-term barbecue.

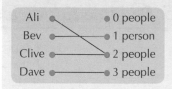

Andy / Ben / Caley / Ed / Fred — lighting barbecue / flipping burgers / making fruit punch / squirting ketchup / clearing up

On a double-date, some hand shaking takes place.
The number of people each person shakes hands with is shown.

Ali — 0 people
Bev — 1 person
Clive — 2 people
Dave — 3 people

You can never have an edge to 0 and an edge to 3 — it's impossible for one person to shake hands with no one and another to shake hands with everyone.

Shape Problems Sound a Bit Odd at First

Sometimes exam questions ask you to represent a <u>shape</u> with a <u>graph</u>.
This converts a nice, easy-to-understand shape into a bunch of joined-up dots. But anyway...

These shapes are represented by the graphs underneath them.

Each vertex represents a face and the arcs connect faces which share an edge.

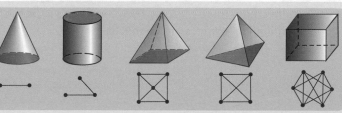

I've got geographical problems — I have no sense of direction...

The situations you can model with a graph are limited only by your imagination. In exams, they're limited only by the examiner's imagination. You might get a situation you've not seen before, but don't panic — just read the question carefully.

Graphs

There are loads of different types of graph. And you need to know all their names. It's not hard — it just takes learning.

Networks have a Number on Each Arc

1) Networks, or weighted graphs, have a number associated with each edge (called the weight of the edge).

2) Weights often give you lengths — like in this network showing points in a nature reserve and the footpaths joining them. They sometimes give you costs or times too.

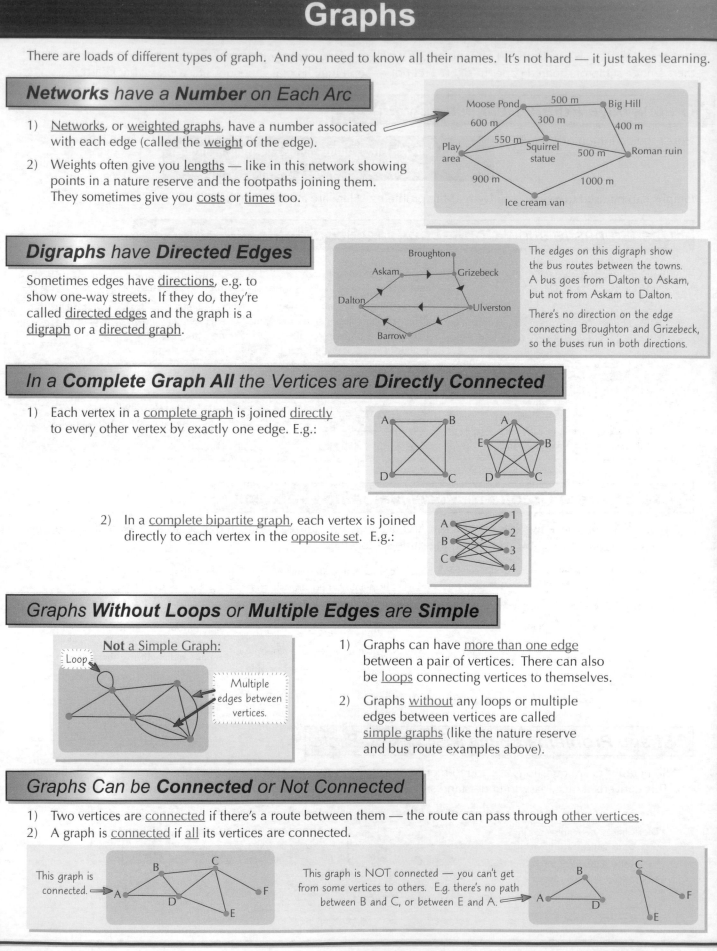

Digraphs have Directed Edges

Sometimes edges have directions, e.g. to show one-way streets. If they do, they're called directed edges and the graph is a digraph or a directed graph.

The edges on this digraph show the bus routes between the towns. A bus goes from Dalton to Askam, but not from Askam to Dalton.

There's no direction on the edge connecting Broughton and Grizebeck, so the buses run in both directions.

In a Complete Graph All the Vertices are Directly Connected

1) Each vertex in a complete graph is joined directly to every other vertex by exactly one edge. E.g.:

2) In a complete bipartite graph, each vertex is joined directly to each vertex in the opposite set. E.g.:

Graphs Without Loops or Multiple Edges are Simple

Not a Simple Graph:

Loop

Multiple edges between vertices.

1) Graphs can have more than one edge between a pair of vertices. There can also be loops connecting vertices to themselves.

2) Graphs without any loops or multiple edges between vertices are called simple graphs (like the nature reserve and bus route examples above).

Graphs Can be Connected or Not Connected

1) Two vertices are connected if there's a route between them — the route can pass through other vertices.
2) A graph is connected if all its vertices are connected.

This graph is connected.

This graph is NOT connected — you can't get from some vertices to others. E.g. there's no path between B and C, or between E and A.

And your leg bone's connected to your foot bone...

A page of lovely definitions. You'll need them very, very soon, so learn them and then scribble them out from memory. Then check back to the page to see what you missed. Graphs are all over the place — the London Underground map is one.

Graphs

More terminology coming up. Make sure you totally get it, or confusion will be the next thing coming up.

Subgraphs are Just *Bits of Another Graph*

1) These are absolute doddles. If you take a graph, and rub a few bits out, then you're left with a <u>subgraph</u>.

2) Here's the posh definition to learn:

> A **subgraph** of graph *G* is a graph where all the vertices and edges belong to *G*.

EXAMPLE

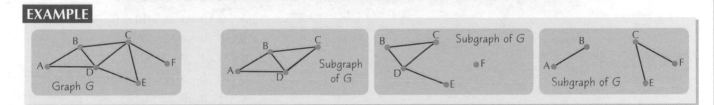

A *Path* is a Route in the Graph Which *Doesn't Repeat Any Vertices*

A path is a <u>sequence of edges</u> that flow on, end to end. The only thing is, you <u>can't</u> go through a vertex more than once.

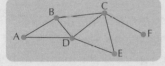

One possible path here is <u>ABDECF</u>. Another is <u>CBAD</u>.

DCECF <u>isn't</u> a path because you go through vertex C more than once.

A *Cycle* is a Path that *Brings you Back* to Your Starting Point

1) A <u>cycle</u> (or <u>circuit</u>) is a <u>closed path</u>. The <u>end</u> vertex is the same as the <u>start</u> vertex.

2) So on the graph above, <u>ABDA</u> is a cycle. Other cycles are <u>ABCDA</u> and <u>CEDBC</u>.

> You still have to follow the rules for paths — so you can't go through a vertex twice. So ABDCEDA isn't a cycle because it goes through vertex D twice.

A *Hamilton Cycle* Goes Through *Each Vertex Once*

1) A <u>Hamilton (or Hamiltonian) cycle</u> is a <u>cycle</u> which goes through <u>each vertex exactly once</u>.

2) Like all cycles, it brings you <u>back to the start vertex</u>.

3) Not all graphs contain Hamilton cycles — those that do are called <u>Hamilton graphs</u>.

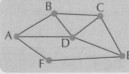

This graph contains the Hamilton cycle <u>ABDCEFA</u>.

A *Walk* is *Absolutely Any* Route in a Graph

1) Like paths, walks are <u>sequence of edges</u> that flow on, end to end.

2) With walks, you <u>can</u> go through vertices and along edges <u>more than once</u>.

3) So on the graph above, <u>BCDBCE</u> is a walk, as is <u>ABDAB</u>.

> Walks or trails that bring you back to your starting vertex are called <u>closed walks</u> or <u>closed trails</u>.

A *Trail* is a Walk that *Doesn't* Repeat any *Edges*

Unlike paths, trails can <u>repeat vertices</u> (but not edges). <u>BDCBA</u> is a trail and so is <u>FCEDCB</u>.

A subgiraph — just the neck or a leg...

It's so, so easy to get these definitions muddled up — they're all pretty similar, but not quite the same. Cycles are paths and trails are walks, and cycles are always closed, and walks and trails can be closed or not. As for paths, well, they can be closed, but then they become cycles. If this rambling isn't clarifying matters, you'd best just learn the definitions.

Graphs

We're now cruising at the correct altitude and you may unfasten your seat belts and move around the cabin. But don't leave the aircraft, it's cold out there and there's no floor.

Incidence Matrices show the *Number of Links* between *Vertices*

1) To draw an <u>incidence (or adjacency) matrix</u> from a graph, go through each space in the matrix and count the <u>number of direct connections</u> from the vertex at the left of the <u>row</u> to the vertex at the top of the <u>column</u>.

EXAMPLE Represent this graph with an incidence matrix.

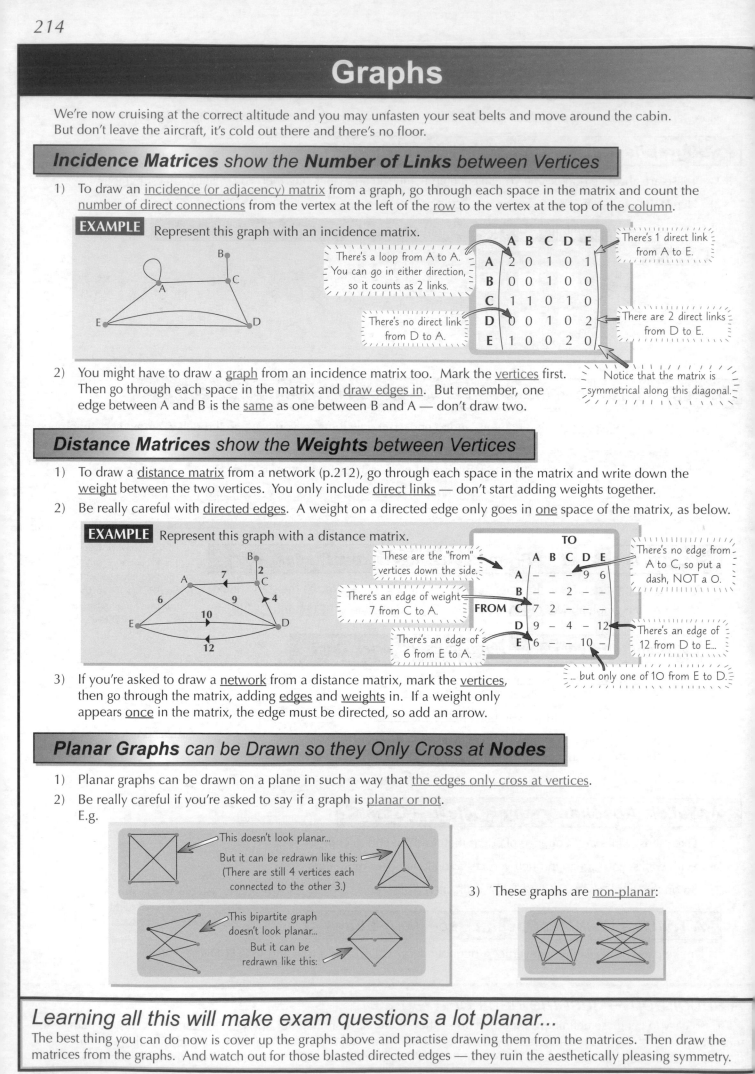

There's a loop from A to A. You can go in either direction, so it counts as 2 links.

There's 1 direct link from A to E.

There's no direct link from D to A.

There are 2 direct links from D to E.

	A	B	C	D	E
A	2	0	1	0	1
B	0	0	1	0	0
C	1	1	0	1	0
D	0	0	1	0	2
E	1	0	0	2	0

Notice that the matrix is symmetrical along this diagonal.

2) You might have to draw a <u>graph</u> from an incidence matrix too. Mark the <u>vertices</u> first. Then go through each space in the matrix and <u>draw edges in</u>. But remember, one edge between A and B is the <u>same</u> as one between B and A — don't draw two.

Distance Matrices show the *Weights* between *Vertices*

1) To draw a <u>distance matrix</u> from a network (p.212), go through each space in the matrix and write down the <u>weight</u> between the two vertices. You only include <u>direct links</u> — don't start adding weights together.

2) Be really careful with <u>directed edges</u>. A weight on a directed edge only goes in <u>one</u> space of the matrix, as below.

EXAMPLE Represent this graph with a distance matrix.

These are the "from" vertices down the side.

There's an edge of weight 7 from C to A.

There's an edge of 6 from E to A.

There's no edge from A to C, so put a dash, NOT a O.

There's an edge of 12 from D to E...

... but only one of 10 from E to D.

		TO				
		A	B	C	D	E
	A	–	–	–	9	6
	B	–	–	2	–	–
FROM	C	7	2	–	–	–
	D	9	–	4	–	12
	E	6	–	–	10	–

3) If you're asked to draw a <u>network</u> from a distance matrix, mark the <u>vertices</u>, then go through the matrix, adding <u>edges</u> and <u>weights</u> in. If a weight only appears <u>once</u> in the matrix, the edge must be directed, so add an arrow.

Planar Graphs can be Drawn so they Only Cross at *Nodes*

1) Planar graphs can be drawn on a plane in such a way that <u>the edges only cross at vertices</u>.

2) Be really careful if you're asked to say if a graph is <u>planar or not</u>. E.g.

This doesn't look planar... But it can be redrawn like this: (There are still 4 vertices each connected to the other 3.)

This bipartite graph doesn't look planar... But it can be redrawn like this:

3) These graphs are <u>non-planar</u>:

Learning all this will make exam questions a lot planar...

The best thing you can do now is cover up the graphs above and practise drawing them from the matrices. Then draw the matrices from the graphs. And watch out for those blasted directed edges — they ruin the aesthetically pleasing symmetry.

Graphs

If these graph definitions were a tunnel, you'd now be seeing a dot of light in the distance.

Trees are Graphs that have No Cycles

See p213 for more on cycles.

They also have to be <u>connected graphs</u> (see p212).

Both graphs here are connected — but <u>only</u> the first is a <u>tree</u> (the graphical type of tree that is).

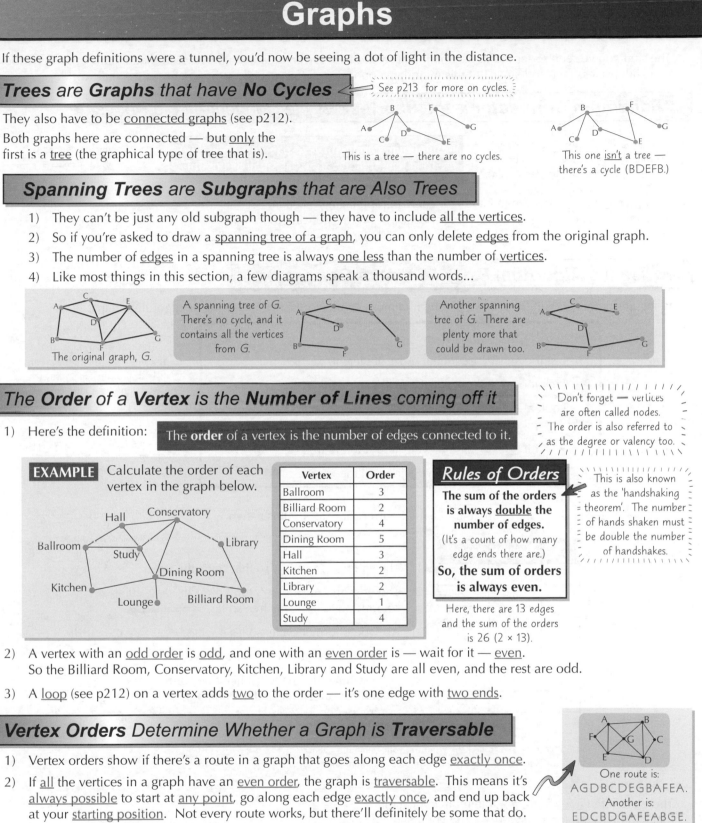

This is a tree — there are no cycles.

This one <u>isn't</u> a tree — there's a cycle (BDEFB.)

Spanning Trees are Subgraphs that are Also Trees

1) They can't be just any old subgraph though — they have to include <u>all the vertices</u>.
2) So if you're asked to draw a <u>spanning tree of a graph</u>, you can only delete <u>edges</u> from the original graph.
3) The number of <u>edges</u> in a spanning tree is always <u>one less</u> than the number of <u>vertices</u>.
4) Like most things in this section, a few diagrams speak a thousand words...

The original graph, G.

A spanning tree of G. There's no cycle, and it contains all the vertices from G.

Another spanning tree of G. There are plenty more that could be drawn too.

The Order of a Vertex is the Number of Lines coming off it

Don't forget — vertices are often called nodes. The order is also referred to as the degree or valency too.

1) Here's the definition:

The **order** of a vertex is the number of edges connected to it.

EXAMPLE Calculate the order of each vertex in the graph below.

Vertex	Order
Ballroom	3
Billiard Room	2
Conservatory	4
Dining Room	5
Hall	3
Kitchen	2
Library	2
Lounge	1
Study	4

Rules of Orders

The sum of the orders is always <u>double</u> the number of edges.
(It's a count of how many edge ends there are.)
So, the sum of orders is always even.

Here, there are 13 edges and the sum of the orders is 26 (2 × 13).

This is also known as the 'handshaking' theorem'. The number of hands shaken must be double the number of handshakes.

2) A vertex with an <u>odd order</u> is <u>odd</u>, and one with an <u>even order</u> is — wait for it — <u>even</u>. So the Billiard Room, Conservatory, Kitchen, Library and Study are all even, and the rest are odd.

3) A <u>loop</u> (see p212) on a vertex adds <u>two</u> to the order — it's one edge with <u>two ends</u>.

Vertex Orders Determine Whether a Graph is Traversable

1) Vertex orders show if there's a route in a graph that goes along each edge <u>exactly once</u>.

2) If <u>all</u> the vertices in a graph have an <u>even order</u>, the graph is <u>traversable</u>. This means it's <u>always possible</u> to start at <u>any point</u>, go along each edge <u>exactly once</u>, and end up back at your <u>starting position</u>. Not every route works, but there'll definitely be some that do.

One route is: AGDBCDEGBAFEA.
Another is: EDCBDGAFEABGE.

3) If <u>exactly two vertices</u> have an <u>odd order</u>, and the rest are even, the graph is <u>semi-traversable</u>. It's possible to go along every edge <u>exactly once</u>, but <u>ONLY</u> if you start at one odd vertex and end up at the <u>other</u> odd vertex.

In this graph, you have to start and end at the odd nodes (A and D). A possible route is:
ABDCA around the square, then ABDCA around the circle, then across the diagonal to D.

4) If a graph has <u>more than two odd vertices</u>, there's <u>no route</u> that travels along each edge exactly once. You have to go along some of them <u>twice</u>.
The Königsberg Bridge problem (p.211) has 4 odd vertices — that's why there was no solution.

Now what would a tree do with a cycle anyway...

See — I didn't put the bit about <u>vertex order</u> in *just* because it's fascinating. (Although it certainly is.) It's important for planning routes that go along each edge in a network. If there are two odd vertices, you start at one and finish at the other.

Minimum Connectors

The stuff you've seen so far in this section might seem like it's been dreamed up by bored mathematicians to provide you with useless facts to learn. But this minimum connector stuff is actually rather handy in the real world.

A *Minimum Connector* is the *Shortest* way to Connect All the Points

See page 215 if you've forgotten what spanning trees are. And remember — an arc is just another name for an edge.

A **minimum connector** is a spanning tree where the total length of the arcs is as **small as possible**.

A minimum connector is also known as a minimum spanning tree (an MST).

Minimum connectors come in handy for cable or pipe-laying companies.
If they need to connect several buildings in a town, say, they'd want to find the cheapest path — this may be the shortest route, or have the easiest ground to dig up.

Kruskal's Algorithm Finds *Minimum Connectors*

Being absolutely certain that you've got the minimum connector is tricky, so using an algorithm helps.

KRUSKAL'S ALGORITHM

1) List the arcs in ascending order of weight.

2) Pick the arc of least weight — this starts the tree.

3) Look at the next arc in your list.
   - if it forms a cycle, DON'T use it and go on to the next arc.
   - if it doesn't form a cycle, add it to the tree.

4) Repeat step 3 until you've joined all the vertices.

This is a 'greedy algorithm'. You make the choice that seems best at each stage, without worrying about later choices.

If there are n vertices in a network, there will always be (n – 1) arcs in a minimum connector.

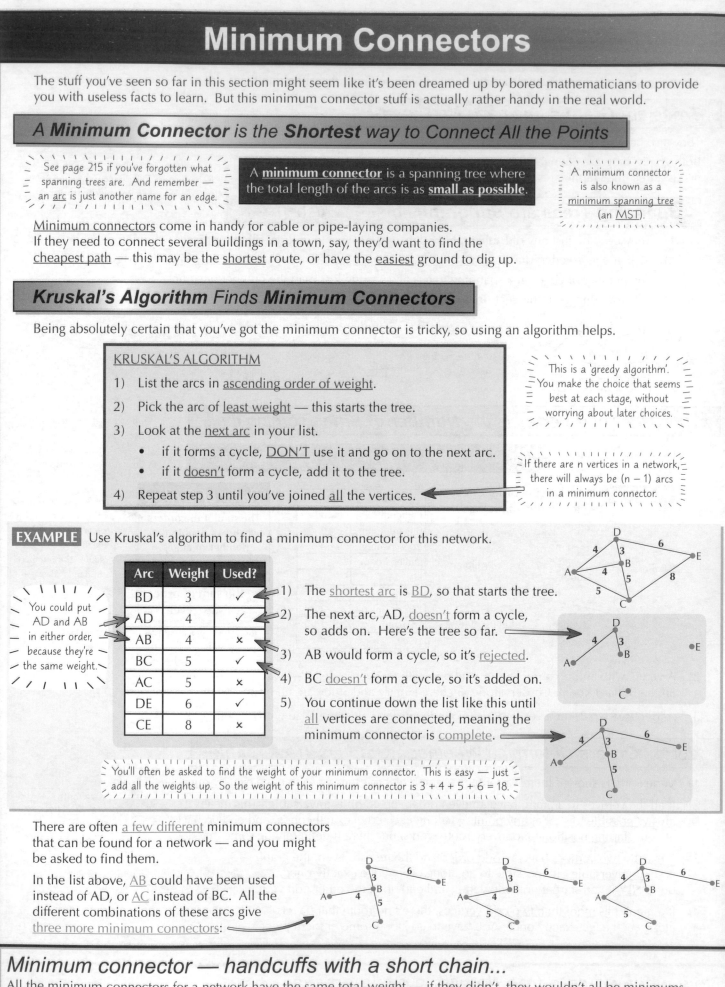

EXAMPLE Use Kruskal's algorithm to find a minimum connector for this network.

Arc	Weight	Used?
BD	3	✓
AD	4	✓
AB	4	✗
BC	5	✓
AC	5	✗
DE	6	✓
CE	8	✗

You could put AD and AB in either order, because they're the same weight.

1) The shortest arc is BD, so that starts the tree.

2) The next arc, AD, doesn't form a cycle, so adds on. Here's the tree so far.

3) AB would form a cycle, so it's rejected.

4) BC doesn't form a cycle, so it's added on.

5) You continue down the list like this until all vertices are connected, meaning the minimum connector is complete.

You'll often be asked to find the weight of your minimum connector. This is easy — just add all the weights up. So the weight of this minimum connector is 3 + 4 + 5 + 6 = 18.

There are often a few different minimum connectors that can be found for a network — and you might be asked to find them.

In the list above, AB could have been used instead of AD, or AC instead of BC. All the different combinations of these arcs give three more minimum connectors:

Minimum connector — handcuffs with a short chain...

All the minimum connectors for a network have the same total weight — if they didn't, they wouldn't all be minimums.
Kruskal's algorithm works fine, but you can't do it straight from matrix forms of graphs, which is what computers often use.
And if you've got a whopping network, this might be important. This is where Prim's algorithm is tops — see the next page...

Minimum Connectors

Prim's algorithm does exactly the same job as Kruskal's algorithm. I'd love to say you only need to learn the one you like best, but that'd be a fib. You've got to learn them both, of course.

Prim's Algorithm Finds Minimum Connectors Too

PRIM'S ALGORITHM

1) Pick a vertex, any vertex — this starts the tree.

2) Choose the arc of least weight that'll join a vertex in the tree to one not yet in the tree.

3) Repeat step 2 until you've joined all the vertices.

> If there's more than one to pick from, just choose randomly.

EXAMPLE   Use Prim's algorithm to find a minimum connector for the network on the right.

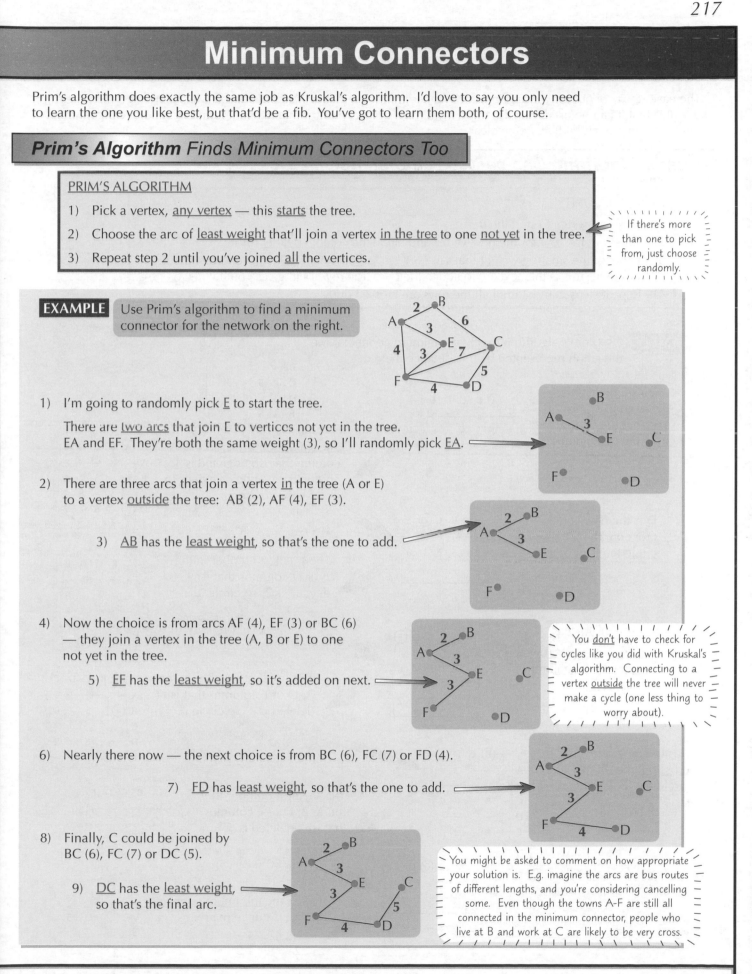

1) I'm going to randomly pick E to start the tree.

   There are two arcs that join E to vertices not yet in the tree. EA and EF. They're both the same weight (3), so I'll randomly pick EA.

2) There are three arcs that join a vertex in the tree (A or E) to a vertex outside the tree: AB (2), AF (4), EF (3).

   3) AB has the least weight, so that's the one to add.

4) Now the choice is from arcs AF (4), EF (3) or BC (6) — they join a vertex in the tree (A, B or E) to one not yet in the tree.

   5) EF has the least weight, so it's added on next.

> You don't have to check for cycles like you did with Kruskal's algorithm. Connecting to a vertex outside the tree will never make a cycle (one less thing to worry about).

6) Nearly there now — the next choice is from BC (6), FC (7) or FD (4).

   7) FD has least weight, so that's the one to add.

8) Finally, C could be joined by BC (6), FC (7) or DC (5).

   9) DC has the least weight, so that's the final arc.

> You might be asked to comment on how appropriate your solution is. E.g. imagine the arcs are bus routes of different lengths, and you're considering cancelling some. Even though the towns A-F are still all connected in the minimum connector, people who live at B and work at C are likely to be very cross.

Wasn't Mr Prim one of the Mr Men?...

Practice, practice, practice is definitely the key for this algorithm too. There are only three steps to memorise, so that's not too tricky. You've just got to apply them accurately — so check you've considered all the possible arcs. Exam questions usually ask you to show your working, or to state the order that you add the arcs in, so winging it with a different method won't do.

Minimum Connectors

The easiest way of putting a graph into a computer is to use a matrix. And the reason why Prim's algorithm is so useful is that it can be used on a <u>distance matrix</u>. It looks like a horrible mess of crossing out and circling randomly, but stay with me, and it'll all come clear.

Prim's Algorithm Can be Used on Distance Matrices

> **PRIM'S ALGORITHM**
>
> 1) Pick <u>any vertex</u> to start the tree.
> 2) Cross out the <u>row</u> for the new vertex and circle the <u>column header</u> for it.
> 3) Look for the <u>smallest weight</u> that's in <u>ANY circled column</u> AND <u>isn't</u> yet crossed out. Circle it. This is the <u>next arc</u> to add to the tree. The row it's in gives you the <u>new vertex</u>.
> 4) <u>Repeat</u> steps 2 and 3 until all the rows are crossed out.

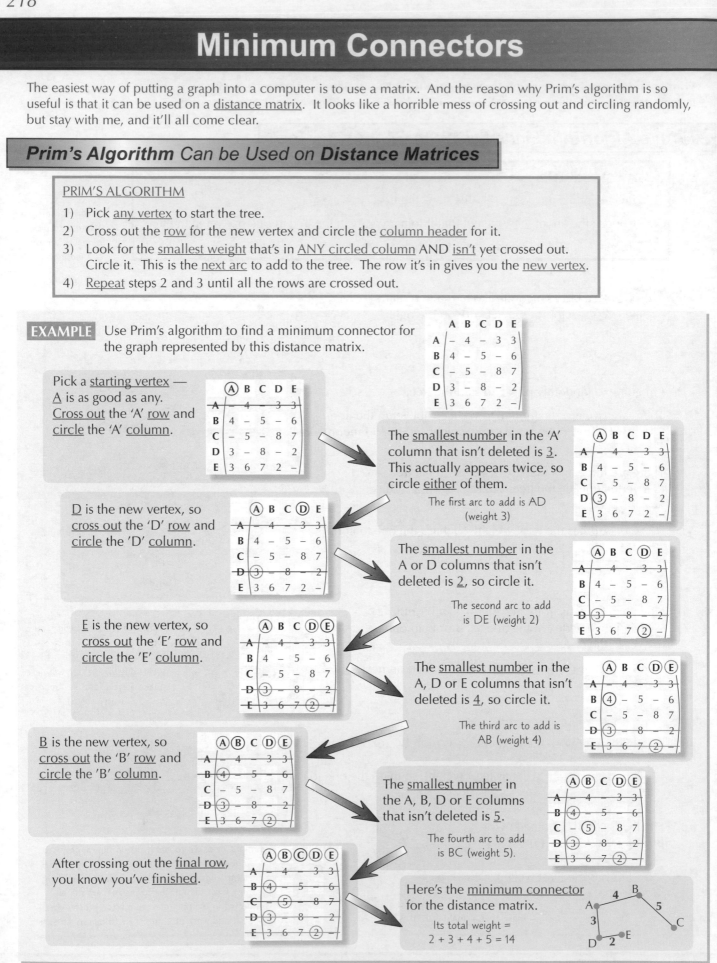

EXAMPLE Use Prim's algorithm to find a minimum connector for the graph represented by this distance matrix.

Pick a <u>starting vertex</u> — A is as good as any. <u>Cross out</u> the 'A' <u>row</u> and <u>circle</u> the 'A' <u>column</u>.

The <u>smallest number</u> in the 'A' column that isn't deleted is <u>3</u>. This actually appears twice, so circle <u>either</u> of them.
The first arc to add is AD (weight 3)

D is the new vertex, so <u>cross out</u> the 'D' <u>row</u> and <u>circle</u> the 'D' <u>column</u>.

The <u>smallest number</u> in the A or D columns that isn't deleted is <u>2</u>, so circle it.
The second arc to add is DE (weight 2)

E is the new vertex, so <u>cross out</u> the 'E' <u>row</u> and <u>circle</u> the 'E' <u>column</u>.

The <u>smallest number</u> in the A, D or E columns that isn't deleted is <u>4</u>, so circle it.
The third arc to add is AB (weight 4)

B is the new vertex, so <u>cross out</u> the 'B' <u>row</u> and <u>circle</u> the 'B' <u>column</u>.

The <u>smallest number</u> in the A, B, D or E columns that isn't deleted is <u>5</u>.
The fourth arc to add is BC (weight 5).

After crossing out the <u>final row</u>, you know you've <u>finished</u>.

Here's the <u>minimum connector</u> for the distance matrix.
Its total weight = 2 + 3 + 4 + 5 = 14

This method also calculates the birthdate of your one true love...

When you're doing this yourself, you don't have to draw out the matrix a zillion times like I've done. Phew, I hear you say. I just wanted you to see all my steps. It took me ages, so do admire them all, and then have a practice for yourself.

Dijkstra's Algorithm

This is another of those algorithms that look really, really complicated. But when you've <u>learnt the steps</u>, you can string them together pretty rapidly. This one does a different job from the last two, so don't just skim the first bit.

Dijkstra's Algorithm Finds the Shortest Path between Two Vertices

1) If you're driving between <u>two cities</u> with a complicated road network between them, it's good to be able to work out which route is <u>quickest</u> (just like satnavs do).

2) <u>Dijkstra's algorithm</u> is a foolproof way to do this. Basically, you <u>label each vertex</u> with the length of the shortest path found so far from the starting point. If you find a <u>shorter path</u>, then you <u>change the label</u>. You keep doing this until you're sure that you've got the shortest distance to it.

Weights can also represent costs — you might want to find the cheapest route.

DIJKSTRA'S ALGORITHM

Once you've given a vertex a final label, you can't change it.

1) Give the <u>Start vertex</u> the <u>final label '0'</u>. This is also called a <u>permanent label</u>.

2) Find all the vertices <u>directly connected</u> to the vertex you've just given a final label to. Give each of these vertices a <u>working value</u> (also called a <u>temporary label</u>).

Dijkstra's algorithm is quadratic (order $O(n^2)$), where n is the number of vertices — see page 202.

$$\text{Working value} = \text{Final label at previous vertex} + \text{weight of arc between previous vertex and this one.}$$

If one of these vertices already has a working value, replace it <u>ONLY</u> if the new working value is <u>lower</u>.

3) Look at the <u>working values</u> of vertices that <u>don't</u> have a final label yet. Pick the <u>smallest</u> and make this the <u>final label</u> of that vertex.

If two vertices have the same smallest working value, pick either.

4) Now repeat steps 2 and 3 until the <u>End vertex</u> has a <u>final label</u> (this is the shortest path length).

5) Trace the route <u>backwards</u> (from the End vertex to the Start vertex). An arc is on the path if:

$$\text{Weight of arc} = \text{Difference in final labels of the arc's vertices}$$

EXAMPLE: Use Dijkstra's algorithm to find the shortest route between A and G.

In the exam, you'll be given a version of the graph to work out the answer on. It'll have <u>boxes</u> to complete at each vertex. Here's what goes in each box:

Order of labelling	Final label
Working values	

① First label the <u>start vertex</u> with the <u>final label '0'</u>. It's the first vertex you've labelled, so stick a 1 in the top left box.

<u>B</u> and <u>C</u> connect to A, so give them <u>working values</u>.

previous final label + connecting arc weight = 0 + 4 = 4

② Make the <u>smallest working value</u> a final label.

3 is the lowest working value, so make that a final label. B is the second vertex to be labelled.

Then give the vertices connecting to B (i.e. <u>D</u> and <u>E</u>) working values.

previous final label + connecting arc weight = 3 + 2 = 5

Dijkstra's Algorithm

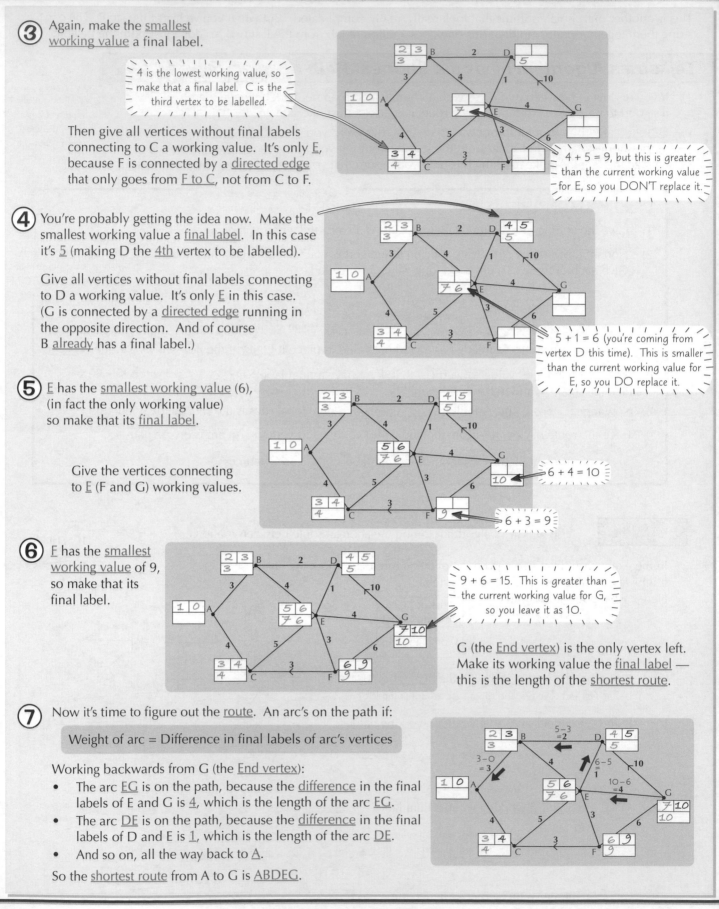

③ Again, make the smallest working value a final label.

4 is the lowest working value, so make that a final label. C is the third vertex to be labelled.

Then give all vertices without final labels connecting to C a working value. It's only E, because F is connected by a directed edge that only goes from F to C, not from C to F.

4 + 5 = 9, but this is greater than the current working value for E, so you DON'T replace it.

④ You're probably getting the idea now. Make the smallest working value a final label. In this case it's 5 (making D the 4th vertex to be labelled).

Give all vertices without final labels connecting to D a working value. It's only E in this case. (G is connected by a directed edge running in the opposite direction. And of course B already has a final label.)

5 + 1 = 6 (you're coming from vertex D this time). This is smaller than the current working value for E, so you DO replace it.

⑤ E has the smallest working value (6), (in fact the only working value) so make that its final label.

Give the vertices connecting to E (F and G) working values.

6 + 4 = 10

6 + 3 = 9

⑥ F has the smallest working value of 9, so make that its final label.

9 + 6 = 15. This is greater than the current working value for G, so you leave it as 10.

G (the End vertex) is the only vertex left. Make its working value the final label — this is the length of the shortest route.

⑦ Now it's time to figure out the route. An arc's on the path if:

> Weight of arc = Difference in final labels of arc's vertices

Working backwards from G (the End vertex):

- The arc EG is on the path, because the difference in the final labels of E and G is 4, which is the length of the arc EG.
- The arc DE is on the path, because the difference in the final labels of D and E is 1, which is the length of the arc DE.
- And so on, all the way back to A.

So the shortest route from A to G is ABDEG.

It's a bit like the Time Warp — now get it right...

Sometimes there's more than one shortest route. If there is, you'll find two possible arcs leading off from a vertex when you're tracing the route back. Remember to read the question carefully — they might want both of the shortest routes.

D1 Section 2 — Practice Questions

Right, now for this algorithm. 1) <u>Try</u> the questions. 2) <u>Check</u> your answers. 3) Reread the page on any you got <u>wrong</u>. 4) Repeat steps 1-3 until you get them all <u>right</u>.

Warm-up Questions

1) Explain what the following are: a) network, b) digraph, c) tree, d) spanning tree

   Questions 2–7 are about the graph on the right.

2) Draw two subgraphs of the graph.

3) Explain why this graph is: a) simple b) planar

4) Describe a possible cycle in the graph.

5) Describe a possible walk and a possible trail in the graph.

6) The graph is currently connected. Delete some edges so that it isn't connected any more.

7) List the order of each node.
   Explain the link between the number of edges and the sum of the orders.

8) Using Dijkstra's algorithm on the graph on page 219: a) Find the shortest route from A to F.
   b) Delete edge BD. Now find the shortest route from A to G.

9) Draw the graph this matrix represents.

$$\begin{array}{c} \\ \\ \textbf{From} \begin{array}{c} \textbf{A} \\ \textbf{B} \\ \textbf{C} \\ \textbf{D} \end{array} \end{array} \overset{\textbf{To}}{\begin{array}{cccc} \textbf{A} & \textbf{B} & \textbf{C} & \textbf{D} \\ \end{array}} \left(\begin{array}{cccc} - & 2 & 3 & 1 \\ 2 & - & - & 4 \\ 3 & - & - & 1 \\ 1 & 5 & - & - \end{array} \right)$$

Now for some questions just like you'll get in the exam. They really are the best sort of practice you can do.

Exam Questions

1   **Figure 1** shows the potential connections for a sprinkler system between greenhouses at a plant nursery.

   The numbers on each arc represent the cost in pounds of each connection.

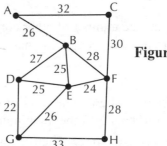

Figure 1

   a)   Use Kruskal's algorithm to find a minimum connector for the network in **Figure 1**.
        List the edges in the order that you consider them and state whether you are adding them to your minimum connector.

        (3 marks)

   b)   State the minimum cost of connecting the sprinkler system.

        (1 mark)

   c)   Draw the minimum connector obtained in a).

        (2 marks)

   d)   If Prim's algorithm had been used to find the minimum connector, starting from E, find which edge would have been the final edge added. Show your working.

        (2 marks)

   e)   State two advantages of Prim's algorithm over Kruskal's algorithm for finding a minimum connector.

        (2 marks)

D1 Section 2 — Practice Questions

Keep going. You can do it. No need for gas and air yet.

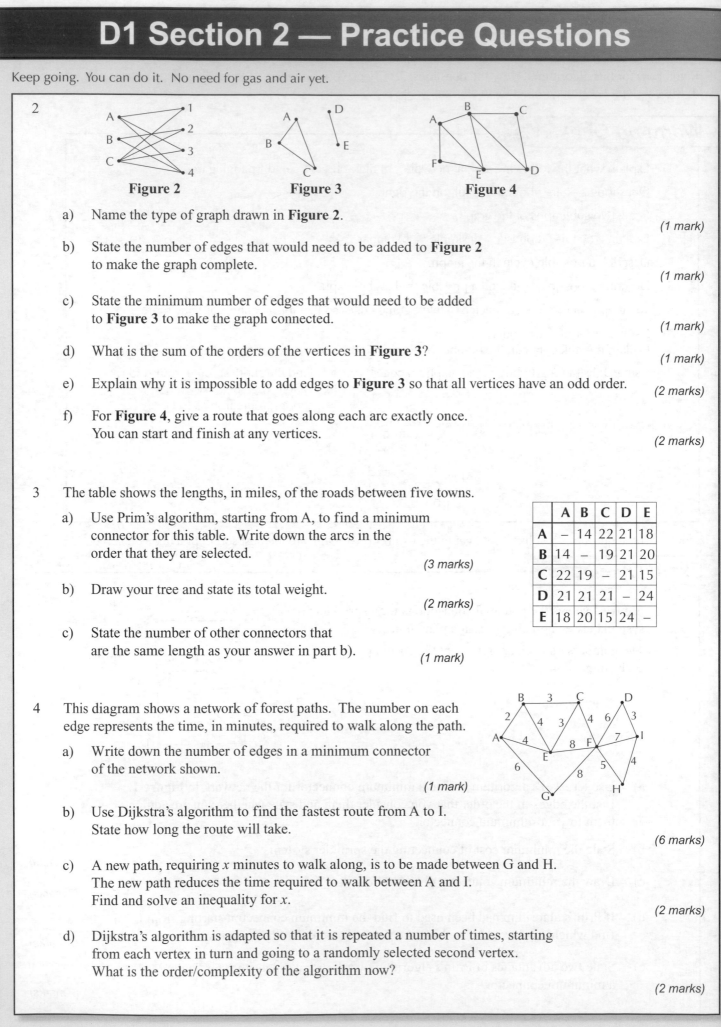

Figure 2   **Figure 3**   **Figure 4**

2

a) Name the type of graph drawn in **Figure 2**.

(1 mark)

b) State the number of edges that would need to be added to **Figure 2** to make the graph complete.

(1 mark)

c) State the minimum number of edges that would need to be added to **Figure 3** to make the graph connected.

(1 mark)

d) What is the sum of the orders of the vertices in **Figure 3**?

(1 mark)

e) Explain why it is impossible to add edges to **Figure 3** so that all vertices have an odd order.

(2 marks)

f) For **Figure 4**, give a route that goes along each arc exactly once. You can start and finish at any vertices.

(2 marks)

3   The table shows the lengths, in miles, of the roads between five towns.

a) Use Prim's algorithm, starting from A, to find a minimum connector for this table. Write down the arcs in the order that they are selected.

(3 marks)

b) Draw your tree and state its total weight.

(2 marks)

c) State the number of other connectors that are the same length as your answer in part b).

(1 mark)

	A	B	C	D	E
A	–	14	22	21	18
B	14	–	19	21	20
C	22	19	–	21	15
D	21	21	21	–	24
E	18	20	15	24	–

4   This diagram shows a network of forest paths. The number on each edge represents the time, in minutes, required to walk along the path.

a) Write down the number of edges in a minimum connector of the network shown.

(1 mark)

b) Use Dijkstra's algorithm to find the fastest route from A to I. State how long the route will take.

(6 marks)

c) A new path, requiring *x* minutes to walk along, is to be made between G and H. The new path reduces the time required to walk between A and I. Find and solve an inequality for *x*.

(2 marks)

d) Dijkstra's algorithm is adapted so that it is repeated a number of times, starting from each vertex in turn and going to a randomly selected second vertex. What is the order/complexity of the algorithm now?

(2 marks)

Activity Networks

A complicated project like building a house involves <u>lots of different activities</u>. Some activities can't be <u>started</u> until others are <u>finished</u>, e.g. you can't put the roof on until the walls are built, and you can't build the walls until the foundations are in place. If you want to get the house built as quickly and cheaply as possible, you have to do a lot of <u>planning</u> (there's no point in the decorator turning up on the same day as the bricklayer and hanging round for 3 months). Luckily, there are a few tricks you can use to help you...

Precedence Tables Show Which Activities Need Doing **Before** Others

<u>Precedence tables</u> show what activities must be <u>finished</u> before others are <u>started</u>. They're not as exciting as an episode of Futurama, but they're pretty easy to draw.

> **EXAMPLE**   Below is a list of activities involved in rustling up an apple pie.
> On the right is a precedence table of the information.

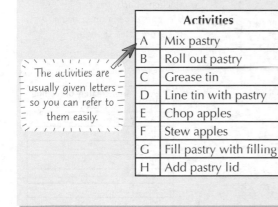

	Activities
A	Mix pastry
B	Roll out pastry
C	Grease tin
D	Line tin with pastry
E	Chop apples
F	Stew apples
G	Fill pastry with filling
H	Add pastry lid

The activities are usually given letters so you can refer to them easily.

Activity	Immediately preceding activities
A	—
B	A
C	—
D	B, C
E	—
F	E
G	D, F
H	G

A (mixing pastry) doesn't depend on anything being done first.

You need to finish A before starting B (mix the pastry before rolling it out).

D depends on both B and C being finished. A must be finished too, but you've already said that B can't start until A is done, so you don't have to show it again.

Activity Networks Show the Information **More Clearly**

1) Precedence tables are OK, but they're not great. Putting the information in an <u>activity network</u> makes it easier to understand, and it looks more impressive too.

2) In activity networks, 'arcs' represent the <u>activities</u>, and 'nodes' represent the <u>completion of activities</u> or '<u>events</u>'.

3) The nodes are <u>numbered</u> as they're added to the network. The first one is numbered <u>zero</u> and is called the <u>source node</u>. The final node is called the <u>sink node</u>.

4) Constructing activity networks can be quite awkward — here's one for the <u>apple pie example</u> above:

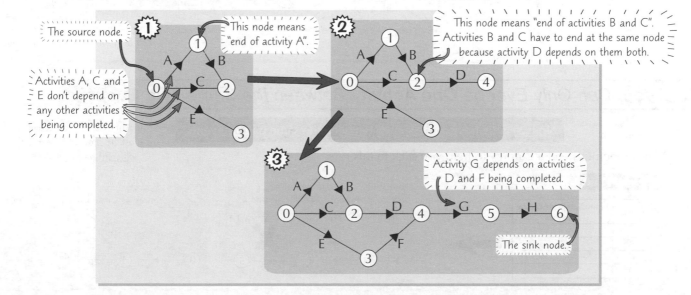

The source node.

This node means "end of activity A".

Activities A, C and E don't depend on any other activities being completed.

This node means "end of activities B and C". Activities B and C have to end at the same node because activity D depends on them both.

Activity G depends on activities D and F being completed.

The sink node.

Arcs are always straight lines — not a general rule for life...

It's very tricky getting the layout of an activity network right first time round, and you're likely to have to do some rubbing out — so draw your activity network in pencil. Getting the layout right does get easier the more you practise though.

Activity Networks

Some situations can only be shown on an activity network using curiously named "<u>dummies</u>". You'll see...

Dummies Help Show the Order that Activities Must be Done in

1) <u>Dummy activities</u> aren't real activities. They just show that <u>one real activity</u> depends on <u>another real activity</u> when it can't be shown clearly otherwise.

2) The information in this <u>precedence table</u> can't be shown on an activity network without a <u>dummy</u>:

EXAMPLE 1:

Show the information in this table in an activity network.

Activity	Immediately preceding activities
A	—
B	A
C	—
D	A, C

Dummy activities are shown by dotted lines.

The dummy activity shows that activity <u>A</u> must be done <u>before</u> activity <u>D</u>.

Activity D must come after the completion of activities A <u>AND</u> C. B doesn't depend on C being completed though.

EXAMPLE 2: Show the information in the table in an activity network. (It's a tricky one that needs two dummies.)

Activity	Immediately preceding activities
A	—
B	—
C	—
D	A
E	B, C
F	C
G	D
H	D, E, F

① The first bit's straightforward. Activities A, B and C don't depend on any other activities. Activity D depends only on A.

② Activity F depends only on activity C, but activity E depends on BOTH B and C. You need a dummy to show this.

③ Activity H depends on both activity E and activity F — so you have to make E and F's arcs end at a shared node.

Activity G depends only on D, but activity H depends on D, E and F. You show this with a dummy.

④ No activities depend on G, so make the 'G' arc end at the sink node. You only ever have one final node.

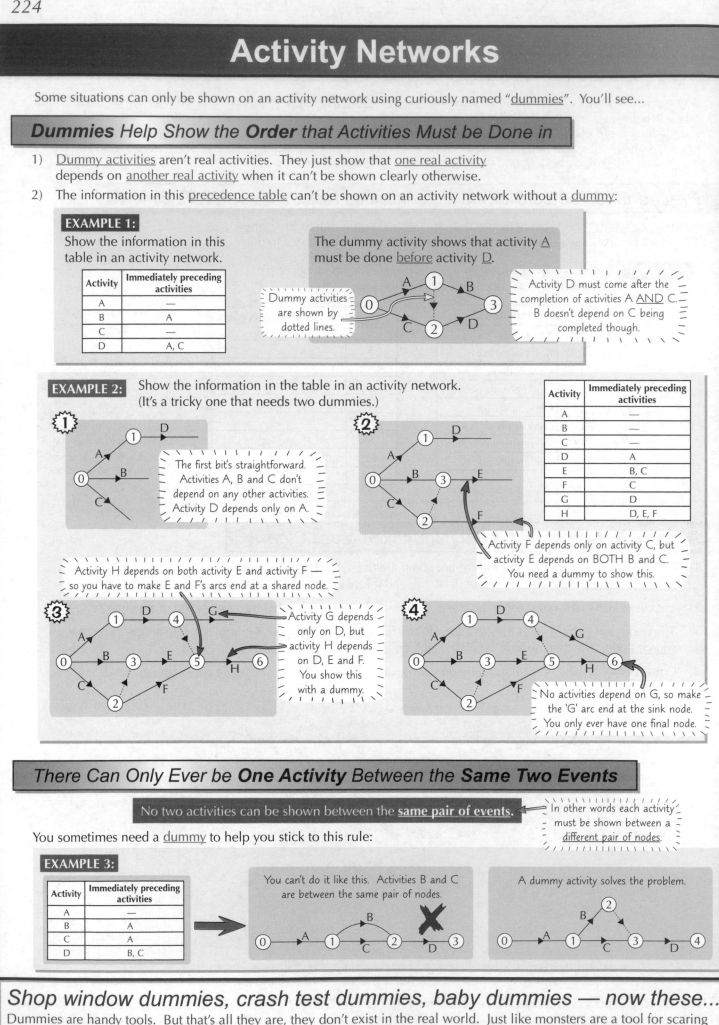

There Can Only Ever be One Activity Between the Same Two Events

No two activities can be shown between the **same pair of events**.

In other words each activity must be shown between a <u>different pair of nodes</u>.

You sometimes need a <u>dummy</u> to help you stick to this rule:

EXAMPLE 3:

Activity	Immediately preceding activities
A	—
B	A
C	A
D	B, C

You can't do it like this. Activities B and C are between the same pair of nodes.

A dummy activity solves the problem.

Shop window dummies, crash test dummies, baby dummies — now these...

Dummies are handy tools. But that's all they are, they don't exist in the real world. Just like monsters are a tool for scaring small children. Oh, shouldn't you do that? Well, cover the precedence tables and draw them from the networks anyway.

Activity Networks with Early and Late Times

When planning real projects, you normally have a <u>deadline</u> to work to. So <u>how long</u> each activity takes is important.

Each Activity has a **Duration**

1) The <u>duration</u> of an activity is <u>how long</u> it takes to complete.

The durations are given here in brackets. They can have the units hours, days, weeks, etc.

2) Each node or 'event' has an <u>early event time</u> and a <u>late event time</u>:

An event is the completion of an activity or activities (see page 223).

EARLY EVENT TIME — the **earliest time** you can reach an event. It depends on the durations of the **preceding activities**.

LATE EVENT TIME — the **latest time** you can get to an event **without** increasing the duration of the entire project.

3) The convention is to use <u>boxes</u> at each node to show the early and late event times.

The early event time goes in the left-hand box.

The late event time goes in the right-hand box.

| 3 | 6 |

Work Out the **Early Event Times** Starting from the **Source**...

You work out an <u>early event time</u> by adding the <u>activity duration</u> to the <u>previous early event time</u>. If there's a <u>choice of paths</u> to a node you use the <u>biggest number</u>. Have a look at the example below (the times are in hours).

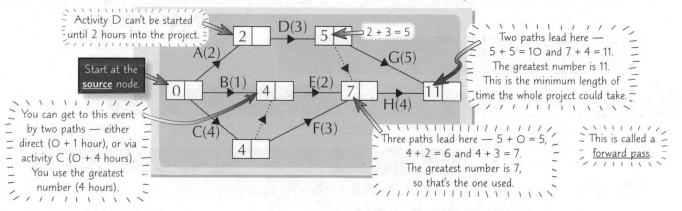

Activity D can't be started until 2 hours into the project.

2 + 3 = 5

Two paths lead here — 5 + 5 = 10 and 7 + 4 = 11. The greatest number is 11. This is the minimum length of time the whole project could take.

Start at the **source** node.

You can get to this event by two paths — either direct (0 + 1 hour), or via activity C (0 + 4 hours). You use the greatest number (4 hours).

Three paths lead here — 5 + 0 = 5, 4 + 2 = 6 and 4 + 3 = 7. The greatest number is 7, so that's the one used.

This is called a <u>forward pass</u>.

...Then Work Out the **Late Event Times** Starting from the **Sink**

To work out <u>late event times</u>, you start at the <u>sink node</u>, and work back towards the source. You subtract each <u>activity duration</u> from its <u>late event time</u>. If there's a choice of paths, you use the <u>smallest number</u> each time.

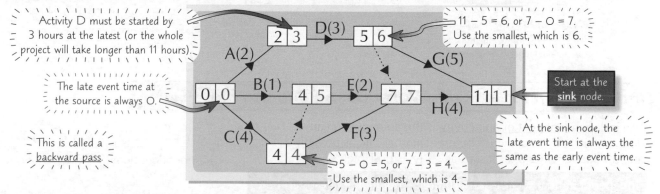

Activity D must be started by 3 hours at the latest (or the whole project will take longer than 11 hours).

11 − 5 = 6, or 7 − 0 = 7. Use the smallest, which is 6.

The late event time at the source is always 0.

Start at the **sink** node.

This is called a <u>backward pass</u>.

At the sink node, the late event time is always the same as the early event time.

5 − 0 = 5, or 7 − 3 = 4. Use the smallest, which is 4.

Help — I'm sinking. Too late... Glugg glugg glugg...

It's good to check at the end that your early event times are all less than or equal to your late event times. Remember, use the biggest numbers to work out early event times. Try imagining that your teammates are running along different length paths to the node. You haven't won until you all arrive there. Then remember that working out late event times is the opposite.

Critical Paths

All the activities for a project have to be done, but with some of them you can take your time and <u>still meet</u> the deadline. With other activities you <u>can't</u> — these are the <u>critical</u> ones.

Critical Activities Must be Completed *Within* their Allotted Time

> If the duration of a **CRITICAL ACTIVITY** increases, the duration of the whole project increases by the same amount.

> A **CRITICAL PATH** runs from the source node to the sink node and is made up of **critical activities**.

The nodes lying on this path are called critical events.

1) All the nodes on a <u>critical path</u> have the same <u>early and late event times</u>.

2) This means they <u>MUST</u> be started at a particular time — there's no 'slack'.

3) <u>Adding up</u> the <u>durations</u> of the activities on the critical path gives you the <u>minimum completion time</u> of the <u>whole project</u> or the '<u>critical time</u>'.

4) You can have an activity network with <u>more than one</u> critical path. The critical paths will all have the same durations.

5) In reality, <u>limited resources</u>, such as workers or machines might mean the project <u>can't</u> be completed within its critical time.

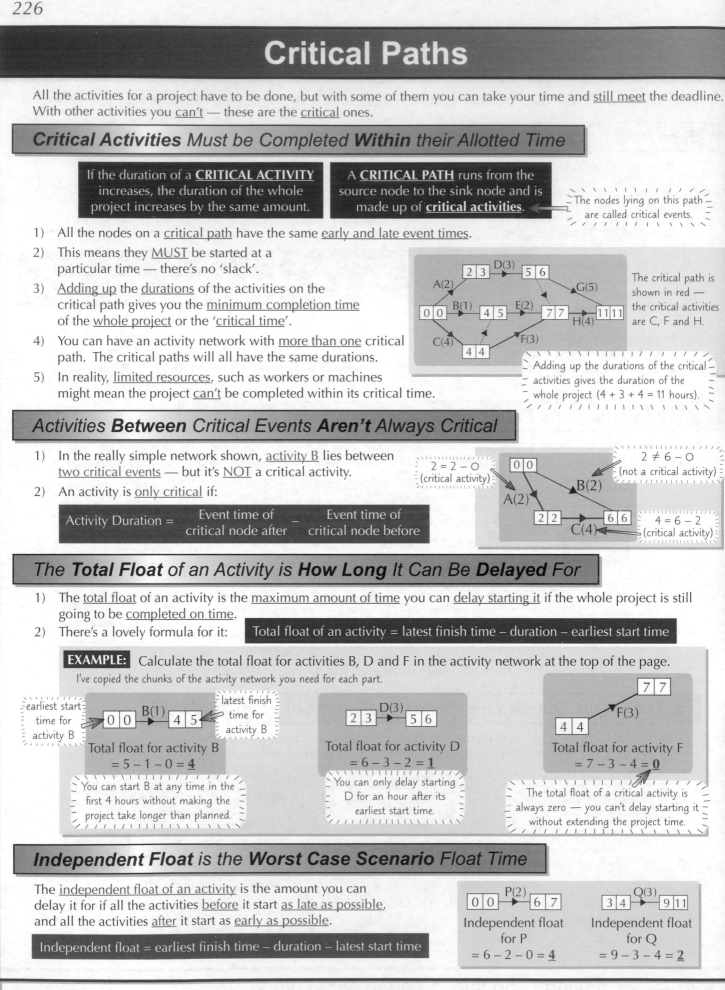

The critical path is shown in red — the critical activities are C, F and H.

Adding up the durations of the critical activities gives the duration of the whole project (4 + 3 + 4 = 11 hours).

Activities *Between* Critical Events *Aren't* Always Critical

1) In the really simple network shown, <u>activity B</u> lies between <u>two critical events</u> — but it's <u>NOT</u> a critical activity.

2) An activity is <u>only critical</u> if:

$$\text{Activity Duration} = \begin{array}{c}\text{Event time of}\\\text{critical node after}\end{array} - \begin{array}{c}\text{Event time of}\\\text{critical node before}\end{array}$$

2 = 2 − 0
(critical activity)

2 ≠ 6 − 0
(not a critical activity)

4 = 6 − 2
(critical activity)

The *Total Float* of an Activity is *How Long* It Can Be *Delayed* For

1) The <u>total float</u> of an activity is the <u>maximum amount of time</u> you can <u>delay starting it</u> if the whole project is still going to be <u>completed on time</u>.

2) There's a lovely formula for it:

> Total float of an activity = latest finish time − duration − earliest start time

> **EXAMPLE:** Calculate the total float for activities B, D and F in the activity network at the top of the page.
>
> I've copied the chunks of the activity network you need for each part.

earliest start time for activity B

latest finish time for activity B

Total float for activity B
= 5 − 1 − 0 = **4**

You can start B at any time in the first 4 hours without making the project take longer than planned.

Total float for activity D
= 6 − 3 − 2 = **1**

You can only delay starting D for an hour after its earliest start time.

Total float for activity F
= 7 − 3 − 4 = **0**

The total float of a critical activity is always zero — you can't delay starting it without extending the project time.

Independent Float is the *Worst Case Scenario* Float Time

The <u>independent float of an activity</u> is the amount you can delay it for if all the activities <u>before</u> it start <u>as late as possible</u>, and all the activities <u>after</u> it start as <u>early as possible</u>.

> Independent float = earliest finish time − duration − latest start time

Independent float for P
= 6 − 2 − 0 = **4**

Independent float for Q
= 9 − 3 − 4 = **2**

Critical path: You're walking on me all wrong...

Make sure you're really hot at finding critical paths and identifying critical activities. Remember, there may be more than one — just use the same rules for finding each of them. There's practice at spotting multiple critical paths on p. 232-233.

Crashing Networks

'Crashing Networks' is possibly the most exciting title in this entire book. Now that you've enjoyed it, enjoy the page. But be warned — this stuff is really hard. There's no algorithm — you've just got to use trial, error and common sense.

Crashing a Network means Reducing the Minimum Time for the Project

1) To reduce the critical time for a project, you have to decrease the duration of an activity in the critical path. Decreasing the duration of a non-critical activity won't have any effect on the overall time for the project.

2) You usually have to add extra resources, such as workers or money (or both) to do this.

3) There's normally a limit to how much you can reduce the duration of an activity, so you might have to decrease more than one activity in the critical path.

4) If there are two critical paths, you have to decrease the length of them both, or the overall time for the project won't change.

Keep Checking for Knock-on Effects

1) The trouble is, changing the duration of one activity can affect other activities.

2) It can mean that another activity either can't be done on time or becomes critical.

3) An activity becoming critical means a new critical path has been created. If you need to reduce the project time any further, you'll have to reduce this new critical path too.

4) Remember this rule:

> Every time you change the duration of an activity, check all activities are still possible and none have become critical.

EXAMPLE: The project shown by the activity network below has a critical time of 17 days, and two critical paths, AHJ and CGJ (shown in red).

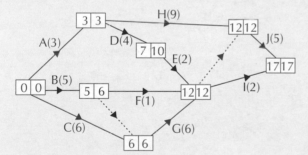

The durations of some of the activities can be reduced by spending more money.

Activity C can be reduced by up to 2 days for £125 a day.
Activity G can be reduced by up to 3 days for £150 a day.
Activity H can be reduced by up to 3 days for £200 a day.
Activity J can be reduced by up to 2 days for £300 a day.

Find the cheapest way of reducing the project time to 13 days.

1) You need to shave 4 days off the project duration to get it down from 17 days to 13 days.

2) There are two critical paths — they both must be reduced by four days.

3) You can't reduce any activity by 4 days, so you'll have to reduce the durations of at least two activities on each critical path.

4) The first critical path has activities A, H and J on it. You can't reduce A, so you have reduce both H and J.

5) Start by reducing activity J. It lies on both critical paths so reducing its duration reduces both critical paths simultaneously. It costs £300 to reduce it by a day, and this is cheaper than the next best alternative of reducing H on one critical path and C on the other (£200 + £125 = £325), so it makes sense to try to decrease it by the maximum amount of time (2 days).

6) Reducing activity J by 2 days brings the project completion time down to 15 days.

7) Now check all non-critical activities are still possible, and haven't become critical. Activity I is the only one that could have been affected with this change, but there's still enough time to complete it and it hasn't become critical.

> There are still 3 days to complete activity I in. It only takes 2 days so it's still not critical.

The critical time is down to 15 days — but there are still two more days to lose. Just how much will it cost? Find out in the next episode...

Crashing Networks

Keep on plodding onwards — just like a little donkey...

EXAMPLE CONTINUED:

8) You're now looking to reduce <u>each</u> critical path (AHJ and CGJ) by <u>2 more days each</u>.

9) The only way to reduce AHJ is to reduce <u>H</u> by <u>2 days</u>. So try that.

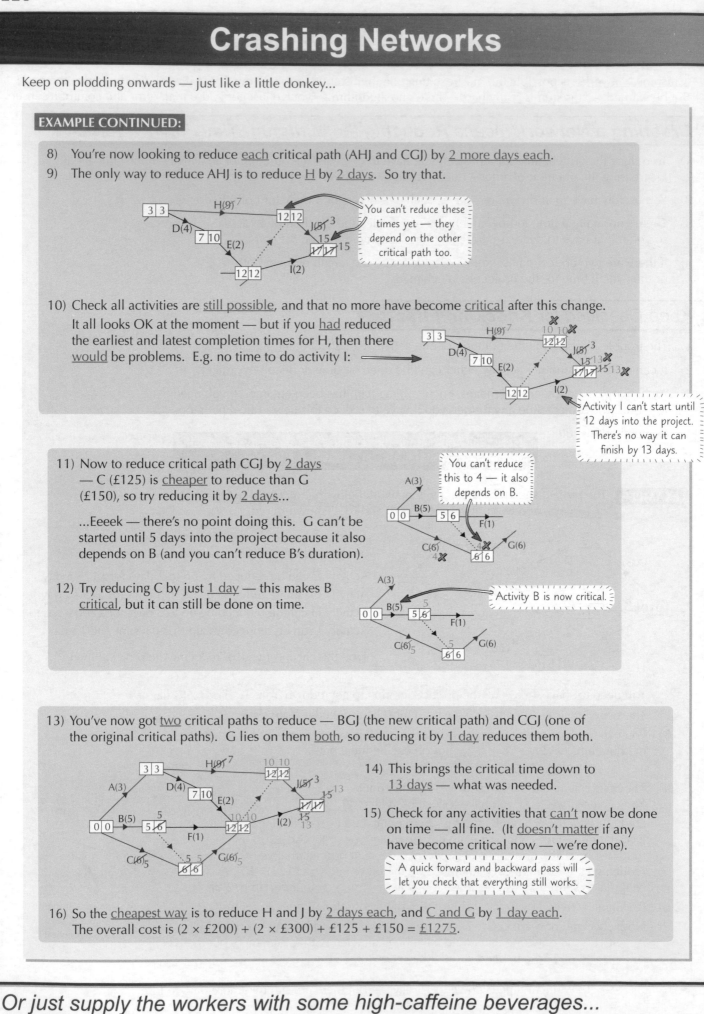

You can't reduce these times yet — they depend on the other critical path too.

10) Check all activities are <u>still possible</u>, and that no more have become <u>critical</u> after this change.
It all looks OK at the moment — but if you <u>had</u> reduced the earliest and latest completion times for H, then there <u>would</u> be problems. E.g. no time to do activity I:

Activity I can't start until 12 days into the project. There's no way it can finish by 13 days.

11) Now to reduce critical path CGJ by <u>2 days</u> — C (£125) is <u>cheaper</u> to reduce than G (£150), so try reducing it by <u>2 days</u>...

...Eeeek — there's no point doing this. G can't be started until 5 days into the project because it also depends on B (and you can't reduce B's duration).

You can't reduce this to 4 — it also depends on B.

12) Try reducing C by just <u>1 day</u> — this makes B <u>critical</u>, but it can still be done on time.

Activity B is now critical.

13) You've now got <u>two</u> critical paths to reduce — BGJ (the new critical path) and CGJ (one of the original critical paths). G lies on them <u>both</u>, so reducing it by <u>1 day</u> reduces them both.

14) This brings the critical time down to <u>13 days</u> — what was needed.

15) Check for any activities that <u>can't</u> now be done on time — all fine. (It <u>doesn't matter</u> if any have become critical now — we're done).

A quick forward and backward pass will let you check that everything still works.

16) So the <u>cheapest way</u> is to reduce H and J by <u>2 days each</u>, and <u>C and G</u> by <u>1 day each</u>. The overall cost is (2 × £200) + (2 × £300) + £125 + £150 = <u>£1275</u>.

Or just supply the workers with some high-caffeine beverages...

So you need to reduce the critical path — or possibly paths. But check, check, check that the rest of the network still works.

Cascade Charts

The cascade chart, commonly known as the Gantt chart — Henry Gantt's greatest triumph. I bet his mum was proud.

Cascade Charts Show Possible Start and Finish Times For Activities

1) Cascade charts let you show the possible time periods that each activity can happen in for the project to be completed on time.

2) Here's how to plot a single activity on a cascade chart:

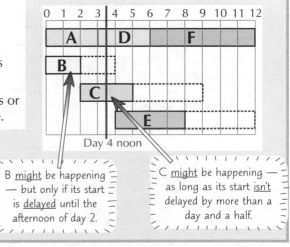

P has a duration of 4 hours. If it starts at 1 hour, it'll finish at 5 hours.

Total float for activity P
= 7 − 4 − 1 = 2

The earliest P can start is 1 hour into the project.

The latest P can finish is at 7 hours.

The total float is 2 hours.

3) This example shows a whole activity network plotted on a cascade chart:

EXAMPLE: Display this information on a cascade chart. The times are all shown in hours.

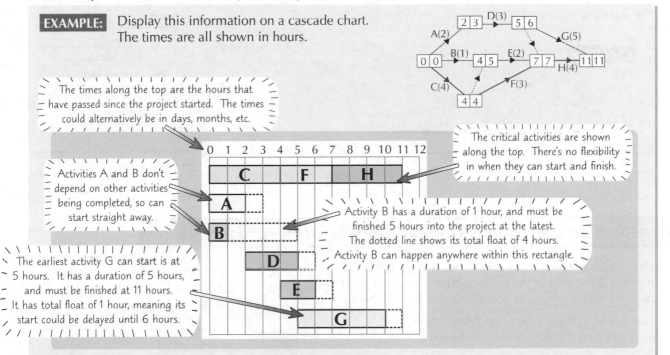

The times along the top are the hours that have passed since the project started. The times could alternatively be in days, months, etc.

The critical activities are shown along the top. There's no flexibility in when they can start and finish.

Activities A and B don't depend on other activities being completed, so can start straight away.

Activity B has a duration of 1 hour, and must be finished 5 hours into the project at the latest. The dotted line shows its total float of 4 hours. Activity B can happen anywhere within this rectangle.

The earliest activity G can start is at 5 hours. It has a duration of 5 hours, and must be finished at 11 hours. It has total float of 1 hour, meaning its start could be delayed until 6 hours.

4) The solid activity rectangles can slide right — as long as they stay within the dotted rectangles. But sliding them might affect other activities. E.g. if A slides forward an hour, then D must too. This means G has to slide later too.

You Have to Interpret Cascade Charts Too

1) You'll sometimes be asked what activities will be happening at a particular time. Some activities will definitely be happening at this time, whereas other activities only might be happening.

2) Don't forget — the times along the top indicate the number of days or hours that have elapsed. So day 4 is between 3 and 4 on the scale.

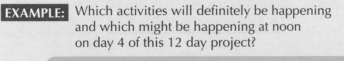

Day 4 noon

EXAMPLE: Which activities will definitely be happening and which might be happening at noon on day 4 of this 12 day project?

Only activity D will definitely be happening on day 4. Activities B and C might be happening.

B might be happening — but only if its start is delayed until the afternoon of day 2.

C might be happening — as long as its start isn't delayed by more than a day and a half.

Can't stand the cascade of information? — best get a hard hat...

It's not actually so bad, this stuff. If I'd written the spec, I reckon I'd have put it on too. To test whether you really know it, copy out the activity network above without the times. Then try to fill them in by just looking at the cascade chart.

Resource Histograms

Resource histograms — now you're back in familiar territory. They're just like, well, histograms.

Resource Histograms Show How Many People Are Needed at any Time

1) Strictly, <u>resource histograms</u> show the '<u>quantity of resources</u>' needed at any moment. It's usually the <u>number of people</u>, but it could be, e.g. machines or space.

2) Resource histograms are drawn from <u>cascade charts</u> — and it makes things a lot easier if you draw your resource histogram <u>right under</u> the cascade chart.

3) Sometimes activities require <u>more than one person</u>. The <u>number of people</u> needed for each activity will be shown either in a table or on the cascade chart (see right).

4) The example on the right is for this activity network:

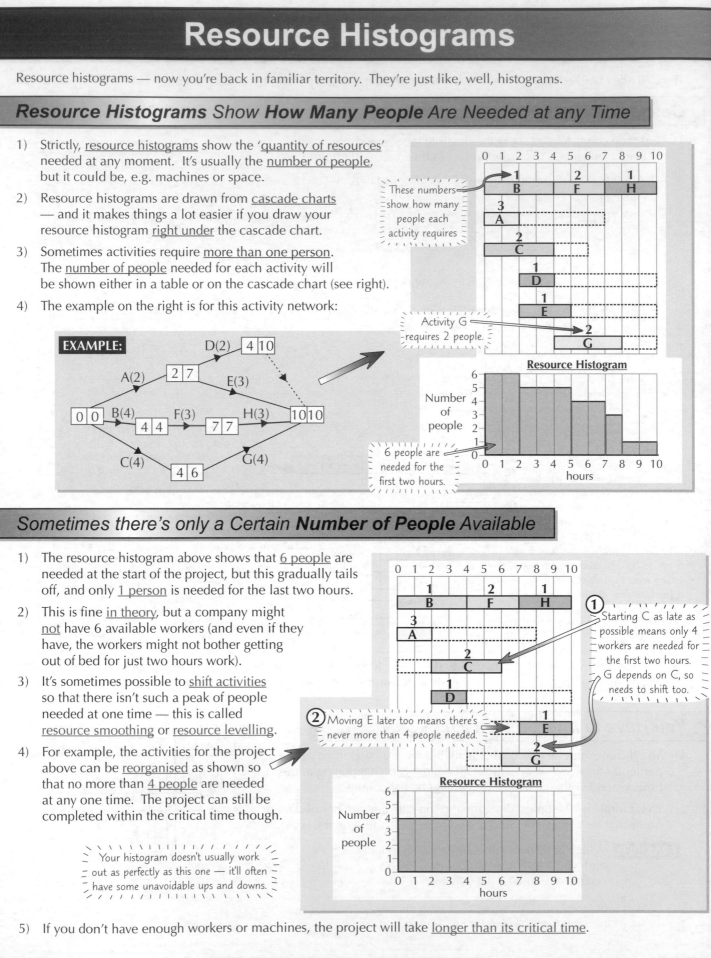

These numbers show how many people each activity requires

Activity G requires 2 people.

Resource Histogram

6 people are needed for the first two hours.

Sometimes there's only a Certain Number of People Available

1) The resource histogram above shows that <u>6 people</u> are needed at the start of the project, but this gradually tails off, and only <u>1 person</u> is needed for the last two hours.

2) This is fine <u>in theory</u>, but a company might <u>not</u> have 6 available workers (and even if they have, the workers might not bother getting out of bed for just two hours work).

3) It's sometimes possible to <u>shift activities</u> so that there isn't such a peak of people needed at one time — this is called <u>resource smoothing</u> or <u>resource levelling</u>.

4) For example, the activities for the project above can be <u>reorganised</u> as shown so that no more than <u>4 people</u> are needed at any one time. The project can still be completed within the critical time though.

① Starting C as late as possible means only 4 workers are needed for the first two hours. G depends on C, so needs to shift too.

② Moving E later too means there's never more than 4 people needed.

Resource Histogram

Your histogram doesn't usually work out as perfectly as this one — it'll often have some unavoidable ups and downs.

5) If you don't have enough workers or machines, the project will take <u>longer than its critical time</u>.

If it takes n mathematicians to change a lightbulb...

Cascade charts and resource histograms are useful tools, but you do need to add a bit of common sense when applying them to a situation. You often have to look at what resources you have and then do a bit of juggling to make things work efficiently.

Scheduling

Cascade charts are useful for working out <u>how many people</u> are needed to complete a project on time. An employer wouldn't want to have people standing about, because they're all going to want to be <u>paid</u>.

Scheduling Diagrams *Show How Many* **Workers** *are Needed*

1) In the exam, you might be asked to give a <u>schedule</u> showing the tasks each worker should do in which <u>order</u>.

2) Scheduling diagrams are a good way to work this out. As well as showing each worker's activities, they show <u>how many workers</u> are needed to complete the project by the deadline.

3) There are some <u>rules</u> to follow when you're scheduling workers:

- Assume that <u>each activity</u> requires <u>one worker</u>.

- Once a worker starts an activity, they have to <u>carry on</u> with it until it's finished. They <u>can't</u> break off from the activity to get another one started.

- Assume that once a worker finishes one activity, they're ready to start on another <u>immediately</u> — workers in Decision Maths don't need a lunch break.

- When picking the next activity for a worker, look for ones that can be <u>started straight away</u>. If there's a <u>choice of activities</u>, they should always start on the one that must be <u>finished soonest</u> (which has the lowest latest finishing time).

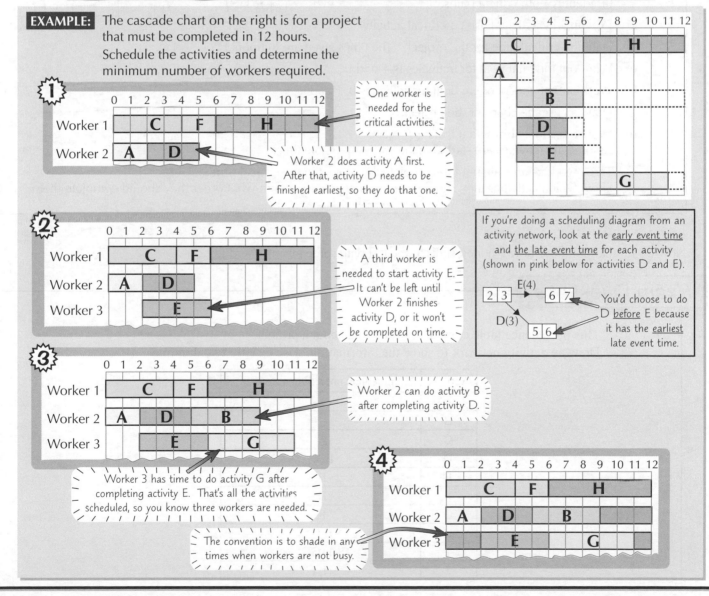

EXAMPLE: The cascade chart on the right is for a project that must be completed in 12 hours. Schedule the activities and determine the minimum number of workers required.

One worker is needed for the critical activities.

Worker 2 does activity A first. After that, activity D needs to be finished earliest, so they do that one.

A third worker is needed to start activity E. It can't be left until Worker 2 finishes activity D, or it won't be completed on time.

If you're doing a scheduling diagram from an activity network, look at the <u>early event time</u> and <u>the late event time</u> for each activity (shown in pink below for activities D and E).

You'd choose to do D <u>before</u> E because it has the <u>earliest</u> late event time.

Worker 2 can do activity B after completing activity D.

Worker 3 has time to do activity G after completing activity E. That's all the activities scheduled, so you know three workers are needed.

The convention is to shade in any times when workers are not busy.

I left my job because of something the boss said — it was "You're fired"...

Of course, in real life, there'll be complications. You might need a worker with specialist skills to do particular activities, and things will happen to scupper your scheduling diagrams, like people being off sick, or machines breaking. But hey, who cares about that — this is maths. Your workers can work nonstop for hours. They don't even need loo breaks.

D1 Section 3 — Practice Questions

Oooh... precedence tables, activity networks, cascade charts, scheduling diagrams.
To make sure you know how to construct and use each of them, try these juicy little questions.

Warm-up Questions

1) Activities A and B don't depend on any other activities. Activity C depends on activity A, activity D depends on activity B, and activity E depends on both activities C and D.

   a) Draw a precedence table to represent this information.

   b) Draw an activity network for the project.

2) Draw an activity network for the precedence table on the right. You'll need two dummies.

3) a) What numbers should replace the red letters *a–g* in this activity network?

   b) (i) Explain what is meant by a critical path.
      (ii) Identify both critical paths.

   c) Explain why activity E isn't a critical activity.

   d) State the critical time for the project. (The times given are in hours.)

   e) Work out the total float for activities B, E and I.

   f) Work out the independent float for activities B, E and I.

   g) Draw a cascade chart for the project.

   h) Draw a resource histogram for this project. Assume all activities are started at the earliest possible time.

   i) Three workers are sufficient to complete the project in the critical time. Show which activities they should each be assigned to, and in what order they should complete them.

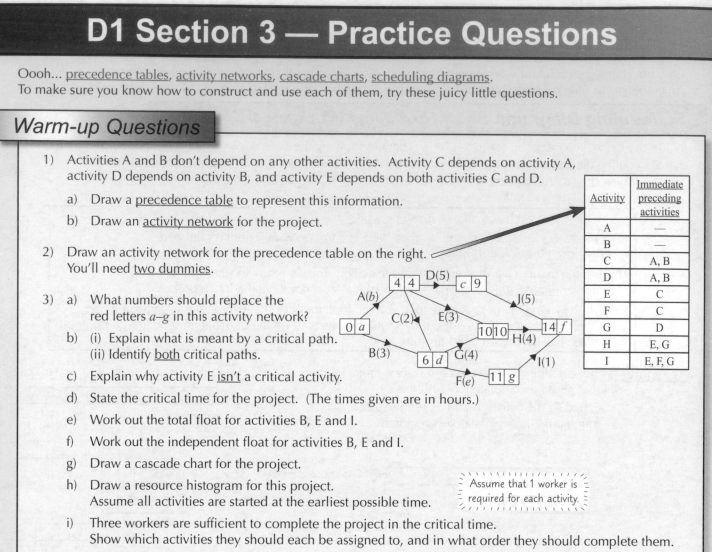

Activity	Immediate preceding activities
A	—
B	—
C	A, B
D	A, B
E	C
F	C
G	D
H	E, G
I	E, F, G

Assume that 1 worker is required for each activity.

Now it's time to put those newly-honed skills to the test with some exam-style questions.

Exam Questions

1 a) This precedence table contains information about a project.
      Draw an activity network to show the information. Use exactly two dummies.

(5 marks)

Activity	Immediate preceding activities
A	—
B	—
C	A
D	B, C
E	B
F	D
G	E
H	F, G
I	F, G
J	H, I

   b) Explain why each dummy is needed.

(2 marks)

D1 Section 3 — Practice Questions

Just <u>two more questions</u> to have a bash at. There's nothing too devilish about them...

2   The network in **Figure 1** shows the activities involved in a process. The number in brackets on each arc gives the time, in days, taken to complete the activity.

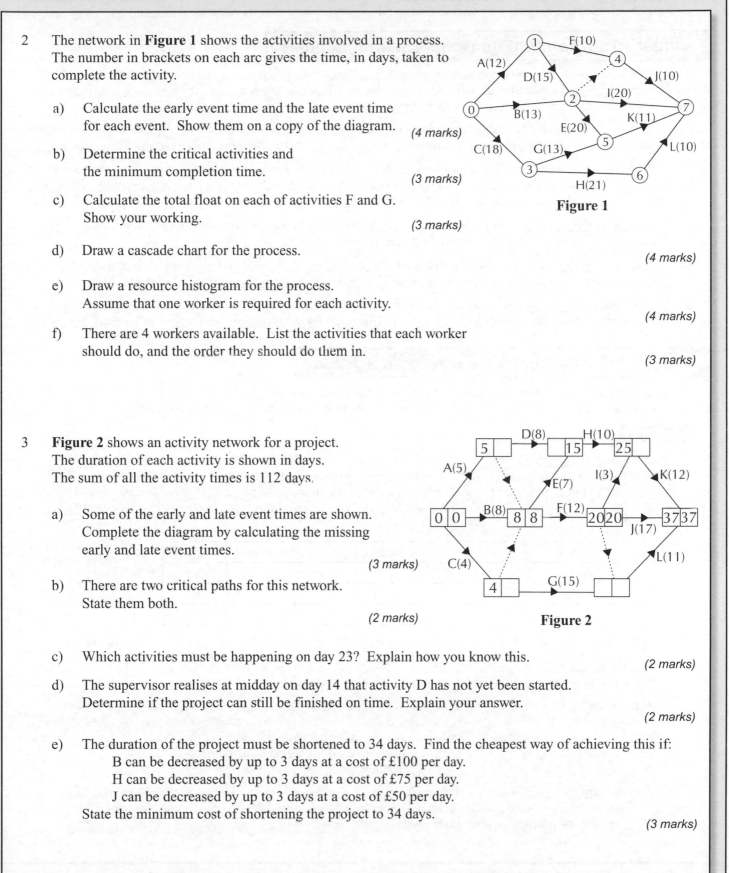

a)   Calculate the early event time and the late event time for each event. Show them on a copy of the diagram.   *(4 marks)*

b)   Determine the critical activities and the minimum completion time.   *(3 marks)*

c)   Calculate the total float on each of activities F and G. Show your working.   *(3 marks)*

d)   Draw a cascade chart for the process.   *(4 marks)*

e)   Draw a resource histogram for the process. Assume that one worker is required for each activity.   *(4 marks)*

f)   There are 4 workers available. List the activities that each worker should do, and the order they should do them in.   *(3 marks)*

Figure 1

3   **Figure 2** shows an activity network for a project. The duration of each activity is shown in days. The sum of all the activity times is 112 days.

a)   Some of the early and late event times are shown. Complete the diagram by calculating the missing early and late event times.   *(3 marks)*

b)   There are two critical paths for this network. State them both.   *(2 marks)*

Figure 2

c)   Which activities must be happening on day 23? Explain how you know this.   *(2 marks)*

d)   The supervisor realises at midday on day 14 that activity D has not yet been started. Determine if the project can still be finished on time. Explain your answer.   *(2 marks)*

e)   The duration of the project must be shortened to 34 days. Find the cheapest way of achieving this if:
        B can be decreased by up to 3 days at a cost of £100 per day.
        H can be decreased by up to 3 days at a cost of £75 per day.
        J can be decreased by up to 3 days at a cost of £50 per day.
    State the minimum cost of shortening the project to 34 days.   *(3 marks)*

Linear Programs

Linear programming is a way of <u>solving problems</u> that have lots of inequalities, often to do with <u>money</u> or <u>business</u>. So if you're a budding entrepreneur, pay attention — this section could help you make your <u>first million</u>. Or just pass D1.

Linear Programming problems use Inequalities

The <u>aim</u> of linear programming is to produce an <u>optimal solution</u> to a <u>problem</u>, e.g. to find the solution that gives the <u>maximum profit</u> to a manufacturer, based on <u>conditions</u> that would affect it, such as <u>limited time</u> or <u>materials</u>. Before you start having a go at linear programming problems, there are a few <u>terms</u> you need to know.

1) In any problem, you'll have things that are being <u>produced</u> (or <u>bought</u> or <u>sold</u> etc.) — e.g. jars of jam or different types of books. The <u>amount</u> of each thing is represented by x, y, z etc. — these are called the <u>decision variables</u>.

2) The <u>constraints</u> are the <u>factors</u> that <u>limit</u> the problem, e.g. a limited amount of workers available. The constraints are written as <u>inequalities</u> in terms of the <u>decision variables</u>. Most problems will have <u>non-negativity constraints</u>. This just means that the decision variables <u>can't</u> be <u>negative</u>. It makes sense really — you can't have −1 books.

3) The <u>objective function</u> is what you're trying to <u>maximise</u> or <u>minimise</u> (e.g. maximise <u>profit</u> or minimise <u>cost</u>). It's usually in the form of a <u>function</u> written in terms of the <u>decision variables</u>.

4) A <u>feasible solution</u> is a solution that <u>satisfies</u> all the <u>constraints</u>. It'll give you a <u>value</u> for each of the <u>decision variables</u>. On a <u>graph</u>, the <u>set</u> of feasible solutions lie in the <u>feasible region</u> (see p.235).

5) You're aiming to <u>optimise</u> the objective function — that's finding a solution within the feasible region that maximises (or minimises) the <u>objective function</u>. This is the <u>optimal solution</u>, and there can be <u>more than one</u>.

Put the Information you're given into a Table

Linear programming questions can look a bit confusing because you're given a lot of <u>information</u> in one go. But if you put all the information in a <u>table</u>, it's much easier to work out the <u>inequalities</u> you need.

EXAMPLE

A company makes garden furniture, and produces both picnic tables and benches. It takes 5 hours to make a picnic table and 2 hours to paint it. It takes 3 hours to make a bench and 1 hour to paint it. In a week, there are 100 hours allocated to construction and 50 hours allocated to painting. Picnic tables are sold for a profit of £30 and benches are sold for a profit of £10. The company wants to maximise their weekly profit.

Putting this information into a table gives:

Item of furniture	Construction time (hours)	Painting time (hours)	Profit (£)
Picnic table	5	2	30
Bench	3	1	10
Total time available:	100	50	

This is an example of how linear programming can be used to solve real-life problems.

Now use the table to identify all the different parts of the problem and come up with the inequalities:

- The <u>decision variables</u> are the <u>number of picnic tables</u> and the <u>number of benches</u>, so let x = number of picnic tables and y = number of benches.

- The <u>constraints</u> are the <u>number of hours available</u> for <u>each stage</u> of manufacture. Making a picnic table takes 5 hours, so x tables will take $5x$ hours. Making a bench takes 3 hours, so y benches will take $3y$ hours. There are a total of 100 hours available. From this, you get the inequality $5x + 3y \leq 100$. Using the same method for the painting hours produces the inequality $2x + y \leq 50$. You also need $x, y \geq 0$. ← *Don't forget the non-negativity constraints.*

- The <u>objective function</u> to be <u>maximised</u> is <u>profit</u>. Each picnic table makes a profit of £30, so x tables make a profit of £$30x$. Each bench makes a profit of £10, so y benches make a profit of £$10y$. Let P be the profit, then the aim is to maximise $P = 30x + 10y$.

I'd like −3 picnic tables please...

In fancy examiner speak, the example above could be written like this: 'maximise $P = 30x + 10y$ subject to the constraints $5x + 3y \leq 100$, $2x + y \leq 50$ and $x, y \geq 0$'. Watch out for constraints such as 'there have to be at least twice as many benches as picnic tables — this would be written as $2x \leq y$. You might have to think about this one to get your head round it.

Feasible Regions

If you're a fan of <u>drawing graphs</u>, you'll love this page. It's a bit like the <u>graphical inequality problems</u> you came across at GCSE. Even if you're not that keen on graphs, or if the mere thought of them brings you out in a <u>rash</u>, don't worry — they're only <u>straight line graphs</u>.

Drawing **Graphs** can help solve **Linear Programming Problems**

<u>Plotting the constraints</u> on a <u>graph</u> is probably the easiest way to <u>solve</u> a linear programming problem — it helps you see the <u>feasible solutions</u> clearly. Get your ruler and graph paper ready.

1) Draw each of the <u>constraints</u> as a <u>line</u> on the graph. All you have to do is <u>change</u> the <u>inequality sign</u> to an <u>equals sign</u> and plot the line. If you find it easier, <u>rearrange</u> the equation into the form $y = mx + c$.

2) Then you have to <u>decide</u> which bit of the graph you <u>want</u> — whether the solution will be <u>above</u> or <u>below</u> the line. This will depend on the <u>inequality sign</u> — <u>rearrange</u> the inequality into the form $y = mx + c$, then think about which sign you'd use. For $y \leq mx + c$ (or <), you want the bit <u>underneath</u> the line, and if it's $y \geq mx + c$ (or >) then you want the bit <u>above</u> the line. If you're not sure, put the <u>coordinates</u> of a point in one region (e.g. the origin) into the equation and see if it <u>satisfies</u> the inequality.

3) Once you've decided which bit you want, <u>shade</u> the region you <u>don't want</u>. This way, when you put all the constraints on the graph, the <u>unshaded region</u> (the bit you want) is easy to see.

4) If the inequality sign is < or >, use a <u>dotted line</u> — this means you <u>don't</u> include the line in the region. If the inequality sign is ≤ or ≥ then use a <u>normal</u> line, so the line is <u>included</u> in the range of solutions.

5) Once you've drawn <u>all</u> the constraints on the graph, you'll be able to solve the problem. Don't forget the <u>non-negativity constraints</u> — they'll limit the graph to the <u>first quadrant</u>.

The **Unshaded Area** is the **Feasible Region**

Your finished graph should have an area, <u>bounded</u> by the lines of the <u>constraints</u>, that <u>hasn't</u> been <u>shaded</u>. This is the <u>feasible region</u> — the <u>coordinates</u> of any point inside the <u>unshaded area</u> will satisfy <u>all</u> the <u>constraints</u>.

EXAMPLE

On a graph, show the constraints $x + y \leq 5$, $3x - y \geq 2$, $y > 1$ and $x, y \geq 0$. Label the feasible region R.

Rearranging the inequalities into '$y = mx + c$' form and choosing the appropriate inequality sign gives: $y \leq 5 - x$, $y \leq 3x - 2$ and $y > 1$. The non-negativity constraints $x, y \geq 0$ are represented by the x- and y- axes.

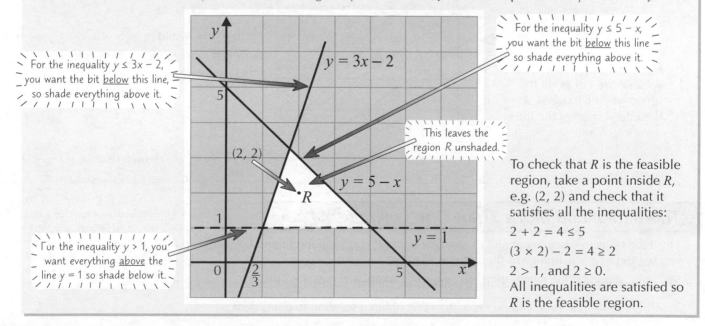

It's feasible that I might become a film star...

...but not very likely — I'm a terrible actor. Anyway, although it's possible that you might get a linear programming problem with more than two variables, you won't have to draw graphs for these ones. You'll only have to graph 2-variable problems.

Optimal Solutions

Don't throw away your <u>graphs</u> just yet — you still need them for the next few pages. You're now getting on to the really useful bit — actually <u>solving</u> the linear programming problem.

Draw a line for the **Objective Function**

All the points in the <u>feasible region</u> (see previous page) satisfy all the <u>constraints</u> in the problem. You need to be able to work out which point (or points) also <u>optimises</u> the <u>objective function</u>. The objective function is usually of the form $Z = ax + by$, where Z either needs to be <u>maximised</u> (e.g. profit) or <u>minimised</u> (e.g. cost) to give the <u>optimal solution</u>.

The Objective Line Method

1. Draw the <u>straight line</u> $Z = ax + by$, choosing a <u>fixed value</u> of Z (a and b will be given in the question). This is called the <u>objective line</u>.

2. Move the line to the <u>right</u>, keeping it <u>parallel</u> to the original line. As you do this, the value of Z <u>increases</u> (if you move the line to the <u>left</u>, the value of Z <u>decreases</u>).

3. If you're trying to <u>maximise</u> Z, the <u>optimal solution</u> will be the <u>last point</u> within the <u>feasible region</u> that the objective line touches as you slide it to the <u>right</u>.

4. If you're trying to <u>minimise</u> Z, the <u>optimal solution</u> will be the <u>last point</u> within the <u>feasible region</u> that the objective line touches as you slide it to the <u>left</u>.

This is sometimes called the ruler method, as a good way to do it is to slide a ruler over the graph parallel to the objective line.

The objective lines have the **Same Gradient**

When you draw your <u>first</u> objective line, you can use <u>any value</u> for Z. Pick one that makes the line <u>easier</u> to draw — e.g. let Z be a <u>multiple</u> of both a and b so that the <u>intercepts</u> with the axes are <u>easy</u> to find.

EXAMPLE Using the example from the previous page, maximise the profit $P = 2x + 3y$.

First, choose a value for P, say $P = 6$. This means that the objective line goes through $(3, 0)$ and $(0, 2)$. Draw this line on the graph.

Slide the objective line to the right until it reaches the last point within R. At this point, P is maximised.

This is the first objective line, where P = 6.

From the diagram, you can see that the last point the objective line touches is the intersection of the lines $y = 5 - x$ and $y = 3x - 2$.

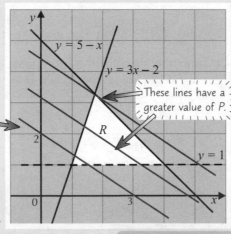

These lines have a greater value of P.

To find the point of intersection, solve these simultaneous equations. This will give you the optimal solution.

Substituting $y = 5 - x$ into $y = 3x - 2$ gives: $5 - x = 3x - 2$

$$7 = 4x \Rightarrow x = \tfrac{7}{4}$$

Putting $x = \tfrac{7}{4}$ into $y = 5 - x$ gives $y = \tfrac{13}{4}$.

Now put these values into the objective function to find P: $P = 2x + 3y$

$$= 2\left(\tfrac{7}{4}\right) + 3\left(\tfrac{13}{4}\right)$$

$$= \tfrac{14}{4} + \tfrac{39}{4} = \tfrac{53}{4} = 13.25$$

So the maximum value of P is 13.25, which occurs at $\left(\tfrac{7}{4}, \tfrac{13}{4}\right)$.

There might be **More Than One** optimal solution

If the optimal solution is on a dotted line, the actual solution will just be a point very very close to it. You don't need to worry about this though.

1) If the objective line is <u>parallel</u> to one of the <u>constraints</u>, you might end up with a <u>section of a line</u> that gives the <u>optimal solution</u>.

2) If this happens, <u>any point</u> along the line is an optimal solution (as long as it's <u>inside</u> the <u>feasible region</u>).

3) This shows that there can be <u>more than one</u> optimal solution to a problem.

Maximise your chance of passing D1...

Make sure you're happy with solving simultaneous equations — if not, have a look back at page 25. You won't have to solve any tricky quadratic equations for this section, but you need to be able to solve linear simultaneous equations quick-smart.

Optimal Solutions

If you object to using the <u>objective line</u>, there is another method. This one uses a lot more <u>simultaneous equations</u>, but you don't have to worry about keeping the ruler <u>parallel</u> or <u>stopping global warming</u> or anything like that.

Optimal Solutions are found at *Vertices*

The <u>optimal solution</u> for the example on the previous page was found at a <u>vertex</u> of the <u>feasible region</u>. This isn't a coincidence — if you have a go at some more linear programming problems, you'll find that the optimal solutions <u>always</u> occur at a vertex (or an <u>edge</u>) of the feasible region. This gives you another way to solve the problem.

The Vertex Method

1. **Find the *x*- and *y*-values of the <u>vertices</u> of the <u>feasible region</u>. You do this by solving the <u>simultaneous equations</u> of the <u>lines</u> that <u>intersect</u> at each vertex.**
2. **Put these values into the <u>objective function</u> $Z = ax + by$ to find the value of Z.**
3. **Look at the Z values and work out which is the <u>optimal value</u>. Depending on your objective function, this might be either the <u>smallest</u> (if you're trying to <u>minimise</u> Z) or the <u>largest</u> (if you're trying to <u>maximise</u> Z).**

If two vertices A and B produce the same Z value, this means that all points along the edge AB are also optimal solutions.

Test *Every* vertex

Even if it looks <u>obvious</u> from the graph, you still have to <u>test</u> each vertex of the feasible region. Sometime the <u>origin</u> will be one of the vertices — it's really easy to test, as the objective function will just be equal to <u>0</u> there. Don't forget vertices on the <u>x-</u> and <u>y-axes</u> too.

You can sometimes just read off the coordinates from your graph (as long as it's accurate).

EXAMPLE

Minimise $Z = 8x + 9y$, subject to the constraints $2x + y \geq 6$, $x - 2y \leq 2$, $x \leq 4$, $y \leq 4$ and $x, y \geq 0$.

Drawing these constraints on a graph produces the diagram below, where *A*, *B*, *C* and *D* are the vertices of the feasible region *R*:

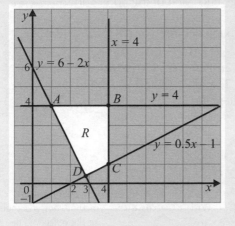

Point *A* is the intersection of the lines $y = 6 - 2x$ and $y = 4$, so *A* has coordinates (1, 4).

Point *B* is the intersection of the lines $x = 4$ and $y = 4$, so *B* has coordinates (4, 4).

Point *C* is the intersection of the lines $x = 4$ and $y = 0.5x - 1$, so *C* has coordinates (4, 1).

Point *D* is the intersection of the lines $y = 6 - 2x$ and $y = 0.5x - 1$, which has coordinates $\left(\frac{14}{5}, \frac{2}{5}\right)$.

You need to use simultaneous equations to find the coordinates of D.

Putting these values into the objective function $Z = 8x + 9y$:

At *A*, $Z = (8 \times 1) + (9 \times 4) = 44$.

At *B*, $Z = (8 \times 4) + (9 \times 4) = 68$.

At *C*, $Z = (8 \times 4) + (9 \times 1) = 41$.

At *D*, $Z = (8 \times 2.8) + (9 \times 0.4) = 26$.

So the minimum value of Z is 26, which occurs when $x = \frac{14}{5}$ and $y = \frac{2}{5}$.

In this example, it was really <u>easy</u> to find the coordinates of *A*, *B* and *C*, as at least one of the values was <u>given</u> by the <u>equation of the line</u>. *D* was a bit harder, as it involved <u>simultaneous equations</u>, but it wasn't too bad.

Your optimal solution might mean that there are some <u>spare capacities</u> — some of the variables that haven't been <u>used up</u>. This usually happens with a <u>constraint</u> that isn't used when finding the <u>optimal solution</u> (i.e. it doesn't go through the vertex that provides the optimal solution. In a <u>real life problem</u>, you might have to <u>interpret</u> this — e.g. there might be <u>spare time</u>, or <u>leftover ingredients</u>.

I'm getting vertigo...

Some questions might give you two different objective functions and ask you to minimise cost and maximise profit for the same set of constraints. The vertex method is really useful here, as once you've worked out the coordinates of the vertices, you can easily put the values into both objective functions without having to do any more work (or draw on confusing lines).

Optimal Integer Solutions

The methods on the previous two pages are all very well and good, but I can't exactly make 2.5 teddy bears, even if it does <u>maximise my profit</u>. There must be a better way, one that doesn't involve <u>mutilating soft toys</u>...

Some problems need **Integer Solutions**

1) Sometimes it's fine to have <u>non-integer solutions</u> to linear programming problems — for example, if you were making different <u>fruit juices</u>, you could realistically have 3.5 litres of one type of juice and 4.5 litres of another.

2) However, if you were making <u>garden furniture</u>, you couldn't make 3.5 tables and 4.5 benches — so you need <u>integer solutions</u>.

3) You won't always be <u>told</u> whether a problem needs integer solutions — you might have to <u>work it out</u> for yourself. It's common sense really — just think about whether you can have <u>fractions</u> of the <u>decision variables</u>.

You can use the **Objective Line Method** or the **Vertex Method**

Some problems have optimal integer solutions that are far away from the vertices — but you don't need to worry about these for D1.

Both of the methods covered on pages 236-237 can be used to find an <u>optimal integer solution</u> — it just depends on how <u>clear</u> your <u>graph</u> is.

1) You use the <u>objective line method</u> in exactly the <u>same way</u> as before, but instead of looking for the last <u>vertex</u> the line touches, you need to look for the last <u>point</u> with <u>integer coordinates</u> in the <u>feasible region</u>. This might be hard to do if your graph isn't very <u>accurate</u>, or if the scale isn't <u>clear</u>.

2) The other way to find the optimal integer solution is to use the <u>vertex method</u> to find which vertex to use. Then, consider all the points with <u>integer coordinates</u> that are <u>close by</u>. Make sure you <u>check</u> whether these points still <u>satisfy</u> the <u>constraints</u> though — test this <u>before</u> you put the values into the objective function.

The **Optimal Integer Solution** must be **Inside** the **Feasible Region**

It's easy to forget that <u>not all</u> the solutions near the optimal vertex will be <u>inside</u> the <u>feasible region</u> — you can check either <u>by eye</u> on an <u>accurate graph</u>, or put the <u>coordinates</u> into each of the <u>constraints</u>.

> **EXAMPLE**   The optimal solution to the problem on the previous page occurred at $\left(\frac{14}{5}, \frac{2}{5}\right)$ $(= (2.8, 0.4))$. Find the optimal integer solution.
>
> Looking at the integers nearby gives you the points (3, 0), (3, 1), (2, 0) and (2, 1) to test. However, the point (3, 0) doesn't satisfy the constraint $x - 2y \leq 2$, and (2, 0) and (2, 1) don't satisfy $2x + y \geq 6$, so the optimal integer solution is at (3, 1), where $Z = (8 \times 3) + (9 \times 1) = 33$.

EXAMPLE

A company makes baby clothes. It makes x sets of girls' clothes and y sets of boys' clothes, for a profit of £6 and £5 respectively, subject to the constraints $x + y \leq 9$, $3x - y \leq 9$, $y \leq 7$ and $x, y \geq 0$. Maximise the profit, $P = 6x + 5y$

This example uses the vertex method, but you could also use the objective line method.

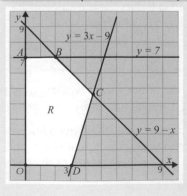

The feasible region is the area $OABCD$, with coordinates $O(0, 0)$, $A(0, 7)$, $B(2, 7)$, $C\left(\frac{9}{2}, \frac{9}{2}\right)$ and $D(3, 0)$.

The value of P at each vertex is O: £0, A: £35, B: £47, C: £49.50 and D: £18.

The maximum value of P is £49.50, which occurs at $\left(\frac{9}{2}, \frac{9}{2}\right)$ $(= (4.5, 4.5))$. However, making 4.5 sets of clothes is not possible, so an integer solution is needed.

The integer coordinates near C are (4, 5), (5, 5), (5, 4) and (4, 4). (5, 5) and (5, 4) don't satisfy the constraint $3x - y \leq 9$ so are outside the feasible region. At (4, 5), $P = £49$, and at (4,4), $P = £44$, so £49 is the maximum profit.

So the company needs to make 4 sets of girls' clothes and 5 sets of boys' clothes to make the maximum profit of £49.

My solution to a problem is to close my eyes and hope it'll go away...

Oo, I do like a nice integer now and then. Like a good cup of tea, integers can really brighten your morning. They're harder to dunk biscuits in, but they do provide sensible solutions to linear programming problems. Watch out for them in the exam.

D1 Section 4 — Practice Questions

This section isn't too bad really — once you've got your head round turning the <u>constraints</u> into <u>inequalities</u>, all you have to do is draw a <u>graph</u> and Bob's your uncle. I wish I had an Uncle Bob. Anyway, here are some warm-up questions for you to have a go at.

Warm-up Questions

1) Give a brief definition of:
   a) <u>decision variables</u>
   b) <u>objective function</u>
   c) <u>optimal solution</u>

2) What does a <u>dotted line</u> on a graph show?

3) What is an <u>objective line</u>?

4) Give one example of a problem that <u>doesn't</u> need <u>integer solutions</u>, and one example that <u>does</u>.

5) A company makes posters in two sizes, large and small. It takes 10 minutes to print each large poster, and 5 minutes to print each small poster. There is a total of 250 minutes per day allocated to printing. It takes 6 minutes to laminate a large poster and 4 minutes for a small poster, with a total of 200 minutes laminating time. The company want to sell at least as many large posters as small, and they want to sell at least 10 small posters. Large posters are sold for a profit of £6 and small posters are sold for a profit of £3.50.

   a) Write this out as a <u>linear programming problem</u>. Identify the <u>decision variables</u>, <u>constraints</u> and <u>objective function</u>.

   b) Show the <u>constraints</u> for this problem <u>graphically</u>. Label the <u>feasible region</u> R.

   c) <u>Maximise</u> the <u>profit</u>, using either the <u>objective line method</u> or the <u>vertex method</u>. Don't worry about integer solutions for now.

   d) Use your answer to part c) to find the <u>optimal integer solution</u>.

Exam questions try and <u>scare</u> you by throwing a lot of <u>information</u> at you all at once. Don't let them bully you, just take them <u>one bit at a time</u> and you'll soon get the better of them. Here are a few for you to do.

Exam Questions

1   Anna is selling red and white roses at a flower stall. She buys the flowers from a wholesaler, where red roses cost 75p each and white roses cost 60p each. Based on previous sales, she has come up with the following constraints:

- She will sell both red roses and white roses.
- She will sell more red roses than white roses.
- She will sell a total of at least 100 flowers.
- The wholesaler has 300 red roses and 200 white roses available.

Let x be the number of red roses she buys and y be the number of white roses she buys. Formulate this information as a linear programming problem. Write out the constraints as inequalities and identify a suitable objective function, stating how it should be optimised. You do not need to solve this problem.

(7 marks)

D1 Section 4 — Practice Questions

In the words of some little <u>Dickensian orphan</u>, 'please sir, I want some more'. Well, I'd be more than happy to oblige — here's another page full of <u>exciting exam questions</u>.

2   A company sells three packs of craft paper, bronze, silver and gold. Each pack is made up of three different types of paper, tissue paper, sugar paper and foil.

- The gold pack is made up of 6 sheets of foil, 15 sheets of sugar paper and 15 sheets of tissue paper.
- The silver pack is made up of 2 sheets of foil, 9 sheets of sugar paper and 4 sheets of tissue paper.
- The bronze pack is made up of 1 sheet of foil, 6 sheets of sugar paper and 1 sheet of tissue paper.
- Each day, there are 30 sheets of foil available, 120 sheets of sugar paper available and 60 sheets of tissue paper available.
- The company is trying to reduce the amount of foil used, so it uses at least three times as many sheets of sugar paper as of foil.

The company makes x gold packs, y silver packs and z bronze packs in a day.

a)   Apart from the non-negativity constraints, write out the other four constraints as inequalities in terms of x, y and z. Simplify each inequality where possible.

(8 marks)

b)   On Monday, the company decides to make the same number of silver packs as bronze packs.

(i)   Show that your inequalities from part a) become

$$2x + y \leq 10$$
$$x + y \leq 8$$
$$3x + y \leq 12$$
$$2y \geq x$$

(3 marks)

(ii)   On graph paper, draw a graph showing the constraints from part (i) above, as well as the non-negativity constraints. Label the feasible region R.

(5 marks)

(iii)   Use your graph to work out the maximum number of packs the company can make on Monday.

(2 marks)

(iv)   Gold packs are sold for a profit of £3.50, silver packs are sold for a profit of £2 and bronze packs are sold for a profit of £1. Use your answers to parts (ii) and (iii) to maximise the profit they make, and state how many of each type of pack they need to sell.

(3 marks)

3   The graph below shows the constraints of a linear programming problem. The feasible region is labelled R.

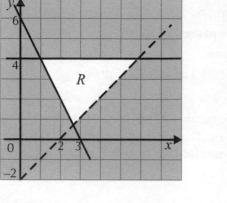

a)   Including the non-negativity constraints, find the inequalities that produce R.

(5 marks)

b)   Find the coordinates of each vertex of R.

(4 marks)

The aim is to minimise $C = 4x + y$.

c)   Find the optimal solution and state where this value occurs.

(3 marks)

Random Variables

You might have come across <u>random variables</u> before — they pop up in Statistics and some other areas of maths. In D1, you have to use them to <u>model real-life situations</u>.

Use **Random Numbers** to **Model** events

1) <u>Random variables</u> are used to <u>simulate</u> real-life events that have a <u>range</u> of possible <u>outcomes</u>. Each outcome will have a <u>probability</u> of how likely it is to occur — e.g. 80% of skaters are male, so the probability that the next skater to turn up at a skate park is male is 0.8.

2) Using the different probabilities, you assign <u>random numbers</u> to <u>each outcome</u>. Then you can <u>generate</u> random numbers and use them to <u>simulate</u> the event.

3) There are lots of different ways of generating random numbers — you can <u>toss a coin</u>, <u>roll a dice</u>, use <u>random number tables</u> or use the <u>random number button</u> on your <u>calculator</u>.

4) Random variables can be used for <u>uniform</u> or <u>non-uniform</u> events. Uniform events are ones where the outcomes have <u>equal probabilities</u> (e.g. getting a certain set of numbers on the lottery) and non-uniform events are those where the probabilities are <u>not equal</u> (e.g. the gender of skaters at a skate park, as above).

Assign numbers to **Different Outcomes**

1) When you're <u>setting up</u> your simulation, you need to decide which <u>random numbers</u> are assigned to each <u>outcome</u>. You have to make this <u>really clear</u> before you start the simulation.

2) Make sure the <u>proportion</u> of random numbers for each outcome matches the <u>probabilities</u> — e.g. for the skate park example above, you'd want 80% of the numbers for male skaters and 20% for female skaters.

3) If there are a lot of <u>different outcomes</u>, it's a good idea to use <u>2-digit random numbers</u> (i.e. 00 to 99) — usually from a <u>table</u> or generated on your <u>calculator</u>.

EXAMPLE The probability that people arriving at a train station will fall into a particular age bracket is shown in the table below:

'Set up the rules' just means 'assign the numbers'.

Age	Under 16	16-24	25-39	40-60	Over 60
Probability	0.1	0.15	0.3	0.25	0.2

First, set up the rules for the simulation: there are quite a few outcomes, so use 2-digit random numbers:

Age	Under 16	16-24	25-39	40-60	Over 60
Probability	0.1	0.15	0.3	0.25	0.2
Random numbers	00-09	10-24	25-54	55-79	80-99

You want 10% of the numbers for the under 16s — just use the first 10 (i.e. 00-09), then 15% for the 16-24s (10-24) etc.

Now generate some random numbers, e.g. 93, 68, 95, 71 and 16.
Use these to model the ages of the next 5 people who arrive at the train station.

All you have to do is look at the random numbers and work out which category each one fits in:
93 = over 60, 68 = 40-60, 95 = over 60, 71 = 40-60 and 16 = 16-24. So in the simulation, the next person to arrive will be over 60, the second person aged 40-60 and so on.

You might have to **Reject** some numbers

1) If you're given probabilities with denominators that aren't <u>factors of 100</u> (e.g. if the probabilities above were $\frac{1}{9}, \frac{2}{9}, \frac{4}{9}, \frac{1}{9}$ and $\frac{1}{9}$), assigning the random numbers 00 - 99 <u>doesn't work</u> — you can't have <u>decimals</u> or <u>fractions</u>.

2) In this case, you can <u>reject</u> some of the random numbers — work out the <u>remainder</u> when 100 is divided by the <u>denominator</u> and reject the numbers left over (here, 100 ÷ 9 = 11 r 1, so you'd reject 1 number — 99).

3) You have to <u>say</u> which numbers you're ignoring when you give the <u>rules</u> of the simulation.

4) If one of the reject numbers comes up when the numbers are <u>generated</u>, just <u>ignore it</u>.

5) In cases like this, it's better to use <u>2-digit</u> random numbers rather than <u>1-digit</u> random numbers — you reject a <u>smaller proportion</u> of 2-digit numbers.

Rejection hurts...

These methods are known as the Monte Carlo methods. Very James Bond. In the exam you might have to 'give an efficient rule' for a simulation — you have to assign as many random numbers as you can to each outcome, ignoring as few as possible.

Simulation Modelling

It would be really fun if you got to make models as part of D1 — I'd make a pirate ship.

Simulations are used to model Queues

1) You can set up simulations to model queuing situations — you use them to predict how long people will have to queue for on average. The queuing time is the length of time between arriving and being served.

2) To set up a queuing simulation, you first need to simulate the time intervals and service times of the customers, using the method on the previous page.
   - TIME INTERVAL is the length of time between customers arriving (so the time interval for customer 2 is how long they arrive after customer 1).
   - SERVICE TIME is how long it takes the customer to be served once they reach the front of the queue.

3) From these two pieces of information, you can work out the queuing time of each customer (see below).

Use a Table to work out Queuing Times

1) First use the time intervals to work out the arrival time of each customer.
   This is the time they arrive after the start of the simulation, so you add each customer's time interval to the previous customer's arrival time. For 3 customers with time intervals of 2, 3 and 6 minutes, the first would arrive at $t = 2$ mins, the second would arrive at $t = 2 + 3 = 5$ mins and the third would arrive at $t = 5 + 6 = 11$ mins.

2) Now you work out the start of service time and end of service time for each customer.
   The first customer (Hugh) is served as soon as he arrives (at $t = 2$ in the example above), but the second customer (Claire) can't be served until Hugh has finished being served. If Hugh's service time was 5, his service end time would be $2 + 5 = 7$. The next customer could then start being served.

3) Now calculate the queuing time: Claire arrived at $t = 5$, but can't be served till $t = 7$, so she has to queue for 2 minutes.

EXAMPLE The problem described above, with service times of 3 minutes for Claire and 4 minutes for the third customer (Amy), could be put in a table like this:

The arrival time is (time interval) + (previous customer's arrival time).

From simulation.

The queuing time is the difference between the arrival time and the start of service...

Claire finishes being served at 10 mins but Amy doesn't arrive till 11 mins so she can't be served until she gets there.

...but if the customer arrives after the previous service has finished, they can be served straight away.

Customer number	Time interval	Arrival time	Start of service	Service time	End of service	Queuing time
1 (Hugh)	2	2	2	5	7	0
2 (Claire)	3	5	7	3	10	2
3 (Amy)	6	11	11	4	15	0

4) Some questions might be a bit different — e.g. the waiting time for a ski lift needing a certain number of people before it can set off. The people may arrive in different-sized groups. In this case, you'd need to know the time intervals and also group size, and you'd add up the time intervals to work out how long the overall waiting time was.

EXAMPLE A ski lift needs to have 20 passengers before it can set off. Using a simulation, the time intervals (in minutes) of the next 8 groups of people arriving are 3, 2, 2, 4, 1, 5, 1, 3.
Using another simulation, their group sizes are 5, 1, 6, 9, 3, 4, 5, 2.
How long will the first passengers have to wait before the lift can set off?

Group number	Time interval	Group size	Total passengers in lift	Arrival time	Can the lift set off?
1	3	5	5	3	No
2	2	1	6	5	No
3	2	6	12	7	No
4	4	9	21	11	Yes

The waiting time is the sum of the time intervals.

You can stop after 4 groups as the lift can now set off. The waiting time is $11 - 3 =$ **8 minutes** (as the first group arrives at $t = 3$ and the fourth group arrives at $t = 11$).

5) To improve a simulation, you should run it again. So in the example above, take another simulation of 8 groups and work out the waiting time again. If you have to find the average waiting time, find the average of all the simulations.

D1 Section 5 — Practice Questions

Phew, you've reached the <u>end</u> of the <u>section</u> — and, except for a small matter of an exam paper (or two), it's the end of <u>D1</u> too. In fact, it's also the end of the <u>entire book</u>.

Warm-up Questions

1) a) Set up a rule for using 1-digit random numbers to simulate the results of a cricket team's matches:

Result	Win	Lose	Draw
Probability	0.3	0.6	0.1

    b) Use the random numbers 1, 3, 7, 5, 7 to simulate the results of the team's next 5 cricket matches.

2) Karen gives guided tours round a museum. There must be at least 5 people on the tour before she can set off. The time intervals of people arriving for the tour are shown below:

Time interval	0	2	4	6	8
Probability	$\frac{1}{4}$	$\frac{1}{6}$	$\frac{1}{3}$	$\frac{1}{6}$	$\frac{1}{12}$

    a) State an efficient rule for using 2-digit random numbers for this simulation.

    b) Use the random numbers 64, 40, 36, 97, 26, 66, 10 and 81 to estimate how long Karen will have to wait before the tour can set off.

    c) The table below shows 4 simulations of the time intervals of 5 people. Work out the waiting times for each one and add your simulation from part b) to the table. Calculate the average waiting time.

Simulation	Time intervals					Waiting time
1	4	4	6	0	4	
2	2	4	6	6	0	
3	2	0	4	8	6	
4	2	4	2	0	4	
5						

    d) How could this estimate be improved?

The exam questions are often <u>pretty long</u>, and divided up into <u>lots of parts</u>. Just do them <u>step by step</u> and you'll be <u>fine</u>.

Exam Question

1   a) This table shows the time intervals of people arriving at a doctor's surgery and their probabilities.

Time interval (mins)	5	10	15	20
Probability	0.25	0.375	0.125	0.25

    State an efficient rule for using 2-digit random numbers to simulate this situation.

    (3 marks)

    b) Use the random numbers 19, 08, 63, 70, 04, 29, 44, 10, 19, 01 to simulate the intervals between the arrival times of the next 10 patients.

    (2 marks)

    c) The time each patient is in with the doctor (to the nearest 5 mins) is modelled below:

Consultation time	5	10	15	20
Probability	0.1	0.55	0.3	0.05

    State an efficient rule for using 2-digit random numbers for this simulation.

    (3 marks)

    d) Use the random numbers 12, 38, 36, 83, 30, 63, 69, 53, 92, 53 to simulate how long the patients from part b) will be in with the doctor.

    (2 marks)

    e) Set up a table to show the waiting times of these patients, and use it to work out the average waiting time.

    (5 marks)

General Certificate of Education
Advanced Subsidiary (AS) and Advanced Level

Decision Mathematics D1 — Practice Exam One

Time Allowed: 1 hour 30 min

Graphical calculators may be used for this exam.

Give any non-exact numerical answers to an appropriate degree of accuracy.

There are 72 marks available for this paper.

Section A (24 marks)

1 The algorithm below calculates square roots correct to 2 decimal places.

Step 1:	Input A
Step 2:	Let $N = 1$
Step 3:	Let $P = A \div N$
Step 4:	Let $Q = P + N$
Step 5:	Let $R = Q \div 2$
Step 6:	If $|R - N| < 0.01$, then go to Step 10
Step 7:	If $|R - N| \geq 0.01$, then go to Step 8
Step 8:	Let $N = R$
Step 9:	Go to Step 3
Step 10:	Write R to 2 decimal places
Step 11:	Stop.

a) Trace the algorithm for $A = 2$.

(6 marks)

b) State the result you would obtain if you traced the algorithm for $A = 9$.

(1 mark)

c) Another algorithm can find a square root to any number of decimal places.
It takes a computer 20 seconds to calculate a square root to 2 decimal places, 80 seconds to calculate it to 4 decimal places and 180 seconds to calculate the square root to 6 decimal places.
What does this tell you about this algorithm's order of complexity?

(1 mark)

2 A graph has 4 nodes, A, B, C, D, and 4 arcs. Nodes A and B have orders of 1 and 3 respectively.

a) Draw two possible connected graphs, where one is simple and the other isn't.

(2 marks)

b) Give an example of a cycle and a trail in your simple graph.

(2 marks)

c) How many arcs would you need to add to turn your simple graph into a complete graph?

(1 mark)

d) Is your simple graph a tree? Explain your answer.

(2 marks)

e) Explain why the graph below is a planar graph.

(1 mark)

3   A supermarket manager collects
     the following data about
     how much male and female
     customers spend in the store.

Amount	£0 – £9.99	£10 – £19.99	£20 – £39.99	Over £40
Male	$\dfrac{3}{10}$	$\dfrac{4}{10}$	$\dfrac{1}{10}$	$\dfrac{2}{10}$
Female	$\dfrac{4}{15}$	$\dfrac{3}{15}$	$\dfrac{5}{15}$	$\dfrac{3}{15}$

a)   Give an efficient rule for using two-digit random numbers to simulate how much
     a customer will spend if they are

     (i)   male.

(2 marks)

     (ii) female.

(3 marks)

b)   Use these random two-digit numbers to simulate the amount the next
     5 female customers will spend.

     39 57 26 77 17

(2 marks)

c)   This simulation is used to estimate the mean spend for female customers.
     State how you could make the estimate more accurate.

(1 mark)

Section B (48 marks)

4   The table below shows the durations and predecessors of activities involved in a construction project.

Activities	Duration (days)	Immediate predecessors
A	6	–
B	11	–
C	9	–
D	5	A
E	8	C
F	10	B
G	4	B, D
H	4	B
I	6	E, H
J	2	F, I

a)   Draw an activity network to show this information.

(5 marks)

b)   Calculate the early event times and the late event times for the activities.
     Mark these on your network using box notation.

(4 marks)

c)   State the project duration in days and list the critical activities.

(2 marks)

d)   Calculate the total float on activity D.

(1 mark)

e)   The project needs to be completed in 21 days.
     The durations of some activities can be reduced
     at extra cost, as shown in the table on the right.
     List the activities that should be speeded up to
     reduce the project duration at minimum cost.
     State how many days each activity should be
     reduced by.

(4 marks)

Activity	Cost per day of reducing duration	Maximum number of days activity can be reduced by
A	£1000	4
B	£2000	5
C	£2000	4
I	£3000	3

5   A charity is selling tickets to its annual charity ball. It has two corporate packages available: business class and premier.

        Each business class package includes 5 tickets and each premier package includes 10 tickets.

        Each business class package includes 2 bottles of wine and each premier package includes 8 bottles of wine.

        There are 300 tickets and 160 bottles of wine available.

        At least 5 of each type of package are sold, and at least 20 packages are sold in total.

        The charity sells x business class packages and y premier packages.

    a)   5 constraints are required when expressing this information as a linear programming problem.

        (i)   Show why the following constraints are required: $x + 2y \leq 60$, $x + 4y \leq 80$.

                                                                                (2 marks)

        (ii)   State three other constraints that must also be used.

                                                                                   (3 marks)

    b)   Each business class package makes a profit of £150 and each premier package makes a profit of £200. The charity wants to calculate the minimum and maximum profit from the ball.

        (i)   On graph paper, draw a diagram to represent this linear programming problem. Clearly label the feasible region and draw on an objective line.

                                                                                         (7 marks)

        (ii)   Find the maximum profit from the ball. Write down how many of each type of package need to be sold to make this profit.

                                                                             (2 marks)

        (iii) Find the minimum profit from the ball. Write down how many of each type of package need to be sold to make this profit.

                                                                              (2 marks)

6   The diagram shows the various cycle paths in a park. The bike hire shop is at G.
A floodlighting system is to be installed so that the cycle paths can be used after dark. There will be a light at each intersection. The number on each edge represents the distance, in metres, between two intersections.

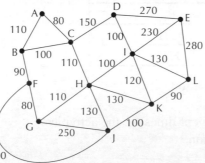

    a)   Cabling must be laid along the paths so that each intersection is connected. Starting from the bike hire shop (G), use Prim's algorithm to find a cabling layout that will use a minimum amount of cable. List the paths in the order they are added.

                                                                                          (4 marks)

    b)   Draw your minimum connector and state its length.

                                                                                          (2 marks)

    c)   The warden used Kruskal's algorithm to find the same minimum connector. Find the tenth and the eleventh edges that the warden added to his connector.

                                                                              (3 marks)

    d)   Use Dijkstra's algorithm to find the shortest route from G to E. Give the route and its length.   *(7 marks)*

General Certificate of Education
Advanced Subsidiary (AS) and Advanced Level

Decision Mathematics D1 — Practice Exam Two

Time Allowed: 1 hour 30 min

Graphical calculators may be used for this exam.

Give any non-exact numerical answers to an appropriate degree of accuracy.

There are 72 marks available for this paper.

Section A (24 marks)

1   Stephanie is packing to go to university. She has boxes that can hold a maximum of 6 kg.
The items she needs to pack into the boxes have the following weights (in kg):

1.8	3.5	2.6	4.1	1.2	0.8	2.0	2.4	3.1

a)   Use the first fit method to pack the items into the boxes.
State how many boxes are used and how much space is wasted.

(3 marks)

b)   Use the first fit decreasing method to pack the items again. You don't need to use an algorithm
to sort the items. State how many boxes are used and how much space is wasted.

(3 marks)

c)   Suggest a reason why the answer to part a) might be a more practical way of packing.

(1 mark)

d)   It is suggested that the full-bin packing method will produce a solution which uses less boxes
than the first fit or first fit decreasing methods. Comment on whether this could be true.

(1 mark)

2   Look at the following linear programming problem:

$$\text{Maximise} \qquad P = 0.75x + 1.5y$$

$$\text{subject to the constraints } 4x + 5y \le 80$$
$$y \le 8$$
$$y \le x$$
$$x, y \ge 0.$$

Use a graphical approach to solve this problem. State the optimal values of x, y and P.

(8 marks)

3   Kalim, Louisa and Melissa need to be matched to four jobs numbered 1 - 4.
The table on the right shows the jobs that each person is willing to do.

Name	Jobs
Kalim	2, 4
Louisa	1, 3
Melissa	2

a)   Show this information on a bipartite graph.

(2 marks)

b)   How many arcs must be added to form a complete bipartite graph?

(1 mark)

c)   List all the paths that start from the node representing Kalim on the graph.

(2 marks)

d)   Explain how you know the bipartite graph is not connected.

(1 mark)

e)   Add as many arcs as you can to the bipartite graph without it becoming connected.
It must remain a bipartite graph so an arc can only be added between a person and a job.
State the number of arcs you have added.

(2 marks)

Section B (48 marks)

4

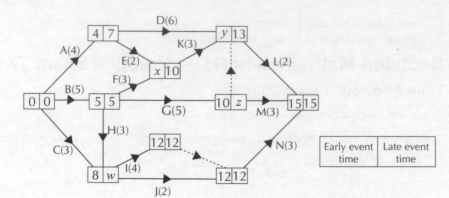

The network above shows the activities involved in a process. The activities are represented by the arcs. The number in brackets on each arc gives the time, in hours, to complete the activity. Some of the early and late event times for events are shown.

a) Give the immediate predecessors for activities F and L.

(2 marks)

b) Find the values of w, x, y and z.

(2 marks)

c) Calculate the independent and total float of activity D.

(2 marks)

d) Draw a cascade chart for the project. Assume that each activity starts as early as possible.

(4 marks)

e) An inspector visits during hour 4 and during hour 10. Assuming the project is on schedule, which activities must be happening during these hours?

(3 marks)

f) Each activity requires 1 worker. There are only 4 workers available to complete this project. Describe how your cascade chart from part d) could be changed so that the project is still completed in 15 hours.

(3 marks)

5 The table shows the distances, in metres, along paths between bird boxes in a reserve.

	A	B	C	D	E	F
A	–	140	240	–	150	170
B	140	–	90	100	170	170
C	240	90	–	210	–	–
D	–	100	210	–	300	60
E	150	170	–	300	–	–
F	170	170	–	60	–	–

a) Use Prim's algorithm, starting from A, to find a minimum connector for this distance matrix. You must list the edges that form your connector in the order that they are selected.

(3 marks)

b) Calculate the total weight of your minimum connector.

(1 mark)

c) One advantage of Prim's algorithm over Kruskal's is that you don't have to check for cycles. Explain why you don't have to check for cycles in Prim's algorithm.

(2 marks)

d) Draw the network.

(3 marks)

e) (i) Name an algorithm that could be used to find the minimum distance of each bird box from bird box C.

(1 mark)

   (ii) Use the algorithm to do this. State which bird box is the greatest distance away and the route that should be taken to reach it.

(6 marks)

6   Ben is selling home-made lollies for a pound each in a park. He wants to sell 7 lollies so he can buy a DVD. This table shows the probabilities of customers arriving at certain time intervals (to the nearest 10 minutes).

Time interval (mins)	10	20	30	40
Probability	$\frac{7}{20}$	$\frac{1}{5}$	$\frac{3}{10}$	$\frac{3}{20}$

a)   2-digit random numbers are to be used to simulate the time interval between customers. State an efficient rule for doing this.

(3 marks)

The probability of a customer buying a certain number of lollies is given in the table below.

Number of lollies	1	2	3	4
Probability	$\frac{5}{12}$	$\frac{1}{12}$	$\frac{1}{3}$	$\frac{1}{6}$

b)   State an efficient rule for using 2-digit random numbers to simulate the number of lollies bought by a customer.

(4 marks)

c)   Use these random numbers to simulate the time intervals between the next 5 customers and how many lollies each will buy. You may not need all the numbers. State after how many minutes Ben will have sold 7 lollies.

46   15   54   66   81   98   67   71   5   12   46   80

(5 marks)

d)   Five other simulations are carried out and the results are shown in the table below. Calculate after how many minutes Ben will have sold 7 lollies in each case. Use your results from all 6 simulations to estimate the mean time that Ben must sell lollies for.

(4 marks)

	Customer 1		Customer 2		Customer 3		Customer 4		Customer 5		Time until 7 lollies are sold (mins)
	Time Interval (mins)	Number of lollies	Time Interval (mins)	Number of lollies	Time Interval (mins)	Number of lollies	Time Interval (mins)	Number of lollies	Time Interval (mins)	Number of lollies	
Simulation 2	30	1	20	1	10	3	30	1	40	1	
Simulation 3	30	4	10	4	30	3	30	1	20	1	
Simulation 4	30	1	20	1	10	1	30	4	10	3	
Simulation 5	20	3	30	1	10	4	20	3	10	2	
Simulation 6	20	3	10	3	30	1	10	1	30	1	

Answers

C1 Section 1 — Algebra Fundamentals
Warm-up Questions

1) a) a & b are constants, x is a variable.

   b) a & b are constants, x is a variable.

   c) a, b & c are constants, y is a variable.

   d) a is a constant, x & y are variables.

2) Identity symbol is $\equiv$.

3) A, C and D are identities.

4) a) x^8 b) a^{15} c) x^6 d) a^8 e) $x^4 y^3 z$ f) $\dfrac{b^2 c^5}{a}$

5) a) 4 b) 2 c) 8 d) 1 e) $\dfrac{1}{7}$

6) a) $x = \pm\sqrt{5}$ b) $x = -2 \pm \sqrt{3}$

7) a) $2\sqrt{7}$ b) $\dfrac{\sqrt{5}}{6}$ c) $3\sqrt{2}$ d) $\dfrac{3}{4}$

8) a) $\dfrac{8}{\sqrt{2}} = \dfrac{8}{\sqrt{2}} \times \dfrac{\sqrt{2}}{\sqrt{2}} = \dfrac{8\sqrt{2}}{2} = 4\sqrt{2}$

   b) $\dfrac{\sqrt{2}}{2} = \dfrac{\sqrt{2}}{(\sqrt{2})^2} = \dfrac{1}{\sqrt{2}}$

9) $136 + 24\sqrt{21}$

10) $3 - \sqrt{7}$

11) a) $a^2 - b^2$ b) $a^2 + 2ab + b^2$

    c) $25y^2 + 210xy$ d) $3x^2 + 10xy + 3y^2 + 13x + 23y + 14$

12) a) $xy(2x + a + 2y)$ b) $a^2 x(1 + b^2 x)$

    c) $8(2y + xy + 7x)$ d) $(x - 2)(x - 3)$

13) a) $\dfrac{52x + 5y}{60}$ b) $\dfrac{5x - 2y}{x^2 y^2}$ c) $\dfrac{x^3 + x^2 - y^2 + xy^2}{x(x^2 - y^2)}$

14) a) $\dfrac{3a}{2b}$ b) $\dfrac{2(p^2 + q^2)}{p^2 - q^2}$ c) 🐦 = 🐦☁️

Exam Questions

1 a) $27^{\frac{1}{3}} = \sqrt[3]{27}$

    $= 3$ *[1 mark]*

  b) $27^{\frac{4}{3}} = \left(27^{\frac{1}{3}}\right)^4$ *[1 mark]*

    $= 3^4 = 3 \times 3 \times 3 \times 3 = 9 \times 9$

    $= 81$ *[1 mark]*

2 a) $(5\sqrt{3})^2 = (5^2)(\sqrt{3})^2 = 25 \cdot 3$

    $= 75$ *[1 mark]*

  b) $(5 + \sqrt{6})(2 - \sqrt{6}) = 10 - 5\sqrt{6} + 2\sqrt{6} - 6$ *[1 mark]*

    $= 4 - 3\sqrt{6}$ *[1 mark]*

3 $10000\sqrt{10} = 10^4 \cdot 10^{\frac{1}{2}}$ *[1 mark]*

    $= 10^{4 + \frac{1}{2}}$ *[1 mark]*

    $= 10^{\frac{9}{2}}$

    so $k = \dfrac{9}{2}$ *[1 mark]*

4 Multiply top and bottom by $3 + \sqrt{5}$ to 'rationalise the denominator':

    $\dfrac{5 + \sqrt{5}}{3 - \sqrt{5}} = \dfrac{(5 + \sqrt{5})(3 + \sqrt{5})}{(3 - \sqrt{5})(3 + \sqrt{5})}$ *[1 mark]*

    $= \dfrac{15 + 5\sqrt{5} + 3\sqrt{5} + 5}{9 - 5}$ *[1 mark]*

    $= \dfrac{20 + 8\sqrt{5}}{4}$ *[1 mark]*

    $= 5 + 2\sqrt{5}$ *[1 mark]*

5 $2x^4 - 32x^2 = 2x^2(x^2 - 16)$

    $= 2x^2(x + 4)(x - 4)$

    [3 marks available in total — 1 mark for each correct factor]

6 $\dfrac{x + 5x^3}{\sqrt{x}} = x^{-\frac{1}{2}}(x + 5x^3)$ *[1 mark]*

    $= x^{\frac{1}{2}} + 5x^{\frac{5}{2}}$ *[1 mark]*

7 $\dfrac{(5 + 4\sqrt{x})^2}{2x} = \dfrac{25 + 40\sqrt{x} + 16x}{2x}$ *[1 mark]*

    $= \dfrac{1}{2}x^{-1}(25 + 40x^{\frac{1}{2}} + 16x)$ *[1 mark]*

    $= \dfrac{25}{2}x^{-1} + 20x^{-\frac{1}{2}} + 8,$

    so $P = 20$ and $Q = 8$ *[1 mark]*

C1 Section 2 — Quadratic Equations
Warm-up Questions

1) a) $(x + 1)^2$ b) $(x - 10)(x - 3)$

   c) $(x + 2)(x - 2)$ d) $(3 - x)(x + 1)$

   e) $(2x + 1)(x - 4)$ f) $(5x - 3)(x + 2)$

2) a) $(x - 2)(x - 1) = 0$, so $x = 2$ or 1

   b) $(x + 4)(x - 3) = 0$, so $x = -4$ or 3

   c) $(2 - x)(x + 1) = 0$, so $x = 2$ or –1

   d) $(x + 4)(x - 4) = 0$, so $x = \pm 4$

   e) $(3x + 2)(x - 7) = 0$, so $x = -2/3$ or 7

   f) $(2x + 1)(2x - 1) = 0$, so $x = \pm 1/2$

   g) $(2x - 3)(x - 1) = 0$, so $x = 3/2$ or 1

3) a) $(x - 2)^2 - 7$; minimum value = –7 at $x = 2$, and this crosses the x-axis at $x = 2 \pm \sqrt{7}$

   b) $\dfrac{21}{4} - \left(x + \dfrac{3}{2}\right)^2$; maximum value = 21/4 at $x = -3/2$, and this crosses the x-axis at $-\dfrac{3}{2} \pm \dfrac{\sqrt{21}}{2}$.

   c) $2(x - 1)^2 + 9$; minimum value = 9 at $x = 1$, and this doesn't cross the x-axis.

   d) $4\left(x - \dfrac{7}{2}\right)^2 - 1$; minimum value = –1 at $x = 7/2$, crosses the x-axis at $x = \dfrac{7}{2} \pm \dfrac{1}{2}$ i.e. $x = 4$ or 3

4) a) $b^2 - 4ac = 16$, so 2 roots

   b) $b^2 - 4ac = 0$, so 1 root

   c) $b^2 - 4ac = -8$, so no roots

   a) $y = x^2 - 2x - 3$ b) $y = x^2 - 6x + 9$ c) $y = 2x^2 + 4x + 3$

5) a) Using the quadratic formula with $a = 3$, $b = -7$ and $c = 3$:

$$x = \frac{-(-7) \pm \sqrt{(-7)^2 - (4 \times 3 \times 3)}}{(2 \times 3)}$$

$$= \frac{7 \pm \sqrt{49 - 36}}{6}$$

$$= \frac{7 \pm \sqrt{13}}{6}$$

so $x = \frac{7 + \sqrt{13}}{6}, x = \frac{7 - \sqrt{13}}{6}$.

b) Using the quadratic formula with $a = 2$, $b = -6$ and $c = -2$:

$$x = \frac{-(-6) \pm \sqrt{(-6)^2 - (4 \times 2 \times -2)}}{(2 \times 2)}$$

$$= \frac{6 \pm \sqrt{36 + 16}}{4}$$

$$= \frac{6 \pm \sqrt{52}}{4}$$

$$= \frac{6 \pm 2\sqrt{13}}{4}$$

$$= \frac{3 \pm \sqrt{13}}{2}$$

so $x = \frac{3 + \sqrt{13}}{2}, x = \frac{3 - \sqrt{13}}{2}$.

c) Using the quadratic formula with $a = 1$, $b = 4$ and $c = -6$:

$$x = \frac{-(4) \pm \sqrt{(4)^2 - (4 \times 1 \times -6)}}{(2 \times 1)}$$

$$= \frac{-4 \pm \sqrt{16 + 24}}{2}$$

$$= \frac{-4 \pm \sqrt{40}}{2}$$

$$= \frac{-4 \pm 2\sqrt{10}}{2}$$

$$= -2 \pm \sqrt{10}$$

so $x = -2 + \sqrt{10}, x = -2 - \sqrt{10}$.

6) $k^2 - (4 \times 1 \times 4) > 0$, so $k^2 > 16$ and so $k > 4$ or $k < -4$.

7) $4x^4 - 5x^2 + 1 = 4(x^2)^2 - 5(x^2) + 1$ so substitute $y = x^2$ to give:
$4y^2 - 5y + 1$. Now solve for y:
$(4y - 1)(y - 1) = 0$, so $y = \frac{1}{4}$ or $y = 1$.
So: $x^2 = \frac{1}{4}$ or $x^2 = 1$, and so $x = \pm\frac{1}{2}$ or $x = \pm 1$.

Exam Questions

1 For equal roots, $b^2 - 4ac = 0$ *[1 mark]*
   $a = 1$, $b = 2k$ and $c = 4k$
   so $(2k)^2 - (4 \times 1 \times 4k) = 0$ *[1 mark]*
   $4k^2 - 16k = 0$
   $4k(k - 4) = 0$ *[1 mark]*
   so $k = 4$ (as k is non-zero). *[1 mark]*

2 a) For distinct real roots, $b^2 - 4ac > 0$ *[1 mark]*
   $a = p$, $b = p + 3$ and $c = 4$
   so $(p + 3)^2 - (4 \times p \times 4) > 0$ *[1 mark]*
   $p^2 + 6p + 9 - 16p > 0$
   $p^2 - 10p + 9 > 0$ *[1 mark]*

b) $p^2 - 10p + 9$ is a u-shaped quadratic, which crosses the
   x-axis when $p^2 - 10p + 9 = 0$, that is when $(p - 9)(p - 1) = 0$
   [1 mark], which occurs at $p = 9$ and $p = 1$ *[1 mark]*. As it's
   u-shaped, $p^2 - 10p + 9 > 0$ when p is outside these values
   [1 mark], that is when $p < 1$ or $p > 9$ *[1 mark]*.

3 Substitute $y = x^{\frac{1}{5}}$ *[1 mark]*, then $2y^2 - 3y - 2 = 0$.
   Factorise quadratic to get $(2y + 1)(y - 2) = 0$ *[1 mark]*.
   Solve for y to get $y = -\frac{1}{2}$ or $y = 2$ *[1 mark]*.
   So, $x^{\frac{1}{5}} = -\frac{1}{2}$ or $x^{\frac{1}{5}} = 2$

   $\Rightarrow x = (-\frac{1}{2})^5 = -\frac{1}{32}$ or $x = 2^5 = 32$ *[1 mark]*

4 Expanding the brackets on the RHS gives the quadratic
   $mx^2 + 4mx + 4m + p$. Equating the coefficients of x^2 gives
   $m = 5$ *[1 mark]*. Equating the coefficients of x gives
   $n = 4m$, so $n = 20$ *[1 mark]*. Equating the constant terms
   gives $14 = 4m + p \Rightarrow p = -6$ *[1 mark]*.

5 a) $a = 12 \div 2 = 6$ *[1 mark]*, so the completed square is
   $(x - 6)^2 + b = x^2 - 12x + 36 + b$. Equating coefficients
   gives $15 = 36 + b$, so $b = 15 - 36 = -21$ *[1 mark]*.
   The final expression is $(x - 6)^2 - 21$.

b) (i) The minimum occurs when the expression in brackets
       is equal to 0, which means the minimum is the value of
       b, which from (a) above is –21 *[1 mark]*.

   (ii) From above, the minimum occurs when the expression
       in brackets is equal to 0, i.e. when $x = 6$ *[1 mark]*.

   *Part b) is dead easy once you've completed the square
   — you can just take your values straight from there.*

6 a) Put $a = 1$, $b = -14$ and $c = 25$ into the quadratic formula:

   $$x = \frac{-(-14) \pm \sqrt{(-14)^2 - (4 \times 1 \times 25)}}{(2 \times 1)}$$

   $$= \frac{14 \pm \sqrt{196 - 100}}{2}$$

   $$= \frac{14 \pm \sqrt{96}}{2}$$

   $$= \frac{14 \pm 4\sqrt{6}}{2}$$

   $$= 7 \pm 2\sqrt{6}$$

   so $x = 7 + 2\sqrt{6}, x = 7 - 2\sqrt{6}$
   *[3 marks available — 1 mark for putting correct values of
   a, b and c into the quadratic formula, 1 mark each for final
   x-values.]*

b)

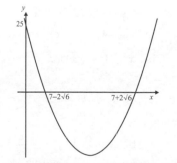

   *[3 marks available — 1 mark for drawing u-shaped curve,
   1 mark for using answers from a) as x-axis intercepts and
   1 mark for correct y-axis intercept (0, 25).]*

c) As the graph is u-shaped, the inequality is < 0 when x is
   between the two intercepts, i.e. $7 - 2\sqrt{6} \le x \le 7 + 2\sqrt{6}$
   [1 mark].

Answers

7 a) (i) $m = 10 \div 2 = 5$ *[1 mark]*, so the expression becomes
             $-(5 - x)^2 + n = -25 + 10x - x^2 + n$. Equating coefficients
             gives $-27 = -25 + n$, so $n = -27 - (-25) = -2$
             [1 mark]. The final expression is $-(5 - x)^2 - 2$.

       (ii) $(5 - x)^2 \geq 0$ for all values of x,
             so $-(5 - x)^2 \leq 0$. Therefore $-(5 - x)^2 - 2 < 0$ for all x,
             i.e. the function is always negative. *[1 mark]*

    b) (i) The y-coordinate is the maximum value, which is -2
             [1 mark], and this occurs when the expression in the
             brackets = 0.
             The x-value that makes the expression in the brackets 0
             is 5 *[1 mark]*, so the coordinates of the maximum point
             are $(5, -2)$.

       (ii)

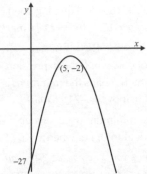

             [2 marks available — 1 mark for drawing n-shaped
             curve that sits below the x-axis, 1 mark for correct
             y-axis intercept (0, −27)]

8   Only one root implies that $b^2 - 4ac = 0$ *[1 mark]*, so
        $p^2 - 4(p - 2)(2) = 0$ *[1 mark]*. Multiply out to get
        $p^2 - 8p + 16 = 0$ *[1 mark]*, which factorises to
        $(p - 4)^2 = 0$, and so $p = 4$ *[1 mark]*.

C1 Section 3 — Inequalities
& Simultaneous Equations
Warm-up Questions

1) a) $x > -\frac{38}{5}$ b) $y \leq \frac{7}{8}$ c) $y \leq -\frac{3}{4}$

2) a) $x > \frac{5}{2}$ b) $x > -4$ c) $x \leq -3$

3) a) $-\frac{1}{3} \leq x \leq 2$ b) $x < 1 - \sqrt{3}$ or $x > 1 + \sqrt{3}$
    c) $x \leq -3$ or $x \geq -2$

4) a) $x \leq -3$ and $x \geq 1$ b) $x < -\frac{1}{2}$ and $x > 1$
    c) $-3 < x < 2$

5) a) $x = -3, y = -4$ b) $x = -\frac{1}{6}, y = -\frac{5}{12}$

6) a) The line and the curve meet at the points $(2, -6)$ and $(7, 4)$.
    b) The line is a tangent to the parabola at the point $(2, 26)$.
    c) The equations have no solution and so the line and the
        curve never meet.

7) a) $\left(\frac{1}{4}, -\frac{13}{4}\right)$ b) $(4, 5)$ c) $(-5, -2)$

Exam Questions

1 a) $3x + 2 \leq x + 6$
           $2x \leq 4$ *[1 mark]*
            $x \leq 2$ *[1 mark]*
    b) $20 - x - x^2 > 0$
           $(4 - x)(5 + x) > 0$ *[1 mark]*

        The graph crosses the x-axis at $x = 4$ and $x = -5$
        [1 mark]. The coefficient of x^2 is negative so the graph is
        n-shaped *[1 mark]*.
        So $20 - x - x^2 > 0$ when $-5 < x < 4$ *[1 mark]*.

    c) From above, x will satisfy both inequalities when
        $-5 < x \leq 2$ *[1 mark]*.

        For this bit, all you need to do is use your answers to parts
        a) and b) and work out which values of x fit in them both.

2 a) $3 \leq 2p + 5 \leq 15$
        This inequality has 3 parts. Subtract 5 from each
        part to give: $-2 \leq 2p \leq 10$ *[1 mark]*.
        Now divide each part by 2 to give: $-1 \leq p \leq 5$
        [1 mark for −1 ≤ p and 1 mark for p ≤ 5].

    b) $q^2 - 9 > 0$
        $(q + 3)(q - 3) > 0$ *[1 mark]*
        The function is 0 at $q = -3$ and $q = 3$ *[1 mark]*.
        The coefficient of x^2 is positive so the graph is u-shaped.
        So $q^2 - 9 > 0$ when $q < -3$ or $q > 3$
        [1 mark for each correct inequality].

        Use D.O.T.S. (Difference of Two Squares) to factorise the
        quadratic — remember that $a^2 - b^2 = (a + b)(a - b)$.

3 a) $(3x + 2)(x - 5)$ *[1 mark]*
    b) $(3x + 2)(x - 5) \leq 0$
        The function is 0 at $x = -\frac{2}{3}$ and $x = 5$ *[1 mark]*.
        The coefficient of x^2 is positive so the graph is u-shaped,
        meaning the function is less than or equal to 0 between
        these x-values.
        I.e. $3x^2 - 13x - 10 \leq 0$ when $-\frac{2}{3} \leq x \leq 5$
        [2 marks, 1 for $-\frac{2}{3} \leq x$ and 1 for $x \leq 5$].

4   First, take the linear equation and rearrange it to get x on
        its own: $x = 6 - y$ *[1 mark]*. Now substitute the equation
        for x into the quadratic equation:
              $(6 - y)^2 + 2y^2 = 36$ *[1 mark]*
              $36 - 12y + y^2 + 2y^2 = 36$
                    $3y^2 - 12y = 0$
                      $y^2 - 4y = 0$
                     $y(y - 4) = 0$ *[1 mark]*
        so $y = 0$ and $y = 4$. *[1 mark]*.
        Now you've got the y-values, put them back into the
        equation for x ($x = 6 - y$) to find the x-values.
        When $y = 0$, $x = 6 - y = 6 - 0 = 6$.
        When $y = 4$, $x = 6 - y = 6 - 4 = 2$.
        So solutions are $x = 6$, $y = 0$ *[1 mark]*
        and $x = 2$, $y = 4$ *[1 mark]*.

Answers

5 a) At points of intersection, $-2x + 4 = -x^2 + 3$ *[1 mark]*
$$x^2 - 2x + 1 = 0$$
$$(x - 1)^2 = 0 \ \textit{[1 mark]}$$
so $x = 1$ *[1 mark]*. When $x = 1$, $y = -2x + 4 = 2$, so there is one point of intersection at (1, 2) *[1 mark]*.

b)

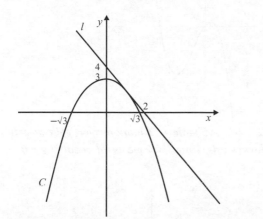

[5 marks available — 1 mark for drawing n-shaped curve, 1 mark for x-axis intercepts at ±√3, 1 mark for maximum point of curve and y-axis intercept at (0, 3). 1 mark for line crossing the y-axis at (0, 4) and the x-axis at (2, 0). 1 mark for line and curve touching in one place.]

6 a)

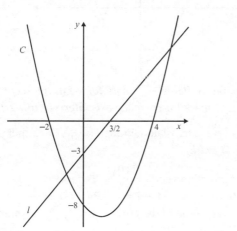

[5 marks available — 1 mark for drawing u-shaped curve, 1 mark for x-axis intercepts at −2 and 4 , 1 mark for y-axis intercept at (0, −8). 1 mark for line crossing the y-axis at (0, −3) and the x-axis at (3/2, 0). 1 mark for line and curve touching in two places.]

b) At points of intersection,
$$2x - 3 = (x + 2)(x - 4)$$
$$2x - 3 = x^2 - 2x - 8 \ \textit{[1 mark]}$$
$$0 = x^2 - 4x - 5 \ \textit{[1 mark]}$$

c) $x^2 - 4x - 5 = 0$
$(x - 5)(x + 1) = 0$ *[1 mark]*
so $x = 5$, $x = -1$ *[1 mark]*.
When $x = 5$, $y = (2 \times 5) - 3 = 7$ and when $x = -1$,
$y = (2 \times -1) - 3 = -5$, so the points of intersection are
(5, 7) *[1 mark]* and (−1, −5) *[1 mark]*.

C1 Section 4 —
Coordinate Geometry and Graphs
Warm-up Questions

1) a) (i) $y + 1 = 3(x-2)$ (ii) $y = 3x - 7$ (iii) $3x - y - 7 = 0$

  b) (i) $y + \frac{1}{3} = \frac{1}{5}x$ (ii) $y = \frac{1}{5}x - \frac{1}{3}$

  (iii) $3x - 15y - 5 = 0$

2) a) $y = \frac{3}{2}x - 4$ **b)** $y = -\frac{1}{2}x + 4$

3) The equation of the required line is $y = \frac{3}{2}x + \frac{15}{2}$.

4) a) $M = (\frac{2 + 12}{2}, \frac{5 - 1}{2}) = (7, 2)$.

  b) length $= \sqrt{(7 - 2)^2 + (2 - 5)^2} = \sqrt{25 + 9} = \sqrt{34}$.

5) a)
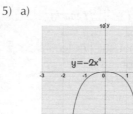

  b)
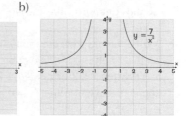

  c)

  d)
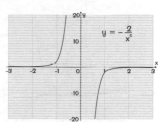

6)
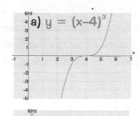
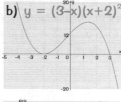

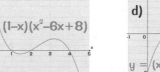
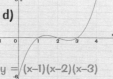
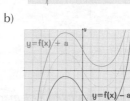

7) a)   **b)**
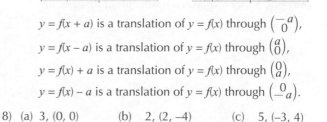

$y = f(x + a)$ is a translation of $y = f(x)$ through $\binom{-a}{0}$,

$y = f(x - a)$ is a translation of $y = f(x)$ through $\binom{a}{0}$,

$y = f(x) + a$ is a translation of $y = f(x)$ through $\binom{0}{a}$,

$y = f(x) - a$ is a translation of $y = f(x)$ through $\binom{0}{-a}$.

8) (a) 3, (0, 0)   **(b)** 2, (2, −4)   **(c)** 5, (−3, 4)

Answers

Exam Questions

1 a) Just rearrange into the form $y = mx + c$ and read off m:
$$3y = 15 - 4x$$
$$y = -\frac{4}{3}x + 5 \quad \textbf{[1 mark]}$$
so the gradient of the line PQ is $-\frac{4}{3}$ **[1 mark]**.

b) Gradient of the line $= -1 \div -\frac{4}{3} = \frac{3}{4}$ **[1 mark]**
So $y = \frac{3}{4}x + c$.
Now use the x- and y- values of R to find c:
$$1 = \frac{3}{4}(3) + c$$
$$1 = \frac{9}{4} + c$$
$$\Rightarrow c = -\frac{5}{4} \quad \textbf{[1 mark]}$$
so the equation of the line is $y = \frac{3}{4}x - \frac{5}{4}$ **[1 mark]**

2 When the brackets are multiplied out, the first term is $2x^3$,
so the graph is a positive cubic graph.
$y = 0$ when $x = 2$ or $x = -\frac{1}{2}$, so the graph touches
the x-axis twice. When $x = 0$, $y = (1)(-2)^2 = 4$.

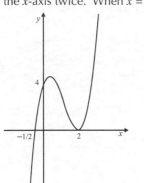

*[4 marks available — 1 mark for correct shape, 1 mark
for x-axis intercept at -1/2, 1 mark for graph touching the
x-axis at 2 and 1 mark for correct y-axis intercept at 4.]*

3 a)

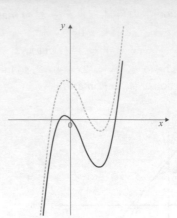

*[2 marks available — 1 mark for horizontal translation to
the right, 1 mark for x-axis intercepts at 3, 5 and 6]*

b)

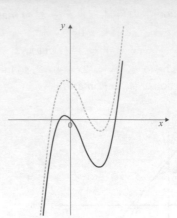

*[2 marks available — 1 mark for vertical translation
downwards, 1 mark for y-axis intercept at y = 0.]*

4 a)

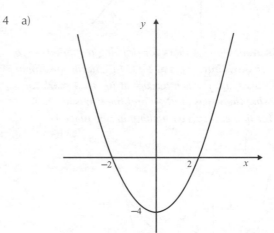

*[2 marks available — 1 mark for x-axis intercepts at -2
and 2, 1 mark for correct y-axis intercept (0, -2)]*

b) The curve is translated through $\begin{pmatrix} -2 \\ 0 \end{pmatrix}$, i.e. a shift of 2 to the
left. **[1 mark]**

c) The translation vector is $\begin{pmatrix} 0 \\ 2 \end{pmatrix}$. **[1 mark]**
$y = f(x) + 2 = x^2 - 4 + 2 = x^2 - 2$ ($a = 0$, $b = -2$).
So the equation of the curve is $y = x^2 - 2$. **[1 mark]**

5 a) Using the formula $y - y_1 = m(x - x_1)$, with the coordinates
of point S for the x- and y- values and $m = -2$,
$$y - (-3) = -2(x - 7) \quad \textbf{[1 mark]}$$
$$y + 3 = -2x + 14 \quad \textbf{[1 mark]}$$
$$y = -2x + 11 \quad \textbf{[1 mark]}$$

b) Putting $x = 5$ into $y = -2x + 11$ gives $y = 1$
[1 mark], so T does lie on the line.

6 a) Gradient of $LK = \frac{8 - 6}{5 - 2} = \frac{2}{3}$ **[1 mark]**
so gradient of $l_1 = -1 \div \frac{2}{3} = -\frac{3}{2}$ **[1 mark]**.
Now, putting this gradient and the x- and y- coordinates of
L into the formula $y - y_1 = m(x - x_1)$ gives:
$$y - 6 = -\frac{3}{2}(x - 2)$$
$$y = -\frac{3}{2}x + 3 + 6$$
$$y = -\frac{3}{2}x + 9 \quad \textbf{[1 mark]}$$
$$\Rightarrow 3x + 2y - 18 = 0 \quad \textbf{[1 mark]}$$

b) Putting $x = 0$ into $y = -\frac{3}{2}x + 9$ gives $y = 9$ *[1 mark]*, so $M = (0, 9)$ *[1 mark]*.

c) Putting $y = 0$ into $3x + 2y - 18 = 0$ gives $x = 6$ *[1 mark]*, so $N = (6, 0)$ *[1 mark]*.

7 a) Putting $(k, 1)$ into $2x - 14y + 6 = 0$ gives $2k - 14 + 6 = 0$ *[1 mark]*, and so $k = 4$ *[1 mark]*.

b) $l = \sqrt{(x_2 - x_1)^2 + (y_2 - y_1)^2}$ *[1 mark]*
$= \sqrt{(4 + 3)^2 + (1 - 0)^2}$ *[1 mark]*
$= \sqrt{50} = 5\sqrt{2}$ *[1 mark]*.

c) Rewriting $2x + y + 5 = 0$ in the form $y = mx + c$ gives $y = -2x - 5$, and so read off the gradient $m = -2$ *[1 mark]*. As lines are parallel, can use same gradient *[1 mark]*. Putting this gradient and the coordinates of Q in the formula $y - y_1 = m(x - x_1)$ gives $y - 1 = -2(x - 4)$, i.e. the line $y = -2x + 9$. *[1 mark]*

8 a) Rearrange equation and complete the square:
$x^2 - 2x + y^2 - 10y + 21 = 0$ *[1 mark]*
$(x - 1)^2 - 1 + (y - 5)^2 - 25 + 21 = 0$ *[1 mark]*
$(x - 1)^2 + (y - 5)^2 = 5$ *[1 mark]*
Compare with $(x - a)^2 + (y - b)^2 = r^2$:
centre $= (1, 5)$ *[1 mark]*, radius $= \sqrt{5} = 2.24$ (to 3 s.f.) *[1 mark]*.

b) The point $(3, 6)$ and centre $(1, 5)$ both lie on the diameter.
Gradient of the diameter $= \frac{6 - 5}{3 - 1} = 0.5$.
$Q(q, 4)$ also lies on the diameter, so $\frac{4 - 6}{q - 3} = 0.5$.
$-2 = 0.5q - 1.5$
So $q = (-2 + 1.5) \div 0.5 = -1$.
[3 marks available — 1 mark for finding the gradient of the diameter, 1 mark for linking this with the point Q, and 1 mark for correct calculation of q.]

c) Tangent at Q is perpendicular to the diameter at Q, so gradient $m = -\frac{1}{0.5} = -2$
$y - y_1 = m(x - x_1)$, and $(-1, 4)$ is a point on the line, so:
$y - 4 = -2(x + 1)$
$y - 4 = -2x - 2$
$2x + y - 2 = 0$ is the equation of the tangent.
[5 marks available — 1 mark for gradient = –1 ÷ gradient of diameter, 1 mark for correct value for gradient, 1 mark for substituting Q in straight-line equation, 2 marks for correct substitution of values in the correct form, or 1 mark if not in the form ax + by + c = 0.]

9 a) The line through P is a diameter, and as such is perpendicular to the chord AB at the midpoint M.
Gradient of AB = Gradient of $AM = \frac{(7 - 10)}{(11 - 9)} = -\frac{3}{2}$.
$\Rightarrow$ Gradient of $PM = \frac{2}{3}$.

Gradient of $PM = \frac{(7 - 3)}{(11 - p)} = \frac{2}{3}$

$\Rightarrow 3(7 - 3) = 2(11 - p)$
$\Rightarrow 12 = 22 - 2p \Rightarrow p = 5$.
[5 marks available — 1 mark for identifying that PM and AM are perpendicular, 1 mark for correct gradient

of AM, 1 mark for correct gradient of PM, 1 mark for substitution of the y-value of P into the gradient or equation of the line, and 1 mark for correct final answer.]

b) The centre of C is $P(5, 3)$, so $a = 5$ *[1 mark]* and $b = 3$ *[1 mark]* in the equation $(x - a)^2 + (y - b)^2 = r^2$. The radius is the length of AP, which can be found using Pythagoras as follows:
$r^2 = AP^2 = (9 - 5)^2 + (10 - 3)^2 = 65$ *[1 mark]*
So the equation of C is:
$(x - 5)^2 + (y - 3)^2 = 65$ *[1 mark]*.

C1 Section 5 — Polynomials
Warm-up Questions

1) $x^3 + 6x^2 + 11x + 6 = (x + 1)(x^2 + 5x + 6)$
$= (x + 1)(x + 2)(x + 3)$.

2) a) $f(x) = (x + 2)(3x^2 - 10x + 15) - 36$
b) $f(x) = (x + 2)(x^2 - 3) + 10$
c) $f(x) = (x + 2)(2x^2 - 4x + 14) - 31$

3) a) (i) You just need to find $f(-1)$.
This is $-6 - 1 + 3 - 12 = -16$.
(ii) Now find $f(1)$. This is $6 - 1 - 3 - 12 = -10$.
(iii) Now find $f(2)$. This is $48 - 4 - 6 - 12 = 26$.

b) (i) $f(-1) = -1$
(ii) $f(1) = 9$
(iii) $f(2) = 38$

c) (i) $f(-1) = -2$
(ii) $f(1) = 0$
(iii) $f(2) = 37$

4) a) You need to find $f(-2)$. This is
$(-2)^4 - 3(-2)^3 + 7(-2)^2 - 12(-2) + 14$
$= 16 + 24 + 28 + 24 + 14 = 106$.

b) You need to find $f(-4/2) = f(-2)$. You found this in part a), so remainder $= 106$. You might also have noticed that $2x + 4$ is a multiple of $x + 2$ (from part a)), so the remainder must be the same.

c) You need to find $f(3)$. This is
$(3)^4 - 3(3)^3 + 7(3)^2 - 12(3) + 14$
$= 81 - 81 + 63 - 36 + 14 = 41$.

d) You need to find $f(6/2) = f(3)$. You found this in part c), so remainder $= 41$. You might also have noticed that $2x - 6$ is a multiple of $x - 3$, so the remainder must be the same.

5) a) You need to find $f(1)$ — if $f(1) = 0$, then $(x - 1)$ is a factor:
$f(1) = 1 - 4 + 3 + 2 - 2 = 0$, so $(x - 1)$ is a factor.

b) You need to find $f(-1)$ — if $f(-1) = 0$, then $(x + 1)$ is a factor:
$f(-1) = -1 - 4 - 3 + 2 - 2 = -8$, so $(x + 1)$ is not a factor.

c) You need to find $f(2)$ — if $f(2) = 0$, then $(x - 2)$ is a factor:
$f(2) = 32 - (4 \times 16) + (3 \times 8) + (2 \times 4) - 2$
$= 32 - 64 + 24 + 8 - 2 = -2$, so $(x - 2)$ is not a factor.

d) The remainder when you divide by $(2x - 2)$ is the same as the remainder when you divide by $x - 1$.

Answers

$(x - 1)$ is a factor (i.e. remainder = 0), so $(2x - 2)$ is also a factor.

6) If $f(x) = 2x^4 + 3x^3 + 5x^2 + cx + d$, then to make sure $f(x)$ is exactly divisible by $(x - 2)(x + 3)$, you have to make sure $f(2) = f(-3) = 0$.
$f(2) = 32 + 24 + 20 + 2c + d = 0$, i.e. $\underline{2c + d = -76}$.
$f(-3) = 162 - 81 + 45 - 3c + d = 0$, i.e. $\underline{3c - d = 126}$.
Add the two underlined equations to get: $5c = 50$, and so $c = 10$. Then $d = -96$.

7) 1   5   10   10   5   1

8) $(1 + x)^{12} = 1 + \dfrac{12}{1}x + \dfrac{12 \times 11}{1 \times 2}x^2 + \dfrac{12 \times 11 \times 10}{1 \times 2 \times 3}x^3 + \dots$
$= 1 + 12x + (6 \times 11)x^2 + (4 \times 11 \times 5)x^3 + \dots$
So the first 4 terms are:
$1 + 12x + 66x^2 + 220x^3$

9) $\dfrac{16 \times 15}{1 \times 2} \times (-2x)^2 = \dfrac{16 \times 15}{2} \times 4x^2$
$= 8 \times 15 \times 4x^2 = 480x^2$

10) $(2 + 3x)^5 = 2^5\left(1 + \dfrac{3}{2}x\right)^5$
$= 2^5\left[1 + \dfrac{5}{1}\left(\dfrac{3}{2}x\right) + \dfrac{5 \times 4}{1 \times 2}\left(\dfrac{3}{2}x\right)^2 + \dots\right]$
x^2 term is $2^5 \times \dfrac{5 \times 4}{1 \times 2}\left(\dfrac{3}{2}x\right)^2$
so coefficient is $2^5 \times \dfrac{5 \times 4}{1 \times 2} \times \dfrac{3^2}{2^2}$
$= 32 \times 10 \times \dfrac{9}{4}$
$= \dfrac{32}{4} \times 10 \times 9$
$= 8 \times 10 \times 9$
$= 720$

Exam Questions

1 a) (i) Remainder = $f(1) = 2(1)^3 - 5(1)^2 - 4(1) + 3$ *[1 mark]*
$= -4$ *[1 mark]*.

(ii) Remainder = $f\left(-\dfrac{1}{2}\right) = 2\left(-\dfrac{1}{8}\right) - 5\left(\dfrac{1}{4}\right) - 4\left(-\dfrac{1}{2}\right) + 3$
[1 mark] $= \dfrac{7}{2}$ *[1 mark]*.

b) If $f(-1) = 0$ then $(x + 1)$ is a factor.
$f(-1) = 2(-1)^3 - 5(-1)^2 - 4(-1) + 3$ *[1 mark]*
$= -2 - 5 + 4 + 3 = 0$, so $(x + 1)$ is a factor of $f(x)$.
[1 mark]

c) $(x + 1)$ is a factor, so divide $2x^3 - 5x^2 - 4x + 3$ by $x + 1$:
$2x^3 - 5x^2 - 4x + 3 - \underline{2x^2}(x + 1) = 2x^3 - 5x^2 - 4x + 3 - 2x^3 - 2x^2$
$= -7x^2 - 4x + 3$.
$-7x^2 - 4x + 3 - (\underline{-7x})(x + 1) = -7x^2 - 4x + 3 + 7x^2 + 7x$
$= 3x + 3$. Finally $3x + 3 - \underline{3}(x + 1) = 0$.
so $2x^3 - 5x^2 - 4x + 3 = (2x^2 - 7x + 3)(x + 1)$.

This is the algebraic division method from p.42. You could also use the method from p.41 — it depends which you prefer.

Factorising the quadratic expression gives:
$f(x) = (2x - 1)(x - 3)(x + 1)$.

[4 marks available — 1 mark for dividing by $x + 1$ to find quadratic factor, 1 mark for correct quadratic factor, 1 mark for attempt to factorise quadratic, 1 mark for correct factorisation of quadratic.]

2 a) $f(p) = (4p^2 + 3p + 1)(p - p) + 5$
$= (4p^2 + 3p + 1) \times 0 + 5$
$= 5$ *[1 mark]*.

b) $f(-1) = -1$.
$f(-1) = (4(-1)^2 + 3(-1) + 1)((-1) - p) + 5$
$= (4 - 3 + 1)(-1 - p) + 5$
$= 2(-1 - p) + 5 = 3 - 2p$ *[1 mark]*
So: $3 - 2p = -1$, $p = 2$ *[1 mark]*.

c) $f(x) = (4x^2 + 3x + 1)(x - 2) + 5$
$f(1) = (4 + 3 + 1)(1 - 2) + 5 = -3$ *[1 mark]*.

3 $(4 + 3x)^5 = 4^5\left(1 + \dfrac{3}{4}x\right)^5$
x^4 term $= 4^5\left[\dfrac{5 \times 4 \times 3 \times 2}{1 \times 2 \times 3 \times 4} \times \left(\dfrac{3}{4}x\right)^4\right]$
So x^4 coefficient $= 4^5\left[\dfrac{5 \times 4 \times 3 \times 2}{1 \times 2 \times 3 \times 4} \times \left(\dfrac{3}{4}\right)^4\right]$
$= 4^5 \times 5 \times \dfrac{3^4}{4^4} = 4 \times 5 \times 3^4 = 20 \times 81 = 1620$.

[4 marks available — 1 mark for 4^5, 1 mark for $^5C_4$, 1 mark for $\left(\dfrac{3}{4}\right)^4$, 1 mark for correct final answer.]

I've said it before and I'll say it again — always try to cancel your fractions to make calculations easier. Here, you needed to spot that the 4^5 and $\dfrac{1}{4^4}$ multiply together to give 4. If binomial expansion is still a tangle of factors, powers and garden gnomes, go back and sort it out — you'll be glad you did.

4 a) As $(x + 4)$ is a factor of $f(x)$, $f(-4) = 0$: *[1 mark]*
$(-4)^3 + p(-4) + 4 = 0$
$-64 - 4p + 4 = 0$
$-60 = 4p$
$p = -15$ *[1 mark]*

b) Told that $x + 4$ is a factor, so factorise by equating coefficients:
$f(x) = (x^3 - 15x + 4) = (x + 4)(x^2 + ?x + 1)$
$= (x + 4)(x^2 - 4x + 1)$ *[1 mark]*
This the method from page 41.
Set $f(x) = 0$ and find the roots of the quadratic:
By completing the square, or using the formula,
$x^2 - 4x + 1 = 0$ has roots $x = 2 \pm \sqrt{3}$. *[1 mark]*
So the roots of $f(x) = 0$ are
$x = 2 + \sqrt{3}, 2 - \sqrt{3}$ and -4. *[1 mark]*

C1 — Practice Exam One

1 Using the remainder theorem, the remainder when dividing $f(x) = x^3 + x^2 - 3x - 1$ by $(x + 2)$ will be equal to the value of $f(-2)$ *[1 mark]*.
$f(-2) = (-2)^3 + (-2)^2 - 3(-2) - 1 = 1$ *[1 mark]*.
So the remainder is 1.

2 a) Rearrange according to Laws of Indices (if you've forgotten, they've got their very own page in Section 1):
$36^{-\frac{1}{2}} = \dfrac{1}{36^{\frac{1}{2}}} = \dfrac{1}{\sqrt{36}}$ *[1 mark]*
$= \dfrac{1}{6}$ *[1 mark]*

Answers

b) First simplify the surd on the bottom of the fraction:

$\sqrt[m]{a^n} = a^{\frac{n}{m}}$ so $\sqrt{a^4} = a^2$ *[1 mark]*

Then rewrite the entire expression so that you're only multiplying things (remember that $\div a^n = \times a^{-n}$):

$\dfrac{a^6 \times a^3}{a^2} \div a^{\frac{1}{2}} = a^6 \times a^3 \times a^{-2} \times a^{-\frac{1}{2}}$ *[1 mark]*

Finally, add the powers together, because $a^m \times a^n = a^{m+n}$:

$= a^{6+3-2-\frac{1}{2}} = a^{\frac{13}{2}}$ *[1 mark]*

Lots of laws to remember there. Make sure you don't multiply powers when you should be adding, and vice versa.

3    $y = \dfrac{x-1}{x} + 3$.

First multiply throughout by x:

$xy = x - 1 + 3x$ *[1 mark]*

Then gather all x-terms on one side and everything else on the other:

$1 = 4x - xy$

Now factorise the right hand side:

$1 = x(4-y)$ *[1 mark]*

And so $x = \dfrac{1}{4-y}$ *[1 mark]*.

4   Multiply out the brackets first:

$(5\sqrt{5} + 2\sqrt{3})^2 = (5\sqrt{5} + 2\sqrt{3})(5\sqrt{5} + 2\sqrt{3})$

$= (5\sqrt{5})^2 + 2(5\sqrt{5} \times 2\sqrt{3}) + (2\sqrt{3})^2$

So now you've got three terms to deal with, and they're all a little bit nasty. The first term is:

$(5\sqrt{5})^2 = 5\sqrt{5} \times 5\sqrt{5}$

$= 5 \times 5 \times \sqrt{5} \times \sqrt{5}$

$= 5 \times 5 \times 5$

$= 125$ *[1 mark]*

The second term is:

$2(5\sqrt{5} \times 2\sqrt{3}) = 2 \times 5 \times 2 \times \sqrt{5} \times \sqrt{3}$

$= 20\sqrt{15}$ *(don't forget, $\sqrt{5} \times \sqrt{3} = \sqrt{5 \times 3}$)* *[1 mark]*

And the third term is:

$2\sqrt{3} \times 2\sqrt{3} = 2 \times 2 \times \sqrt{3} \times \sqrt{3}$

$= 2 \times 2 \times 3 = 12$ *[1 mark]*

So all you have to do now is add the three terms together:

$125 + 20\sqrt{15} + 12 = 137 + 20\sqrt{15}$ *[1 mark]*

So $a = 137$, $b = 20$ and $c = 15$.

5 a) Using the binomial expansion formula:

$(1+x)^n =$
$1 + \dfrac{n}{1}x + \dfrac{n(n-1)}{1 \times 2}x^2 + \dfrac{n(n-1)(n-2)}{1 \times 2 \times 3}x^3 + \dots + x^n$

Expand the expression $(1 + ax)^{10}$ into this form:

$1 + \dfrac{10}{1}(ax) + \dfrac{10 \times 9}{1 \times 2}(ax)^2 + \dfrac{10 \times 9 \times 8}{1 \times 2 \times 3}(ax)^3 + \dots$ *[1 mark]*

Then simplify each coefficient:

$(1+ax)^{10} = 1 + 10ax + 45a^2x^2 + 120a^3x^3 + \dots$ *[1 mark]*

b) *Pay attention to the number at the front of the bracket. If it's not a 1, you have to rearrange everything so it is a 1. Fiddly but important.*

First take a factor of 2 to get it in the form $(1 + ax)^n$:

$(2 + 3x)^5 = \left[2\left(1 + \dfrac{3}{2}x\right)\right]^5 = 2^5\left(1 + \dfrac{3}{2}x\right)^5 = 32\left(1 + \dfrac{3}{2}x\right)^5$

Now expand:

$32\left[1 + \dfrac{5}{1}\left(\dfrac{3}{2}x\right) + \dfrac{5 \times 4}{1 \times 2}\left(\dfrac{3}{2}x\right)^2 + \dots\right]$ *[1 mark]*

You only need the x^2 term, so simplify that one:

$32 \times \dfrac{20}{2} \times \left(\dfrac{3}{2}\right)^2 \times x^2$

$= \left(32 \times 10 \times \dfrac{9}{4}\right)x^2$

$= (8 \times 10 \times 9)x^2 = 720x^2$

So the coefficient of x^2 is 720   *[1 mark]*

6 a) Start by finding a — it's the coefficient of x halved:

$x^2 - 6x + 5 = (x-3)^2 + b$ *[1 mark]*

Multiply out to get $x^2 - 6x + 9 + b = x^2 - 6x + 5$

Simplify to find b: $9 + b = 5$ so $b = 5 - 9 = -4$

So the answer is $x^2 - 6x + 5 = (x-3)^2 - 4$ *[1 mark]*

b) To factorise $x^2 - 6x + 5$ you need two numbers that add up to -6 and multiply to give 5. Easy peasy...

$x^2 - 6x + 5 = (x-1)(x-5)$ *[2 marks for correct answer, or 1 mark if there's a sign error]*

7 a) k is the y-value when $x = 4$, so substitute $x = 4$ into the equation of the line to find y:

$y + (2 \times 4) - 5 = 0$

$y = 5 - 8$

$y = -3$ so $k = -3$ *[1 mark]*

b) Remember — the gradients of two perpendicular lines multiply together to make -1. This means that the gradient of the new line will be: $\dfrac{-1}{\text{the gradient of AB}}$

The gradient of a straight line is the coefficient of x when the equation of the line is written in the form $y = mx + c$.

$y + 2x - 5 = 0$ becomes $y = -2x + 5$, so the gradient of AB $= -2$. *[1 mark]*

Now you know the gradient of the new line will be $\dfrac{-1}{-2}$, which equals $\dfrac{1}{2}$. *[1 mark]*

Finally, get the equation of the new line using $y - y_1 = m(x - x_1)$ and A (1, 3) — the point it passes through: $y - 3 = \dfrac{1}{2}(x-1)$ *[1 mark]*

$y = \dfrac{1}{2}x - \dfrac{1}{2} + 3 = \dfrac{1}{2}x + \dfrac{5}{2}$

$y = \dfrac{x+5}{2}$ *[1 mark]*

Remember the process, remember the formulas, and you'll be fine. But the only way to make sure you know it is practice. If you forgot anything, go back to the coordinate geometry section and go through it till it sinks in...

8   If the quadratic $ax^2 + bx + c = 0$ has no real roots, this means the discriminant gives a negative value:

$b^2 - 4ac < 0$ *[1 mark]*. So:

$(-4)^2 - [4 \times 1 \times (k-1)] < 0$ *[1 mark]*

$\Rightarrow 16 - (4k - 4) < 0$

$\Rightarrow 20 - 4k < 0$ *[1 mark]*

$20 < 4k$

$k > 5$ *[1 mark]*

Answers

9 a) $4x + 7 > 7x + 4$
Subtract $4x + 4$ from both sides which gives
$3 > 3x$ *[1 mark]*
$1 > x$ *or* $x < 1$ *[1 mark]*

b) You've got to find the minimum value of $(x - 5)(x - 3)$ and when k is less than that, $(x - 5)(x - 3) > k$ will be true for all possible values of x.
As always, it helps to sketch a graph and think about what the function looks like:

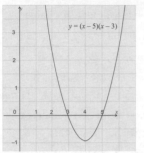

Remember, it's a symmetrical graph, so the minimum is halfway between $x = 3$ and $x = 5$
— i.e. when $x = 4$. *[1 mark]*
Put this x-value into the equation to find the lowest possible y-value: $(x - 5)(x - 3) = (4 - 5)(4 - 3)$ *[1 mark]*
$= -1 \times 1 = -1$ *[1 mark]*
So for the range of values $k < -1$ it is true that $(x - 5)(x - 3) > k$ for all possible values of x.

You can also find the minimum value by completing the square — when you've got your quadratic in the form $(x + m)^2 + n$, the minimum value occurs at n.

10 a) As one of these equations is a quadratic, you need the substitution method, so substitute $y = 7 - x$ into $y = x^2 + 3x - 5$ to get:
$7 - x = x^2 + 3x - 5$ *[1 mark]*

Rearrange again to get everything on one side of the equation, and then factorise it:
$0 = x^2 + 4x - 12$
$(x + 6)(x - 2) = 0$ *[1 mark]*
Which gives two values : $x = -6$ and $x = 2$ *[1 mark]*
Don't forget to find the corresponding values of y as well:
$y = 7 - x$
So when $x = -6$
$y = 7 - -6 = 7 + 6$
$y = 13$ *[1 mark]*
And when $x = 2$
$y = 7 - 2$
$y = 5$ *[1 mark]*

So the curves meet at $(-6, 13)$ and $(2, 5)$.

Simultaneous equations — you should be able to do them standing on your head... although don't try that in the exam...

b) Complete the square by halving the coefficient of x to find the number in the brackets (a):
$x^2 + 3x - 5 = \left(x + \frac{3}{2}\right)^2 + b$

Now simplify this equation to find b:
$b = x^2 + 3x - 5 - \left[\left(x + \frac{3}{2}\right)^2\right]$
$b = x^2 + 3x - 5 - x^2 - 3x - \frac{9}{4}$
$b = -5 - \frac{9}{4} = -\frac{29}{4}$
So you can express $x^2 + 3x - 5$ as:
$\left(x + \frac{3}{2}\right)^2 - \frac{29}{4}$

[3 marks available — 1 mark for correct value of a, 1 mark for correct value of b, 1 mark for correct working.]

c) The graph of $y = \left(x + \frac{3}{2}\right)^2 - \frac{29}{4}$ is a translation of the graph of $y = x^2$ through $\left(\begin{smallmatrix} -\frac{3}{2} \\ -\frac{29}{4} \end{smallmatrix}\right)$, so the graph is:

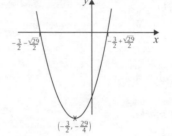

The turning point of $y = x^2$ is at $(0, 0)$, so the turning point of the translated graph is $\left(-\frac{3}{2}, -\frac{29}{4}\right)$, as shown.
The translated graph crosses the x-axis when $y = 0$:
$0 = \left(x + \frac{3}{2}\right)^2 - \frac{29}{4}$
$\left(x + \frac{3}{2}\right)^2 = \frac{29}{4}$
$x + \frac{3}{2} = \pm \sqrt{\frac{29}{4}}$
$x = -\frac{3}{2} \pm \frac{\sqrt{29}}{2}$

So the graph intersects the x-axis at $x = -\frac{3}{2} + \frac{\sqrt{29}}{2}$
and $x = -\frac{3}{2} - \frac{\sqrt{29}}{2}$, as shown.

[3 marks available — 1 mark for translated quadratic graph, 1 mark for correct x-axis intersections, 1 mark for correct turning point.]

11 a) Multiply out the brackets and rearrange to get zero on one side:
$(x - 1)(x^2 + x + 1) = 2x^2 - 17$
$\Rightarrow x^3 - 1 = 2x^2 - 17$ *[1 mark]*
$\Rightarrow x^3 - 2x^2 + 16 = 0$ *[1 mark]*

b) To show whether $(x + 2)$ is a factor of f(x) you need the factor theorem, which says that $(x - a)$ is a factor of a polynomial f(x) if and only if f(a) = 0. So if $(x + 2)$ is a factor of f(x), f(-2) = 0. *[1 mark]*
f(x) $= x^3 - 2x^2 + 16$
f(-2) $= (-2)^3 - 2 \times (-2)^2 + 16$
$= -8 - 8 + 16$
$= 0$ *[1 mark]*
f(-2) = 0, therefore $(x + 2)$ is a factor of f(x) *[1 mark]*

Answers

c) From part b) you know that $(x + 2)$ is a factor of f(x).
Dividing f(x) by $(x + 2)$ gives:
$x^3 - 2x^2 + 16 - \underline{x^2}(x + 2) = x^3 - 2x^2 + 16 - x^3 - 2x^2$
$= -4x^2 + 16$
$-4x^2 + 16 - (\underline{-4x})(x + 2) = -4x^2 + 16 + 4x^2 + 8x = 8x + 16$
$8x + 16 - \underline{8}(x + 2) = 0$.
So $x^3 - 2x^2 + 16 = (x + 2)(x^2 - 4x + 8)$
[3 marks available — 1 mark for each correct term in the quadratic.]

d) To find $(x^3 - 2x^2 + 3x - 3) \div (x - 1)$ keep subtracting lumps of $(x - 1)$ to get rid of all powers of x.
First get rid of the x^3 term by subtracting x^2 lots of $(x - 1)$:
$(x^3 - 2x^2 + 3x - 3) - \underline{x^2}(x - 1)$
$= x^3 - 2x^2 + 3x - 3 - x^3 + x^2$
$= -x^2 + 3x - 3$
Now do the same with the bit you've got left to get rid of the x^2 term:
$-x^2 + 3x - 3 + \underline{x}(x - 1)$
$= -x^2 + 3x - 3 + x^2 - x$
$= 2x - 3$
Finally, get rid of the x term in the bit that's left:
$2x - 3 - \underline{2}(x - 1) = 2x - 3 - 2x + 2$
$= -1$
Which all means that $(x^3 - 2x^2 + 3x - 3) \div (x - 1)$
$= x^2 - x + 2$ with a remainder -1.
[4 marks available — 1 mark for each correct term and 1 mark for remainder.]

12 a) The circle intersects the x-axis when $y = 0$, i.e.:
$x^2 - 6x - 3 = 0$
Use the quadratic formula to find x:
$x = \dfrac{6 \pm \sqrt{(-6)^2 - (4 \times 1 \times -3)}}{2 \times 1}$ *[1 mark]*
$= 3 \pm \dfrac{\sqrt{48}}{2}$ *[1 mark]* $= 3 \pm 2\sqrt{3}$.

So the coordinates of intersection with the x-axis are:
$(3 + 2\sqrt{3}, 0)$ *[1 mark]* and $(3 - 2\sqrt{3}, 0)$ *[1 mark]*.

b) $x^2 - 6x + y^2 = 3$
$(x - 3)^2 - 9 + y^2 = 3$ *[1 mark]*
$(x - 3)^2 + y^2 = 12$ *[1 mark]*.

c) $r = \sqrt{12} = 2\sqrt{3}$ *[1 mark]*
Q has coordinates $(3, 0)$ *[1 mark]*.

d) (i) Use the distance formula $d = \sqrt{(x_2 - x_1)^2 + (y_2 - y_1)^2}$:
$d = \sqrt{(5 - 3)^2 + (4 - 0)^2}$ *[1 mark]*
$= \sqrt{4 + 16} = \sqrt{20}$ *[1 mark]* $= 2\sqrt{5}$ *[1 mark]*.
(ii) Distance from Q to P is $2\sqrt{5}$.
Radius of C is $2\sqrt{3}$.
$2\sqrt{5} > 2\sqrt{3}$, so P lies outside C.
[2 marks available — 1 mark for correct answer, 1 mark for reason]

At the end of the exam, it's tradition to have a comforting cup of tea and vow never to look at a quadratic equation ever again. That was just a practice though, so don't celebrate just yet... Oh alright, you can have a cuppa I suppose...

C1 — Practice Exam Two

1 Solve $x^3 - 4x^2 - 7x + 10 = 0$ by factorising it. They've given you the factor $(x - 1)$, so first you need to find the quadratic that multiplies with that factor to give the original equation.
The first and last terms of the quadratic are simple to find — what multiplies with x to give x^3 and what multiplies with -1 to give $+10$?
$(x - 1)(x^2 ..... - 10)$
Now multiply that out and see if anything's missing:
$(x - 1)(x^2 - 10) = x^3 - x^2 - 10x + 10$
To get the correct coefficients for x^2 and x you need an additional: $- 3x^2$ and $+ 3x$ *[1 mark]*.
$(- 3x)(x - 1) = - 3x^2 + 3x$
So you know that the quadratic needs $-3x$ in it, which gives: $(x - 1)(x^2 - 3x - 10)$ *[1 mark]*.
The quadratic further factorises into $(x - 5)(x + 2)$, so
$x^3 - 4x^2 - 7x + 10 = (x - 1)(x - 5)(x + 2)$ *[1 mark]*
Now solve the equation $(x - 1)(x - 5)(x + 2) = 0$
So $x = 1$, 5 or $- 2$ *[1 mark]*
No two ways about it — questions like those are a bit taxing. The only way is to practise and practise till you know exactly what you're looking for. And then practise some more...

2 a) Just multiply out the brackets:
$(\sqrt{3} + 1)(\sqrt{3} - 1) = 3 - \sqrt{3} + \sqrt{3} - 1$ *[1 mark]*
$= 2$ *[1 mark]*

b) To rationalise the denominator, you want to get rid of the surd on the bottom line of the fraction. To do this, use the difference of two squares — e.g. if the denominator's $\sqrt{a} + b$, you multiply by $\sqrt{a} - b$:
$\dfrac{\sqrt{3} - 1}{\sqrt{3} + 1} \times \dfrac{\sqrt{3} - 1}{\sqrt{3} - 1}$ *[1 mark]*
$= \dfrac{3 - 2\sqrt{3} + 1}{2}$ *[1 mark]*
$= 2 - \sqrt{3}$ *[1 mark]*

3 a) Complete the square by halving the coefficient of x to find the number in the brackets (m):
$x^2 - 7x + 17 = \left(x - \dfrac{7}{2}\right)^2 + n$
Now simplify this equation to find n:
$n = x^2 - 7x + 17 - \left[\left(x - \dfrac{7}{2}\right)^2\right]$
$n = x^2 - 7x + 17 - x^2 + \dfrac{14x}{2} - \dfrac{49}{4}$
$n = 17 - \dfrac{49}{4} = \dfrac{19}{4}$
So you can express $x^2 - 7x + 17$ as:
$\left(x - \dfrac{7}{2}\right)^2 + \dfrac{19}{4}$

[3 marks available — 1 mark for correct value of m, 1 mark for correct value of n, 1 mark for correct working.]

b) The maximum value of $f(x)$ will be when the denominator is as small as possible — so you want the minimum value of $x^2 - 7x + 17$. Using the completed square above, you can see that the minimum value is $\dfrac{19}{4}$ because the squared part can equal but never be below 0 *[1 mark]*.

Answers

So max value of $f(x)$ is $\frac{1}{19/4} = 1 \times \frac{4}{19} = \frac{4}{19}$ *[1 mark]* .

You've got to put on your thinking cap for that one — but they give you a big hint by getting you to complete the square first.

4 To find the values where $9x^2 + 4x < 0$, you need to start by solving $9x^2 + 4x = 0$. Factorising the quadratic:

$x(9x + 4) = 0$, so $x = 0$ *[1 mark]* or:

$9x = -4 \Rightarrow x = -\frac{4}{9}$ *[1 mark]*.

The graph looks like this:

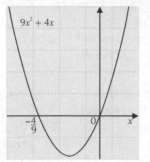

From the graph, you can see that $9x^2 + 4x < 0$ when $-\frac{4}{9} < x < 0$ *[1 mark]*.

If you made a mistake, do not pass GO, do not collect £200, and move your tiny top hat back to the pages on quadratic inequalities...

5 $(2 + x)^5 = 2^5\left(1 + \frac{1}{2}x\right)^5$ *[1 mark]*

The term in x^3 is given by: $2^5\left[\frac{5 \times 4 \times 3}{1 \times 2 \times 3} \times \left(\frac{1}{2}x\right)^3\right]$ *[1 mark]*

$= \frac{2^5}{2^3}[10x^3] = 2^2[10x^3] = 40x^3$

So the coefficient of x^3 is 40 *[1 mark]*.

6 Factorising $3n^2 - 12$ gives:

$3n^2 - 12 = 3(n^2 - 4)$

$\qquad\qquad = 3(n + 2)(n - 2)$ *[1 mark]*

If n is odd, then $n + 2$ and $n - 2$ will also be odd, so:

$3n^2 - 12 = 3(n + 2)(n - 2) = (\text{odd}) \times (\text{odd}) \times (\text{odd}) = (\text{odd})$.

[1 mark]

Similarly, if n is even, then $n + 2$ and $n - 2$ will also be even, so:

$3n^2 - 12 = 3(n + 2)(n - 2) = (\text{odd}) \times (\text{even}) \times (\text{even}) = (\text{even})$.

[1 mark]

This type of question pops up in exams quite often, and they can be tricky little devils. It often helps to try and factorise, simplify or rearrange the expression they give you — looking at it in a different way could give you some inspiration. If you prefer, you could write 'n odd' as 2k + 1 and 'n even' as 2k, as on p. 8, and go from there. Or you could always just explain the answer in words rather than algebraically, but you need to make sure the examiner understands what you are trying to say. Decisions, decisions.

7 If the function only has one root, then $b^2 - 4ac = 0$ *[1 mark]*. For this equation, $a = 3$, $b = k$ and $c = 12$. Use this formula to find k:

$k^2 - (4 \times 3 \times 12) = 0$ *[1 mark]*

$k^2 - 144 = 0$

$k^2 = 144$

$k = \pm 12$ *[1 mark]*

Of course, it's no good remembering the general formula if you don't know what a, b and c stand for. Imagine forgetting that it's $ax^2 + bx + c$ — you'd feel a right wally.

8 $x^4 - 6x^2 + 8 = 0$

$y = x^2 \Rightarrow y^2 - 6y + 8 = 0$ *[1 mark]*

$(y - 2)(y - 4) = 0$ *[1 mark]*

So $y = 2$, or $y = 4$

$\Rightarrow x^2 = 2$, or $x^2 = 4$ *[1 mark]*

So, $x = \pm\sqrt{2}$ *[1 mark]*, or $x = \pm 2$ *[1 mark]*.

9 a) (i) $10^0 = 1$ *[1 mark]*.

   Remember — anything to the power O is equal to 1.

   (ii) $81^{-\frac{1}{2}} = \frac{1}{81^{\frac{1}{2}}} = \frac{1}{\sqrt{81}} = \pm\frac{1}{9}$

   [2 marks — 1 for $\frac{1}{9}$, 1 for $-\frac{1}{9}$].

   b) $\frac{a^2 b}{a^3} - \frac{b}{a} + \frac{b^2 c^3 d}{bc^2} = \frac{b}{a} - \frac{b}{a} + bcd$ *[1 mark]*

   $= bcd$ *[1 mark]*

10 a) (i) Remainder $= f(-3) = (-3)^3 - 6(-3)^2 - (-3) + 30$ *[1 mark]*

   $= -48$ *[1 mark]*.

   (ii) Remainder $= f\left(\frac{1}{2}\right) = \left(\frac{1}{8}\right) - 6\left(\frac{1}{4}\right) - \left(\frac{1}{2}\right) + 30$ *[1 mark]*

   $= \left(\frac{1}{8}\right) - \left(\frac{12}{8}\right) - \left(\frac{4}{8}\right) + \left(\frac{240}{8}\right) = \frac{225}{8}$ *[1 mark]*.

   b) If $(x - 3)$ is a factor then $f(3) = 0$.

   $f(3) = (3)^3 - 6(3)^2 - (3) + 30$ *[1 mark]*

   $= 27 - 54 - 3 + 30 = 0$,

   so $(x - 3)$ is a factor of $f(x)$ *[1 mark]*.

   c) $(x - 3)$ is a factor, so divide $x^3 - 6x^2 - x + 30$ by $x - 3$:

   $x^3 - 6x^2 - x + 30 - \underline{x^2}(x - 3) = x^3 - 6x^2 - x + 30 - x^3 + 3x^2$

   $= -3x^2 - x + 30$.

   $-3x^2 - x + 30 - (\underline{-3x})(x - 3) = -3x^2 - x + 30 + 3x^2 - 9x$

   $= -10x + 30$. Finally $-10x + 30 - (\underline{-10})(x - 3) = 0$.

   so $x^3 - 6x^2 - x + 30 = (x^2 - 3x - 10)(x - 3)$.

   This is the method from p.42.

   Factorising the quadratic expression gives:

   $f(x) = (x - 5)(x + 2)(x - 3)$.

   [4 marks available — 1 mark for dividing by x – 3 to find quadratic factor, 1 mark for correct quadratic factor, 1 mark for attempt to factorise quadratic, 1 mark for correct factorisation of quadratic.]

   d) The translation $\begin{pmatrix} 1 \\ 0 \end{pmatrix}$ is a shift of '1 to the right', so the graph of $y = f(x)$ is mapped to the graph of $y = f(x - 1)$ *[1 mark]*.

   $f(x - 1) = (x^2 - 2x + 1)(x - 1) - 6(x^2 - 2x + 1) - (x - 1) + 30$

   [1 mark]

   $= x^3 - 2x^2 + x - x^2 + 2x - 1 - 6x^2 + 12x - 6 - x + 1 + 30$

   $= x^3 - 9x^2 + 14x + 24$ *[1 mark]*.

Answers

11 a) A is on the *y*-axis, so the *x*-coordinate is 0. Just put $x = 0$ into the equation and solve:

$0^2 - (6 \times 0) + y^2 - 4y = 0$ *[1 mark]*

$y^2 - 4y = 0$

$y(y - 4) = 0$

$y = 0$ or $y = 4$

$y = 0$ is the origin, so A is at $(0, 4)$ *[1 mark]*

b) You're basically completing the square for *x* and *y* separately, so halve the coefficient of *x* to find *a*, and halve the coefficient of *y* to find *b*. For each one you'll end up with a number you don't want, which you need to take away each time:

Completing the square for $x^2 - 6x$ gives $(x - 3)^2$
but $(x - 3)^2 = x^2 - 6x + 9$ so you need to take 9 away:
$(x - 3)^2 - 9$ *[1 mark]*
Now the same for $y^2 - 4y$: $(y - 2)^2 = y^2 - 4y + 4$ so take away 4 which gives: $(y - 2)^2 - 4$ *[1 mark]*

Put these new expressions back into the original equation:
$(x - 3)^2 - 9 + (y - 2)^2 - 4 = 0$

$\Rightarrow (x - 3)^2 + (y - 2)^2 = 13$ *[1 mark]*

c) In the general equation for a circle $(x - a)^2 + (y - b)^2 = r^2$, the centre is (a, b) and the radius is *r*. So for the equation in part b) — $a = 3$, $b = 2$, $r = \sqrt{13}$.
Hence, the centre is $(3, 2)$ *[1 mark]*
and the radius is $\sqrt{13}$. *[1 mark]*

d) The tangent is perpendicular to the radius.
The radius between A $(0, 4)$ and centre $(3, 2)$
has a gradient of: $\frac{y_2 - y_1}{x_2 - x_1} = \frac{2 - 4}{3 - 0} = -\frac{2}{3}$ *[1 mark]*
Using the gradient rule, the tangent at A has a gradient of:
$\frac{-1}{-\frac{2}{3}} = \frac{3}{2}$ *[1 mark]*
Finally use $y - y_1 = m(x - x_1)$ to find the equation of the tangent to the circle at point A:
$y - 4 = \frac{3}{2}(x - 0)$ *[1 mark]*

$y = \frac{3}{2}x + 4$ *[1 mark]*

The tangent is perpendicular to the radius? That sounds like a useful life fact — like how to boil an egg or tie your laces. If you didn't know it, go back to the circles section and learn it...

12 a) To find the coordinates of *A*, solve the two lines as simultaneous equations:
$l_1: x - y + 1 = 0$
$l_2: 2x + y - 8 = 0$
Add the two equations together to get rid of *y*:
$x + 2x + 1 - 8 - y + y = 0$ *[1 mark]*
$3x - 7 = 0$
$x = \frac{7}{3}$ *[1 mark]*

Now put $x = \frac{7}{3}$ back into l_1 to find *y*:
$\frac{7}{3} - y + 1 = 0$
$y = \frac{7}{3} + 1 = \frac{10}{3}$

So *A* is $\left(\frac{7}{3}, \frac{10}{3}\right)$ *[1 mark]*

Still with me? Deep breath... there's a whole lot more geometry a-coming your way...

b) There's a lot of information here, so draw a quick sketch to make things a bit clearer:

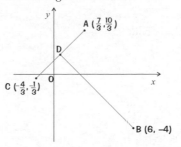

To find the equation of line BD, you need its gradient. But before you can find the gradient, you need to find the coordinates of point *D* — the midpoint of AC. To find the midpoint of two points, find the average of the *x*-values and the average of the *y*-values:
$D = \left(\frac{x_a + x_c}{2}, \frac{y_a + y_c}{2}\right) = \left(\frac{\frac{7}{3} + \frac{-4}{3}}{2}, \frac{\frac{10}{3} + \frac{-1}{3}}{2}\right)$ *[1 mark]*

$D = \left(\frac{1}{2}, \frac{3}{2}\right)$ *[1 mark]*

To find the gradient (*m*) of BD, use this rule: $m_{BD} = \frac{y_D - y_B}{x_D - x_B}$

Gradient $= \frac{\frac{3}{2} - -4}{\frac{1}{2} - 6} = \frac{\frac{3}{2} + \frac{8}{2}}{\frac{1}{2} - \frac{12}{2}} = \frac{3 + 8}{1 - 12} = -1$ *[1 mark]*

Now you can find the equation of BD. Input the known values of *x* and *y* at B $(6, -4)$ and the gradient (-1) into $y = mx + c$, which gives:
$-4 = (-1 \times 6) + c$ *[1 mark]*
$-4 + 6 = c$
$c = 2$

So the equation for BD is $y = -x + 2$ *[1 mark]*

But the question asks for it in the form $ax + by + c = 0$
So rearrange to get: $x + y - 2 = 0$ *[1 mark]*

Line blah, point blah, midpoint blah... it's easy to feel bamboozled when reading a long list of geometry babble, which is why it helps to DRAW A GRAPH. It's up to you, but I know what I'd do...

c) Look at the sketch in part b). To prove triangle ABD is a right-angled triangle, you need to prove that lines AD and BD are perpendicular — in other words, prove the product of their gradients equals -1.

You already know the gradient of BD = -1.
Use the same rule to find the gradient of AD:
$m_{AD} = \frac{y_D - y_A}{x_D - x_A} = \frac{\frac{3}{2} - \frac{10}{3}}{\frac{1}{2} - \frac{7}{3}} = \frac{\frac{9}{6} - \frac{20}{6}}{\frac{3}{6} - \frac{14}{6}} = \frac{9 - 20}{3 - 14} = 1$ *[1 mark]*

$m_{BD} \times m_{AD}$ *[1 mark]*
$= -1 \times 1 = -1$ *[1 mark]*
So triangle ABD is a right-angled triangle.

Oh my giddy goat, we've finished. You'd better go and have a lie down, otherwise all the numbers will fall out of your head and we'd have to start again...

Answers

C2 Section 1 — Logs and Exponentials
Warm-up Questions

1) a) $3^3 = 27$ so $\log_3 27 = 3$

   b) To get fractions you need negative powers
   $3^{-3} = 1/27$
   $\log_3 (1/27) = -3$

   c) Logs are subtracted so divide
   $\log_3 18 - \log_3 2 = \log_3 (18 \div 2)$
   $= \log_3 9$
   $= 2 \;(3^2 = 9)$

2) a) Logs are added so you multiply —
   remember $2 \log 5 = \log 5^2$.
   $\log 3 + 2 \log 5 = \log (3 \times 5^2)$
   $= \log 75$

   b) Logs are subtracted so you divide and the power half means
   square root
   $\frac{1}{2} \log 36 - \log 3 = \log (36^{\frac{1}{2}} \div 3)$
   $= \log (6 \div 3)$
   $= \log 2$

   c) Logs are subtracted so you divide and the power quarter
   means fourth root
   $\log 2 - \frac{1}{4} \log 16 = \log (2 \div 16^{\frac{1}{4}})$
   $= \log (2 \div 2)$
   $= \log 1 = 0$

3) This only looks tricky because of the algebra, just remember
   the laws: $\log_b (x^2 - 1) - \log_b (x - 1) = \log_b \{(x^2 - 1)/(x - 1)\}$
   Then use the difference of two squares:
   $(x^2 - 1) = (x - 1)(x + 1)$ and cancel to get
   $\log_b (x^2 - 1) - \log_b (x - 1) = \log_b (x + 1)$

4) a) Filling in the answers is just a case of using the calculator

x	-3	-2	-1	0	1	2	3
y	0.0156	0.0625	0.25	1	4	16	64

   Check that it agrees with what we know about the graphs.
   It goes through the common point (0, 1), and it follows the
   standard shape.

   b) Then you just need to draw the graph, and use a scale that's
   just right.

   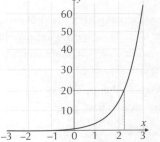

   c) The question tells you to use the graph to get your answer,
   so you'll need to include the construction lines, but check
   the answer with a calculator.

   $x = \log 20 / \log 4 = 2.16$, but you can't justify this accuracy
   if your graph's not up to it, so 2.2 is a good estimate.

5) a) $x = \log_{10} 240 / \log_{10} 10 = \log_{10} 240 = 2.380$

   b) $x = 10^{5.3} = 199526.2... = 200000$ (to 3 s.f.)

   c) $2x + 1 = \log_{10} 1500 = 3.176$, so $2x = 2.176$, so $x = 1.088$

   d) $(x - 1) \log 4 = \log 200$, so $x - 1 = \log 200 / \log 4 = 3.822$,
   so $x = 4.822$

6) First solve for $1.5^P > 1\,000\,000$
   $P \times \log_{10} 1.5 > \log_{10} 1\,000\,000$,
   so $P > (\log_{10} 1\,000\,000) / (\log_{10} 1.5)$, $P > 34.07$.
   We need the next biggest integer, so this will be $P = 35$.

Exam Questions

1 a) $2^x = 9$, so taking logs of both sides gives
   $\log 2^x = \log 9$

   *This is usually the first step in getting x on its own
   — then you can use your trusty log laws...*

   $\Rightarrow x \log 2 = \log 9$
   $\Rightarrow x = \dfrac{\log 9}{\log 2} = 3.17$ to 2 d.p.
   *[3 marks available — 1 mark for taking logs
   of both sides, 1 mark for x log 2 = log 9,
   and 1 mark for correct final answer.]*

   b) $2^{2x} = (2^x)^2$ (from the laws of indices) *[1 mark]*,
   so let $y = 2^x$ and $y^2 = 2^{2x}$. This gives a quadratic in y:
   $y^2 - 13y + 36 = 0$

   Now the big question is — will it factorise? You betcha...

   $(y - 9)(y - 4) = 0$, so $y = 9$ or $y = 4$, that is,
   $\Rightarrow 2^x = 9$ *[1 mark]* or $2^x = 4$ *[1 mark]*

   From a), for $2^x = 9$, $x = 3.17$ to 2 d.p. *[1 mark]*
   and for $2^x = 4$, $x = 2$ (since $2^2 = 4$) *[1 mark]*.

2 $\log_7 (y + 3) + \log_7 (2y + 1) = 1$
   $\Rightarrow \log_7 ((y + 3)(2y + 1)) = 1$

   To remove the $\log_7$, do 7 to the power of each side:
   $(y + 3)(2y + 1) = 7^1 = 7$

   Multiply out, rearrange, and re-factorise:
   $2y^2 + 7y + 3 = 7$
   $\Rightarrow 2y^2 + 7y - 4 = 0$
   $\Rightarrow (2y - 1)(y + 4) = 0$
   $\Rightarrow y = \frac{1}{2}$ or $y = -4$,
   but since $y > 0$, $y = \frac{1}{2}$ is the only solution.

   *[5 marks available — 1 mark for combining the
   two logs, 1 mark for 7 to the power of each
   side, 1 mark for the correct factorisation of the
   quadratic, 1 mark for correct solutions and 1 mark
   for stating that only y = ½ is a valid solution.]*

3 a) $\log_3 x = -\frac{1}{2}$, so do 3 to the power of each side to
   remove the log:
   $x = 3^{-\frac{1}{2}}$ *[1 mark]*
   $\Rightarrow x = \dfrac{1}{3^{\frac{1}{2}}}$ *[1 mark]* $\Rightarrow x = \dfrac{1}{\sqrt{3}}$ *[1 mark]*.

b) $2 \log_3 x = -4$

$\Rightarrow \log_3 x = -2$, and 3 to the power of each side gives:

$x = 3^{-2}$ *[1 mark]*

$\Rightarrow x = \frac{1}{9}$ *[1 mark]*

4 a) $6^{(3x + 2)} = 9$, so taking logs of both sides gives:

$(3x + 2) \log 6 = \log 9$ *[1 mark]*

$\Rightarrow 3x + 2 = \frac{\log 9}{\log 6} = 1.2262...$ *[1 mark]*

$\Rightarrow x = (1.2262... - 2) \div 3 = -0.258$ to 3 s.f. *[1 mark]*

b) $3^{(y^2 - 4)} = 7^{(y + 2)}$, so taking logs of both sides gives:

$(y^2 - 4) \log 3 = (y + 2) \log 7$ *[1 mark]*

$\Rightarrow \frac{(y^2 - 4)}{(y + 2)} = \frac{\log 7}{\log 3} = 1.7712...$ *[1 mark]*

The top of the fraction is a 'difference of two squares' so it will simplify as follows...

$\frac{(y - 2)(y + 2)}{(y + 2)} = 1.7712...$ *[1 mark]*

$\Rightarrow y - 2 = 1.7712...$ *[1 mark]* $\Rightarrow y = 3.77$ to 3 s.f. *[1 mark]*

5 a) $\log_4 p - \log_4 q = \frac{1}{2}$, so using the log laws:

$\log_4 \left(\frac{p}{q}\right) = \frac{1}{2}$

Doing 4 to the power of both sides gives:

$\frac{p}{q} = 4^{\frac{1}{2}} = \sqrt{4} = 2$

$\Rightarrow p = 2q$

[3 marks available — 1 mark for combining the two logs, 1 mark for 4 to the power of each side, 1 mark for the correct final working.]

b) Since $p = 2q$ (from (a)), the equation can be written:

$\log_2 (2q) + \log_2 q = 7$ *[1 mark]*

This simplifies to:

$\log_2 (2q^2) = 7$ *[1 mark]*

Doing 2 to the power of both sides gives:

$2q^2 = 2^7 = 128$ *[1 mark]*

$\Rightarrow q^2 = 64$, $\Rightarrow q = 8$ (since p and q are positive) *[1 mark]*

$p = 2q \Rightarrow p = 16$ *[1 mark]*

6 a) (i) $\log_a 20 - 2 \log_a 2$

$= \log_a 20 - \log_a (2^2)$ *[1 mark]*

$= \log_a (20 \div 2^2)$ *[1 mark]*

$= \log_a 5$ *[1 mark]*

(ii) $\frac{1}{2} \log_a 16 + \frac{1}{3} \log_a 27$

$= \log_a (16^{\frac{1}{2}}) + \log_a (27^{\frac{1}{3}})$ *[1 mark]*

$= \log_a (16^{\frac{1}{2}} \times 27^{\frac{1}{3}})$ *[1 mark]*

$= \log_a (4 \times 3) = \log_a 12$ *[1 mark]*

b) (i) $\log_2 64 = 6$ *[1 mark]* (since $2^6 = 64$)

(ii) $2 \log_3 9 = \log_3 (9^2) = \log_3 81$ *[1 mark]*

$\log_3 81 = 4$ *[1 mark]* (since $3^4 = 81$)

c) (i) $\log_6 25 = \frac{\log 25}{\log 6} = 1.7965$ to 4 d.p. *[1 mark]*

(ii) $\log_3 10 + \log_3 2 = \log_3 (10 \times 2) = \log_3 20$ *[1 mark]*

$\log_3 20 = \frac{\log 20}{\log 3} = 2.7268$ to 4 d.p. *[1 mark]*

7 a)

t	1	2	3	4	5
$\log_{10} p$	1	1.114	1.230	1.380	1.544

[1 mark for all 3 values correct]

b)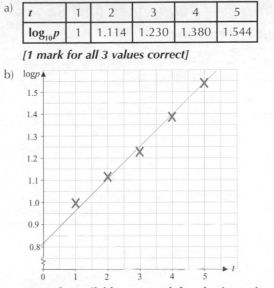

[2 marks available — 1 mark for plotting points correctly, 1 mark for drawing line of best fit]

c) You are given the equation $p = ab^t$. Using the laws of logs, this rearranges to:

$\log p = t \log b + \log a$

Comparing this to $y = mx + c$ shows that the gradient of the graph is equal to $\log b$ *[1 mark]*, and the vertical-axis intercept is equal to $\log a$ *[1 mark]*.

Use gradient $= \frac{y_2 - y_1}{x_2 - x_1}$ with points (x_1, y_1) and (x_2, y_2) chosen from your graph to find $\log b$.

e.g. taking the points (3, 1.25) and (4, 1.40):

gradient $= \frac{1.40 - 1.25}{4 - 3}$ *[1 mark]* $= 0.15$ *[1 mark]*.

So $\log b = 0.15 \Rightarrow b = 1.41$ (2 d.p.) *[1 mark]*.

Now read off your vertical-axis intercept to find $\log a$:

$\log a = 0.82$ *[1 mark]* $\Rightarrow a = 6.61$ (2 d.p.) *[1 mark]*.

Subbing these values into $p = ab^t$ then gives the equation:

$p = 6.61(1.41)^t$ *[1 mark]*.

d) $t = 10 \Rightarrow p = 6.61(1.41)^{10} = 205.30$.

So the author's income will be approximately £ 205 000. *[1 mark]*

Don't worry if your values aren't exactly the same as in this solution. It will depend on the line of best fit you have drawn — everybody's will be slightly different. The examiners have a range of answers which are allowed, so as long as yours are within that range then you'll be fine. If you really struggled with this question then take a look back at page 54 to try and get your head around it all.

Answers

C2 Section 2 — Sequences and Series
Warm-up Questions

1) a) nth term $= 4n - 2$ b) nth term $= 0.5n - 0.3$

   c) nth term $= -3n + 24$ d) nth term $= -6n + 82$

2) First work out n: $a = 5$, $l = 65$, $d = 3$
   so, $65 = 5 + 3(n - 1)$
   so, $n = 21$

   Now use: $S_{21} = 21 \times \dfrac{(5 + 65)}{2}$
   so, $S_{21} = 735$

   They're not gonna hand it to you on a plate — you often have to work out a and d from the question. Luckily it's pretty simple. Phew.

3) a) Common difference $(d) = 4$

   b) 15th term $= 63$ c) $S_{10} = 250$

4) $S_{10} = 205$

5) a) $a = 2$, $r = -3$

   You find r by putting the information you're given into the formula for u_2: $u_2 = u_1 \times r$, so $-6 = 2 \times r \Rightarrow r = -3$.

   10th term, $u_{10} = ar^9$
   $= 2 \times (-3)^9$ $= -39366$

   b) $S_{10} = \dfrac{2(1 - (-3)^{10})}{1 - (-3)} = \dfrac{1 - (-3)^{10}}{2} = -29524$

6) a) $a = 2$, $r = 4$, so $S_{12} = \dfrac{2(4^{12} - 1)}{4 - 1} = 11,184,810$

   b) $a = 30$, $r = \frac{1}{2}$, so $S_{12} = \dfrac{30\left(1 - \left[\frac{1}{2}\right]^{12}\right)}{1 - \frac{1}{2}} = 59.985$ (to 3 d.p.)

7) $a = 2$, $r = 3$
   You need $ar^{n-1} = 1458$, i.e. $2 \times 3^{n-1} = 1458$, i.e. $3^{n-1} = 729$.
   Then, use logs to find that:
   $\log 3^{n-1} = \log 729$
   $(n - 1)\log 3 = \log 729$
   $n - 1 = \dfrac{\log 729}{\log 3}$
   $n - 1 = 6$, i.e. $n = 7$, the 7th term $= 1458$.

   See C2 Section 1 for more on logs.

Exam Questions

1 a) $h_2 = h_{1+1} = 2 \times 5 + 2 = 12$ *[1 mark]*
   $h_3 = h_{2+1} = 2 \times 12 + 2 = 26$ *[1 mark]*
   $h_4 = 2h_3 + 2 = 54$ *[1 mark]*

  b) $\sum\limits_{r=3}^{6} h_r = h_3 + h_4 + h_5 + h_6$
   $h_5 = 2h_4 + 2 = 110$ *[1 mark]*
   $h_6 = 2(110) + 2 = 222$
   so $\sum\limits_{r=3}^{6} h_r = 26 + 54 + 110 + 222$ *[1 mark]*
   $= 412$ *[1 mark]*

   Nothing hard here, just pop the numbers in. Pop, pop, pop...

2 a) $a_2 = 3k + 11$ *[1 mark]*
   $a_3 = 3a_2 + 11$
   $= 3(3k + 11) + 11 = 9k + 33 + 11$
   $= 9k + 44$ *[1 mark]*
   $a_4 = 3a_3 + 11$
   $= 3(9k + 44) + 11$
   $= 27k + 143$ *[1 mark]*

  b) $\sum\limits_{r=1}^{4} a_r = k + (3k + 11) + (9k + 44) + (27k + 143)$
   $= 40k + 198$ *[1 mark]*
   $40k + 198 = 278$
   $40k = 278 - 198 = 80$ *[1 mark]*
   $k = 2$ *[1 mark]*

3 Use the nth term formula: $a_n = a_1 + (n - 1)d$:
   $a + (7 - 1)d = a + 6d$ *[1 mark]*
   You know that $a_7 = 580$ so
   $a + 6d = 580$ *[1 mark]*
   And you know that $S_{15} = 9525$, so using the series formula:
   $S_{15} = \dfrac{15}{2}[2a + (15 - 1)d] = 9525$ *[1 mark]*
   $= \dfrac{15}{2}(2a + 14d) = 9525$, i.e. $15a + 105d = 9525$
   then you can divide everything by 15 to give:
   $a + 7d = 635$ *[1 mark]*
   then solve them simultaneously:
   $(a + 7d) - (a + 6d) = d = 635 - 580$ *[1 mark]*
   $d = 55$ *[1 mark]*
   and finally use this value of d to find a:
   $a + (6 \times 55) = 580$
   $a = 580 - 330$
   $= 250$ *[1 mark]*

   A lot of steps needed for that one, but don't panic if the question seems complicated. If you're stuck, write down all the sequence and series formulas — then see what formulas you can fill in using the info in the question. A light bulb should go 'bing'. Hopefully...

4 a) $a_{31} = 22 + (31 - 1)(-1.1)$ *[1 mark]*
   $= 22 + 30(-1.1)$
   $= 22 - 33 = -11$ *[1 mark]*

  b) $a_k = 0$
   $a_1 + (k - 1)d = 0$
   $22 + (k - 1) \times -1.1 = 0$ *[1 mark]*
   $k - 1 = \dfrac{-22}{-1.1} = \dfrac{220}{11} = 20$
   $k = 20 + 1 = 21$ *[1 mark]*

  c) We want to find the first value of n for which $S_n < 0$.
   Using the formula for sum of a series:
   $S_n = \dfrac{n}{2}[2 \times 22 + (n - 1)(-1.1)] < 0$ *[1 mark]*
   $S_n = \dfrac{n}{2}(44 - 1.1n + 1.1) < 0$
   $\dfrac{n}{2}(45.1 - 1.1n) < 0$ *[1 mark]*
   $\dfrac{n}{2}(45.1 - 1.1n) = 0$
   $\Rightarrow \dfrac{n}{2} = 0$ or $45.1 - 1.1n = 0$
   $\Rightarrow n = 0$ or $n = 41$ *[1 mark]*

265

Answers

The coefficient of n^2 is negative so graph is n-shaped.
Need to find negative part, so $n < 0$ or $n > 41$.
Since n cannot be negative then $n > 41$.
Now we just want the first (i.e. lowest) value of n for which this is true, which is $n = 42$. *[1 mark]*

5 a) $a = 6$
$d = 8$ *[1 mark]*
$a_n = 6 + 8(n - 1)$ *[1 mark]*
$= 8n - 2$ *[1 mark]*

b) $S_{10} = \frac{10}{2}[2 \times 6 + (10 - 1)8]$ *[1 mark]*
$= 5 \times (12 + 72)$ *[1 mark]*
$= 420$ *[1 mark]*

c) First find an expression for S_k:
$S_k = \frac{k}{2}[2 \times 6 + 8(k - 1)]$
$= \frac{k}{2} \times (12 + 8k - 8)$
$= \frac{k}{2}(8k + 4)$ *[1 mark]*
$= \frac{8k^2 + 4k}{2} = 4k^2 + 2k$ *[1 mark]*

Then, you know that the total sum will be less than 2450, because he hadn't yet reached that limit by day k, so:
$4k^2 + 2k < 2450$
$\Rightarrow 2k^2 + k < 1225$
$\Rightarrow 2k^2 + k - 1225 < 0$
$\Rightarrow (2k - 49)(k + 25) < 0$ *[1 mark]*

Don't forget the difference between series and sequences. Part c is about a series — the cumulative sum. So don't use the wrong equations, or you'll get very muddled indeed.

d) Since $(2k - 49)(k + 25) < 0$,
$2k - 49 = 0$ or $k + 25 = 0$
$k = 24.5$ or $k = -25$ *[1 mark]*
Coefficient of k^2 is positive so graph is u-shaped.
Need negative part, so $-25 < k < 24.5$.
k will be the largest whole number that satisfies the inequality, i.e. $k = 24$. *[1 mark]*

6 a) The ratio $= 1.3$, which is > 1, so the sequence is divergent.
[1 mark]

b) $u_3 = 12 \times 1.3^2 = 20.28$ *[1 mark]*
$u_{10} = 12 \times 1.3^9 = 127.25$ *[1 mark]*

7 a) $S_\infty = \frac{a}{1 - r} = \frac{20}{1 - \frac{3}{4}} = \frac{20}{\frac{1}{4}} = 80$
*[2 marks available — 1 mark for formula,
1 mark for correct answer]*

b) $u_{15} = ar^{14} = 20 \times \left(\frac{3}{4}\right)^{14} = 0.356$ (to 3 sig. fig.)
*[2 marks available — 1 mark for formula,
1 mark for correct answer]*

c) Use the formula for the sum of a geometric series to write an expression for S_n:
$S_n = \frac{a(1 - r^n)}{1 - r} = \frac{20\left(1 - \frac{3}{4}^n\right)}{1 - \frac{3}{4}}$ *[1 mark]*

so $\frac{20\left(1 - \frac{3}{4}^n\right)}{1 - \frac{3}{4}} > 79.76$

Now rearrange and use logs to get n on its own:
$\frac{20\left(1 - \frac{3}{4}^n\right)}{1 - \frac{3}{4}} > 79.76 \Rightarrow 20\left(1 - \frac{3}{4}^n\right) > 19.94$
$\Rightarrow 1 - \frac{3}{4}^n > 0.997 \Rightarrow 0.003 > 0.75^n$ *[1 mark]*
$\Rightarrow \log 0.003 > n \log 0.75$ *[1 mark]*
$\Rightarrow \frac{\log 0.003}{\log 0.75} < n$ *[1 mark]*

Bit tricky that last bit. If $x < 1$, then $\log x$ has a negative value — and when dividing by a negative value on either side of an inequality sign you need to change the direction of the inequality.
$\frac{\log 0.003}{\log 0.75} = 20.1929.... $ So $n > 20.1929....$

But n must be an integer, as it is a term not a value, therefore $n = 21$ *[1 mark]*

Don't get too calculator-happy and forget that n will be an integer — you'd have lost that mark if you'd just put 20.1929...

8 a) $u_n = ar^{n-1}$ where $a = 1$ and $r = 1.5$,
so $u_5 = 1 \times (1.5)^4$ *[1 mark]*
$= 5.06$ km to the nearest 10m *[1 mark]*
Make sure you get the ratios right here. If the values increase by 0.5 each time then the ratio is 1.5 — a ratio of 0.5 would decrease the value.

b) $a = 2$ and $r = 1.2$ *[1 mark]*
$u_9 = 2 \times (1.2)^8 = 8.60$ km
$u_{10} = 2 \times (1.2)^9 = 10.32$ km *[1 mark]*
$u_9 < 10$ km and $u_{10} > 10$ km
so day 10 is the first day Chris runs more than 10 km. *[1 mark]*

c) In 10 days, Alex ran a total of 30 km *[1 mark]*
Use the formula for the sum of first n terms: $S_n = \frac{a(1 - r^n)}{1 - r}$.
Chris ran a total of: $\frac{2(1 - 1.2^{10})}{1 - 1.2} = 51.917$ km *[1 mark]*
Heather ran a total of: $\frac{1(1 - 1.5^{10})}{1 - 1.5} = 113.330$ km
[1 mark]

So they raised £$(30 + 51.917 + 113.330)$
$= £195.25$ *[1 mark]*

9 a) $S_\infty = \frac{a}{1 - r}$ and $u_2 = ar$ *[1 mark]*
So $36 = \frac{a}{1 - r}$ i.e. $36 - 36r = a$ *[1 mark]*
and $5 = ar$. *[1 mark]*
Substituting for a gives: $5 = (36 - 36r)r = 36r - 36r^2$
i.e. $36r^2 - 36r + 5 = 0$ *[1 mark]*

b) Factorising gives: $(6r - 1)(6r - 5) = 0$
So $r = \frac{1}{6}$ or $r = \frac{5}{6}$. *[1 mark for each correct value]*
If $r = \frac{1}{6}$ and $ar = 5$ then $\frac{a}{6} = 5$ i.e. $a = 30$
If $r = \frac{5}{6}$ and $ar = 5$ then $\frac{5a}{6} = 5$ i.e. $a = 6$
[1 mark for each correct value]
Keep an eye on what you're being asked to find. Values in a sequence can be any number (oh, the possibilities), but the term positions are always whole numbers. So if you calculate a position and end up with a decimal number... something's not right.

C2 — ANSWERS

Answers

C2 Section 3 — Trigonometry
Warm-up Questions

1) $\cos 30° = \frac{\sqrt{3}}{2}$, $\sin 30° = \frac{1}{2}$, $\tan 30° = \frac{1}{\sqrt{3}}$

$\cos 45° = \frac{1}{\sqrt{2}}$, $\sin 45° = \frac{1}{\sqrt{2}}$, $\tan 45° = 1$

$\cos 60° = \frac{1}{2}$, $\sin 60° = \frac{\sqrt{3}}{2}$, $\tan 60° = \sqrt{3}$

2) Sine Rule: $\frac{x}{\sin X} = \frac{y}{\sin Y} = \frac{z}{\sin Z}$

Cosine Rule: $x^2 = y^2 + z^2 - 2yz\cos X$

Area: $\frac{1}{2}xy\sin Z$

3) $\tan x \equiv \frac{\sin x}{\cos x}$; $\cos^2 x \equiv 1 - \sin^2 x$

4) a) B = 125°, a = 3.66 m, c = 3.10 m, area is 4.64 m²

   b) r = 20.05 km, P = 1.49°, Q = 168.51°

5) Freda's angles are 22.3°, 49.5°, 108.2°

6) One triangle: c = 4.98, C = 72.07°, B = 72.93°
   Other possible triangle: c = 3.22, C = 37.93°, B = 107.07°

7)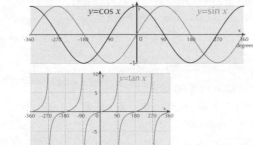

8) a)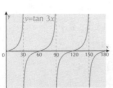

   b)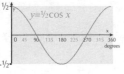

9) a) (i) θ = 240°, 300°.

   (ii) θ = 135°, 315°.

   (iii) θ = 135°, 225°.

   b) (i) θ = 33.0°, 57.0°, 123.0°, 147.0°, –33.0°, –57.0°, –123.0°, –147.0°

   (ii) θ = 8.7°, 81.3°, –98.7°, –171.3°

   (iii) θ = 179.8°

10) x = 70.5°, 120°, 240°, 289.5°.

11) x = –30°

12) $(\sin y + \cos y)^2 + (\cos y - \sin y)^2$
$\equiv (\sin^2 y + 2\sin y\cos y + \cos^2 y) +$
$\quad (\cos^2 y - 2\cos y\sin y + \sin^2 y)$
$\equiv 2(\sin^2 y + \cos^2 y) \equiv 2$

13) $\dfrac{\sin^4 x + \sin^2 x\cos^2 x}{\cos^2 x - 1} \equiv -1$

LHS:

$\dfrac{\sin^2 x(\sin^2 x + \cos^2 x)}{(1 - \sin^2 x) - 1}$

$\equiv \dfrac{\sin^2 x}{-\sin^2 x} \equiv -1 \equiv$ RHS

Exam Questions

1 a) $3 \cos x = 2 \sin x$, and $\tan x = \frac{\sin x}{\cos x}$,

   You need to substitute tan in somewhere, so look at how you can rearrange to get sin/cos in the equation...

   Divide through by cos x to give:

   $3\frac{\cos x}{\cos x} = 2\frac{\sin x}{\cos x}$
   $\Rightarrow 3 = 2 \tan x$

   $\Rightarrow \tan x = \frac{3}{2}$ (or = 1.5).

   [2 marks available — 1 mark for correct substitution of tan x, 1 mark for correct final answer.]

   b) Using tan x = 1.5
   x = 56.3° *[1 mark]*
   and a 2nd solution can be found from
   x = 180° + 56.3° = 236.3° *[1 mark]*.

   Don't forget the other solution! Either use the CAST diagram or sketch a graph to help.

2 a) Using the cosine rule with $\triangle AMC$:
   $a^2 = b^2 + c^2 - 2bc\cos A$
   $2.30^2 = 2.20^2 + 2.20^2 - (2 \times 2.20 \times 2.20 \times \cos\theta)$
   $\cos\theta = \frac{5.29 - 4.84 - 4.84}{-9.68} = 0.4535...$
   $\theta = \cos^{-1} 0.4535... = 1.10$ rad to 3 s.f.

   [2 marks available — 1 mark for correct substitution into cosine rule formula, 1 mark for correct answer in radians.]

   ...or, you could divide it into 2 right-angled triangles and then use: $\theta = 2\sin^{-1}\frac{1.15}{2.20} = 1.10$ rad. Whatever works.

   b) Arc length $S = r\theta = 2.20 \times 1.10$ *[1 mark]*
   = 2.42 m *[1 mark]*.
   Perimeter of slab = 2.42 + 1.5 + 1.5 = 5.42 m
   [1 mark].

   c) Area of slab =
   Area $\triangle ABC$ + Area $\triangle AMC$ – Area sector AMC.

   Area of the triangles can be found using $\frac{1}{2}ab\sin C$.

   Area of sector can be found using $\frac{1}{2}r^2\theta$.

   So area of slab = $\left(\frac{1}{2} \times 1.50 \times 1.50 \times \sin 1.75\right) +$
   $\left(\frac{1}{2} \times 2.20 \times 2.20 \times \sin 1.10\right) - \left(\frac{1}{2} \times 2.20^2 \times 1.10\right)$
   = 1.107 + 2.157 - 2.662 = 0.602 m² to 3 s.f.

   [5 marks available — 1 mark for correct calculation of each of the three shapes, 1 mark for combining the three shapes in the correct way, 1 mark for correct final answer.]

Answers

3 $2 - \sin x = 2\cos^2 x$, and $\cos^2 x = 1 - \sin^2 x$

$\Rightarrow 2 - \sin x = 2(1 - \sin^2 x)$

$\Rightarrow 2 - \sin x = 2 - 2\sin^2 x$

$\Rightarrow 2\sin^2 x - \sin x = 0$

Now simply factorise and all will become clear...

$\sin x(2 \sin x - 1) = 0 \Rightarrow \sin x = 0$ or $\sin x = \frac{1}{2}$.

For $\sin x = 0$, $x = 0$, π and 2π.

For $\sin x = \frac{1}{2}$, $x = \frac{\pi}{6}$ and $\pi - \frac{\pi}{6} = \frac{5\pi}{6}$.

[6 marks available — 1 mark for correct substitution using trig identity, 1 mark for factorising quadratic in sin x, 1 mark for finding correct values of sin x, 1 mark for all three solutions when sin x = 0, 1 mark for each of the other 2 correct solutions.]

4 a) $(1 + 2 \cos x)(3 \tan^2 x - 1) = 0$

$\Rightarrow 1 + 2 \cos x = 0 \Rightarrow \cos x = -\frac{1}{2}$.

OR:

$3 \tan^2 x - 1 = 0 \Rightarrow \tan^2 x = \frac{1}{3} \Rightarrow \tan x = \frac{1}{\sqrt{3}}$ or $-\frac{1}{\sqrt{3}}$.

For $\cos x = -\frac{1}{2}$

$x = \frac{2\pi}{3}$ and $-\frac{2\pi}{3}$.

Drawing the cos x graph helps you find the second one here, and don't forget the limits are $-\pi \le x \le \pi$.

For $\tan x = \frac{1}{\sqrt{3}}$

$x = \frac{\pi}{6}$ and $-\pi + \frac{\pi}{6} = -\frac{5\pi}{6}$.

For $\tan x = -\frac{1}{\sqrt{3}}$

$x = -\frac{\pi}{6}$ and $-\frac{\pi}{6} + \pi = \frac{5\pi}{6}$.

Again, look at the graph of tan x if you're unsure.

[6 marks available — 1 mark for each correct solution.]

b) $3 \cos^2 x = \sin^2 x \Rightarrow 3 = \frac{\sin^2 x}{\cos^2 x}$

$\Rightarrow 3 = \tan^2 x \Rightarrow \tan x = \pm\sqrt{3}$

For $\tan x = \sqrt{3}$, $x = \frac{\pi}{3}$ and $\frac{\pi}{3} - \pi = -\frac{2\pi}{3}$.

For $\tan x = -\sqrt{3}$, $x = -\frac{\pi}{3}$ and $-\frac{\pi}{3} + \pi = \frac{2\pi}{3}$.

[4 marks available — 1 mark for each correct solution.]

5 a) Area of cross-section = $\frac{1}{2}r^2\theta$

$= \frac{1}{2} \times 20^2 \times \frac{\pi}{4} = 50\pi$ cm².

Volume = area of cross-section × height, so

$V = 50\pi \times 10 = 500\pi$ cm³.

[3 marks available — 1 mark for correct use of area formula, 1 mark for 50π, and 1 mark for correct final answer.]

b) Surface area is made up of 2 × cross-sectional area + 2 × side rectangles + 1 curved end rectangle.

Cross-sectional area = 50π (from part a))

Area of each side rectangle = $10 \times 20 = 200$

Area of end rectangle = $10 \times$ arc length

$= 10 \times (20 \times \frac{\pi}{4})$

$= 50\pi$.

$S = (2 \times 50\pi) + (2 \times 200) + 50\pi = (150\pi + 400)$ cm².

[5 marks available — 1 mark for each correct shape area, 1 mark for correct combination, and 1 mark for correct final answer.]

6 a)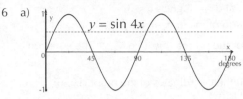

[2 marks available — 1 mark for correct y = sin x graph, 1 mark for 2 repetitions of the sine wave between 0 and 180°.]

b) $\sin 4x = 0.5$

$4x = 30°$

$x = 7.5°$ is one solution. *[1 mark]*

The graph in b) shows there are 4 solutions between 0 and 180°, which, by the symmetry of the graph, lie 7.5° from where the graph cuts the x-axis, as follows:

$x = 45° - 7.5° = 37.5°$. *[1 mark]*

$x = 90° + 7.5° = 97.5°$. *[1 mark]*

$x = 135° - 7.5° = 127.5°$. *[1 mark]*

7 a) Using the cosine rule:

$a^2 = b^2 + c^2 - 2bc\cos A$

If XY is a, then angle $A = 180° - 100° = 80°$.

$XY^2 = 150^2 + 250^2 - (2 \times 150 \times 250 \times \cos 80°)$

$XY^2 = 71976.3867$

$XY = \sqrt{71976.3867} = 268.28$ m (to 2 d.p.)

$= 268$ m to the nearest m.

[2 marks available — 1 mark for correct substitution into cosine rule formula, and 1 mark for correct answer.]

b) Using the sine rule:

$\frac{a}{\sin A} = \frac{b}{\sin B}$, so $\frac{250}{\sin\theta} = \frac{268.2842}{\sin 80°}$ (from part a)).

Rearranging gives:

$\frac{\sin\theta}{\sin 80°} = \frac{250}{268.2842} = 0.93$ to 2 d.p.

[3 marks available — 1 mark for correct substitution into sine rule formula, 1 mark for rearrangement into the correct form, and 1 mark for correct final answer.]

C2 Section 4 — Differentiation
Warm-up Questions

Oh goody, let's get started...

1) a) $\frac{dy}{dx} = 2x$ b) $\frac{dy}{dx} = 4x^3 + \frac{1}{2\sqrt{x}}$

c) $\frac{dy}{dx} = -\frac{14}{x^3} + \frac{3}{2\sqrt{x^3}} + 36x^2$

2) a) $\frac{dy}{dx} = 4x = 8$

b) $\frac{dy}{dx} = 8x - 1 = 15$

c) $\frac{dy}{dx} = 3x^2 - 14x = -16$

3) Differentiate $v = 17t^2 - 10t$ to give: $\frac{dv}{dt} = 34t - 10$

so, when $t = 4$, $\frac{dv}{dt} = 126$ ml/s.

Answers

4) The tangent and normal must go through (16, 6).

Differentiate to find $\frac{dy}{dx} = \frac{3}{2}\sqrt{x} - 3$, so gradient at (16, 6) is 3.

Therefore tangent can be written $y_T = 3x + c_T$;

putting $x = 16$ and $y = 6$ gives $6 = 3 \times 16 + c_T$, so $c_T = -42$,

and the equation of the tangent is $y_T = 3x - 42$.

The gradient of the normal must be $-\frac{1}{3}$, so the equation of

the normal is $y_N = -\frac{1}{3}x + c_N$

Substituting in the coordinates of the point (16, 6)

gives $6 = -\frac{16}{3} + c_N \Rightarrow c_N = \frac{34}{3}$; so the normal is

$y_N = -\frac{1}{3}x + \frac{34}{3} = \frac{1}{3}(34 - x)$.

5) For both curves, when $x = 4$, $y = 2$, so they meet at
(4, 2). Differentiating the first curve gives

$\frac{dy}{dx} = x^2 - 4x - 4$, which at $x = 4$ is equal to –4.

Differentiating the other curve gives $\frac{dy}{dx} = \frac{1}{2\sqrt{x}}$, and so the
gradient at (4, 2) is ¼. If you multiply these two gradients
together you get –1, so the two curves are perpendicular at
$x = 4$.

6) $\frac{dy}{dx} = 3x^2 - \frac{3}{x^2}$; this is zero at (1, 4) and (–1, –4).

$\frac{d^2y}{dx^2} = 6x + \frac{6}{x^3}$; at $x = 1$ this is positive,

so (1, 4) is a minimum; at $x = -1$ this is negative,
so (–1, –4) is a maximum.

7) Maximum is when $\frac{dh}{dm} = 0$.

So, $\frac{m}{5} - \frac{3m^2}{800} = m\left(\frac{1}{5} - \frac{3m}{800}\right) = 0$

Since $m \neq 0$, $\frac{1}{5} - \frac{3m}{800} = 0$

$\Rightarrow \frac{3m}{800} = \frac{1}{5}$

$\Rightarrow m = \frac{800}{15} = 53.3\,\text{g}$ to 3 s.f.

So, $h_{max} = \frac{53.3^2}{10} - \frac{53.3^3}{800} = 94.8\,\text{m}$ to 3 s.f.

8) a) $m = \frac{y_2 - y_1}{x_2 - x_1} = \frac{6 - 2}{4 - 2} = 2$.

b) Take another point on the curve, C, which is closer to A
than B is, then find the gradient of the chord AC.

*Those questions covered the basics of differentiation, so if you got
them all correct, bravely venture into the murky realm of Exam
Questions. If you struggled, have a cuppa to fuel your noggin —
then read the section again until it all makes sense.*

Exam Questions

1 Rewrite the expression in powers of x, so it

becomes $x^{-\frac{1}{2}} + x^{-1}$ *[1 mark]*. Then differentiate to get

$\frac{dy}{dx} = -\frac{1}{2}x^{-\frac{3}{2}} - x^{-2}$ *[1 mark for each correct term]*.

Putting $x = 4$ into the derivative gives:

$-\frac{1}{2}4^{-\frac{3}{2}} - 4^{-2} = -\frac{1}{2}(\sqrt{4})^{-3} - \frac{1}{4^2}$

$= -\frac{1}{2} \cdot \frac{1}{2^3} - \frac{1}{16} = -\frac{1}{2} \cdot \frac{1}{8} - \frac{1}{16}$

$= -\frac{1}{16} - \frac{1}{16} = -\frac{1}{8}$ *[1 method mark, 1 answer mark]*

2 a) Rewrite all the terms as powers of x:

$y = x^7 + \frac{2}{x^3} = x^7 + 2x^{-3}$ *[1 mark]*

and then differentiate each term:

$\frac{dy}{dx} = 7x^6 + (-3)2x^{-4}$

$= 7x^6 - \frac{6}{x^4}$ *[1 mark]*

b) This is a second-order derivative
— just differentiate the answer for part a):

$\frac{d^2y}{dx^2} = \frac{d}{dx}(7x^6 - 6x^{-4})$ *[1 mark]*

$= (7 \times 6)x^5 - (6 \times -4)x^{-5}$

$= 42x^5 + \frac{24}{x^5}$ *[1 mark]*

3 a) $f(2 + h) = (2 + h)^2 + 8 = 4 + 4h + h^2 + 8$

$= h^2 + 4h + 12$ *[1 mark]*.

b) $\frac{f(2 + h) - f(2)}{h} = \frac{(h^2 + 4h + 12) - (2^2 + 8)}{h}$ *[1 mark]*

$= \frac{h^2 + 4h}{h} = h + 4$ *[1 mark]*

c) The gradient is equal to $\underset{h \to 0}{Lim}\frac{f(2 + h) - f(2)}{h} =$

$\underset{h \to 0}{Lim}(h + 4) = 4$.

*[2 marks available — 1 mark for using that the limit as
$h \to 0$ gives the gradient, 1 mark for correct answer].*

4 a) $\frac{dy}{dx} = (3 \times mx^{(3-1)}) - (2 \times x^{(2-1)}) + 8(1 \times x^{(1-1)})$

$= 3mx^2 - 2x + 8$

[1 method mark, 1 answer mark]

b) Rearranging the equation of the line parallel to the normal
gives the equation: $y = 3 - 4x$, so it has a gradient of –4
[1 mark]. The normal also has gradient –4 because it is
parallel to this line *[1 mark]*. The gradient of the tangent is
–1 ÷ the gradient of the normal = –1 ÷ –4 = ¼ *[1 mark]*.

c) (i) So you know that when $x = 5$, the gradient

$3mx^2 - 2x + 8 = \frac{1}{4}$. *[1 mark]*

Now find the value of m:

$m(3 \times 5^2) - (2 \times 5) + 8 = \frac{1}{4}$ *[1 mark]*

$75m - 2 = \frac{1}{4}$

$m = \frac{9}{4} \times \frac{1}{75} = \frac{9}{300} = \frac{3}{100} = 0.03$ *[1 mark]*

(ii) When $x = 5$, then:

$y = \left(\frac{3}{100} \times 5^3\right) - (5^2) + (8 \times 5) + 2$ *[1 mark]*

$= \frac{375}{100} - 25 + 40 + 2$

$= \frac{375}{100} + 17 = \frac{2075}{100}$

$= 20.75$ *[1 mark]*

*They've given you all the information you need, in a funny
roundabout kinda way. Get comfortable figuring out gradients
of normals and tangents and then applying them to curves
— otherwise the exam will be very UNcomfortable. You have
been warned...*

Answers

5 a) $\frac{dy}{dx} = 6x^2 - 8x - 4$

[2 marks for all 3 terms correct or 1 mark for 2 terms.]

b) To find the gradient, put $x = 2$ into the answer to part a):
$6(2^2) - 8(2) - 4 = 24 - 16 - 4 = 4$ ***[1 mark]***.

c) The gradient of the normal is $-1 \div$ the gradient of the
tangent $= -1 \div 4 = -\frac{1}{4}$ ***[1 mark]***. At $x = 2$, the y-value is
$2(2^3) - 4(2^2) - 4(2) + 12 = 16 - 16 - 8 + 12 = 4$ ***[1 mark]***.
Putting these values into the formula $(y - y_1) = m(x - x_1)$
gives $(y - 4) = -\frac{1}{4}(x - 2) \Rightarrow y = -\frac{1}{4}x + \frac{1}{2} + 4 \Rightarrow$
$y = -\frac{1}{4}x + 4\frac{1}{2}$ ***[1 mark]***.

You could also give your answer in the form x + 4y = 18 by
multiplying through by 4 to get rid of the fractions.

6 a) Find the value of x that gives the minimum
value of y — the stationary point of curve y.

Differentiate, and then solve $\frac{dy}{dx} = 0$:

$\frac{dy}{dx} = \frac{1}{\sqrt{x}} - \frac{27}{x^2}$ ***[1 mark for each term]***

$\frac{1}{\sqrt{x}} - \frac{27}{x^2} = 0$ ***[1 mark]*** $\Rightarrow \frac{1}{\sqrt{x}} = \frac{27}{x^2}$

$x^2 \div x^{1/2} = 27 \Rightarrow x^{3/2} = 27$ ***[1 mark]***

$x = \sqrt[3]{27^2} = 9$. ***[1 mark]***

So, 9 miles per hour gives the minimum coal consumption.

b) $\frac{d^2y}{dx^2} = \frac{54}{x^3} - \frac{1}{2\sqrt{x^3}}$ ***[1 mark]***

At the stationary point $x = 9$,

so $\frac{54}{9^3} - \frac{1}{2\sqrt{9^3}} = 0.05555...$ which is positive,

therefore the stationary point is a minimum. ***[1 mark]***

c) $y = 2\sqrt{9} + \frac{27}{9} = 9$ ***[1 mark]***

7 a) $y = 6 + \frac{4x^3 - 15x^2 + 12x}{6} = 6 + \frac{2}{3}x^3 - \frac{5}{2}x^2 + 2x$

$\frac{dy}{dx} = 2x^2 - 5x + 2$

[1 mark for each correct term]

b) Stationary points occur when $2x^2 - 5x + 2 = 0$. ***[1 mark]***
Factorising the equation gives: $(2x - 1)(x - 2) = 0$

So stationary points occur when $x = 2$ ***[1 mark]*** and

$x = \frac{1}{2}$ ***[1 mark]***.
When $x = 2$:

$y = 6 + \frac{4(2^3) - 15(2^2) + (12 \times 2)}{6} = 5\frac{1}{3}$ ***[1 mark]***

When $x = \frac{1}{2}$:

$y = 6 + \frac{4\left(\frac{1}{2}\right)^3 - 15\left(\frac{1}{2}\right)^2 + 12\left(\frac{1}{2}\right)}{6} = 6\frac{11}{24}$ ***[1 mark]***

So coordinates of the stationary points on the
curve are $\left(2, 5\frac{1}{3}\right)$ and $\left(\frac{1}{2}, 6\frac{11}{24}\right)$.

c) Differentiate again to find $\frac{d^2y}{dx^2} = 4x - 5$. ***[1 mark]***

When $x = 2$ this gives $\Rightarrow 4(2) - 5 = 3$, which is positive,

therefore the curve has a minimum at $\left(2, 5\frac{1}{3}\right)$. ***[1 mark]***

When $x = \frac{1}{2}$ this gives $\Rightarrow 4(\frac{1}{2}) - 5 = -3$, which is negative,

so the maximum is at $\left(\frac{1}{2}, 6\frac{11}{24}\right)$. ***[1 mark]***

8 a) First step, multiply out function to get $y = 3x^3 - 8x^2 + 3x + 2$

$\frac{dy}{dx} = 9x^2 - 16x + 3 = 0$ at the stationary point. ***[1 mark]***

Solve using the quadratic formula:

$x = \frac{16 \pm \sqrt{(-16)^2 - (4 \times 9 \times 3)}}{2 \times 9} = \frac{16 \pm 2\sqrt{37}}{18}$

$x = 1.56$ and 0.213 ***[1 mark]***. Substituting these values for
x into the original equation for y gives: $y = -1.40$ and 2.31
So the stationary points have coordinates:
$(1.56, -1.40)$ ***[1 mark]*** and $(0.213, 2.31)$ ***[1 mark]***

b) $\frac{d^2y}{dx^2} = 18x - 16$ ***[1 mark]***

At $x = 1.56$, $\frac{d^2y}{dx^2} = 12.1$ is > 0,

so it's a minimum ***[1 mark]***

At $x = 0.213$, $\frac{d^2y}{dx^2} = -12.2$ is < 0,

so it's a maximum ***[1 mark]***

c) y is a positive cubic function, with stationary points as
found in parts a) and b). The curve crosses the y-axis
when $x = 0$, so $y = 2$ ***[1 mark]***. The initial cubic equation
can be factorised to find where it intersects the x-axis:
$y = (x - 1)(3x^2 - 5x - 2)$
$y = (x - 1)(3x + 1)(x - 2)$
so $y = 0$ when $x = 1, -\frac{1}{3}$ and 2 ***[1 mark]***.

The sketch looks like this:

[1 mark]

$y = 3x^3 - 8x^2 + 3x + 2$

9 a) Surface area $= [2 \times (d \times x)] + \left[2 \times \left(d \times \frac{x}{2}\right)\right] + \left[x \times \frac{x}{2}\right]$

$= 2dx + \frac{2dx}{2} + \frac{x^2}{2}$ ***[1 mark]***

surface area $= 72$ so $3dx + \frac{x^2}{2} = 72$

$\Rightarrow x^2 + 6dx = 144$ ***[1 mark]***

$d = \frac{144 - x^2}{6x}$ ***[1 mark]***

Volume $=$ width $\times$ height $\times$ depth $= \frac{x}{2} \times x \times d$

$= \frac{x^2}{2} \times \frac{144 - x^2}{6x} = \frac{144x^2 - x^4}{12x} = 12x - \frac{x^3}{12}$ ***[1 mark]***

b) Differentiate V and then solve for when $\frac{dV}{dx} = 0$:

$\frac{dV}{dx} = 12 - \frac{x^2}{4}$ ***[1 mark for each correct term]***

$12 - \frac{x^2}{4} = 0$ ***[1 mark]*** $\frac{x^2}{4} = 12$

$x^2 = 48$

$x = \sqrt{48} = 4\sqrt{3}$ m ***[1 mark]***

c) $\frac{d^2V}{dx^2} = -\frac{x}{2}$ ***[1 mark]***

so when $x = 4\sqrt{3}$, $\frac{d^2V}{dx^2} = -2\sqrt{3}$ ***[1 mark]***

$\frac{d^2V}{dx^2}$ is negative, so it's a maximum point. ***[1 mark]***

$x = 4\sqrt{3}$ at V_{max}, so $V_{max} = (12 \times 4\sqrt{3}) - \frac{(4\sqrt{3})^3}{12}$

$V_{max} = 55.4$ m^3 ***[1 mark]***

10 a) Rewrite the expression in powers of x, so it becomes:

$\frac{x^2 + 3x^{\frac{3}{2}}}{x^{\frac{1}{2}}}$ *[1 mark]*

Then divide the top of the fraction by the bottom:

$\frac{x^2}{x^{\frac{1}{2}}} + \frac{3x^{\frac{3}{2}}}{x^{\frac{1}{2}}}$

$= x^{\frac{3}{2}} + 3x$

So $p = \frac{3}{2}$ *[1 mark]* and $q = 1$ *[1 mark]*.

b) Use your answer to part a) to rewrite the equation as:

$y = 3x^3 + 5 + x^{\frac{3}{2}} + 3x$ *[1 mark]*.

Then differentiate each term to give:

$\frac{dy}{dx} = 9x^2 + \frac{3}{2}x^{\frac{1}{2}} + 3$ *[1 mark for each correct term]*.

11 a) $f'(x) = 2x^3 - 3 = 0$ at the stationary point. *[1 mark]*

$2x^3 = 3 \Rightarrow x = 1.145$ *[1 mark]*, which gives:

$y = f(1.145) = \frac{1}{2}(1.145)^4 - 3(1.145) = -2.576$ *[1 mark]*

So coordinates of the stationary point are $(1.145, -2.576)$.

b) $f''(x) = 6x^2$ *[1 mark]* so at the stationary point:

$f''(1.145) = 7.87$, which is positive, so it is a minimum. *[1 mark]*

c) (i) As the stationary point is a minimum, $f'(x) > 0$ to the right of the stationary point. So the function is increasing when $x > 1.145$ *[1 mark]*

(ii) As the stationary point is a minimum, $f'(x) < 0$ to the left of the stationary point. So the function is decreasing when $x < 1.145$ *[1 mark]*

d) Intersects the x-axis when:

$y = \frac{1}{2}x^4 - 3x = 0$

$x(\frac{1}{2}x^3 - 3) = 0$

$\Rightarrow x = 0$

or $x = \sqrt[3]{6} = 1.82$ *[1 mark]*

So the graph looks like this

[1 mark]

C2 Section 5 — Integration
Warm-up Questions

1) a) $2x^5 + C$ **b)** $\frac{3x^2}{2} + \frac{5x^3}{3} + C$ **c)** $\frac{3}{4}x^4 + \frac{2}{3}x^3 + C$

2) Integrating gives $y = 3x^2 - 7x + C$; then substitute $x = 1$ and $y = 0$ to find that $C = 4$. So the equation of the curve is $y = 3x^2 - 7x + 4$.

3) Check whether there are limits to integrate between. If there are, then it's a definite integral; if not, it's an indefinite integral.

4) a) $\int_0^1 (4x^3 + 3x^2 + 2x + 1)dx$

$= [x^4 + x^3 + x^2 + x]_0^1$

$= 4 - 0 = 4$

b) $\int_1^2 \left(\frac{8}{x^5} + \frac{3}{\sqrt{x}}\right)dx = \left[-\frac{2}{x^4} + 6\sqrt{x}\right]_1^2$

$= \left(-\frac{2}{16} + 6\sqrt{2}\right) - (-2 + 6) = -\frac{33}{8} + 6\sqrt{2}$

c) $\int_1^6 \frac{3}{x^2} dx = \left[\frac{-3}{x}\right]_1^6 = -\frac{1}{2} - (-3) = \frac{5}{2}$

5) a) $\int_{-3}^3 (9 - x^2)dx = \left[9x - \frac{x^3}{3}\right]_{-3}^3$

$= 18 - (-18) = 36$

b) $\int_1^\infty \frac{3}{x^2}dx = \left[-\frac{3}{x}\right]_1^\infty$

$= 0 - (-3) = 3$

6) $\int_1^8 y\, dx = \int_1^8 x^{-\frac{1}{3}}dx = \left[\frac{3}{2}x^{\frac{2}{3}}\right]_1^8$

$= \left(\frac{3}{2} \times 8^{\frac{2}{3}}\right) - \left(\frac{3}{2} \times 1^{\frac{2}{3}}\right) = \left(\frac{3}{2} \times 4\right) - \left(\frac{3}{2} \times 1\right) = \frac{9}{2}$

7) a) $h = \frac{(3 - 0)}{3} = 1$

$x_0 = 0$: $y_0 = \sqrt{9} = 3$

$x_1 = 1$: $y_1 = \sqrt{8} = 2.8284$

$x_2 = 2$: $y_2 = \sqrt{5} = 2.2361$

$x_3 = 3$: $y_3 = \sqrt{0} = 0$

$\int_a^b y\, dx \approx \frac{1}{2}[(3 + 0) + 2(2.8284 + 2.2361)]$

$= 6.5645 \approx 6.56$

b) $h = \frac{(1.2 - 0.2)}{5} = 0.2$

$x_0 = 0.2$: $y_0 = 0.2^{0.04} = 0.93765$

$x_1 = 0.4$: $y_1 = 0.4^{0.16} = 0.86363$

$x_2 = 0.6$: $y_2 = 0.6^{0.36} = 0.83202$

$x_3 = 0.8$: $y_3 = 0.8^{0.64} = 0.86692$

$x_4 = 1$: $y_4 = 1^1 = 1$

$x_5 = 1.2$: $y_5 = 1.2^{1.44} = 1.30023$

$\int_a^b y\, dx \approx \frac{0.2}{2}\left[(0.93765 + 1.30023) + 2(0.86363 + 0.83202 + 0.86692 + 1)\right]$

$= 0.1 \times 9.36302 \approx 0.936$

8) a) $A = \int_0^2 (x^3 - 5x^2 + 6x)dx$

$= \left[\frac{x^4}{4} - \frac{5}{3}x^3 + 3x^2\right]_0^2 = \frac{8}{3}$

b) $A = \int_1^4 2\sqrt{x}\, dx = \left[\frac{4}{3}x^{\frac{3}{2}}\right]_1^4 = \frac{28}{3}$

c) $A = \int_0^2 2x^2 dx + \int_2^6 (12 - 2x)dx$

$= \left[\frac{2}{3}x^3\right]_0^2 + [12x - x^2]_2^6$

$= \frac{16}{3} + 16 = \frac{64}{3}$

Instead of integrating $(12 - 2x)$ between 2 and 6, you could have found the area of the triangle with base 4 and height 8.

d) $A = \int_1^4 (x + 3)dx - \int_1^4 (x^2 - 4x + 7)dx$

$= \left[\frac{x^2}{2} + 3x\right]_1^4 - \left[\frac{x^3}{3} - 2x^2 + 7x\right]_1^4$

$= \frac{33}{2} - 12 = \frac{9}{2}$

Answers

Exam Questions

1 a) $f(x) = \dfrac{x^{\frac{1}{2}}}{\frac{1}{2}} + 4x - \dfrac{5x^4}{4} + C$

and then simplify each term further if possible...

$= 2\sqrt{x} + 4x - \dfrac{5x^4}{4} + C$

[3 marks available — 1 mark for each term. Lose 1 mark if C missing or terms not simplified, e.g. ÷½ not converted to ×2. Note — you don't need to put surds in for it to be simplified — indices are fine.]

b) First rewrite everything in terms of powers of x:

$f'(x) = 2x + 3x^{-2}$

Now you can integrate each term (don't forget to add C):

$f(x) = \dfrac{2x^2}{2} + \dfrac{3x^{-1}}{-1} + C$

Then simplify each term:

$f(x) = x^2 - \dfrac{3}{x} + C$

[2 marks available — 1 mark for each term. Lose 1 mark if C missing or terms not simplified.]

c) Following the same process as in part b):

$f'(x) = 6x^2 - \dfrac{1}{3}x^{-\frac{1}{2}}$

$f(x) = \dfrac{6x^3}{3} + \dfrac{1}{3}(x^{\frac{1}{2}} \div \frac{1}{2}) + C$

$f(x) = 2x^3 + \dfrac{2}{3}\sqrt{x} + C$

[2 marks available — 1 mark for each term. Lose 1 mark if C missing or terms not simplified.]

2 To find $f(x)$ you integrate $f'(x)$, but it helps to write all terms in powers of x, so $5\sqrt{x} = 5x^{\frac{1}{2}}$ and $\dfrac{6}{x^2} = 6x^{-2}$ ***[1 mark]***

Now integrate each term:

$\int (2x + 5x^{\frac{1}{2}} + 6x^{-2})dx = \dfrac{2x^2}{2} + \left(5x^{\frac{3}{2}} \div \frac{3}{2}\right) + \left(\dfrac{6x^{-1}}{-1}\right) + C$

$f(x) = x^2 + \dfrac{10\sqrt{x^3}}{3} - \dfrac{6}{x} + C$

[2 marks for correct terms, 1 mark for +C]

You've been given a point on the curve so you can calculate the value of C:

If $y = 7$ when $x = 3$, then

$3^2 - \dfrac{6}{3} + \dfrac{10\sqrt{3^3}}{3} + C = 7$ ***[1 mark]***

$9 - 2 + 10\sqrt{3} + C = 7$

$7 + 10\sqrt{3} + C = 7$

$C = -10\sqrt{3}$

$f(x) = x^2 - \dfrac{6}{x} + \dfrac{10\sqrt{x^3}}{3} - 10\sqrt{3}$ ***[1 mark]***

3 a) Rearrange the terms so each is written as a power of x, showing your working:

$\dfrac{1}{\sqrt{36x}} = \dfrac{1}{\sqrt{36}\sqrt{x}} = \dfrac{1}{6} \times \dfrac{1}{\sqrt{x}} = \dfrac{1}{6}x^{-\frac{1}{2}}$ ***[1 mark]***

$2\left(\sqrt{\dfrac{1}{x^3}}\right) = 2\left(\dfrac{1}{x^3}\right)^{\frac{1}{2}} = 2(x^{-3})^{\frac{1}{2}}$

$= 2(x^{(-3 \times \frac{1}{2})}) = 2x^{-\frac{3}{2}}$ ***[1 mark]***

This shows that $f'(x) = \dfrac{1}{6}x^{-\frac{1}{2}} - 2x^{-\frac{3}{2}}$ — so $A = \dfrac{1}{6}$ and $B = 2$ ***[1 mark]***

b) Integrate $f'(x)$ to find $f(x)$:

$f(x) = \left(\dfrac{1}{6} \times x^{\frac{1}{2}} \div \frac{1}{2}\right) - \left(2x^{-\frac{1}{2}} \div -\frac{1}{2}\right) + C$ ***[1 mark]***

$= \dfrac{1}{3}x^{\frac{1}{2}} + \left(-2 \div -\frac{1}{2}\right)\left(\dfrac{1}{\sqrt{x}}\right) + C$

$= \dfrac{\sqrt{x}}{3} + \dfrac{4}{\sqrt{x}} + C$ ***[1 mark]***

Now use the coordinates (1, 7) to find the value of C:

$7 = \dfrac{\sqrt{1}}{3} + \dfrac{4}{\sqrt{1}} + C$ ***[1 mark]***

$7 - \dfrac{1}{3} - 4 = C$

$C = \dfrac{8}{3}$

So $y = \dfrac{\sqrt{x}}{3} + \dfrac{4}{\sqrt{x}} + \dfrac{8}{3}$ ***[1 mark]***

Well, aren't we having lovely integrating fun. Keep toddling through, and it'll be time for tea and biscuits in no time.

4 a) Multiply out the brackets and simplify the terms:

$(5 + 2\sqrt{x})^2 = (5 + 2\sqrt{x})(5 + 2\sqrt{x})$

$= 25 + 10\sqrt{x} + 10\sqrt{x} + 4x$

$= 25 + 20\sqrt{x} + 4x$

So $a = 25$, $b = 20$ and $c = 4$

[3 marks: one for each constant]

b) Integrate your answer from a), treating each term separately:

$\int (25 + 20\sqrt{x} + 4x)dx = 25x + \left(20x^{\frac{3}{2}} \div \frac{3}{2}\right) + \left(\dfrac{4x^2}{2}\right) + C$

$= 25x + \dfrac{40\sqrt{x^3}}{3} + 2x^2 + C$

[3 marks available — 1 for each term. Lose 1 mark if C missing or answers not simplified (surds not necessary)]

Don't forget to add C, don't forget to add C, don't forget to add C. Once, twice, thrice I beg of you, because it's very important.

5 $\int_2^7 (2x - 6x^2 + \sqrt{x})dx = \left[x^2 - 2x^3 + \dfrac{2\sqrt{x^3}}{3}\right]_2^7$

[1 mark for each correct term]

$= \left(7^2 - (2 \times 7^3) + \dfrac{2\sqrt{7^3}}{3}\right) - \left(2^2 - (2 \times 2^3) + \dfrac{2\sqrt{2^3}}{3}\right)$

[1 mark]

$= -624.6531605 - (-10.11438192)$

$= -614.5387786 = -614.5388$ to 4 d.p. ***[1 mark]***

6 a) The tangent at (1, 2) has the same gradient as the curve at that point, so use $f'(x)$ to calculate the gradient:

$f'(1) = 1^3 - 2$ ***[1 mark]***

$= -1$ ***[1 mark]***

Put this into the straight-line equation $y - y_1 = m(x - x_1)$:

$y - 2 = -1(x - 1)$ ***[1 mark]***

$y = -x + 1 + 2$

$y = -x + 3$ ***[1 mark]***

No need to go off on a tangent here — just find the gradient and then find the equation. Boom. Done. And move swiftly on...

Answers

b) $f(x) = \int \left(x^3 - \frac{2}{x^2}\right)dx = \int (x^3 - 2x^{-2})dx$ *[1 mark]*

$= \frac{x^4}{4} - 2\frac{x^{-1}}{-1} + C = \frac{x^4}{4} + 2x^{-1} + C$ *[1 mark]*

$= \frac{x^4}{4} + \frac{2}{x} + C$

Now use the coordinates (1, 2) to find the value of C:

$2 = \frac{1^4}{4} + \frac{2}{1} + C$ *[1 mark]*

$2 - \frac{1}{4} - 2 = C$

$C = -\frac{1}{4}$ *[1 mark]*

So $f(x) = \frac{x^4}{4} + \frac{2}{x} - \frac{1}{4}$ *[1 mark]*

7 a) (i) $h = \frac{8-2}{3} = 2$ *[1 mark]*

$x_0 = 2\ y_0 = \sqrt{(3 \times 2^3)} + \frac{2}{\sqrt{2}} = 6.31319$

$x_1 = 4\ y_1 = \sqrt{(3 \times 4^3)} + \frac{2}{\sqrt{4}} = 14.85641$

$x_2 = 6\ y_2 = \sqrt{(3 \times 6^3)} + \frac{2}{\sqrt{6}} = 26.27234$

$x_3 = 8\ y_3 = \sqrt{(3 \times 8^3)} + \frac{2}{\sqrt{8}} = 39.89894$ *[1 mark]*

$\int_2^8 y\, dx \approx \frac{2}{2}[6.31319 + 2(14.85641 + 26.27234)$

$+ 39.89894]$ *[1 mark]*

$= 128.46963 \approx 128.47$ to 2 d.p. *[1 mark]*

(ii) $h = \frac{5-1}{4} = 1$ *[1 mark]*

$x_0 = 1\ y_0 = \frac{1^3 - 2}{4} = -0.25$

$x_1 = 2\ y_1 = \frac{2^3 - 2}{4} = 1.5$

$x_2 = 3\ y_2 = \frac{3^3 - 2}{4} = 6.25$

$x_3 = 4\ y_3 = \frac{4^3 - 2}{4} = 15.5$

$x_4 = 5\ y_4 = \frac{5^3 - 2}{4} = 30.75$ *[1 mark]*

$\int_1^5 y\, dx \approx \frac{1}{2}[-0.25 + 2(1.5 + 6.25 + 15.5) + 30.75]$

[1 mark]

$= 38.5$ *[1 mark]*

b) Increase the number of intervals calculated. *[1 mark]*

8 a) Multiply out the brackets in $f'(x)$:

$(x-1)(3x-1) = 3x^2 - x - 3x + 1$

$= 3x^2 - 4x + 1$ *[1 mark]*

Now $f(x) = \int (3x^2 - 4x + 1)dx$

$= \frac{3x^3}{3} - \frac{4x^2}{2} + \frac{x}{1} + C$ *[1 mark]*

$= x^3 - 2x^2 + x + C$ *[1 mark]*

Input the x and y coordinates to find C:

$10 = 3^3 - 2(3^2) + 3 + C$ *[1 mark]*

$10 - 27 + 18 - 3 = C$

$C = -2$ *[1 mark]*

So $f(x) = x^3 - 2x^2 + x - 2$ *[1 mark]*

b) First calculate the gradient of $f(x)$ when $x = 3$:

$f'(3) = 3(3^2) - (4 \times 3) + 1$

$= 27 - 12 + 1$

$= 16$ *[1 mark]*

Use the fact that the tangent gradient multiplied by the normal gradient must equal –1 to find the gradient of the

normal (n): $16 \times n = -1$ therefore $n = -\frac{1}{16}$ *[1 mark]*.

Put n and $P(3, 10)$ into the formula for the equation of a line and rearrange until it's in the form $y = \frac{a-x}{b}$:

$y - 10 = -\frac{1}{16}(x - 3)$ *[1 mark]*

$y = \frac{3}{16} - \frac{x}{16} + 10$

$y = \frac{163 - x}{16}$

So $a = 163$ and $b = 16$. *[1 mark]*

9 $n = 5, h = \frac{4 - 1.5}{5} = 0.5$ *[1 mark]*

$x_1 = 2.0, x_2 = 2.5, x_3 = 3.0$ *[1 mark]*

$y_0 = 2.8182$ *[1 mark]*, $y_3 = 6.1716$ *[1 mark]*,

$y_4 = 7.1364$ *[1 mark]*

$\int_{1.5}^4 y\, dx \approx \frac{0.5}{2}[2.8182 + 2(4 + 5.1216 + 6.1716 + 7.1364) + 8]$

[1 mark] $= 13.91935 = 13.9$ to 3 s.f. *[1 mark]*

10 The limits are the x-values when $y = 0$, so first solve
$(x-3)^2(x+1) = 0$: *[1 mark]*

$(x-3)(x-3)(x+1) = 0$

$x = 3$ *[1 mark]* and $x = -1$ *[1 mark]*

Hence, to find the area, calculate:

$\int_{-1}^3 (x-3)^2(x+1)dx = \int_{-1}^3 (x^3 - 5x^2 + 3x + 9)\, dx$ *[1 mark]*

$= \left[\frac{x^4}{4} - \frac{5}{3}x^3 + \frac{3}{2}x^2 + 9x\right]_{-1}^3$ *[1 mark]*

$= \left(\frac{3^4}{4} - \frac{5}{3}3^3 + \frac{3}{2}3^2 + (9 \times 3)\right) -$

$\left(\frac{(-1)^4}{4} - \left(\frac{5}{3} \times (-1)^3\right) + \left(\frac{3}{2} \times (-1)^2\right) + (9 \times (-1))\right)$ *[1 mark]*

$= 15\frac{3}{4} - -5\frac{7}{12}$ *[1 mark]*

$= 21\frac{1}{3}$ *[1 mark]*

11 a) $m = \frac{y_2 - y_1}{x_2 - x_1} = \frac{0 - -5}{-1 - 4} = -1$ *[1 mark]*

$y - y_1 = m(x - x_1)$

$y - -5 = -1(x - 4)$ so $y + 5 = 4 - x$

$y = -x - 1$ *[1 mark]*

b) Multiply out the brackets and then integrate:

$(x+1)(x-5) = x^2 - 4x - 5$ *[1 mark]*

$\int_{-1}^4 (x^2 - 4x - 5)\, dx = \left[\frac{x^3}{3} - 2x^2 - 5x\right]_{-1}^4$ *[1 mark]*

$= \left(\frac{4^3}{3} - 2(4^2) - (5 \times 4)\right)$

$- \left(\frac{(-1)^3}{3} - 2(-1)^2 - (5 \times -1)\right)$ *[1 mark]*

$= -30\frac{2}{3} - 2\frac{2}{3}$ *[1 mark]* $= -33\frac{1}{3}$ *[1 mark]*

c) Subtract the area under the curve from the area under the line to leave the area in between. The area under the line is a triangle (where $b = 5$ and $h = -5$), so use the formula for the area of a triangle to calculate it *[1 mark]*:

$A = \frac{1}{2}bh = \frac{1}{2} \times 5 \times -5 = -12.5$ *[1 mark]*

$A = -12\frac{1}{2} - -33\frac{1}{3}$ *[1 mark]*

$= 20\frac{5}{6}$ *[1 mark]*

Answers

C2 — Practice Exam One

1 a) Consider the following triangle:

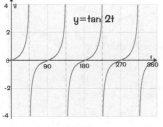

You are given that $\cos\theta = \frac{\sqrt{3}}{2}$, which, using trigonometry, means that $\frac{\text{Adj.}}{\text{Hyp.}} = \frac{\sqrt{3}}{2}$, and so Adj. $= \sqrt{3}$ and Hyp $= 2$:

[1 mark]

Now using Pythagoras:

Opp. $= \sqrt{2^2 - (\sqrt{3}^2)} = \sqrt{4-3} = 1$. So:

[1 mark]

And so $\sin\theta = \frac{\text{Opp.}}{\text{Hyp.}} = \frac{1}{2}$ *[1 mark]*

b) Using the triangle from part a):

$\tan\theta = \frac{\text{Opp.}}{\text{Adj.}} = \frac{1}{\sqrt{3}}$ *[1 mark]*

2 Differentiate the function to find the gradient:

$y = \sqrt{x} - \frac{1}{x^3} = x^{\frac{1}{2}} - x^{-3}$ *[1 mark]*

$\frac{dy}{dx} = \frac{1}{2}x^{-\frac{1}{2}} + 3x^{-4}$ *[1 mark]*

Plug in $x = 1$: $\frac{dy}{dx} = \frac{1}{2}(1)^{-\frac{1}{2}} + 3(1)^{-4} = \frac{1}{2} + 3 = \frac{7}{2}$

[1 mark]

3 a) In the laws of logs: $\log_a a = 1$. So $\log_3 3 = 1$. *[1 mark]*

b) Use the laws of logs to rewrite the expression:

$\log_a 4 + 3\log_a 2 = \log_a(4 \times 2^3) = \log_a 32$. *[1 mark]*

Therefore $\log_a x = \log_a 32$ so $x = 32$. *[1 mark]*

4 a) The graph of $y = \tan 2t$ is going to be the same shape as $\tan x$, but squashed horizontally by a factor of 2. So the graph will be periodic with a period of $90°$ instead of $180°$.

$y = \tan 2t$

[2 marks available — 1 mark for shape, 1 mark for 90° period.]

b) Using $\tan = \frac{\sin}{\cos}$:

$\sin 2t = \sqrt{2}\cos 2t \Rightarrow \tan 2t = \sqrt{2}$ *[1 mark]*

$2t = \tan^{-1}\sqrt{2} = 54.7356...$

$t = 27.37°$ (to 2 d.p.) *[1 mark]*

That's only one solution, but you can see from the graph in part a) that there's got to be four. You also know from part a) that

the graph repeats every 90°, so just add 90° on three times to get the other answers:

$t = 117.37°, 207.37°$ and $297.37°$ *[1 mark]*

5 Use the trig identity $\tan\theta \equiv \frac{\sin\theta}{\cos\theta}$:

$\tan^2\theta + \frac{\tan\theta}{\cos\theta} = 1 \Rightarrow \frac{\sin^2\theta}{\cos^2\theta} + \frac{\sin\theta}{\cos^2\theta} = 1$ *[1 mark]*

Put over a common denominator: $\frac{\sin^2\theta + \sin\theta}{\cos^2\theta} = 1$

$\Rightarrow \sin^2\theta + \sin\theta = \cos^2\theta$

Now use the identity $\cos^2\theta \equiv 1 - \sin^2\theta$ to give:

$\sin^2\theta + \sin\theta = 1 - \sin^2\theta$ *[1 mark]*

$\Rightarrow 2\sin^2\theta + \sin\theta - 1 = 0$ *[1 mark]*.

6 $\int_1^4 (3x^2 + \sqrt{x})dx = \int_1^4 (3x^2 + x^{\frac{1}{2}})dx$

$= \left[x^3 + \frac{2}{3}x^{\frac{3}{2}}\right]_1^4$ *[1 mark]*

$= \left(4^3 + \frac{2}{3}(4)^{\frac{3}{2}}\right) - \left(1 + \frac{2}{3}\right)$ *[1 mark]*

$= 67\frac{2}{3}$ *[1 mark]*.

7 a) Look up the trapezium formula in the nice formula booklet they give you:

$\int_a^b y\, dx \approx \frac{h}{2}[y_0 + y_n + 2(y_1 + y_2 + ...y_{n-1})]$

and remember that n is the number of intervals (in this case 4), and h is the width of each strip:

$h = \frac{b-a}{n} = \frac{2-0}{4} = 0.5$ *[1 mark]*

Work out each y value:

$x_0 = 0$ $y_0 = 2^{0^2} = 2^0 = 1$

$x_1 = 0.5$ $y_1 = 2^{0.5^2} = 2^{0.25} = 1.189$ (3 d.p.)

$x_2 = 1$ $y_2 = 2^{1^2} = 2^1 = 2$

$x_3 = 1.5$ $y_3 = 2^{1.5^2} = 2^{2.25} = 4.757$ (3 d.p)

$x_4 = 2$ $y_4 = 2^{2^2} = 2^4 = 16$ *[1 mark]*

And put all these values into the formula:

$\int_0^2 2^{x^2} dx \approx \frac{0.5}{2}[1 + 16 + 2(1.189 + 2 + 4.757)]$ *[1 mark]*

$= \frac{1}{4}(17 + 15.892)$

$= 8.22$ (3 s.f.) *[1 mark]*

b) Look at the diagram of the curve — it's U-shaped. A trapezium on each strip goes higher than the curve and so has a greater area than that under the curve. So the trapezium rule gives an overestimate for the area. *[1 mark]*

8 a) $f(x + h) = (x + h)^2 - 1$

$= x^2 + 2hx + h^2$

So $\frac{f(x+h) - f(x)}{h} = \frac{x^2 + 2hx + h^2 - 1 - x^2 + 1}{h}$ *[1 mark]*

$= \frac{2hx + h^2}{h} = 2x + h$ *[1 mark]*

b) The gradient at $x = 2$ is given by:

$\lim_{h \to 0}\left(\frac{f(2+h) - f(2)}{h}\right)$ *[1 mark]*

$= \lim_{h \to 0}(2(2) + h) = \lim_{h \to 0}(4 + h)$ *[1 mark]*

$= 4 + 0 = 4$ *[1 mark]*.

9 a) Use the formula for the sum to infinity of a series,
$$S_\infty = \frac{a}{1-r}.$$
You are told that the sum to infinity is 10 times the first term, so:
$$10a = \frac{a}{1-r}$$
$$10 = \frac{1}{1-r}$$
$$10 - 10r = 1$$
$$10r = 9$$
$$\Rightarrow r = 0.9$$
[3 marks available — 1 mark for correct use of formula, 1 mark for correct working, 1 mark for final answer]

b) Now use the formula for the nth term of a series, $u_n = ar^{n-1}$. You are told that the third term is 81, so:
$$u_3 = ar^{3-1}$$
$$\Rightarrow 81 = ar^2 \text{ [1 mark]}$$
$$81 = a \times 0.9^2$$
$$a = 81 \div 0.9^2 = 100 \text{ [1 mark].}$$

10 a) The curve and the line intersect where:
$$x^2 - 4x + 6 = -x + 4$$
Rearrange and factorise:
$$x^2 - 3x + 2 = 0$$
$$(x - 1)(x - 2) = 0$$
$$\Rightarrow x = 1 \text{ and } x = 2$$
To find the y-coordinates, put the x-values in $y = -x + 4$:
when $x = 1$, $y = -1 + 4 = 3$
when $x = 2$, $y = -2 + 4 = 2$
so the two points of intersection are $(1, 3)$ and $(2, 2)$.

[5 marks available — 1 mark for forming quadratic, 1 mark for each x-value, 1 mark for each y-value]

b)
$$\int_1^2 (x^2 - 4x + 6)dx = \left[\frac{x^3}{3} - 2x^2 + 6x\right]_1^2$$
$$= \left(\frac{8}{3} - 8 + 12\right) - \left(\frac{1}{3} - 2 + 6\right)$$
$$= \frac{7}{3}$$

[3 marks available — 1 mark for all terms integrated correctly, 1 mark for correctly substituting in limits, 1 mark for correct final answer]

c) The shaded area is equal to the area under the line $y = -x + 4$ between $x = 1$ and $x = 2$ minus the area under the curve $y = x^2 - 4x + 6$ between $x = 1$ and $x = 2$. The area under the line $y = -x + 4$ is the area of the trapezium:

This area is given by: $\left(\frac{2+3}{2}\right) \times 1$ *[1 mark]* $= \frac{5}{2}$ *[1 mark]*.

So the required area is equal to:
$\frac{5}{2} - \frac{7}{3}$ *[1 mark]* $= \frac{15}{6} - \frac{14}{6} = \frac{1}{6}$ *[1 mark]*.

11 a) x is the adjacent side of a right-angled triangle with an angle θ and hypotenuse r — so use the cos formula:
$$\cos \theta = \frac{\text{adjacent}}{\text{hypotenuse}} = \frac{x}{r}$$
and so $x = r \cos \theta$

Similarly, as the stage is symmetrical, using the sine formula:
$$\sin \theta = \frac{\text{opposite}}{\text{hypotenuse}} = \frac{y}{r}$$
and so $y = r \sin \theta$
[1 mark]

b) Looking at the diagram, most of the perimeter is simple — $q + q + 2r$. But the top and curved lengths need a bit of thinking.
First the top length — you can see this is $2x$ so, using the expression for x found in a), you can write this as $2r \cos \theta$.
For the curved lengths — the shaded areas are sectors of circles, and the formula for the length of one arc is given by: $r\theta$

Now add them all up to get the total perimeter:
$q + q + 2r + 2r\cos \theta + r\theta + r\theta = 2[q + r(1 + \theta + \cos \theta)]$.

And do the same sort of thing for the area — break it down into a rectangle, a triangle and two sectors:
Area of rectangle = width × height = $2qr$

Area of triangle = $\frac{1}{2} \times$ width × height $= \frac{1}{2}(2r\cos \theta)(r\sin \theta)$
$$= r^2 \cos \theta \sin \theta$$

Area of 1 shaded sector = $\frac{1}{2}r^2\theta$

So the total area = $2qr + r^2\cos \theta \sin \theta + r^2\theta$
$$= 2qr + r^2(\cos \theta \sin \theta + \theta).$$

[4 marks available — 1 mark for all individual lengths correct, 1 mark for all individual areas correct, 1 mark for each correct expression.]

Crumbs, that looked very intimidating. The best thing to do with questions like that is stay calm and break them into small chunks. And knowing all the formulas doesn't hurt...

c) Substitute the given values of P and θ into the equation for the perimeter: $P = 2[q + r(1 + \theta + \cos \theta)]$
$$\Rightarrow 40 = 2\left[q + r\left(1 + \frac{\pi}{3} + \cos \frac{\pi}{3}\right)\right]$$
$$\Rightarrow 20 = q + r\left(\frac{3}{2} + \frac{\pi}{3}\right) \text{ [1 mark]}$$
And then into the equation for the area:
$A = 2qr + r^2(\cos \theta \sin \theta + \theta)$
$$\Rightarrow A = 2qr + r^2\left(\cos \frac{\pi}{3}\sin \frac{\pi}{3} + \frac{\pi}{3}\right)$$
$$= 2qr + r^2\left(\frac{\sqrt{3}}{4} + \frac{\pi}{3}\right) \text{ [1 mark]}$$
To rearrange this formula for area into the form shown in the question, you need to get rid of q. Rearrange the perimeter formula to get an expression for q in terms of r, then substitute that into the area equation:

$q = 20 - r\left(\frac{3}{2} + \frac{\pi}{3}\right)$

$A = 2qr + r^2\left(\frac{\sqrt{3}}{4} + \frac{\pi}{3}\right)$

$\quad = 2r\left[20 - r\left(\frac{3}{2} + \frac{\pi}{3}\right)\right] + r^2\left(\frac{\sqrt{3}}{4} + \frac{\pi}{3}\right)$

$\quad = 40r - 2r^2\left(\frac{3}{2} + \frac{\pi}{3}\right) + r^2\left(\frac{\sqrt{3}}{4} + \frac{\pi}{3}\right)$

$\quad = 40r - r^2\left[2\left(\frac{3}{2} + \frac{\pi}{3}\right) - \left(\frac{\sqrt{3}}{4} + \frac{\pi}{3}\right)\right]$ **[1 mark]**

And since $\left[2\left(\frac{3}{2} + \frac{\pi}{3}\right) - \left(\frac{\sqrt{3}}{4} + \frac{\pi}{3}\right)\right] = 3.614$ to 3 d.p.

this means: $A = 40r - 3.614r^2$ **[1 mark]**

d) Plug $A = 12$ into your equation from c):

$12 = 40r - 3.614r^2$

$3.614r^2 - 40r + 12 = 0$

Use the quadratic formula to solve for r:

$r = \dfrac{40 \pm \sqrt{(-40)^2 - (4 \times 3.614 \times 12)}}{2 \times 3.614}$ **[1 mark]**

$r = \dfrac{40 \pm 37.76...}{7.228}$

So $r = 10.8$ m **[1 mark]** or $r = 0.309$ m **[1 mark]**.

12 a) $y = ab^t$

Taking logs of both sides:

$\log y = \log ab^t$

Then using laws of logs:

$\log y = \log a + \log b^t$ **[1 mark]**

$\log y = \log a + t\log b$ **[1 mark]**

or: $\log y = t\log b + \log a$, as required.

b)

t	1	2	3	4	5
$\log_{10} y$	0	0.301	0.602	0.903	1.146

[1 mark]

c)

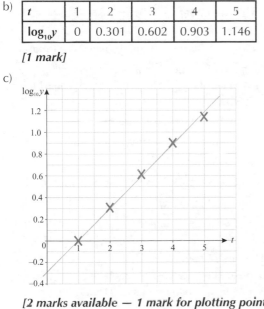

[2 marks available — 1 mark for plotting points correctly, 1 mark for drawing line of best fit.]

d) Comparing $\log y = t\log b + \log a$ to $y = mx + c$ gives that $\log b = m$, the gradient of the graph, and $\log a = c$, the vertical-axis intercept of the graph.

Use points from your graph to calculate the gradient, m:

For example, using the points (2, 0.3) and (1, 0):

$m = \dfrac{y_2 - y_1}{x_2 - x_1} = \dfrac{0.3 - 0}{2 - 1} = 0.3$ **[1 mark]**

So $\log b = 0.3 \Rightarrow b = 2.0$ (2 s.f.) **[1 mark]**

Now estimate the vertical-axis intercept to find $\log a$:

$\log a = -0.29$ **[1 mark]** $\Rightarrow a = 0.51$ (2 s.f.) **[1 mark]**.

Don't worry if your values of a and b are slightly different to this — it depends on your line of best fit. They should be pretty similar to the values given here though.

e) From part d), the equation describing the increase in attendance is $y = 0.51(2.0)^t$.

y is the average attendance in hundreds, so an attendance of 5000 gives a y-value of $y = 50$. Use your equation to find the corresponding t-value:

$50 = 0.51(2.0)^t$ **[1 mark]**

$98.039... = 2.0^t$

$\log(98.039...) = \log(2.0^t)$

$\log(98.039...) = t\log(2.0)$

$t = \log(98.039...) \div \log(2.0) = 6.615...$ **[1 mark]**

So the attendance reaches 5000 in the seventh year after the 2004/05 season, i.e. the 2011/12 season **[1 mark]**.

That was fun.

C2 — Practice Exam Two

1 To convert degrees to radians, divide by 180° and multiply by π: **[1 mark]**

$\dfrac{225°}{180°} \times \pi = \dfrac{5}{4}\pi$ **[1 mark]**.

2 Differentiating $f(x)$ gives:

$f'(x) = 2x - 3$ **[1 mark]**

Then $f(x)$ is increasing when $f'(x) > 0$.

i.e. $2x - 3 > 0$ **[1 mark]**

$2x > 3$

$x > 1.5$

So $f(x)$ is increasing for $x > 1.5$ **[1 mark]**.

3 a) $a^1 = a$, so $\log_a a = 1$. **[1 mark]**

b) Take logs of both sides and use laws of logs:

$\log 4^{(2x+1)} = \log 9$ **[1 mark]**

$\Rightarrow (2x + 1)\log 4 = \log 9$ **[1 mark]**

$\Rightarrow 2x + 1 = \log 9 \div \log 4$

$\Rightarrow x = \dfrac{1}{2}\left(\dfrac{\log 9}{\log 4} - 1\right) = 0.292$ (3 s.f.) **[1 mark]**

4 The graph of $y = \sin x$ is mapped onto the graph of $y = \sin\frac{x}{2}$ via a stretch parallel to the x-axis of scale factor 2.

The graph should appear as follows:

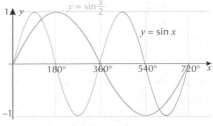

[3 marks available — 1 mark for sin x correct, 1 mark for sin $\frac{x}{2}$ correct, 1 mark for correct axis labelling]

Answers

5 a) Use the formula for sector area:

Area $= \frac{1}{2}r^2\theta = \frac{1}{2} \times (4)^2 \times 0.2$ *[1 mark]*

$= 1.6$ cm^2 *[1 mark]*.

b) Use the formula for arc length:

Arc length $= r\theta = 4 \times 0.2$ *[1 mark]*

$= 0.8$ cm *[1 mark]*

So the perimeter of the whole sector is:

$4 + 4 + 0.8 = 8.8$ cm *[1 mark]*.

6 Integrate $\frac{dy}{dx} = x^{-2} + 2x^{-\frac{1}{3}} + 1$ to find y:

$y = -x^{-1} + 3x^{\frac{2}{3}} + x + C$.

Plug in $x = 1$, $y = 3$ to find C:

$3 = -(1)^{-1} + 3(1)^{\frac{2}{3}} + 1 + C$

$3 = -1 + 3 + 1 + C$

$\Rightarrow C = 0$

So the equation of the curve is $y = -\frac{1}{x} + 3x^{\frac{2}{3}} + x$.

[5 marks available — 1 mark for correctly integrating 1 term, 1 mark for correctly integrating all terms, 1 mark for substituting in x and y values to find C, 1 mark for finding C, 1 mark for correct final answer.]

7 You are given that 15 and 19 are consecutive terms, so the common difference, $d = 19 - 15 = 4$ *[1 mark]*.

Use $u_n = a + (n-1)d$ to find a:

$u_4 = 15 = a + (3 \times 4)$

$\Rightarrow a = 15 - 12 = 3$ *[1 mark]*.

Now use $S_n = \frac{n}{2}(2a + (n-1)d)$ to find the sum of the first ten terms:

$S_{10} = 5(6 + [9 \times 4])$ *[1 mark]* $= 210$ *[1 mark]*.

8 a) Use the cosine rule: $a^2 = b^2 + c^2 - 2bc \cos A$, where $b = 10$, $c = 7$ and angle A $= 60°$:

$a^2 = 10^2 + 7^2 - 2 \times 10 \times 7 \times \cos 60°$ *[1 mark]*

$\Rightarrow a^2 = 149 - 140 \cos 60°$

$\Rightarrow a^2 = 149 - 140(0.5)$

$\Rightarrow a^2 = 79$

$\Rightarrow a = \sqrt{79} = 8.89$ cm to 3 s.f. *[1 mark]*

b) Now you can use the sine rule to find the angles:

$\frac{a}{\sin A} = \frac{b}{\sin B} = \frac{c}{\sin C}$

θ is the angle opposite the 10 cm side. So if we call the 10 cm side 'side b', then $\theta =$ angle B. Putting the known values into the sine rule gives:

$\frac{\sqrt{79}}{\sin 60°} = \frac{10}{\sin \theta}$ *[1 mark]*

$\sin \theta = \frac{10 \times \sin 60°}{\sqrt{79}} = 0.9744$

$\Rightarrow \theta = \sin^{-1}0.9744 = 77.0°$ to 3 s.f. *[1 mark]*

Now, you know 2 of the angles in the triangle, and as the angles in a triangle add up to 180°,

$\phi = 180 - 60 - 77 = 43°$ *[1 mark]*.

To summarise: $\theta = 77°$ and $\phi = 43°$.

9 a) Use the formula:

$\int_a^b y\, dx \approx \frac{h}{2}[y_0 + y_n + 2(y_1 + y_2 + ...y_{n-1})]$

Remember that n is the number of strips (in this case 3), and h is the width of each strip:

$h = \frac{b-a}{n} = \frac{3-0}{3} = 1$ *[1 mark]*

Work out each y value:

$x_0 = 0 \qquad y_0 = \sqrt{(3+0)} = \sqrt{3} = 1.732$ (3 d.p.)

$x_1 = 1 \qquad y_1 = \sqrt{(3+1)} = \sqrt{4} = 2$

$x_2 = 2 \qquad y_2 = \sqrt{(3+4)} = \sqrt{7} = 2.646$ (3 d.p.)

$x_3 = 3 \qquad y_3 = \sqrt{(3+9)} = \sqrt{12} = 3.464$ (3 d.p.) *[1 mark]*

And put all these values into the formula:

$\int_0^2 \sqrt{3+x^2}\, dx \approx \frac{1}{2}[1.732 + 3.464 + 2(2 + 2.646)]$ *[1 mark]*

$= 7.24$ (3 s.f.) *[1 mark]*

b) Improve your estimate by using more strips / more ordinates. *[1 mark]*

10 a) Arc length $= r\theta$, so the arc length of the sector $= 0.5r$ *[1 mark]*.

The perimeter of the sector is then $0.5r + 2r = 2.5r = \frac{5}{2}r$ *[1 mark]*

Sector area $= \frac{1}{2}r^2\theta = \frac{1}{2} \times r^2 \times 0.5 = \frac{1}{4}r^2$ *[1 mark]*.

The area and perimeter are equal, so:

$\frac{5}{2}r = \frac{1}{4}r^2$ *[1 mark]*. Multiply throughout by 4 to get:

$10r = r^2$

$r^2 - 10r = 0$

$r(r - 10) = 0$ *[1 mark]*

$\Rightarrow r = 0$ or $r = 10$.

r is a radius, so assume $r > 0$, and so $r = 10$ *[1 mark]*.

b) (i) Use the cosine rule, $a^2 = b^2 + c^2 - 2bc\cos A$:

$x^2 = 10^2 + 10^2 - (2 \times 10 \times 10)\cos 0.5$ *[1 mark]*

$x^2 = 24.48$

$\Rightarrow x = 4.95$ cm (3 s.f.) *[1 mark]*

(ii) Use the formula for the area of a triangle,

Area $= \frac{1}{2}ab\sin C$:

Area of $OAB = (\frac{1}{2} \times 10 \times 10)\sin 0.5$ *[1 mark]*

$= 23.97$ cm^2 *[1 mark]*.

Area of sector from part a) $= \frac{1}{2}r^2\theta = \frac{1}{2} \times 10^2 \times 0.5$ *[1 mark]*

$= 25$ cm^2 *[1 mark]*.

So the area of the shaded region is:

$25 - 23.97 = 1.03$ cm^2 (3 s.f.) *[1 mark]*.

11 a)

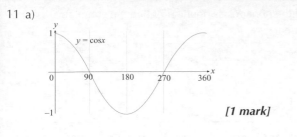

[1 mark]

b) Remember that $\sin^2 x + \cos^2 x \equiv 1$, so with a little rearranging you can replace the $\sin^2$ with a $1 - \cos^2$:

$2[1 - \cos^2 x] = 1 + \cos x$ *[1 mark]*

Now multiply out the bracket and rearrange:

$2[1 - \cos^2 x] = 1 + \cos x$
$\Rightarrow 2 - 2\cos^2 x = 1 + \cos x$ *[1 mark]*
$\Rightarrow 2\cos^2 x + \cos x - 1 = 0$ *[1 mark]*

c) $2\cos^2 x + \cos x - 1 = 0$ factorises to give:
$(2\cos x - 1)(\cos x + 1) = 0$

so $\cos x = \frac{1}{2}$ or $\cos x = -1$ *[1 mark]*

By taking the inverse cosine of these you get:

$x = \cos^{-1}\left(\frac{1}{2}\right) = 60°$ *[1 mark]*
$x = \cos^{-1}(-1) = 180°$ *[1 mark]*

The graph from part a) shows there are three possible solutions, as the curve intersects the line $y = \frac{1}{2}$ twice.

The other solution is $x = 360° - 60° = 300°$. *[1 mark]*
So the three solutions are:
$x = 60°$, $x = 180°$ and $x = 300°$.

d) (i) The graph is 'stretched' parallel to the y-axis with scale factor $\frac{1}{2}$. i.e. it's 'squashed' rather than stretched.

[2 marks available — 1 mark for stretch,
1 mark for scale factor $\frac{1}{2}$.]

(ii)

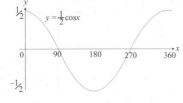

[1 mark]

12 a) Here's the prism again:

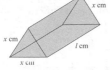

The volume of a triangular prism is given by:
Volume = Area of triangle × Length of prism

The area of the triangle can be found using Area = $\frac{1}{2}ab\sin C$
The triangle is equilateral, so $C = 60°$, and so:

Area = $\frac{1}{2} \times x \times x \times \sin 60° = \frac{\sqrt{3}}{4}x^2$.

So volume = $\frac{\sqrt{3}}{4}x^2 l$ *[1 mark]*

You are given that the volume is $60\sqrt{3}$, so:

$60\sqrt{3} = \frac{\sqrt{3}}{4}x^2 l$ *[1 mark]*

$240 = x^2 l$

$\Rightarrow l = \frac{240}{x^2}$ *[1 mark]*.

b) The prism is made up of two triangular faces of side x cm and three rectangular faces of area $(x \times l)$ cm^2, so its surface area is given by:

$A = 2\left(\frac{1}{2} \times x \times \frac{\sqrt{3}}{2}x\right) + 3\left(\frac{240}{x^2} \times x\right)$ *[1 mark]*

$= \frac{\sqrt{3}}{2}x^2 + \frac{720}{x}$, as required. *[1 mark]*

c) Differentiate to find stationary points:

$\frac{dA}{dx} = \sqrt{3}x - \frac{720}{x^2}$ *[1 mark]*

$\sqrt{3}x - \frac{720}{x^2} = 0 \Rightarrow \sqrt{3}x = \frac{720}{x^2}$

$x^3 = \frac{720}{\sqrt{3}}$

So $x = 7.46$ (3 s.f.) *[1 mark]*.

d) Differentiate again:

$\frac{d^2 A}{dx^2} = \sqrt{3} + \frac{1440}{x^3}$ *[1 mark]*

Plug in $x^3 = \frac{720}{\sqrt{3}}$ from part c):

$\frac{d^2 A}{dx^2} = \sqrt{3} + \frac{1440\sqrt{3}}{720}$ *[1 mark]*,

which is positive, so it is a minimum *[1 mark]*.

e) Plug $x = 7.463$ back into the equation for the surface area:

$A = \frac{\sqrt{3}}{2}x^2 + \frac{720}{x} = \frac{\sqrt{3}}{2}(7.463)^2 + \frac{720}{7.463}$ *[1 mark]*

$= 145$ cm^2 (3 s.f.) *[1 mark]*

Gee to the whizzle, I thought we'd never finish C2, but hurrah!
Run for your lives, before the maths sucks you back in again...

Answers

S1 Section 1 — Data Presentation
Warm-up Questions

1)

Length of call	Lower class boundary (lcb)	Upper class boundary (ucb)	Class width	Frequency	Frequency density = Height of column
0 - 2	0	2.5	2.5	10	4
3 - 5	2.5	5.5	3	6	2
6 - 8	5.5	8.5	3	3	1
9 - 15	8.5	15.5	7	1	0.143

Lots of fiddly details here — a table helps you get them right.

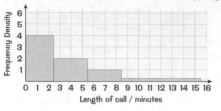

2) 12.8, 13.2, 13.5, 14.3, 14.3, 14.6, 14.8, 15.2, 15.9, 16.1, 16.1, 16.2, 16.3, 17.0, 17.2 (all in cm)

3) $\Sigma f = 16$, $\Sigma fx = 22$, so mean = $22 \div 16 = 1.375$
Median position = $17 \div 2 = 8.5$, so median = 1
Mode = 0, Midrange = $(4 + 0) \div 2 = 2$.

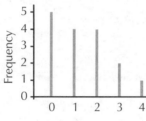

4)

Speed	mid-class value x	Number of cars f		fx
30 - 34	32	12	(12)	384
35 - 39	37	37	(49)	1369
40 - 44	42	9		378
45 - 50	47.5	2		95
Totals		60		2226

Estimated mean = $2226 \div 60 = \underline{37.1\ mph}$
Median position is $61 \div 2 = 30.5$.
This is in class 35 - 39.
$30.5 - 12 = 18.5$, so median is 18.5th value in class.
Class width = 5, so median is:

$34.5 + \left(18.5 \times \dfrac{5}{37}\right) = \underline{37\ mph}$

Modal class is $\underline{35 - 39\ mph}$.

Easy eh? It doesn't hurt to double-check your mid-class values though.

5) Put the 20 items of data in order:
1, 4, 5, 5, 5, 5, 5, 6, 6, 7, 7, 8, 10, 10, 12, 15, 20, 20, 30, 50
Then the median position is 10.5, and since the 10th and the 11th items are both 7, the median = $\underline{7}$.
Lower quartile = $\underline{5}$.
Upper quartile = $(12 + 15) \div 2 = \underline{13.5}$.

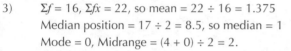

This data is positively skewed. Most 15-year-olds earned a small amount of pocket money. A few got very large amounts.

6) Find the upper class boundaries and the cumulative frequencies:

Distance	Upper class boundary (ucb)	f	Cumulative frequency (CF)
< 0	0	0	0
0 - 2	2	10	10
2 - 4	4	5	15
4 - 6	6	3	18
6 - 8	8	2	20

Now draw the cumulative frequency diagram:

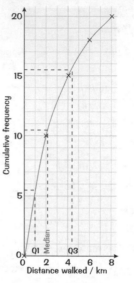

Now you can read off the values of the median (the 10.5th value) and the quartiles (the 5.5th and 15.5th values). This gives a value for the median of $\underline{2.1\ km}$, and values for Q_1 and Q_3 of 1.0 km and 4.3 km respectively. So the interquartile range is $4.3 - 1.0 = \underline{3.3\ km}$.

Because you have grouped data, you could also use the 10th value for the median and the 5th and 15th values for the quartiles. Either would be okay in the exam, but make sure you understand why.

7) $\text{Mean} = \dfrac{11 + 12 + 14 + 17 + 21 + 23 + 27}{7}$
$= \dfrac{125}{7} = 17.9$ to 3 sig. fig.

$\text{r.m.s.d.} = \sqrt{\dfrac{11^2 + 12^2 + 14^2 + 17^2 + 21^2 + 23^2 + 27^2}{7} - \left(\dfrac{125}{7}\right)^2}$
$= \sqrt{30.98} = 5.57$ to 3 sig. fig.

Just numbers and a formula. Simple.

8) Use mid-class values, and remember to multiply the "mean of the squares minus the square of the mean" by $\dfrac{n}{n-1}$, because this is data from a <u>sample</u>.

Score	Mid-class value, x	x^2	f	fx	fx^2
100 - 106	103	10609	6	618	63654
107 - 113	110	12100	11	1210	133100
114 - 120	117	13689	22	2574	301158
121 - 127	124	15376	9	1116	138384
128 - 134	131	17161	2	262	34322
Totals			50 $(= \Sigma f)$	5780 $(= \Sigma fx)$	670618 $(= \Sigma fx^2)$

$\text{Mean} = \dfrac{5780}{50} = 115.6$

$\text{Variance} = \dfrac{50}{49}\left[\dfrac{670618}{50} - 115.6^2\right] = 50$

9) IQR = 88 − 62 = 26, so 1.5 × IQR = 39.
So upper fence = 88 + 39 = 127.
This means that:
a) 121 is not an outlier.   **b)** 134 is an outlier.
Lower fence = 62 − 39 = 23.
This means that: **c)** 29 is not an outlier.

10) Let $y = x − 20$.
Then
$\bar{y} = \bar{x} − 20$ or $\bar{x} = \bar{y} + 20$
$\sum y = 125$ and $\sum y^2 = 221$
So $\bar{y} = \frac{125}{100} = 1.25$ and $\bar{x} = 1.25 + 20 = \underline{21.25}$
m.s.d. of $y = \frac{221}{100} − 1.25^2 = 0.6475$,
and so r.m.s.d. of y = 0.805 to 3 sig.fig.
Therefore <u>r.m.s.d. of x = 0.805</u> to 3 sig. fig.
If you got in a muddle, look back at stuff about coding.

Exam Questions

1 a) Let $y = x − 30$.
$\bar{y} = \frac{228}{19} = 12$ and so $\bar{x} = \bar{y} + 30 = 42$ *[1 mark]*
m.s.d. of $y = \frac{3040}{19} − 12^2 = 16$ *[1 mark]*,
and so r.m.s.d. of y = 4.
But r.m.s.d. of x = r.m.s.d. of y,
and so <u>r.m.s.d. of x = 4</u> *[1 mark]*

b) $\bar{x} = \frac{\sum x}{19} = 42$
And so $\sum x = 42 × 19 = \underline{798}$ *[1 mark]*
m.s.d. of $x = \frac{\sum x^2}{19} − \bar{x}^2 = \frac{\sum x^2}{19} − 42^2 = 16$ *[1 mark]*
And so $\sum x^2 = (16 + 42^2) × 19 = \underline{33\,820}$ *[1 mark]*
A bit harder...

c) New $\sum x = 798 + 32 = 830$ *[1 mark]*
So new $\bar{x} = \frac{830}{20} = \underline{41.5}$ *[1 mark]*
New $\sum x^2 = 33\,820 + 32^2 = 34\,844$ *[1 mark]*
So new m.s.d. $= \frac{34\,844}{20} − 41.5^2 = 19.95$
and new <u>r.m.s.d. = 4.47</u> to 3 sig.fig. *[1 mark]*

2 a) (i) Times = 2, 3, 4, 4, 5, 5, 5, 7, 10, 12
Median position = 5.5, so median = 5 minutes
[1 mark]
(ii) Lower quartile = 4 minutes *[1 mark]*
Upper quartile = 7 minutes *[1 mark]*

b)

**[6 marks available overall — 1 mark for each
median in the right place, 1 mark for each pair of
quartiles shown correctly, and 1 mark for each pair
of lines showing the extremes correctly drawn.]**

c) Various statements could be made,
e.g. the times for Worker B are longer than those for Worker
A, on average.
The IQR for both workers is the same — generally they
both work with the same consistency.
The range for Worker A is larger than that for Worker B.
Worker A had a few items he/she could iron very quickly
and a few which took a long time.
[1 mark for any sensible answer]

d) Worker A would be better to employ. The median time is
less than for Worker B, and the upper quartile is less than
the median of Worker B. Worker A would generally iron
more items in a given time than worker B.
[1 mark for any sensible answer]
*Don't be put off by these questions — you just have to show you
understand what the data is telling you*

3 a) $\bar{a} = \frac{60.3}{20} = 3.015$ g *[1 mark]*

b) Variance of brand A $= \frac{20}{19}\left[\frac{219}{20} − 3.015^2\right]$ *[1 mark]*
$= 1.950$ g² *[1 mark]*
So standard deviation of brand A
$= 1.40$ g to 3 sig.fig. *[1 mark]*

c) E.g. Brand A chocolate drops are heavier on
average than brand B. Brand B chocolate drops
are closer to their mean weight than brand A.
[1 mark for each of 2 sensible statements]
"Mmm, chocolate drops" does not count as a sensible statement...

d) Mean of A and B $= \frac{\sum a + \sum b}{50} = \frac{60.3 + (30 × 2.95)}{50}$
$= 2.976$ g *[1 mark]*
$\frac{30}{29}\left[\frac{\sum b^2}{30} − 2.95^2\right] = 1$, and so $\sum b^2 = 290.075$ *[1 mark]*
Variance of A and $B = \frac{50}{49}\left[\frac{\sum a^2 + \sum b^2}{50} − 2.976^2\right]$
$= \frac{50}{49}\left[\frac{219 + 290.075}{50} − 2.976^2\right]$
$= 1.352$ *[1 mark]*

So standard deviation $= \sqrt{1.352} = 1.16$ g to 3 sig. fig
[1 mark]

*Work through each step carefully so you don't make silly mistakes
and lose any lovely marks.*

4 a) Total number of people = 38
Median position = (38 + 1) ÷ 2 = 19.5 *[1 mark]*
19th value = 15; 20th value = 16,
so median = <u>15.5 hits</u> *[1 mark]*.
Mode = <u>15 hits</u> *[1 mark]*

b) Lower quartile = 10th value = 14
Upper quartile = 29th value = 17
[1 mark for at least one correct value]
So interquartile range = 17 − 14 = 3 *[1 mark]*.

Upper fence = 17 + (1.5 × 3) = 21.5.
This means that 25 is an outlier *[1 mark]*.

c)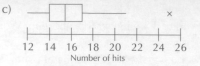

12 14 16 18 20 22 24 26
Number of hits

[1 mark]

As the whisker on the right-hand side is much longer than the left-hand whisker, the distribution seems to be positively skewed. *[1 mark]*

Box plots... everyone's favourite.

d) If 25 was removed then the right-hand 'tail' of the box plot would be much shorter, and the distribution would be more symmetrical *[1 mark]*.

5 a)

Profit	Class width	Frequency	Frequency density = Height of column
4.5 - 5.0	0.5	24	48
5.0 - 5.5	0.5	26	52
5.5 - 6.0	0.5	21	42
6.0 - 6.5	0.5	19	38
6.5 - 8.0	1.5	10	6.67

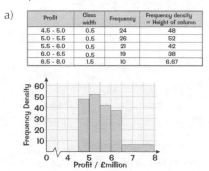

[1 mark for correct axes, plus 2 marks if all bars drawn correctly, or 1 mark for at least 3 bars correct.]

b) The modal profit is between £5 million and £5.5 million. The range of the profits is at most £3.5 million. The distribution is positively skewed — only a few businesses make a high profit.
[1 mark per sensible comment, up to a maximum of 2.]

Not too tricky — not too tricky at all.

6 a) There are 30 males, so median is in 31 ÷ 2 = 15.5th position. Take the mean of the 15th and 16th readings to get median = (62 + 65) ÷ 2 = 63.5 *[1 mark]*

b) The female median is 64.5 (halfway between the 8th and 9th readings). The female median is higher than the male median. The females scored better than the males on average.
Female range = 79 − 55 = 24.
Male range = 79 − 43 = 36
The female range is less than the male range. Their scores are more consistent than the males'.
[Up to 2 marks available for any sensible comments]

7 Find the total area underneath the histogram using the grid squares *[1 mark]*:
2 + 1.5 + 2 + 2 + 1.5 + 4 + 5 + 3 + 4 = 25 *[1 mark]*
So each grid square represents 2 lions *[1 mark]*.
The number of squares for lengths above 220 cm is 7 *[1 mark]*, which represents 7 × 2 = 14 lions *[1 mark]*.

S1 Section 2 — Probability

Warm-up Questions

1) a) This question is asking, "How many ways are there to pick 4 from 12?" This is just:
$$\binom{12}{4} = \frac{12!}{4! \times 8!} = 495$$

b) Now you need to find the number of ways to pick 2 Westerns and the number of ways to pick 2 romantic comedies.

There are $\binom{5}{2} = \frac{5!}{2! \times 3!} = 10$ pairs of Westerns and

$\binom{7}{2} = \frac{7!}{2! \times 5!} = 21$ pairs of romantic comedies.

So altogether, there are 10 × 21 = 210 different combinations containing equal numbers of Westerns and romantic comedies.

This is a slightly unrealistic question, because in reality I would always go for the romcoms.

2) a) The sample space would be as below:

		Dice					
		1	2	3	4	5	6
Coin	H	2	4	6	8	10	12
	T	5	6	7	8	9	10

b) There are 12 outcomes in total, and 9 of these are more than 5, so P(score >5) = 9/12 = 3/4

c) There are 6 outcomes which have a tail showing, and 3 of these are even, so P(even score given that you throw a tail) = 3/6 = 1/2

Hmm, a bit fiddly but not too bad.

3) Draw a sample space diagram

```
   6 | 7  8  9  10 11 12
   5 | 6  7  8  9  10 11
2nd Dice
   4 | 5  6  7  8  9  10
   3 | 4  5  6  7  8  9
   2 | 3  4  5  6  7  8
   1 | 2  3  4  5  6  7
     +------------------- 1st Dice
       1  2  3  4  5  6
```

There are 36 outcomes altogether.

a) 15 outcomes are prime (since 2, 3, 5, 7 and 11 are prime), so P(prime) = 15/36 = 5/12

b) 7 outcomes are square numbers (4 and 9), so P(square) = 7/36

c) Being prime and a square number are exclusive events, so P(prime or square) = 15/36 + 7/36 = 22/36 = 11/18

You have to think outside the probability box for this one, but it's basic maths really.

4) a) 20% of the people eat chips, and 10% of these is 2% — so 2% eat both chips and sausages.

Now you can draw the Venn diagram:

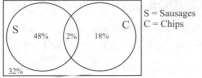

S = Sausages
C = Chips

By reading the numbers in the appropriate sets from the diagram you can see...

b) 18% eat chips but not sausages.

c) 18% + 48% = 66% eat chips or sausages, but not both.

These questions do make you work up an appetite... mmm, sausages...

5) a)

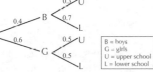

B = boys
G = girls
U = upper school
L = lower school

b) Choosing an upper school pupil means either 'boy and upper' or 'girl and upper'.
P(boy and upper) = 0.4 × 0.3 = 0.12.
P(girl and upper) = 0.6 × 0.5 = 0.30.
So P(Upper) = 0.12 + 0.30 = 0.42.

6) Draw a tree diagram:

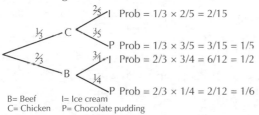

B = Beef   I = Ice cream
C = Chicken   P = Chocolate pudding

a) P(chicken or ice cream but not both) = P(C∩P) + P(B∩I)
= 1/5 + 1/2 = 7/10

b) P(ice cream) = P(C∩I) + P(B∩I) = 2/15 + 1/2 = 19/30

c) P(chicken|ice cream) = P(C∩I) ÷ P(I)
= (2/15) ÷ (19/30) = 4/19

You aren't asked to draw a tree diagram, but it makes it a lot easier if you do.

Exam Questions

1 a) The Venn diagram would look something like this:

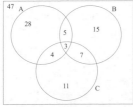

[1 mark for the central figure correct, 2 marks for '5', '7' and '4' correct (get 1 mark for 2 correct), 1 mark for '28', '15' and '11' correct, plus 1 mark for a box with '47' outside the circles.]

b) (i) Add up the numbers in all the circles to get 73 people out of 120 buy at least 1 type of soap *[1 mark]*. So the probability = 73/120 *[1 mark]*

(ii) Add up the numbers in the intersections to get 5 + 3 + 4 + 7 = 19, meaning that 19 people buy at least two soaps *[1 mark]*, so the probability a person buys at least two types = 19/120 *[1 mark]*.

(iii) 28 + 11 + 15 = 54 people buy only 1 soap *[1 mark]*, and of these 15 buy soap B *[1 mark]*.

So probability of a person who only buys one type of soap buying type B is 15/54 = 5/18 *[1 mark]*

2 a)

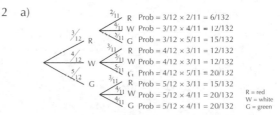

R = red
W = white
G = green

[3 marks available — 1 mark for each set of 3 branches on the right-hand side correct]

b) The second counter is green means one of three outcomes 'red then green' or 'white then green' or 'green then green'. So P(2nd is green) = 15/132 + 20/132 + 20/132 *[1 mark]* = 55/132 = 5/12 *[1 mark]*

c) For both to be red there's only one outcome: 'red then red' *[1 mark]*. P(both red) = 6/132 = 1/22 *[1 mark]*

d) 'Both same colour' is the complementary event of 'not both same colour'. So P(not same colour) = 1 − P(both same colour) *[1 mark]*. Both same colour is either R and R or W and W or G and G.
P(not same colour) = 1 − [6/132 + 12/132 + 20/132]
[1 mark] = 1 − 38/132 = 94/132 = 47/66 *[1 mark]*
(Alternatively, 1 mark for showing P(RW or RG or WR or WG or GR or GW), 1 mark for adding the 6 correct probabilities and 1 mark for the correct answer.)

Ooh, that was a long one. Shouldn't be too tricky though, as long as your tree diagram was nice and clear.

3 a) (i) J and K are independent, so
P(J ∩ K) = P(J) × P(K) = 0.7 × 0.1 = 0.07 *[1 mark]*

(ii) P(J ∪ K) = P(J) + P(K) − P(J ∩ K) *[1 mark]*
= 0.7 + 0.1 − 0.07 = 0.73 *[1 mark]*

b) Drawing a quick Venn Diagram often helps:

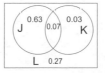

P(L|K') = P(L ∩ K') ÷ P(K')
Now L ∩ K' = L — think about it — all of L is contained in K', so L ∩ K' (the 'bits in both L and K') are just the bits in L. Therefore P(L ∩ K') = P(L) = 1 − P(K ∪ J) = 1 − 0.73 = 0.27
[1 mark]

Answers

$P(K') = 1 - P(K) = 1 - 0.1 = 0.9$ *[1 mark]*
And so $P(L|K') = 0.27 \div 0.9 = 0.3$ *[1 mark]*

That was a bit complicated — you just need to put your thinking cap on and DON'T PANIC.

4   Draw a tree diagram:

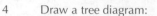

B= Biased dice shows 6
F= Fair dice shows 6

a) $P(B') = 0.8$ *[1 mark]*

b)   Either at least one of the dice shows a 6 or neither of them do, so these are complementary events. Call F the event 'the fair dice shows a 6'.
Then $P(F \cup B) = 1 - P(F' \cap B')$ *[1 mark]*
$= 1 - (4/5 \times 5/6) = 1 - 2/3 = 1/3$ *[1 mark]*

c)   P(exactly one 6 | at least one 6)
= P(exactly one 6 ∩ at least one 6) ÷ P(at least one 6).
The next step might be a bit easier to get your head round if you draw a Venn diagram:

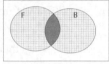

'exactly one 6' ∩ 'at least one 6' = 'exactly one 6'
(Look at the diagram — 'exactly one 6' is the cross-hatched area, and 'at least one 6' is the cross-hatched area <u>plus</u> the grey bit. So the bit in common to both is just the cross-hatched area.)
Now, that means P(exactly one 6 ∩ at least one 6) =
$P(B \cap F') + P(B' \cap F)$ — this is the cross-hatched area in the Venn diagram,
i.e. P(exactly one 6 ∩ at least one 6) = (1/5 × 5/6) + (4/5 × 1/6) = 9/30 = 3/10 (using the fact that B and F are independent) *[1 mark]*
P(at least one 6) = 1/3 (from b)).
And all of this means P(exactly one 6 | at least one 6)
= 3/10 ÷ 1/3 *[1 mark]* = 9/10 *[1 mark]*

Blauuurgh — the noise of a mind boggling. Part c is difficult to get your head round, but it's just a matter of remembering the right conditional probability formula, breaking it down into separate parts and working through it step by step. Yay.

S1 Section 3 —
Discrete Random Variables
Warm-up Questions

1) a)   All the probabilities have to add up to 1.
So $0.5 + k + k + 3k = 0.5 + 5k = 1$, i.e. $5k = 0.5$, i.e. $k = 0.1$.

   b) $P(Y < 2) = P(Y = 0) + P(Y = 1) = 0.5 + 0.1 = 0.6$.

2) a) $E(W) = \sum w P(W = w)$
$= (0.2 \times 0.2) + (0.3 \times 0.2) + (0.4 \times 0.3) + (0.5 \times 0.3)$
$= 0.37$

   b) $Var(W) = \sum w^2 P(W = w) - \mu^2$
$= (0.04 \times 0.2) + (0.09 \times 0.2)$
$+ (0.16 \times 0.3) + (0.25 \times 0.3) - 0.37^2$
$= 0.149 - 0.37^2 = 0.0121$

   c) $P(W > 0.3) = P(W = 0.4) + P(W = 0.5) = 0.3 + 0.3 = 0.6$

3) a)   As always, the probabilities have to add up to 1, so
$k = 1 - \left(\frac{1}{6} + \frac{1}{2} + \frac{5}{24}\right) = 1 - \frac{21}{24} = \frac{3}{24} = \frac{1}{8}$

   b) $E(X) = \left(1 \times \frac{1}{6}\right) + \left(2 \times \frac{1}{2}\right) + \left(3 \times \frac{1}{8}\right) + \left(4 \times \frac{5}{24}\right)$
$= \frac{4 + 24 + 9 + 20}{24} = \frac{57}{24} = \frac{19}{8}$

   c) $E(X^2) = \left(1^2 \times \frac{1}{6}\right) + \left(2^2 \times \frac{1}{2}\right) + \left(3^2 \times \frac{1}{8}\right) + \left(4^2 \times \frac{5}{24}\right)$
$= \frac{4 + 48 + 27 + 80}{24} = \frac{159}{24} = \frac{53}{8}$
$Var(X) = E(X^2) - [E(X)]^2 = \frac{53}{8} - \left(\frac{19}{8}\right)^2$
$= \frac{424 - 361}{64} = \frac{63}{64}$

   d) $P(X \leq 3) = P(X = 1) + P(X = 2) + P(X = 3)$
$= \frac{1}{6} + \frac{1}{2} + \frac{1}{8} = \frac{4 + 12 + 3}{24} = \frac{19}{24}$

4) a) $E(X) = (1 \times 0.1) + (2 \times 0.2) + (3 \times 0.25) + (4 \times 0.2)$
$+ (5 \times 0.1) + (6 \times 0.15) = 3.45$

   b) $Var(X) = E(X^2) - (E(X))^2$
$E(X^2) = (1 \times 0.1) + (4 \times 0.2) + (9 \times 0.25) + (16 \times 0.2)$
$+ (25 \times 0.1) + (36 \times 0.15) = 14.25$
So $Var(X) = 14.25 - 3.45^2 = 2.3475$

   c) $P(3 < X \leq 5) = P(X = 4) + P(X = 5) = 0.2 + 0.1 = 0.3$

5) a) $E(X) = (0 \times 0.4) + (1 \times 0.3) + (2 \times 0.2) + (3 \times 0.1) = 1$

   b) $Var(X) = E(X^2) - (E(X))^2$
$= (0 \times 0.4) + (1 \times 0.3) + (4 \times 0.2) + (9 \times 0.1) - 1^2$
$= 2 - 1 = 1$

6) a)   There are 10 possible values of X, and so $k = 1 \div 10 = 0.1$.

   b) $E(X) = 0.1 \times (0 + 1 + 2 + ... + 9) = 4.5$

   c) $Var(X) = 0.1 \times (0 + 1 + 4 + ... + 81) - 4.5^2$
$= 28.5 - 20.25 = 8.25$

Answers

Exam Questions

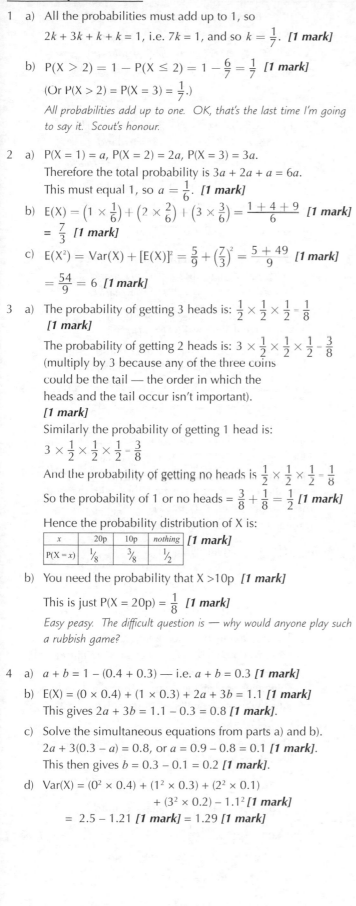

1 a) All the probabilities must add up to 1, so
   $2k + 3k + k + k = 1$, i.e. $7k = 1$, and so $k = \frac{1}{7}$. *[1 mark]*

   b) $P(X > 2) = 1 - P(X \le 2) = 1 - \frac{6}{7} = \frac{1}{7}$ *[1 mark]*
   (Or $P(X > 2) = P(X = 3) = \frac{1}{7}$.)

   All probabilities add up to one. OK, that's the last time I'm going to say it. Scout's honour.

2 a) $P(X = 1) = a$, $P(X = 2) = 2a$, $P(X = 3) = 3a$.
   Therefore the total probability is $3a + 2a + a = 6a$.
   This must equal 1, so $a = \frac{1}{6}$. *[1 mark]*

   b) $E(X) = \left(1 \times \frac{1}{6}\right) + \left(2 \times \frac{2}{6}\right) + \left(3 \times \frac{3}{6}\right) = \frac{1 + 4 + 9}{6}$ *[1 mark]*
   $= \frac{7}{3}$ *[1 mark]*

   c) $E(X^2) = Var(X) + [E(X)]^2 = \frac{5}{9} + \left(\frac{7}{3}\right)^2 = \frac{5 + 49}{9}$ *[1 mark]*
   $= \frac{54}{9} = 6$ *[1 mark]*

3 a) The probability of getting 3 heads is: $\frac{1}{2} \times \frac{1}{2} \times \frac{1}{2} = \frac{1}{8}$
   [1 mark]

   The probability of getting 2 heads is: $3 \times \frac{1}{2} \times \frac{1}{2} \times \frac{1}{2} = \frac{3}{8}$
   (multiply by 3 because any of the three coins
   could be the tail — the order in which the
   heads and the tail occur isn't important).
   [1 mark]
   Similarly the probability of getting 1 head is:
   $3 \times \frac{1}{2} \times \frac{1}{2} \times \frac{1}{2} = \frac{3}{8}$
   And the probability of getting no heads is $\frac{1}{2} \times \frac{1}{2} \times \frac{1}{2} = \frac{1}{8}$
   So the probability of 1 or no heads $= \frac{3}{8} + \frac{1}{8} = \frac{1}{2}$ *[1 mark]*

   Hence the probability distribution of X is:

x	20p	10p	*nothing*
P(X = x)	1/8	3/8	1/2
   [1 mark]

   b) You need the probability that X >10p *[1 mark]*
   This is just $P(X = 20p) = \frac{1}{8}$ *[1 mark]*

   Easy peasy. The difficult question is — why would anyone play such a rubbish game?

4 a) $a + b = 1 - (0.4 + 0.3)$ — i.e. $a + b = 0.3$ *[1 mark]*

   b) $E(X) = (0 \times 0.4) + (1 \times 0.3) + 2a + 3b = 1.1$ *[1 mark]*
   This gives $2a + 3b = 1.1 - 0.3 = 0.8$ *[1 mark]*.

   c) Solve the simultaneous equations from parts a) and b).
   $2a + 3(0.3 - a) = 0.8$, or $a = 0.9 - 0.8 = 0.1$ *[1 mark]*.
   This then gives $b = 0.3 - 0.1 = 0.2$ *[1 mark]*.

   d) $Var(X) = (0^2 \times 0.4) + (1^2 \times 0.3) + (2^2 \times 0.1)$
   $+ (3^2 \times 0.2) - 1.1^2$ *[1 mark]*
   $= 2.5 - 1.21$ *[1 mark]* $= 1.29$ *[1 mark]*

S1 Section 4 — The Binomial Distribution

Warm-up Questions

1) a) There are 21 objects altogether, so if <u>all</u> the balls were
   different colours, there would be 21! ways to arrange them.
   But since 15 of the objects are identical, you need to divide
   this figure by 15!. So there are 21! ÷ 15! = 39 070 080
   possible arrangements.

   b) There are $\frac{16!}{4!4!4!4!} = 63\,063\,000$ possible arrangements.

   You'd be a while counting all these on your fingers.

2) a) (i) $P(5\,heads) = 0.5^5 \times 0.5^5 \times \binom{10}{5}$
   $= 0.5^{10} \times \frac{10!}{5!5!} = 0.246$ (to 3 sig.fig.).

   (ii) $P(9\,heads) = 0.5^9 \times 0.5 \times \binom{10}{9}$
   $= 0.5^{10} \times \frac{10!}{9!1!} = 0.00977$ (to 3 sig.fig.).

   b) (i) Since $P(5\,heads) = 0.246$, I would expect to get
   '5 heads' in $0.246 \times 40 \approx 9.8$ out of the 40 trials.

   (ii) Since $P(9\,heads) = 0.00977$, I would expect to get
   '9 heads' in $0.00977 \times 40 \approx 0.4$ out of the 40 trials.

3) a) Binomial — there are a fixed number of independent trials
   (30) with two possible results ('prime' / 'not prime'), a
   constant probability of success, and the random variable is
   the total number of successes.

   b) Binomial — there are a fixed number of independent trials
   (however many students are in the class) with two possible
   results ('heads' / 'tails'), a constant probability of success,
   and the random variable is the total number of successes.

   c) Not binomial — the probability of being dealt an ace
   changes each time, since the total number of cards
   decreases as each card is dealt.

   d) Not binomial — the number of trials is not fixed.

   It's weird to have to write actual sentences in a maths exam, but be ready for it.

4) a) Use tables with $n = 10$ and $p = 0.5$.
   If X represents the number of heads, then:
   $P(X \ge 5) = 1 - P(X < 5) = 1 - P(X \le 4)$
   $= 1 - 0.3770 = 0.6230$

   b) $P(X \ge 9) = 1 - P(X < 9) = 1 - P(X \le 8)$
   $= 1 - 0.9893 = 0.0107$

   You do have to be prepared to monkey around with the numbers the tables give you.

5) a) You can't use tables here (because they don't include
   $p = 0.27$), so you have to use the probability function.

   $P(X = 4) = \binom{14}{4} \times 0.27^4 \times (1 - 0.27)^{10}$
   $= 0.229$ (to 3 sig.fig.)

Answers

b) $P(X < 2) = P(X = 0) + P(X = 1)$

$= \binom{14}{0} \times 0.27^0 \times (1 - 0.27)^{14}$

$+ \binom{14}{1} \times 0.27^1 \times (1 - 0.27)^{13}$

$= 0.012204... + 0.063195...$

$= 0.0754$ (to 3 sig.fig.)

c) $P(5 < X \le 8) = P(X = 6) + P(X = 7) + P(X = 8)$

$= \binom{14}{6} \times 0.27^6 \times (1 - 0.27)^8$

$+ \binom{14}{7} \times 0.27^7 \times (1 - 0.27)^7$

$+ \binom{14}{8} \times 0.27^8 \times (1 - 0.27)^6$

$= 0.093825... + 0.039660... + 0.012835...$

$= 0.146$ (to 3 sig.fig.)

6) For parts a)-c), use tables with $n = 18$ and $p = 0.15$.

a) $P(X \le 3) = 0.7202$

b) $P(X \le 7) = 0.9973$

c) $P(X \le 15) = 1.0000$

Now use tables with $n = 15$ and $p = 0.65$.

d) $P(Y \le 3) = 0.0005$

e) $P(Y \le 7) = 0.1132$

f) $P(Y \le 15) = 1$ (since 15 is the maximum possible value).

Not much to say about that — if you can read the tables, you're home and dry (more or less).

7) From tables:

a) $P(X \le 15) = 0.9997$

b) $P(X < 4) = P(X \le 3) = 0.8535$

c) $P(X > 7) = 1 - P(X \le 7) = 1 - 0.6535 = 0.3465$

d) $P(X \ge 4) = 1 - P(X < 4) = 1 - P(X \le 3)$

$= 1 - 0.0031 = 0.9969$

e) $P(X = 10) = P(X \le 10) - P(X \le 9)$

$= 0.0480 - 0.0171 = 0.0309$

f) $P(X = 7) = P(X \le 7) - P(X \le 6) = 0.4744 - 0.2241 = 0.2503$

For e) and f), you could just use the binomial probability function.

8) a) mean $= 20 \times 0.4 = 8$; variance $= 20 \times 0.4 \times 0.6 = 4.8$

b) mean $= 40 \times 0.15 = 6$; variance $= 40 \times 0.15 \times 0.85 = 5.1$

c) mean $= 25 \times 0.45 = 11.25$;
variance $= 25 \times 0.45 \times 0.55 = 6.1875$

d) mean $= 50 \times 0.8 = 40$; variance $= 50 \times 0.8 \times 0.2 = 8$

e) mean $= 30 \times 0.7 = 21$; variance $= 30 \times 0.7 \times 0.3 = 6.3$

f) mean $= 45 \times 0.012 = 0.54$;
variance $= 45 \times 0.012 \times 0.988 = 0.53352$

Exam Questions

1 a) (i) $P(X < 8) = P(X \le 7)$ *[1 mark]* $= 0.5618$ *[1 mark]*

(ii) $P(X = 5) = P(X \le 5) - P(X \le 4)$ *[1 mark]*

$= 0.1582 - 0.0573 = 0.1009$ *[1 mark]*

Or you could use the probability function for part (ii):

$P(X = 5) = \binom{12}{5} \times 0.6^5 \times 0.4^7 = 0.1009$

(iii) $P(3 < X \le 7) = P(X \le 7) - P(X \le 3)$ *[1 mark]*

$= 0.5618 - 0.0153 = 0.5465$ *[1 mark]*

b) (i) $P(Y = 14) = 0.8^{14} \times 0.2^7 \times \frac{21!}{14!7!}$ *[1 mark]*

$= 0.0655$ (to 3 sig. fig.) *[1 mark]*

(ii) $E(Y) = 21 \times 0.8 = 16.8$ *[1 mark]*

(iii) $Var(Y) = 21 \times 0.8 \times 0.2 = 3.36$ *[1 mark]*

2 a) (i) Let X represent the number of apples that contain a maggot. Then $X \sim B(20, 0.15)$ *[1 mark]*.
$P(X < 6) = P(X \le 5) = 0.9327$ *[1 mark]*

(ii) $P(X > 2) = 1 - P(X \le 2)$ *[1 mark]*

$= 1 - 0.4049 = 0.5951$ *[1 mark]*

(iii) $P(X = 7) = P(X \le 7) - P(X \le 6)$ *[1 mark]*

$= 0.9941 - 0.9781 = 0.0160$ *[1 mark]*

Or you could use the probability function for part (iii):

$P(X = 7) = \binom{20}{7} \times 0.15^7 \times 0.85^{13} = 0.0160$

b) The probability that a crate contains more than 2 apples with maggots is 0.5951 (from part a) (ii)).
So define a random variable Y, where Y is the number of crates that contain more than 2 apples with maggots.
Then $Y \sim B(3, 0.5951)$ *[1 mark]*.
You need to find $P(Y = 2) + P(Y = 3)$. This is:

$0.5951^2 \times (1 - 0.5951) \times \binom{3}{2}$

$+ 0.5951^3 \times (1 - 0.5951)^0 \times \binom{3}{3}$ *[1 mark]*

$= 0.4302 + 0.2108 = 0.641$ (to 3 d.p.) *[1 mark]*

3 a) (i) The probability of Simon being able to solve each crossword needs to remain the same *[1 mark]*, and all the outcomes need to be independent (i.e. Simon solving or not solving a puzzle one day should not affect whether he will be able to solve it on another day) *[1 mark]*.

(ii) The total number of puzzles he solves (or the number he fails to solve) *[1 mark]*.

b) $P(X = 4) = p^4 \times (1 - p)^{14} \times \frac{18!}{4!14!}$ *[1 mark]*

$P(X = 5) = p^5 \times (1 - p)^{13} \times \frac{18!}{5!13!}$ *[1 mark]*

So $p^4 \times (1 - p)^{14} \times \frac{18!}{4!14!} = p^5 \times (1 - p)^{13} \times \frac{18!}{5!13!}$ *[1 mark]*

Dividing by things that occur on both sides gives:

$\frac{1-p}{14} = \frac{p}{5}$ *[1 mark]*, or $5 = 19p$.

This means $p = \frac{5}{19}$ *[1 mark]*.

Answers

S1 Section 5 —
Hypothesis Testing
Warm-up Questions

1) a) A two-tailed test should be used — Salma doesn't know if the coin is biased towards heads or tails.

   b) H_0: $p = 0.5$, H_1: $p \neq 0.5$

2) The number (or proportion) of 'successes' in a random sample taken from the distribution.

3) a) H_0: $p = 0.2$, H_1: $p < 0.2$, $\alpha = 0.05$ and $x = 2$:
   Under H_0, $X \sim B(20, 0.2)$
   $P(X \leq 2) = 0.2061$
   $0.2061 > 0.05$, so there is insufficient evidence at the 5% level of significance to reject H_0.

   b) H_0: $p = 0.4$, H_1: $p > 0.4$, $\alpha = 0.01$ and $x = 15$:
   Under H_0, $X \sim B(20, 0.4)$
   $P(X \geq 15) = 1 - P(X \leq 14) = 1 - 0.9984 = 0.0016$
   $0.0016 < 0.01$, so there is evidence at the 1% level of significance to reject H_0.

   Trust me... a significant amount of practice is critical when it comes to hypothesis testing.

4) H_0: $p = 0.3$, H_1: $p < 0.3$, $\alpha = 0.05$
   Under H_0, $X \sim B(10, 0.3)$
   Critical region = biggest possible set of 'low' values of X with a total probability of ≤ 0.05.
   $P(X \leq 0) = 0.0282$, $P(X \leq 1) = 0.1493$,
   so CR is $X = 0$.

5) H_0: $p = 0.09$, H_1: $p < 0.09$, $\alpha = 0.05$ and $x = 1$:
   Under H_0, $X \sim B(50, 0.09)$.
   $P(X \leq 1) = P(X = 0) + P(X = 1)$
   $= \binom{50}{0} \times 0.09^0 \times 0.91^{50} + \binom{50}{1} \times 0.09^1 \times 0.91^{49}$
   $= 0.008955... + 0.044283... = 0.053$ (to 3 d.p.).
   So $P(X \leq 1) > 0.05$, and this means that there is insufficient evidence at the 5% level of significance to reject H_0.

Exam Questions

1 a) Binomial *[1 mark]*

  b) (i) Start by stating the hypotheses:
      H_0: $p = 0.2$ and H_1: $p > 0.2$ *[1 mark for both correct]*
      X = number of tiramisu orders in sample
      Under H_0, $X \sim B(20, 0.2)$ *[1 mark]*
      $\alpha = 0.05$

      <u>Either:</u>
      Use the binomial tables to find the probability of getting a value greater than or equal to 7, under H_0:
      $P(X \geq 7) = 1 - P(X \leq 6)$ *[1 mark]*
      $= 1 - 0.9133 = 0.0867$ *[1 mark]*
      $0.0867 > 0.05$, so the result isn't significant. *[1 mark]*

<u>Or:</u>
Use the binomial tables to find the critical region:
$P(X \geq 7) = 1 - P(X \leq 6) = 1 - 0.9133 = 0.0867$
$P(X \geq 8) = 1 - P(X \leq 7) = 1 - 0.9679 = 0.0321$
[1 mark for attempting to find the smallest value of x such that $P(X \geq x) \leq 0.05$.]
$0.0321 < 0.05$, so the CR is $X \geq 8$ *[1 mark]*.
7 isn't in the CR, so the result isn't significant. *[1 mark]*

So, there is insufficient evidence at the 5% level of significance to support the chef's theory that the proportion of dessert eaters ordering tiramisu on a Saturday is greater than on weekdays.
[1 mark for a suitable conclusion]

  (ii) You're looking for the smallest value of x such that $P(X \geq x) \leq 0.05$.
      You know $X = 7$ isn't significant from part (i).
      Try 8: $P(X \geq 8) = 0.0321 < 0.05$,
      so the answer is 8 tiramisu orders *[1 mark]*.

      Part (ii) here is really just asking for the lower boundary of the critical region. So if you answered part (i) by finding the critical region, you've already worked out the answer. Bonus.

2 a) H_0: $p = 0.3$ and H_0: $p \neq 0.3$
   X = number of sampled residents against the plan
   Under H_0, $X \sim B(18, 0.3)$ *[1 mark]*
   It's a two-tailed test, so the critical region is split into two.
   For the lower end:
   $P(X \leq 2) = 0.0600$ and $P(X \leq 1) = 0.0142$ *[1 mark]*.
   For the upper end:
   $P(X \geq 9) = 1 - P(X < 9) = 1 - P(X \leq 8)$
   $= 1 - 0.9404 = 0.0596$,
   $P(X \geq 10) = 1 - P(X < 10) = 1 - P(X \leq 9)$
   $= 1 - 0.9790 = 0.0210$ *[1 mark]*.
   So CR is $X \leq 1$ *[1 mark]* and $X \geq 10$ *[1 mark]*

   Don't forget — the values in the critical region can have a total probability no greater than the significance level.

  b) The value 3 doesn't lie in the critical region *[1 mark]*, so there is insufficient evidence to reject the claim that the proportion of residents against the plan is 30% *[1 mark]*.
  (Allow follow-through for a correct conclusion drawn from an incorrectly calculated critical region in part a).)

Answers

S1 — Practice Exam One

1) a) The mean is $\dfrac{\sum x}{10} = \dfrac{500}{10} = 50$ *[1 mark]*.

The mean square deviation is 'the mean of the squares minus the square of the mean'. And the root mean square deviation is just the square root of the mean square deviation.

m.s.d. $= \dfrac{\sum x^2}{10} - 50^2$

$= \dfrac{25\,622}{10} - 2500 = 62.2$ *[1 mark]*

So r.m.s.d. $= \sqrt{62.2} = 7.89$ *[1 mark]*.

b) (i) The mean will be unchanged *[1 mark]*, because the new value is equal to the original mean *[1 mark]*.

(ii) The root mean square deviation will decrease *[1 mark]*. This is because the root mean square deviation measures the deviation of values from the mean. So by adding a new value that's equal to the mean, you're not adding to the total deviation from the mean, but you now have to divide by 11 (not 10) when you work out the mean square deviation *[1 mark]*.

Understanding what the root mean square deviation actually is can help you get your head round questions like this.

2) a) The events are mutually exclusive, so they can't both happen. Hence $P(A \cap B) = 0$ *[1 mark]*.

b) For mutually exclusive events, $P(A \cup B) = P(A) + P(B)$ *[1 mark]*. So $P(A \cup B) = 0.3 + 0.4 = 0.7$ *[1 mark]*.

c) The probability that neither event happens is equal to $1 - P(A \cup B)$ *[1 mark]* $= 1 - 0.7 = 0.3$ *[1 mark]*.

d) $P(A \mid B)$ is the probability of A, given that B has already happened. But since A and B are mutually exclusive, they can't both happen — so $P(A \mid B)$ must equal zero. You can use the formula for conditional probability to get the same answer:

$P(A \mid B) = \dfrac{P(A \cap B)}{P(B)}$.

[1 mark for the correct answer, and 1 mark for a reasonable explanation.]

3) a) $p = 0.2$, since the probabilities have to add up to 1 *[1 mark]*.

Easy.

b) $P(X \geq 20p) = P(X = 20p) + P(X = 50p) + P(X = 100p)$
$= 0.2 \times 3 = 0.6$ *[1 mark]*.

c) $E(X) = \sum x P(X = x)$
$\quad = 0.2 \times (0 + 10 + 20 + 50 + 100)$ *[1 mark]*
$\quad = 36$ *[1 mark]*

d) $Var(X) = \sum x^2 P(X = x) - \{E(X)\}^2$
$= 0.2 \times (0 + 100 + 400 + 2500 + 10\,000) - 36^2$ *[1 mark]*
$= 1304$ *[1 mark]*

Don't forget to subtract the square of the mean.

e) X is a random variable that shows what's paid out. The expected value of X is 36p, so a charge of 40p will average a profit of 4p per game *[1 mark]*. This is unlikely to be sufficient to cover the owner's costs *[1 mark for any sensible comment]*.

You've got to think a bit about this one.

4) a) Because the cards are not being replaced, the probability of choosing a picture card does not remain constant *[1 mark]*.

b) (i) Since the cards are now being replaced after each pick, Y will follow a binomial distribution.
Since $\dfrac{12}{52} = \dfrac{3}{13}$, $Y \sim B(3, \dfrac{3}{13})$ *[1 mark]*.

$P(Y = 2) = \dbinom{3}{2} \times \left(\dfrac{3}{13}\right)^2 \times \dfrac{10}{13}$ *[1 mark]*
$= \dfrac{270}{13^3} = \dfrac{270}{2197}$
$= 0.123$ (to 3 sig.fig.) *[1 mark]*.

(ii) $E(Y) = 3 \times \dfrac{3}{13} = \dfrac{9}{13} = 0.692$ (to 3 sig.fig.) *[1 mark]*.

c) P(exactly 2 picture cards) $= 0.123$ (from part b)(i)).
So, expected number of 'exactly 2 picture cards' in 50 trials is 0.123×50 *[1 mark]* $= 6.15$ (or 6.14 if the unrounded probability from b)(i) was used) *[1 mark]*.

5) a) X = number of people in the sample of 20 who have done judo before. Then $X \sim B(20, p)$.
$H_0: p = 0.2$ and $H_1: p \neq 0.2$
So under H_0, $X \sim B(20, 0.2)$ *[1 mark]*
It's a two-tailed test, so the critical region is split into two, with a probability of ≤ 0.025 in each tail.
For the lower tail:
$P(X \leq 0) = 0.0115$ and $P(X \leq 1) = 0.0692$. *[1 mark]*
For the upper tail:
$P(X \geq 9) = 1 - 0.9900 = 0.0100$ and
$P(X \geq 8) = 1 - 0.9679 = 0.0321$. *[1 mark]*
So CR is $X = 0$ *[1 mark]* and $X \geq 9$ *[1 mark]*

b) 7 does not lie in the critical region, so do not reject H_0 *[1 mark]*. There is no evidence at the 5% level to suggest that the proportion who have done judo before isn't one fifth *[1 mark]*.

6) a) If C is the event 'has had a crash' and G is the event 'wears glasses', then the tree diagram is as follows:

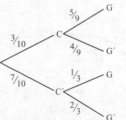

[1 mark for each correct pair of branches, but lose 1 mark for not cancelling down fractions.]

b) $P(C') = \dfrac{7}{10}$ *[1 mark]*

c) The easiest way is to work out the probabilities of the two branches ending in G by multiplying along each branch, and then adding the results
(i.e. $P(G) = P(G \cap C) + P(G \cap C')$).
$P(G \cap C) = \frac{3}{10} \times \frac{5}{9} = \frac{15}{90} = \frac{1}{6}$ *[1 mark]*,
and $P(G \cap C') = \frac{7}{10} \times \frac{1}{3} = \frac{7}{30}$ *[1 mark]*.
Adding these together you get:
$P(G) = \frac{1}{6} + \frac{7}{30} = \frac{5+7}{30} = \frac{12}{30} = \frac{2}{5}$ *[1 mark]*.

d) You need to find: $P(C \mid G) = \frac{P(C \cap G)}{P(G)}$ *[1 mark]*.
You've just worked out $P(C \cap G)$ and $P(G)$, so
$P(C \mid G) = \frac{1}{6} \div \frac{2}{5}$ *[1 mark]*
$= \frac{1}{6} \times \frac{5}{2} = \frac{5}{12}$ *[1 mark]*.

e) There are various possible 'arrangements' of the three older people (i.e. 35 or over) and the one younger person (i.e. less than 35) if you record the order in which they are selected. The probability of one of these arrangements is
$\frac{13}{30} \times \frac{12}{29} \times \frac{11}{28} \times \frac{17}{27} = \frac{29172}{657720} = \frac{2431}{54810}$ *[1 mark]*.

Since there are 4 possible arrangements of the four people, the probability of any of these occurring must be:
$4 \times \frac{2431}{54810}$ *[1 mark]* $= \frac{9724}{54810} = \frac{4862}{27405}$
$= 0.177$ (to 3 sig.fig.) *[1 mark]*
Watch out for these 'number of arrangements' questions. You could tackle it with another tree diagram if you wanted, but remember the probabilities change with each selection.

f) (i) P(not taken to garage) $= \frac{10}{30} = \frac{1}{3}$ *[1 mark]*

(ii) P(at most one type of work)
$= \frac{2+2+11+10}{30}$ *[1 mark]* $= \frac{25}{30} = \frac{5}{6}$ *[1 mark]*
Don't forget to include the 10 for 'no work'.

(iii) P(exactly two types of work)
$\frac{2+1+1}{30}$ *[1 mark]* $= \frac{4}{30} = \frac{2}{15}$ *[1 mark]*
Here you only want the numbers that are in exactly two circles.

7) a) 4.1 metres (the upper quartile) *[1 mark]*.

b) They represent outliers — data values that are a long way away from the rest of the readings *[1 mark]*.

c) The median is the (11 + 1)/2 = 6th value *[1 mark]*, which lies in the interval 4 – 5 metres. There are 4 values before 4 m, so the 6th value is 2 readings along this interval. The interval contains 4 readings and so can be divided into 4 parts of width ¼. So the median is given by:
$4 + \left(2 \times \frac{1}{4}\right)$ *[1 mark]* $= 4.5$ m *[1 mark]*

d)

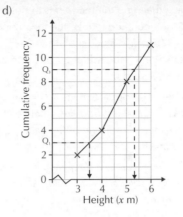

[1 mark for all points plotted correctly and 1 mark for a correctly drawn line or curve.]

e) Q_1 is in position 3 and Q_3 is in position 9.
So, using the graph (see above), Q_1 is 3.5 m *[1 mark]* and Q_3 is 5.3 m *[1 mark]*.
The interquartile range is 5.3 – 3.5 = 1.8 m *[1 mark]*.

f)

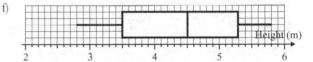

[1 mark for the median shown correctly, 1 mark for the upper quartile, 1 mark for the lower quartile, and 1 mark for both the minimum and the maximum shown correctly.]

g) The giraffes in the zoo are generally taller, with a higher median *[1 mark]*, and higher upper and lower quartiles *[1 mark]*. The two populations seem similarly varied, since they have similar ranges (ignoring the outliers), although the IQR for the giraffes in the zoo is greater than for the giraffes in the game reserve *[1 mark]*. The skew of both distributions is negative (though only slightly negative for the zoo's giraffes) *[1 mark]*.

S1 — Practice Exam Two

1) a) (i) It's best to add a couple of extra rows to the table:

Number of days (x)	1	2	3	4	5	6	7	8
Frequency (f)	5	3	1	0	0	0	0	1
fx	5	6	3	0	0	0	0	8
fx^2	5	12	9	0	0	0	0	64

Then $\sum f = 10$ and $\sum fx = 22$ *[1 mark]*, which gives
$\bar{x} = \frac{\sum fx}{\sum f} = \frac{22}{10} = 2.2$ *[1 mark]*

(ii) $\sum fx^2 = 90$. So:
$s^2 = \frac{n}{n-1}\left[\frac{\sum fx^2}{\sum f} - \left(\frac{\sum fx}{\sum f}\right)^2\right] = \frac{10}{9}\left[\frac{90}{10} - 2.2^2\right]$ *[1 mark]*
$= \frac{10}{9} \times 4.16 = \frac{41.6}{9}$
$\Rightarrow s = \sqrt{\frac{41.6}{9}} = 2.15$ (to 3 sig. fig.) *[1 mark]*

Answers

(iii) There are 10 values, meaning the median is in position $(10 + 1) \div 2 = 5.5$, so you need to take the mean of the 5th and 6th values *[1 mark]*. Since the 5th value is 1 and the 6th is 2, this will be the midpoint of 1 and 2. So the median = 1.5 *[1 mark]*.

b) No, the range is not a very appropriate measure because the outlier of 8 *[1 mark]* will make it unrepresentative of the data set as a whole (since all but one of the data values are either 1, 2 or 3) *[1 mark]*.

There are usually loads of numbers in these 'data analysis' questions. So take your time, do things carefully, and watch that your fingers don't accidentally hit the wrong calculator buttons.

2) a) You want to find the number of different combinations of 5 people from 9, which is:
$\binom{9}{5}$ *[1 mark]* $= \frac{9!}{5!4!} = \frac{362\,880}{2880} = 126$ *[1 mark]*

b) The only selection that results in more men than women is if there are 3 men and 2 women *[1 mark]* (there can't be more than 3 men as only 3 auditioned).
3 men and 2 women can be selected in:
$\binom{3}{3} \times \binom{6}{2} = \frac{3!}{3!0!} \times \frac{6!}{2!4!} = 15$ ways *[1 mark]*
So the number of combinations that have more women than men is $126 - 15$ *[1 mark]* $= 111$ *[1 mark]*. The probability that the choirmaster randomly selects one of these combinations is: $\frac{111}{126} = \frac{37}{42}$ or 0.881 (to 3 s.f.) *[1 mark]*

3) a) (i) The probabilities must sum to 1, so:
$0.1 + 0.2 + p + q + 0.2 = 1$, or $p + q = 0.5$ *[1 mark]*.
$E(X) = 6.3$, so $(0.1 \times 2) + (0.2 \times 4) +$
$\qquad\qquad (p \times 6) + (q \times 8) + (0.2 \times 10) = 6.3$,
or $6p + 8q = 3.3$ *[1 mark]*.

(ii) Rearrange the first equation to give an expression for p, then substitute this into the second equation.
$p = 0.5 - q$, so
$6 \times (0.5 - q) + 8q = 3.3$ *[1 mark]*,
which gives $2q = 0.3$. This means $q = 0.15$ *[1 mark]*.
Then $p = 0.5 - q = 0.5 - 0.15$, i.e. $p = 0.35$ *[1 mark]*.

Even though simultaneous equations aren't part of S1, you're still expected to know how to solve them.

b) $Var(X) = E(X^2) - [E(X)]^2$
$E(X^2) = (0.1 \times 2^2) + (0.2 \times 4^2) + (0.35 \times 6^2)$
$\qquad + (0.15 \times 8^2) + (0.2 \times 10^2)$
$\qquad = 45.8$ *[1 mark]*
So $Var(X) = 45.8 - 6.3^2$ *[1 mark]* $= 6.11$ *[1 mark]*.

4) a) Let H be hard centre, N be nutty and S be soft centre.

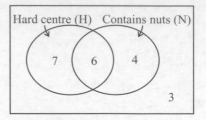

Other answers are possible, e.g. showing S and N instead of H and N.
[1 mark for two appropriate sets (e.g. H and N, or S and N, etc.), plus 1 mark for all numbers correctly marked on the diagram.]

b) (i) $P(S) = \dfrac{\text{Number of soft centres}}{\text{Total number of chocolates}}$
$\qquad = \dfrac{4 + 3}{20} = \dfrac{7}{20}$ *[1 mark]*

(ii) $P(H \mid N)$
$= \dfrac{\text{Number of chocolates in both H and N}}{\text{Number of chocolates in N}}$ *[1 mark]*
$= \dfrac{6}{10} = \dfrac{3}{5}$ *[1 mark]*

In part (ii), you're "given that the chocolate contains a nut", so you only need to look at the circle containing nutty chocolates — you can ignore the rest of the diagram.

c) P(pick hard centre with 1st pick) $= \dfrac{13}{20} \times \dfrac{7}{19} \times \dfrac{6}{18}$
$\qquad\qquad = \dfrac{546}{6840} = \dfrac{91}{1140}$ *[1 mark]*

This is P(HSS), but you also need to add P(SHS) and P(SSH). In fact, P(HSS) = P(SHS) = P(SSH), so you need to multiply the above answer by 3 *[1 mark]*.

So P(pick one hard centre) $= 3 \times \dfrac{91}{1140} = \dfrac{91}{380}$ *[1 mark]*.

Don't forget that the hard centre could be the first one picked out of the box, or the second or the third — and you need to take the fact that there are 'different arrangements' into account when you work out your probability.

5) a) $P(X > 1) = 1 - P(X \le 1)$.
From tables, $P(X \le 1) = 0.3917$ *[1 mark]*.
So $P(X > 1) = 1 - 0.3917 = 0.6083$
$= 0.608$ (to 3 sig. fig.) *[1 mark]*.

b) $P(2 < X \le 6) = P(X \le 6) - P(X \le 2)$ *[1 mark]*
$= 0.9976 - 0.6769$ *[1 mark]* $= 0.3207$
$= 0.321$ (to 3 sig. fig.) *[1 mark]*

6) a) Mean $= \dfrac{\sum x}{n} = \dfrac{66.5}{12}$ *[1 mark]*
$\qquad\qquad = 5.54$ (or £5540) (to 3 sig. fig.) *[1 mark]*.

Mean square deviation =
$\dfrac{\sum x^2}{n} - \left(\dfrac{\sum x}{n}\right)^2 = \dfrac{390.97}{12} - \left(\dfrac{66.5}{12}\right)^2$ *[1 mark]*
$= 1.87$ (to 3 sig. fig.) *[1 mark]*.

b) The ordered list of the 12 data points is:
3.8, 4.1, 4.2, 4.6, 4.9, 5.5, 5.8, 5.9, 6.0, 6.2, 6.4, 9.1.

The position of the median is $\frac{1}{2}(n + 1) = \frac{1}{2}(12 + 1) = 6.5$,
so take the average of the 6th and 7th values.

So the median Q_2 is: $\frac{1}{2}(5.5 + 5.8) = 5.65$ *[1 mark]*.

Since $12 \div 4 = 3$, the lower quartile is the average of the
3rd and 4th values.

So the lower quartile Q_1 is: $\frac{1}{2}(4.2 + 4.6) = 4.4$ *[1 mark]*.

Since $12 \div 4 \times 3 = 9$, the upper quartile is the average of
the 9th and 10th values.

So the upper quartile Q_3 is: $\frac{1}{2}(6.0 + 6.2) = 6.1$ *[1 mark]*.

c) The lower fence is given by:
$Q_1 - 1.5 \times (Q_3 - Q_1) = 4.4 - 1.5 \times (6.1 - 4.4) = 1.85$
[1 mark]. So there are no outliers below the lower fence
[1 mark]. The upper fence is given by:
$Q_3 + 1.5 \times (Q_3 - Q_1) = 6.1 + 1.5 \times (6.1 - 4.4) = 8.65$
[1 mark]. So there is one outlier — the value of 9.1
[1 mark].

d) You need to use the mid-class values. It's best to add some
extra rows to the table.

Sales (£'000s)	0-3	3-6	6-7	7-8	8-9	9-10
Number of weeks, f	3	6	9	11	13	10
Mid-class value, y	1.5	4.5	6.5	7.5	8.5	9.5
$f \times y$	4.5	27	58.5	82.5	110.5	95

$\bar{y} = \dfrac{\sum fy}{\sum f} = \dfrac{378}{52}$ *[1 mark]*

$= 7.27$ or £7270 (to 3 sig.fig.) *[1 mark]*

Numbers, numbers everywhere.

e) It's time for another table — this time showing frequency
density = frequency ÷ class width.

Sales (£'000s)	Class width (£'000s)	Frequency	Frequency Density
$0 \leq y < 3$	3	3	1
$3 \leq y < 6$	3	6	2
$6 \leq y < 7$	1	9	9
$7 \leq y < 8$	1	11	11
$8 \leq y < 9$	1	13	13
$9 \leq y < 10$	1	10	10

Now you can draw the histogram:

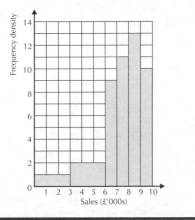

*[1 mark for calculating the frequency densities, 1 mark
for clearly labelled correct axes, 1 mark for all bars the
correct width, 1 mark for all bars the correct height.]*

f) Negative skew *[1 mark]*

7 a) Let X represent the number in the sample who use the pool.
$X \sim B(10, 0.45)$

(i) $P(X = 2) = \binom{10}{2} \times p^2 \times q^8$ *[1 mark]*

$= \dfrac{10!}{2!8!} \times 0.45^2 \times 0.55^8$ *[1 mark]* $= 0.0763$ *[1 mark]*

(ii) $P(X < 5) = P(X \leq 4)$ *[1 mark]* $= 0.5044$ *[1 mark]*

(iii) $P(X \geq 3) = 1 - P(X \leq 2)$ *[1 mark]* $= 1 - 0.0996$ *[1 mark]*
$= 0.9004$ *[1 mark]*

(iv) $E(X) = np = 10 \times 0.45$ *[1 mark]* $= 4.5$ *[1 mark]*

b) (i) Let p = proportion of gym's members who use the pool.
[1 mark]
$H_0: p = 0.45$ *[1 mark]* and $H_1: p < 0.45$ *[1 mark]*.
H_1 has this form because the manager thinks that the
proportion has decreased. *[1 mark]*

(ii) Y = number of people in sample of 16 who use the
pool. Under H_0, $Y \sim B(16, 0.45)$ *[1 mark]*
Using the binomial tables, $P(Y \leq 3) = 0.0281$ *[1 mark]*.
Since $0.0281 < 0.05$, you should reject H_0. *[1 mark]*
So there is evidence at the 5% level of significance to
suggest that the popularity of the pool has decreased.
[1 mark]

Answers

M1 Section 1 — Vectors
Warm-up Questions

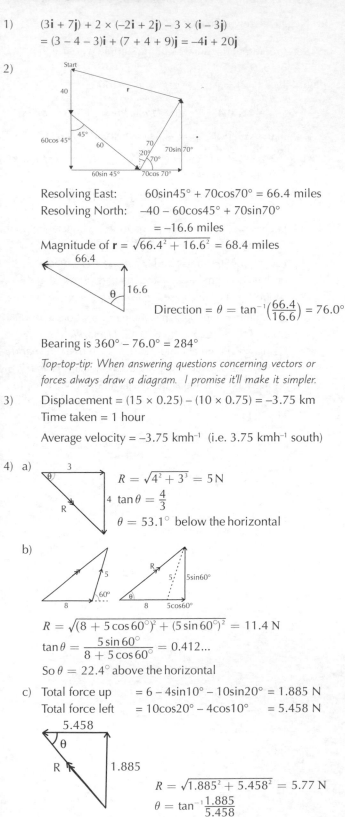

1) $(3\mathbf{i} + 7\mathbf{j}) + 2 \times (-2\mathbf{i} + 2\mathbf{j}) - 3 \times (\mathbf{i} - 3\mathbf{j})$
$= (3 - 4 - 3)\mathbf{i} + (7 + 4 + 9)\mathbf{j} = -4\mathbf{i} + 20\mathbf{j}$

2)

Resolving East:　$60\sin45° + 70\cos70° = 66.4$ miles

Resolving North:　$-40 - 60\cos45° + 70\sin70°$
$= -16.6$ miles

Magnitude of $\mathbf{r} = \sqrt{66.4^2 + 16.6^2} = 68.4$ miles

Direction $= \theta = \tan^{-1}\left(\dfrac{66.4}{16.6}\right) = 76.0°$

Bearing is $360° - 76.0° = 284°$

Top-top-tip: When answering questions concerning vectors or forces always draw a diagram. I promise it'll make it simpler.

3) Displacement $= (15 \times 0.25) - (10 \times 0.75) = -3.75$ km
Time taken $= 1$ hour
Average velocity $= -3.75$ kmh^{-1} (i.e. 3.75 kmh^{-1} south)

4) a) $R = \sqrt{4^2 + 3^3} = 5\,\text{N}$
$\tan\theta = \dfrac{4}{3}$
$\theta = 53.1°$ below the horizontal

b) $R = \sqrt{(8 + 5\cos60°)^2 + (5\sin60°)^2} = 11.4\,\text{N}$
$\tan\theta = \dfrac{5\sin60°}{8 + 5\cos60°} = 0.412...$
So $\theta = 22.4°$ above the horizontal

c) Total force up　$= 6 - 4\sin10° - 10\sin20° = 1.885\,\text{N}$
Total force left　$= 10\cos20° - 4\cos10° = 5.458\,\text{N}$

$R = \sqrt{1.885^2 + 5.458^2} = 5.77\,\text{N}$
$\theta = \tan^{-1}\dfrac{1.885}{5.458}$
$= 19.1°$ above the horizontal

Exam Questions

1 Resolve horizontally: $0 + 5\cos30° = 4.330\,\text{N}$
Resolve vertically:　$4 - 5\sin30° = 1.5\,\text{N}$

$\theta = \tan^{-1}\left(\dfrac{1.5}{4.330}\right) = 19.1°$

i.e. $\theta = 19.1°$ above the horizontal
Magnitude $= \sqrt{1.5^2 + 4.330^2} = 4.58\,\text{N}$

[4 marks available in total]:
- *1 mark for resolving horizontally*
- *1 mark for resolving vertically*
- *1 mark for calculating the direction*
- *1 mark for calculating the magnitude*

Triangles — how do I love thee? Let me count the ways...
...one big way, really. They're just super useful when resolving things.

2 a) $\mathbf{R} = \mathbf{P} + \mathbf{Q} = (2\mathbf{i} - 11\mathbf{j}) + (7\mathbf{i} + 5\mathbf{j}) = (9\mathbf{i} - 6\mathbf{j})\,\text{N}$

[2 marks available in total]:
- *1 mark for correct workings*
- *1 mark for correct resultant*

b) $|\mathbf{R}| = \sqrt{9^2 + (-6)^2} = 10.8\,\text{N}$

[2 marks available in total]:
- *1 mark for correct workings*
- *1 mark for correct magnitude*

3 a)

Resolve vertically:
$4\sin30° = 2$
Resolve horizontally:
$7 + 4\cos30° = 10.464...$

$R = \sqrt{2^2 + (7 + 4\cos30°)^2}$
$= 10.7\,\text{N}$ (3 s.f.)

[4 marks available in total]:
- *1 mark for diagram*
- *1 mark for resolving vertically*
- *1 mark for resolving horizontally*
- *1 mark for correct magnitude*

b) $\tan\alpha = \dfrac{2}{10.5} = 0.19$
$\alpha = 10.8°$

[2 marks available in total]:
- *1 mark for correct workings*
- *1 mark for correct value of α*

4

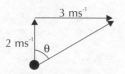

Magnitude $= \sqrt{2^2 + 3^2} = \sqrt{13} = 3.61\,\text{ms}^{-1}$
$\theta = \tan^{-1}\left(\dfrac{3}{2}\right) = 56.3°$
So angle to river bank is $90° - 56.3° = 33.7°$

Answers

[4 marks available in total]:
- ***1 mark for a diagram***
- ***1 mark for calculating the magnitude of the velocity***
- ***1 mark for correct workings***
- ***1 mark for calculating the angle from the bank***

M1 Section 2 — Kinematics
Warm-up Questions

1) $u = 3$; $v = 9$; $a = a$; $s = s$; $t = 2$. Use $s = ½(u + v)t$
$s = ½(3 + 9) \times 2$ $\quad s = ½(12) \times 2 = 12$ m

2) 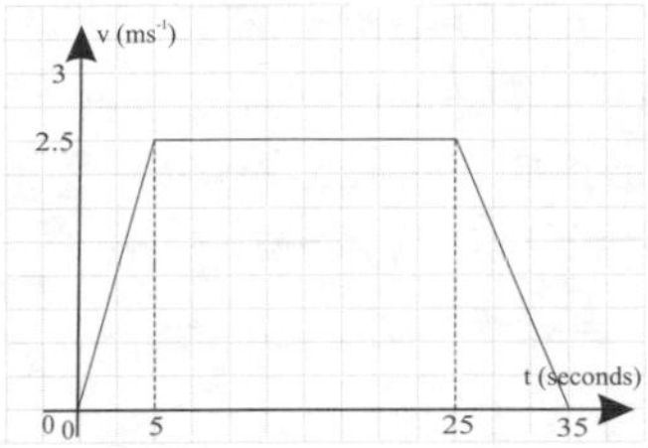

distance = $(5 \times 2.5) \div 2 + (20 \times 2.5) + (10 \times 2.5) \div 2$
$= 68.75$ m

3) velocity = area under (t, a) graph
a) $t = 3$, velocity = $(3 \times 5) \div 2 = 7.5$ ms^{-1}
b) $t = 5$, velocity = $7.5 + (2 \times 5) = 17.5$ ms^{-1}
c) $t = 6$, velocity = $17.5 + (1 \times 5) \div 2 = 20$ ms^{-1}

4) a) $\mathbf{r} = \int \mathbf{v}\,dt = 2t^2\mathbf{i} + \frac{t^4}{4}\mathbf{j} + \mathbf{C}$
When $t = 0$, the particle is at the origin $\Rightarrow \mathbf{C} = 0\mathbf{i} + 0\mathbf{j}$.
So, $\mathbf{r} = 2t^2\mathbf{i} + \frac{t^4}{4}\mathbf{j}$

b) $\mathbf{a} = \frac{d\mathbf{v}}{dt} = 4\mathbf{i} + 3t^2\mathbf{j}$

c) From a), $\mathbf{r} = 2t^2\mathbf{i} + \frac{t^4}{4}\mathbf{j}$, so take $x = 2t^2$ and $y = \frac{t^4}{4}$.
$x = 2t^2 \Rightarrow t = \sqrt{\frac{x}{2}}$

So $y = \frac{\left(\sqrt{\frac{x}{2}}\right)^4}{4} = \frac{\left(\frac{x^2}{4}\right)}{4} = \frac{x^2}{16}$.
So the equation of the path of the particle is $y = \frac{x^2}{16}$.

Exam Questions

1 a) Using $u = v - at$
$u = 17 - (9.8 \times 1.2)$
So, $u = 5.24$ ms^{-1}
[3 marks available in total]:
- ***1 mark for using appropriate equation***
- ***1 mark for correct workings***
- ***1 mark for correct value of u***

These kind of questions are trivial if you've memorised all those constant acceleration equations. If you haven't, you know what to do now (turn to p. 165).

b) Using $s = ut + \frac{1}{2}at^2$
$s = (17 \times 2.1) + \frac{1}{2}(9.8 \times 2.1^2)$
So, $s = 57.31$
$h = \frac{s}{14} = 4.09$ m
[4 marks available in total]:
- ***1 mark for using appropriate equation***
- ***1 mark for correct value of s***
- ***1 mark for correct workings***
- ***1 mark for correct value of h***

2 For the first particle:
$\mathbf{s}_A = \mathbf{s}_Q + \mathbf{v}t$
$= (\mathbf{i} + 2\mathbf{j}) + 8(3\mathbf{i} + \mathbf{j}) = (\mathbf{i} + 2\mathbf{j}) + (24\mathbf{i} + 8\mathbf{j}) = (25\mathbf{i} + 10\mathbf{j})$ m
$\mathbf{s}_B = \mathbf{s}_A + \mathbf{v}t$
$= (25\mathbf{i} + 10\mathbf{j}) + (-20\mathbf{i} + 10\mathbf{j}) = (5\mathbf{i} + 20\mathbf{j})$ m
[4 marks available in total]:
- ***1 mark for correct workings for S_A***
- ***1 mark for correct value of S_A***
- ***1 mark for correct workings for S_B***
- ***1 mark for correct value of S_B***

Argh. My head hurts with the sheer quantity of **i***s and* **j***s in those workings. Better to take it a step at a time (it's good for your health).*

3 a) 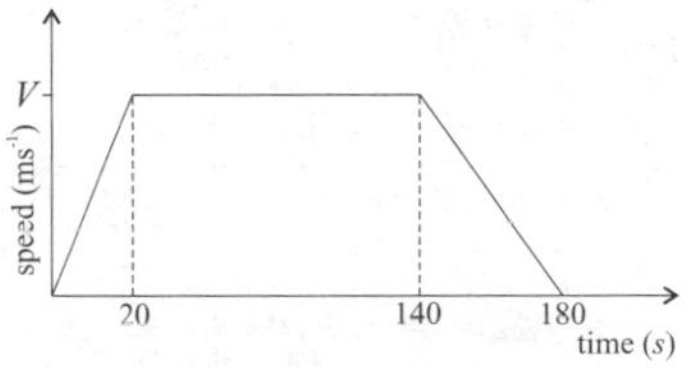

[3 marks available in total]:
- ***1 mark for the correct shape***
- ***1 mark for the correct times***
- ***1 mark for correctly marking V on the vertical axis***

b) Area under graph (area of trapezium) = distance
$\frac{1}{2}(120 + 180)V = 2100$
$V = \frac{2100}{150} = 14$ ms^{-1}
[3 marks available in total]:
- ***1 mark for using Area under graph = distance***
- ***1 mark for correct workings***
- ***1 mark for correct value of V***

The area could also be worked out in other ways, say, using two triangles and a rectangle. Best to use whatever's easiest for you.

c) Distance = area under graph
$= ½ \times 40 \times 14 = 280$ m
[2 marks available in total]:
- ***1 mark for using Area under graph = distance***
- ***1 mark for correct value***

d) Using $a = \frac{v - u}{t}$.
Acceleration period:
$t = 20$, $v = 14$, $u = 0$
$a = (14 - 0) \div 20 = 0.7$ ms^{-2}
Deceleration period:
$t = 40$, $v = 0$, $u = 14$
$a = (0 - 14) \div 40 = -0.35$ ms^{-2}

Answers

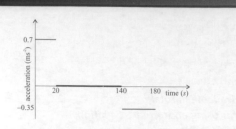

[3 marks available in total]:
- 1 mark for correct shape
- 1 mark for correct value of acceleration (0.7 ms⁻²)
- 1 mark for correct value of deceleration (0.35 ms⁻²)

Yep, sometimes you're not given the values you need to label a graph and you have to work them out yourself. All good practice.

4 a) $a = 0 \Rightarrow \dfrac{dv}{dt} = 0$.

So, in the interval $0 \le t \le 4$,

$a = \dfrac{dv}{dt} = 9 - 6t$ [1 mark]

Set $a = 0$:

$0 = 9 - 6t \Rightarrow t = 1.5$ s [1 mark]

b) $s = \int v \, dt$

$= \dfrac{9t^2}{2} - t^3 + c$ for $0 \le t \le 4$. [1 mark]

When $t = 0$, P is at the origin, i.e. $s = 0 \Rightarrow c = 0$ [1 mark]

So, at $t = 4$: $s = \dfrac{9}{2}(16) - 64 = 8$ m [1 mark]

c) $s = \int v \, dt = \int -12 dt = -12t + k$ for $t > 4$. [1 mark]
From part b), when $t = 4$ s, $s = 8$ m. Use these as initial conditions to find k:

$8 = -12(4) + k \Rightarrow k = 8 + 48 = 56$. [1 mark]
So $s = -12t + 56$. Set $s = 0$ to find when the particle is back at the origin:

$0 = -12t + 56 \Rightarrow t = 56 \div 12 = 4.67$ s (3 s.f.) [1 mark]

You could have done this without integrating, as the speed is constant — but a little light integration never hurt anybody now, did it?

5 a) $u = u$; $v = 20$; $a = 9.8$; $s = 8$.
Using $v^2 = u^2 + 2as$
$20^2 = u^2 + (2 \times 9.8 \times 8)$
$u = -\sqrt{400 - 156.8}$
So, $u = -15.6$ ms⁻¹

[3 marks available in total]:
- 1 mark for using appropriate equation
- 1 mark for correct workings
- 1 mark for correct value of u

The initial velocity is negative, as the rocket is projected upwards.

b) Using $v = u + at$
$20 = -15.59 + 9.8t$
So, $9.8t = 35.59$
hence $t = 3.63$ s (3 s.f.)

[3 marks available in total]:
- 1 mark for using appropriate equation
- 1 mark for correct workings
- 1 mark for correct value of t

Constant use of those constant acceleration equations...
See, I wasn't fooling around — learn them.

6 a) $\mathbf{v} = \dot{\mathbf{r}} = (6t^2 - 14t)\mathbf{i} + (6t - 12t^2)\mathbf{j}$ ms⁻¹.

[2 marks available in total — 1 mark for attempting to differentiate the position vector, 1 mark for correctly differentiating both components]

b) $\mathbf{v} = \left(\dfrac{6}{4} - \dfrac{14}{2}\right)\mathbf{i} + \left(\dfrac{6}{2} - \dfrac{12}{4}\right)\mathbf{j}$ [1 mark]

$= -5.5\mathbf{i} + 0\mathbf{j}$

Speed $= \sqrt{(-5.5)^2 + 0^2} = 5.5$ ms⁻¹ [1 mark]
The component of velocity in the direction of north is zero, and the component in the direction of east is negative, so the particle is moving due west [1 mark]

c) $\mathbf{a} = \dot{\mathbf{v}}$ [1 mark]
$= (12t - 14)\mathbf{i} + (6 - 24t)\mathbf{j}$ [1 mark]
At $t = 2$, $\mathbf{a} = 10\mathbf{i} - 42\mathbf{j}$ ms⁻¹ [1 mark]

d) Use $\mathbf{F} = m\mathbf{a}$ [1 mark] to find the force at $t = 2$:
$\mathbf{F} = 4(10\mathbf{i} - 42\mathbf{j}) = 40\mathbf{i} - 168\mathbf{j}$ N [1 mark]

7 a) Speed $= \sqrt{7^2 + (-3)^2} = \sqrt{58}$
$= 7.62$ ms⁻¹

[2 marks available in total]:
- 1 mark for correct workings
- 1 mark for correct value

A bit of a classic here, and easy if you remember that for a vector ($x\mathbf{i} + y\mathbf{j}$) then the magnitude $= \sqrt{x^2 + y^2}$.

b) Angle from horizontal $= \tan^{-1}\left(\dfrac{-3}{7}\right)$
$= -23.2°$ (i.e. 23° south of east)
The bearing is measured from north
so, bearing $= 90 + 23.2 = 113°$

[3 marks available in total]:
- 1 mark for correct workings
- 1 mark for calculating angle
- 1 mark for correct bearing

Bearings are measured from the north, because that's where Polar bears live, and where the Be[a]ring Strait is — maybe...

c) Position at $t = 4$:
$(\mathbf{i} + 5\mathbf{j}) + 4(7\mathbf{i} - 3\mathbf{j}) = (29\mathbf{i} - 7\mathbf{j})$ m
Displacement to $15\mathbf{i}$:
$15\mathbf{i} - (29\mathbf{i} - 7\mathbf{j}) = (-14\mathbf{i} + 7\mathbf{j})$ m
Velocity $= \dfrac{\mathbf{s}}{t} = (-14\mathbf{i} + 7\mathbf{j})/3.5 = (-4\mathbf{i} + 2\mathbf{j})$
So, $a = -4$ and $b = 2$

[4 marks available in total]:
- 1 mark for calculating position at t = 4
- 1 mark for calculating displacement to 15i
- 1 mark for correct workings
- 1 mark for correct values of a and b

8 a) $a = \dot{v} = 6 - 2t$ ms⁻². [1 mark]

b)
$s = \int_0^3 v \, dt = \left[3t^2 - \dfrac{t^3}{3}\right]_0^3 = 3(3)^2 - \dfrac{3^3}{3} = 18$ m.

[3 marks available in total — 1 mark for integrating, 1 mark for substituting in limits, 1 mark for correct answer]

Answers

M1 Section 3 — Forces
Warm-up Questions

1) a) 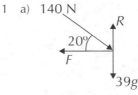 Small point mass, no air resistance, no wind, released from rest.

   b) Small point mass, no air resistance, no wind, released from rest.

   c) Same assumptions as in a) and b), although it might not be safe to ignore wind if outside as table tennis balls are very light.

   You need to get familiar with modelling and all the terminology used in M1 — it's going to be really tricky to figure out M1 questions if you're not.

2) Assumptions: Point mass, one point of contact with ground, constant driving force D from engine, constant friction, F, includes road resistance and air resistance, acceleration = 0 as it's moving at 25mph (in a straight line).

3)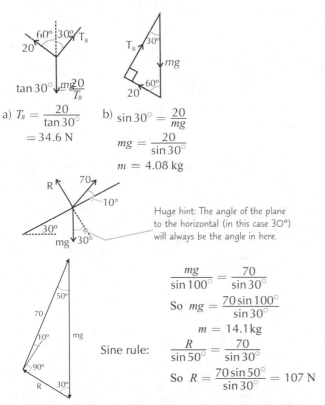

   a) $T_B = \dfrac{20}{\tan 30^\circ}$
   $= 34.6\,\text{N}$

   b) $\sin 30^\circ = \dfrac{20}{mg}$
   $mg = \dfrac{20}{\sin 30^\circ}$
   $m = 4.08\,\text{kg}$

4)

   Huge hint: The angle of the plane to the horizontal (in this case 30°) will always be the angle in here.

   $\dfrac{mg}{\sin 100^\circ} = \dfrac{70}{\sin 30^\circ}$

   So $mg = \dfrac{70 \sin 100^\circ}{\sin 30^\circ}$

   $m = 14.1\,\text{kg}$

   Sine rule: $\dfrac{R}{\sin 50^\circ} = \dfrac{70}{\sin 30^\circ}$

   So $R = \dfrac{70 \sin 50^\circ}{\sin 30^\circ} = 107\,\text{N}$

   Yet another example of how triangles might just save your life mark for the M1 module. Although you could also have solved it by resolving forces parallel and perpendicular to the slope if that floats your boat.

5)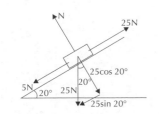

Force perpendicular to the slope: $N = 25\cos 20^\circ = 23.5\,\text{N}$
Force parallel to the slope: $25 - 25\sin 20^\circ - 5 = 11.4\,\text{N}$.
So the resultant force is 11.4 N up the slope.

Exam Questions

1   a)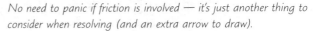

   [2 marks available in total]:
   • *1 mark for drawing 4 correct arrows*
   • *1 mark for correctly labelling the arrows*

   b) Resolve vertically:
   $R = 39g + 140\sin 20^\circ = 430\,\text{N}$
   Resolve horizontally:
   $F = 140\cos 20^\circ = 132\,\text{N}$

   [4 marks available in total]:
   • *1 mark for resolving vertically*
   • *1 mark for resolving horizontally*
   • *1 mark for correct reaction magnitude*
   • *1 mark for correct friction magnitude*

   No need to panic if friction is involved — it's just another thing to consider when resolving (and an extra arrow to draw).

2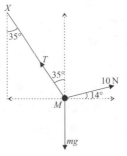

   Resolving vertically: $mg = 10\sin 14^\circ + T\cos 35^\circ$
   Need to find T.
   Resolving horizontally: $T\sin 35^\circ = 10\cos 14^\circ$
   So, $T = \dfrac{10\cos 14^\circ}{\sin 35^\circ} = 16.92\,\text{N}$
   So $mg = 10\sin 14^\circ + 16.92\cos 35^\circ = 16.28\,\text{N}$
   Therefore, the mass of $M = \dfrac{16.28}{g} = 1.66\,\text{kg}$

   [4 marks available in total]:
   • *1 mark for resolving vertically*
   • *1 mark for resolving horizontally*
   • *1 mark for correct value of T*
   • *1 mark for correct mass of M*

3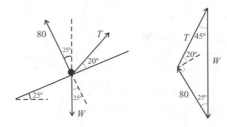

a) $\dfrac{T}{\sin 25°} = \dfrac{80}{\sin 45°}$

So, $T = \dfrac{80 \sin 25°}{\sin 45°} = 47.8$ N

[3 marks available in total]:
- *1 mark for diagram*
- *1 mark for correct workings*
- *1 mark for correct value of T*

b) $\dfrac{W}{\sin 110°} = \dfrac{80}{\sin 45°}$

So, $W = \dfrac{80 \sin 110°}{\sin 45°} = 106$ N

[2 marks available in total]:
- *1 mark for correct workings*
- *1 mark for correct value of W*

4 a) Resolving horizontally:

$T\cos 50° = 58$ N

so, $T = \dfrac{58}{\cos 50°} = 90.2$ N

[3 marks available in total]:
- *1 mark for resolving horizontally*
- *1 mark for correct workings*
- *1 mark for correct value of T*

b) Resolving vertically:

$mg = T\sin 50° = 90.2\sin 50°$

so, $mg = 69.12...$ and $m = 7.05$ kg (3 s.f.)

[3 marks available in total]:
- *1 mark for resolving vertically*
- *1 mark for correct workings*
- *1 mark for correct value of m*

5 a)

$\sin \theta = \dfrac{12}{15}$, so, $\theta = 53.1°$

[2 marks available in total]:
- *1 mark for correct workings*
- *1 mark for the correct value of θ*

b) $15^2 = W^2 + 12^2$

$W = \sqrt{15^2 - 12^2} = 9$ N

[2 marks available in total]:
- *1 mark for correct workings*
- *1 mark for correct value of W*

c) Remove W and the particle moves in the opposite direction to W, i.e. upwards. This resultant of the two remaining forces is 9 N upwards, because the particle was in equilibrium beforehand.

[2 marks available in total]:
- *1 mark for correct magnitude*
- *1 mark for correct direction*

The word 'state' in an exam question means that you shouldn't need to do any extra calculation to answer it.

M1 Section 4 — Newton's Laws of Motion
Warm-up Questions

1) Resolve horizontally: $F_{net} = ma$

$2 = 1.5a$ so $a = 1\frac{1}{3}$ ms^{-2}

$v = u + at$ $v = 0 + (1\frac{1}{3} \times 3) = 4$ ms^{-1}

And we're off. I hope that bit of resolving was simple enough (if not you might want to go revise).

2) $\mathbf{F}_{net} = (24\mathbf{i} + 18\mathbf{j}) + (6\mathbf{i} + 22\mathbf{j}) = 30\mathbf{i} + 40\mathbf{j}$

magnitude of $\mathbf{F}_{net} = \sqrt{30^2 + 40^2} = 50$ N

$F_{net} = ma$, so $50 = 8a$, which gives $a = 6.25$ ms^{-2}

$\tan\alpha = \dfrac{40}{30}$, i.e. $\alpha = 53.1°$

$s = ut + \frac{1}{2}at^2$, $s = 0 \times 3 + \frac{1}{2} \times 6.25 \times 3^2 = 28.1$ m (3 s.f.)

3) Using $\mathbf{F} = m\mathbf{a}$:

$\begin{pmatrix} 6 \\ 4 \\ 2 \end{pmatrix} = 2\mathbf{a}$

$\Rightarrow \mathbf{a} = \dfrac{1}{2}\begin{pmatrix} 6 \\ 4 \\ 2 \end{pmatrix} = \begin{pmatrix} 3 \\ 2 \\ 1 \end{pmatrix}$ ms^{-2}.

4) Taking tractor and trailer together (and calling the resistance force on the trailer R):

Resolving horizontally: $F_{net} = ma$

$1500 - R - 1000 = 3000 \times 0$

$R = 500$ N

For trailer alone:

Resolving horizontally:

$F_{net} = ma$

$T - 500 = 1000 \times 0$

$T = 500$ N

T could be found instead by looking at the horizontal forces acting on the tractor alone.

5) Resolving downwards for A:

$F_{net} = ma$

$4g - T = 4 \times 1.2$

$T = 4g - 4.8$ ①

Resolving upwards for B:

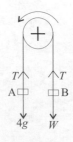

$F_{net} = ma$

$T - W = \dfrac{W}{g} \times 1.2$ ②

Sub ① into ② :

$(4g - 4.8) - W = \dfrac{W}{g}(1.2)$

$4g - 4.8 = W(1 + \dfrac{1.2}{g})$

So $W = 30.6$ N

Here the particles are connected over a pulley, rather than in a straight line, but the key is still resolving — downwards and upwards instead of horizontally and vertically. No need for any panic then. Phew.

6) For B, resolving vertically:

$F_{net} = ma$

$4g - T = 4a$

$T = 4g - 4a$ ①

For A , resolving in ↗ direction:

$F_{net} = ma$

$T - 3g\sin40° = 3a$ ②

Sub ① into ②:

$4g - 4a - 3g\sin40° = 3a$

$4g - 3g\sin40° = 7a$

$a = 2.90$ ms^{-2} (to 3 s.f.)

Sub into ① :

$T = 4g - (4 \times 2.9) = 27.6$ N (to 3 s.f.)

If equilibrium, then for B:

$T = 4g$

Then for A:

Resolving in ↗ direction:

$F_{net} = ma$

$T - 3g\sin40° - P = 0$

$4g - 3g\sin40° = P$

$P = 20.3$ N (to 3 s.f.)

Exam Questions

1 a) Considering the car and the caravan together:

Resolving horizontally:

$F_{net} = ma$

$2500 - 1200 = 2000a$

$a = 0.65$ ms^{-2}

[3 marks available in total]:
* *1 mark for resolving horizontally*
* *1 mark for correct workings*
* *1 mark for correct value of a*

b) Either: *Caravan*
Resolving horizontally:

$F_{net} = ma$

$T - 200 = 500 \times 0.65$

$T = 525$ N

[2 marks available in total]:
* *1 mark for resolving horizontally*
* *1 mark for correct value of T*

Or: *Car*
Resolving horizontally:

$F_{net} = ma$

$2500 - (1000 + T) = 1500 \times 0.65$

$2500 - 1000 - T = 975$

$1500 - 975 = T$

$T = 525$ N

[2 marks available in total]:
* *1 mark for resolving horizontally*
* *1 mark for correct value of T*

Two different methods, one correct answer. At the end of the day, it doesn't matter which you use (but show your diagrams and workings), although it's certainly a bonus if you manage to pick the simpler way and save a bit of time in the exam.

2 a) $(8\mathbf{i} - 3\mathbf{j}) = (x\mathbf{i} + y\mathbf{j}) + (5\mathbf{i} + \mathbf{j})$
So, $x\mathbf{i} + y\mathbf{j} = (8\mathbf{i} - 3\mathbf{j}) - (5\mathbf{i} + \mathbf{j})$, so $x = 3$ and $y = -4$
[2 marks available in total]:
* *1 mark for correct value of x*
* *1 mark for correct value of y*

b) Magnitude of resultant force $= \sqrt{8^2 + (-3)^2} = \sqrt{73}$
Using $F = ma$:
$8.5 = 2.5a$, so $a = 3.42$ ms^{-2} (3 s.f.)
[3 marks available in total]:
* *1 mark using F = ma*
* *1 mark for correct workings*
* *1 mark for correct value of a*

3 a) Resolving forces acting on A:
$7g - T = 7a$
Resolving forces acting on B:
$T - 3g = 3a$, so $T = 3a + 3g$
Substituting T:
$7g - 3a - 3g = 7a$, so $4g = 10a$
hence $a = 3.92$ ms^{-2}
Using $t = \dfrac{(v - u)}{a}$:
$t = (5.9 - 0) \div 3.92$
So, $t = 1.51$ s (to 3 s.f.)
[4 marks available in total]:
* *1 mark for resolving forces*
* *1 mark for correct value of a*
* *1 mark for correct workings*
* *1 mark for correct value of t*

b) Using $s = \dfrac{(v^2 - u^2)}{2a}$
$s = (5.9^2 - 0^2) \div (2 \times 3.92)$
$s = 4.44$ m (to 3 s.f.)
[2 marks available in total]:
* *1 mark for correct workings*
* *1 mark for correct value of s*

Answers

c) When A hits the ground, speed of A = speed of B = 5.9 ms⁻¹
B will then continue to rise, momentarily stop and then fall freely under gravity. String will be taut again when displacement of B = 0.

So, $a = -9.8$, $s = 0$, $u = 5.9$

Using $s = ut + \frac{1}{2}at^2$:

$0 = 5.9t + \frac{1}{2}(-9.8)t^2 = 5.9t - 4.9t^2$

Solve for t:

$4.9t^2 = 5.9t$, so $t(4.9t - 5.9) = 0$

and so $t = 0$ s, or $t = 5.9 \div 4.9 = 1.20$ s

So the string becomes taut again at $t = 1.20$ s (3 s.f.)

[4 marks available in total]:
- **1 mark for using $s = ut + \frac{1}{2}at^2$**
- **1 mark for correct workings**
- **1 mark for solving for t**
- **1 mark for correct value of t**

4 a) Constant velocity, so, $a = 0$
Resolve horizontally:

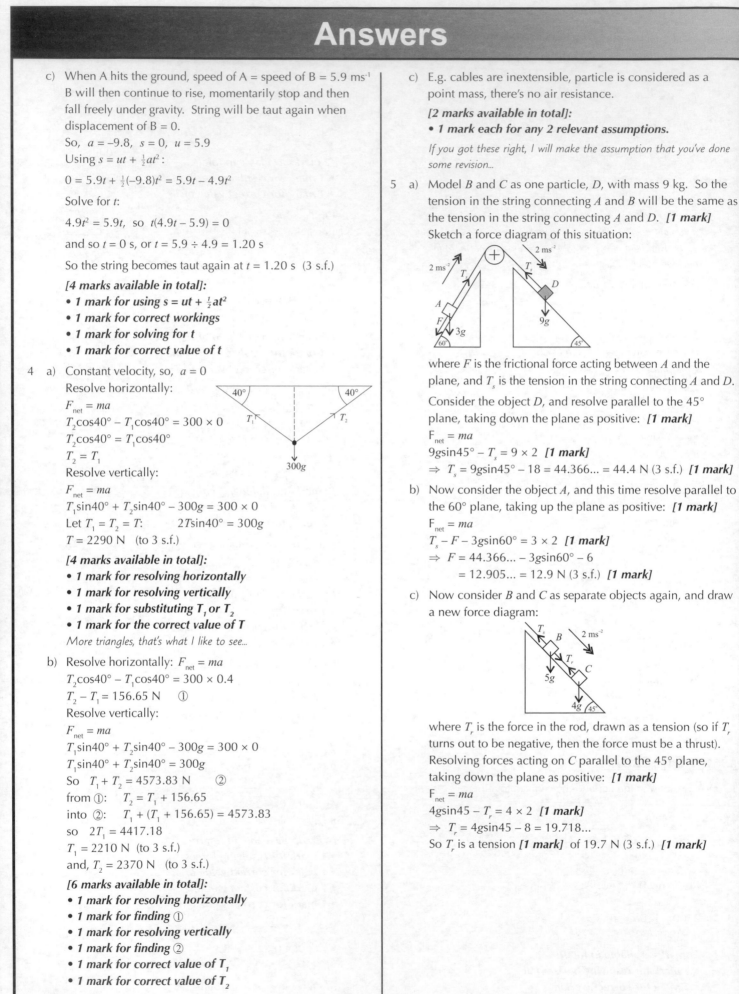

$F_{net} = ma$
$T_2\cos40° - T_1\cos40° = 300 \times 0$
$T_2\cos40° = T_1\cos40°$
$T_2 = T_1$
Resolve vertically:
$F_{net} = ma$
$T_1\sin40° + T_2\sin40° - 300g = 300 \times 0$
Let $T_1 = T_2 = T$: $2T\sin40° = 300g$
$T = 2290$ N (to 3 s.f.)

[4 marks available in total]:
- **1 mark for resolving horizontally**
- **1 mark for resolving vertically**
- **1 mark for substituting T_1 or T_2**
- **1 mark for the correct value of T**

More triangles, that's what I like to see...

b) Resolve horizontally: $F_{net} = ma$
$T_2\cos40° - T_1\cos40° = 300 \times 0.4$
$T_2 - T_1 = 156.65$ N   ①
Resolve vertically:
$F_{net} = ma$
$T_1\sin40° + T_2\sin40° - 300g = 300 \times 0$
$T_1\sin40° + T_2\sin40° = 300g$
So $T_1 + T_2 = 4573.83$ N   ②
from ①: $T_2 = T_1 + 156.65$
into ②: $T_1 + (T_1 + 156.65) = 4573.83$
so $2T_1 = 4417.18$
$T_1 = 2210$ N (to 3 s.f.)
and, $T_2 = 2370$ N (to 3 s.f.)

[6 marks available in total]:
- **1 mark for resolving horizontally**
- **1 mark for finding ①**
- **1 mark for resolving vertically**
- **1 mark for finding ②**
- **1 mark for correct value of T_1**
- **1 mark for correct value of T_2**

c) E.g. cables are inextensible, particle is considered as a point mass, there's no air resistance.

[2 marks available in total]:
- **1 mark each for any 2 relevant assumptions.**

If you got these right, I will make the assumption that you've done some revision...

5 a) Model B and C as one particle, D, with mass 9 kg. So the tension in the string connecting A and B will be the same as the tension in the string connecting A and D. **[1 mark]**
Sketch a force diagram of this situation:

where F is the frictional force acting between A and the plane, and T_s is the tension in the string connecting A and D.

Consider the object D, and resolve parallel to the 45° plane, taking down the plane as positive: **[1 mark]**
$F_{net} = ma$
$9g\sin45° - T_s = 9 \times 2$ **[1 mark]**
$\Rightarrow T_s = 9g\sin45° - 18 = 44.366... = 44.4$ N (3 s.f.) **[1 mark]**

b) Now consider the object A, and this time resolve parallel to the 60° plane, taking up the plane as positive: **[1 mark]**
$F_{net} = ma$
$T_s - F - 3g\sin60° = 3 \times 2$ **[1 mark]**
$\Rightarrow F = 44.366... - 3g\sin60° - 6$
$= 12.905... = 12.9$ N (3 s.f.) **[1 mark]**

c) Now consider B and C as separate objects again, and draw a new force diagram:

where T_r is the force in the rod, drawn as a tension (so if T_r turns out to be negative, then the force must be a thrust). Resolving forces acting on C parallel to the 45° plane, taking down the plane as positive: **[1 mark]**
$F_{net} = ma$
$4g\sin45 - T_r = 4 \times 2$ **[1 mark]**
$\Rightarrow T_r = 4g\sin45 - 8 = 19.718...$
So T_r is a tension **[1 mark]** of 19.7 N (3 s.f.) **[1 mark]**

Answers

M1 Section 5 — Projectiles
Warm-up Questions

1)

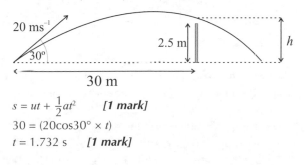

So, parallel to the horizontal, the initial velocity is $u\cos\alpha$.

2) Resolving horizontally (taking right as +ve):
$u = 120$; $s = 60$; $a = 0$; $t = ?$

$s = ut + \frac{1}{2}at^2$

$60 = 120t + \frac{1}{2} \times 0 \times t^2$

$t = 0.5$ s

Resolving vertically (taking down as +ve):
$u = 0$; $s = ?$; $a = 9.8$; $t = 0.5$

$s = ut + \frac{1}{2}at^2$

$= (0 \times 0.5) + (0.5 \times 9.8 \times 0.5^2)$

$= 1.23$ m   (to 3 s.f.)

3) Resolving vertically (taking up as +ve):
$u = 22\sin\alpha$; $a = -9.8$; $t = 4$; $s = 0$

$s = 0$ because the ball lands at the same vertical level it started at.

$s = ut + \frac{1}{2}at^2$

$0 = 22\sin\alpha \times 4 + (0.5 \times -9.8 \times 4^2)$

Rearranging: $\sin\alpha = \frac{78.4}{88}$

$\Rightarrow \alpha = 63.0°$ (3 s.f.)

There are other ways to answer this question — you could use $v = u + at$ and use $t = 2$, which is the time taken to reach the highest point, when $v = 0$. I like my way though.

4) The minimum speed of the particle occurs when the particle is at the highest point of its flight, when the vertical component of its velocity is zero. (The horizontal component of its velocity is the same throughout the particle's motion.) When the vertical component of velocity is zero, the particle's speed is equal to the horizontal component of velocity.

So, minimum speed = $20\cos20° = 18.8$ ms^{-1} (3 s.f.).

Exam Questions

1 Resolving horizontally, taking right as +ve :
$u = 20\cos30°$; $s = 30$; $a = 0$; $t = ?$

20 ms^{-1}

2.5 m h

30°

30 m

$s = ut + \frac{1}{2}at^2$ *[1 mark]*

$30 = (20\cos30° \times t)$

$t = 1.732$ s   *[1 mark]*

Resolving vertically, taking up as +ve:
$s = h$; $u = 20\sin30°$; $t = 1.732$; $a = -9.8$

$s = ut + \frac{1}{2}at^2$ *[1 mark]*

$h = (20\sin30° \times 1.732) + (\frac{1}{2} \times -9.8 \times 1.732^2)$

$= 2.62$ m (to 3 s.f.)   *[1 mark]*

Therefore the ball goes over the crossbar. *[1 mark]*

Assumptions: e.g. ball is a point mass/no air or wind resistance/no spin on the ball *[1 mark]*

That was always my problem when I was taking free kicks — I didn't model the flight of the ball properly before kicking it, so no wonder I never scored.

2 a) $\tan\alpha = \frac{3}{4} \Rightarrow \sin\alpha = \frac{3}{5}$ and $\cos\alpha = \frac{4}{5}$ *[1 mark]*

Resolving vertically, taking down as +ve:
$u = u_y = 15\sin\alpha = 9$; *[1 mark]*
$s = 11$; $a = 9.8$; $t = ?$

$s = ut + \frac{1}{2}at^2$ *[1 mark]*

$11 = 9t + 4.9t^2$ *[1 mark]*

Use the quadratic formula to find:

$t = 0.839$ s (3 s.f.) *[1 mark]*

b) Resolving horizontally, taking right as +ve:
$u = u_x = 15\cos\alpha = 15 \times \frac{4}{5} = 12$; *[1 mark]*
$s = ?$; $t = 0.8390$ s

$OB = 12 \times 0.8390$ *[1 mark]*

$= 10.07$ m

So stone misses H by $10.07 - 9 = 1.07$ m (3 s.f.) *[1 mark]*

c) Resolving vertically, taking down as +ve:
$u = u_y = 9$; $s = 11$;

$a = 9.8$; $v = v_y$

$v^2 = u^2 + 2as$ *[1 mark]*

$v_y^2 = 9^2 + (2 \times 9.8 \times 11) = 296.6$ *[1 mark]*

Resolving horizontally, taking right as +ve:

$v_x = u_x = 12$ *[1 mark]*.

So speed of landing = $\sqrt{v_x^2 + v_y^2}$

$= \sqrt{12^2 + 296.6}$ *[1 mark]* $= 21.0$ ms^{-1} (3 s.f.) *[1 mark]*

d)

v_y

θ

v_x

The angle, θ, that the direction of motion makes with the horizontal can be found using trigonometry: $\tan\theta = \frac{v_y}{v_x}$.

From part c), $v_y = \sqrt{296.6} = 17.22$ and $v_x = 12$, so:

$\tan\theta = \frac{17.22}{12}$ *[1 mark]* $= 1.435$

$\Rightarrow \theta = 55.1°$ (3 s.f.) *[1 mark]*.

What a lovely way to finish off M1. If there was anything you struggled with then take a look back at the relevant pages, then it's on to the practice exams.

Answers

M1 — Practice Exam One

1 a) With uniform motion questions, always start by writing down the data you have and the data you need.

$u = 15$, $v = 40$, $a = ?$, $t = 4$, $s = ?$

You need to find a, so '$v = u + at$' is the equation you need. Rearrange to make a the subject and substitute in:

$a = \dfrac{v - u}{t} = \dfrac{40 - 15}{4} = 6.25$ ms^{-2}

[2 marks available in total]:

• *1 mark for using '$v = u + at$' or equivalent*
• *1 mark for correct value of a*

b) $u = 40$, $v = 26$, $a = -2.8$, $t = ?$, $s = ?$

You need t, so it's '$v = u + at$'. Rearrange and substitute:

$t = \dfrac{v - u}{a} = \dfrac{26 - 40}{-2.8} = 5$ s

[2 marks available in total]:

• *1 mark for using '$v = u + at$' or equivalent*
• *1 mark for correct value of t*

c) You've now got all the other quantities except the two distances, so you can use any of the formulas with s in.

I'm going for '$s = \frac{1}{2}(u + v)t$' because it's nice and easy:

A to B: $s = \frac{1}{2}(u + v)t = \frac{1}{2}(15 + 40) \times 4 = 110$ m

B to C: $s = \frac{1}{2}(u + v)t = \frac{1}{2}(40 + 26) \times 5 = 165$ m

AC = 275 m

[3 marks available in total]:

• *1 mark for using '$s = \frac{1}{2}(u + v)t$' or equivalent*
• *1 mark for either intermediate distance correct*
• *1 mark for the correct value of AC*

You REALLY need to know those equations.

2 a) Integrate the velocity to find the displacement *[1 mark]*:

$s = \int v\,\mathrm{d}t = \frac{11}{2}t^2 - \frac{2}{3}t^3 + c$ for $0 \le t \le 5$ *[1 mark]*.

When $t = 0$, $s = 0 \Rightarrow c = 0$ *[1 mark]*.

So, when $t = 5$:

$s = \frac{11}{2}(25) - \frac{2}{3}(125) = 54.2$ m (3 s.f.) *[1 mark]*

b) Maximum v occurs when $a = 0$ *[1 mark]*.

Differentiate to find a:

$a = \dfrac{\mathrm{d}v}{\mathrm{d}t} = 56 - 8t$ *[1 mark]*

$a = 0 \Rightarrow t = 56 \div 8 = 7$ *[1 mark]*.

When $t = 7$, $v = -175 + 56(7) - 4(7)^2 = 21$ ms^{-1} *[1 mark]*.

Make sure you know the time interval each part of the question is asking about. Here, part a) asks about the motion for $0 \le t \le 5$, whereas part b) asks about the motion for $t > 5$. You don't want to end up using the wrong equation — that wouldn't be good at all.

3 a) The forces are given in terms of components, so to find the resultant force you just add them as vectors:

$\mathbf{F} = \mathbf{F}_1 + \mathbf{F}_2 = (3\mathbf{i} + 2\mathbf{j})$ N $+ (2\mathbf{i} - \mathbf{j})$ N $= (5\mathbf{i} + \mathbf{j})$ N

To find the angle of the resultant force, it's just trig as usual...

angle $= \alpha = \tan^{-1}\left(\frac{1}{5}\right) = 11.3°$

[3 marks available in total]:

• *1 mark for adding vectors to get resultant force*
• *1 mark for using $\tan^{-1}$ or equivalent correctly*
• *1 mark for correct answer*

b) There are a couple of ways of doing this, but both involve Pythagoras and '$F = ma$'. First way:

Find the magnitude of the resultant force:

$|\mathbf{F}| = \sqrt{(5^2 + 1^2)} = \sqrt{26} = 5.10$ N

Then use Newton's second law — $F = ma$:

Rearrange to give: $a = \dfrac{F}{m} = \dfrac{5.10}{0.5} = 10.2$ ms^{-2}

(Second way uses $\mathbf{F} = m\mathbf{a}$ to find vector form of acc^n, then Pythagoras to find magnitude. Either way is fine.)

Magnitude of acceleration = 10.2 ms^{-2}

[4 marks available in total]:

• *1 mark for using '$F = ma$'*
• *1 for correct calculation of either magnitude of force or vector form of acceleration (whichever method is used)*
• *1 mark for correct workings*
• *1 for correct value of a*

Here we go again — "split vector into components, use Pythagoras to find magnitude, ya de ya de ya". Yawn...

4 a) It's usually a good idea to draw a diagram to make it clear what's going on:

(Taking right as positive)

Resolve horizontal forces acting on the car only:

$F_{net} = ma$ *[1 mark]*

$\Rightarrow 4300 - 400 - T = 1600 \times 0.8$ *[1 mark]*

$\Rightarrow T = 4300 - 400 - (1600 \times 0.8) = 2620$ N *[1 mark]*.

b) Resolve forces acting on the boat only:

$F_{net} = ma$ *[1 mark]*

$T - R = 3000 \times 0.8$ *[1 mark]*

$\Rightarrow R = 2620 - (3000 \times 0.8) = 220$ N *[1 mark]*.

5 a) Here's a nice little diagram to help you out:

where T is the tension in the string, $F = 12$ N is the friction between the block and the surface, mg is the block's weight and R is the reaction force of the surface acting on the block.

Resolving perpendicular to the slope:

$R - mg\cos 30° = 0$ *[1 mark]*

$R = 5 \times 9.8 \times \cos 30° = 42.435... = 42.4$ N (3 s.f.) *[1 mark]*

Answers

b) Resolving forces parallel to slope:
$T = F + mg\sin30°$ *[1 mark]*
$T = 12 + (5 \times 9.8 \times \sin30°)$
$T = 36.5$ N *[1 mark]*

c) The block now slides down the slope, so friction acts up the slope, opposing the motion:

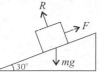

Again, resolving parallel to the slope:
$F_{net} = F - mg\sin30°$ (taking up the slope as positive)
$= 12 - (5 \times 9.8 \times \sin30°)$ *[1 mark]*
$= -12.5$ N *[1 mark]*

d) $F_{net} = ma$ *[1 mark]*
$\Rightarrow a = -12.5 \div 5 = -2.5$ ms^{-2} (3 s.f.) *[1 mark]*
So the block accelerates **down** the slope at a rate of 2.5 ms^{-2}.

6 a) Consider vertical motion, taking up as positive:
$a = -g$, $u = U\sin\alpha$, $v = 0$, $s = ?$:
Use $v^2 = u^2 + 2as$ *[1 mark]*:
$0 = U^2\sin^2\alpha - 2gs$ *[1 mark]*
$\Rightarrow s = \dfrac{U^2\sin^2\alpha}{2g}$ *[1 mark]*.
The frog is initially 0.5 m above the ground, so the maximum height, h, it reaches is:
$h = \dfrac{1}{2} + \dfrac{U^2\sin^2\alpha}{2g} = \dfrac{g + U^2\sin^2\alpha}{2g}$ m, as required *[1 mark]*.

b) Still considering vertical motion, use $v = u + at$ *[1 mark]*:
$0 = U\sin\alpha - gt$ *[1 mark]* $\Rightarrow t = \dfrac{U\sin\alpha}{g}$ s *[1 mark]*.

c) You first need to find the horizontal and vertical components of the frog's motion when it lands.
Vertically:
$u = U\sin\alpha$, $a = -g$, $s = -0.5$, $v = v_V$.
Use $v^2 = u^2 + 2as$ *[1 mark]*:
$v_V^2 = U^2\sin^2\alpha + g$ *[1 mark]*.
Horizontally, $v_H = u_H = U\cos\alpha$, as acceleration is zero *[1 mark]*.
So, $V = \sqrt{v_V^2 + v_H^2} = \sqrt{U^2\sin^2\alpha + g + U^2\cos^2\alpha}$ *[1 mark]*
$= \sqrt{U^2(\sin^2\alpha + \cos^2\alpha) + g}$
$= \sqrt{U^2 + g}$ ms^{-1}, as required *[1 mark]*.

d) Resolving horizontally (taking right as +ve):
$u_x = U\cos45° = \dfrac{U}{\sqrt{2}}$ $a = 0$
$s = x$ $t = t$
Using $s = ut + \dfrac{1}{2}at^2$:
$x = \dfrac{U}{\sqrt{2}} \times t$ *[1 mark]*
Rearrange to make t the subject:
$t = \dfrac{\sqrt{2}x}{U}$ — **eqn 1**
Now resolving vertically (taking up as +ve):
$u_y = U\sin45° = \dfrac{U}{\sqrt{2}}$ $a = -g$
$s = y - \dfrac{1}{2}$ $t = t$

Don't forget that the frog starts from 0.5 m above the ground — that's where $s = y - \dfrac{1}{2}$ comes from.

Using $s = ut + \dfrac{1}{2}at^2$:
$y - \dfrac{1}{2} = \left(\dfrac{U}{\sqrt{2}} \times t\right) - \dfrac{1}{2}gt^2$
$\Rightarrow y = \dfrac{Ut}{\sqrt{2}} - \dfrac{1}{2}gt^2 + \dfrac{1}{2}$ — **eqn 2** *[1 mark]*
Now sub **eqn 1** into **eqn 2** to eliminate t:
$y = \dfrac{U\sqrt{2}x}{U\sqrt{2}} - \dfrac{2gx^2}{2U^2} + \dfrac{1}{2}$ *[1 mark]*
Which simplifies and rearranges to:
$y = \dfrac{1}{2} + x - \dfrac{gx^2}{U^2}$, as required. *[1 mark]*

e) The point P has x-value $x = 0.5$ and y-value $y = 0$, so, using the expression from part d):
$0 = \dfrac{1}{2} + \dfrac{1}{2} - \dfrac{g\left(\frac{1}{2}\right)^2}{U^2}$ *[1 mark]*
$0 = 1 - \dfrac{g}{4U^2}$ *[1 mark]*
$1 = \dfrac{g}{4U^2}$
$U = \dfrac{\sqrt{g}}{2} = 1.57$ ms^{-1} (3 s.f.) *[1 mark]*

7 a) Hold onto your hats — this is a long, long question...

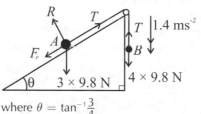

where $\theta = \tan^{-1}\dfrac{3}{4}$
[1 mark for adding all the correct forces]

b) (i) The pulley is smooth and the string is light. *[1 mark]*
(ii) The string is inextensible and B hangs freely *[1 mark]*

c) Particle A remains on the angled plane, so the normal reaction must be equal to the component of the weight force in the opposite direction:

$\tan\theta = \dfrac{3}{4}$ so $\cos\theta = \dfrac{4}{5}$
So $R = 3 \times 9.8 \times \dfrac{4}{5} = 23.52$ N
So, normal reaction = 23.5 N (3 s.f.)

[2 marks available in total]:
• *1 mark for resolving perpendicular*
• *1 mark for correct value of R*

Answers

d) You don't know anything about the friction force on *A* yet, so start by looking at *B*, since that's only affected by weight and tension:

$$B \bullet \quad \downarrow 1.4 \text{ ms}^{-2}$$

(with T pointing up and 4×9.8 N pointing down)

Use '$F = ma$' for *B*:

$(4 \times 9.8) - T = 4 \times 1.4$

So, $T = 33.6$ N

[2 marks available in total]:
* *1 mark for using '$F = ma$'*
* *1 mark for correct value of T*

e) Now you know the tension, you can use '$F = ma$' on particle *A* to find the friction (in case you get confused — the 'F' in '$F = ma$' means 'resultant force', not 'friction'). Start with a diagram (always helps):

(Diagram: 1.4 ms^{-2}, R, T, A, F_r, $3 \times 9.8\sin\theta$ N, $3 \times 9.8\cos\theta$ N)

For *A*: Resultant force = ma

$T - F_r - (3 \times 9.8 \sin\theta) = 3 \times 1.4$

Note that $\tan\theta = \frac{3}{4}$ so $\sin\theta = \frac{3}{5}$

Substitute in value of *T* from part (d):

$33.6 - F_r - 17.64 = 4.2$

So, $F_r = 11.76 = 11.8$ N (3 s.f.)

[3 marks available in total]:
* *1 mark for using '$F = ma$'*
* *1 mark for correct expression for resultant force*
* *1 mark for correct value of F_r*

f) This is fairly straightforward — it's just uniform acceleration, so it's the usual equations:

Motion of *B*: $u = 0$, $v = ?$, $a = 1.4$, $s = ?$, $t = 2$

It's *s* you're after, so use '$s = ut + \frac{1}{2}at^2$':

$s = 0 + \left(\frac{1}{2} \times 1.4 \times 4\right) = 2.8$ m

Particle B moves 2.8 m before the string breaks.

[2 marks available in total]:
* *1 mark for using '$s = ut + \frac{1}{2}at^2$' or equivalent*
* *1 mark for correct value of s*

g) This is easier than it looks (phew). Remember, while *A* and *B* are attached, they move together at the same speed. So you can use the data from part f) to find the speed of (both) *A* and *B* when the string breaks:

$v = u + at = 0 + 1.4 \times 2 = 2.8$ ms^{-1}

Then draw yourself another diagram to show particle *A* immediately after the string breaks:

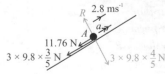

(Diagram: R, 2.8 ms^{-1}, A, a, 11.76 N, $3 \times 9.8 \times \frac{3}{5}$ N, $3 \times 9.8 \times \frac{4}{5}$ N)

You need to work out the acceleration, so you need '$F = ma$':

$-11.76 - \left(3 \times 9.8 \times \frac{3}{5}\right) = 3a$

So, $a = -9.8$ ms^{-2}

Don't stop there — now you've got to find how far *A* travels before it comes to rest. It's the usual equations:

For *A*: $u = 2.8$, $v = 0$, $a = -9.8$, $s = ?$, $t = ?$

You're after *s*, so use '$v^2 = u^2 + 2as$':

Rearrange to give:

$s = \frac{v^2 - u^2}{2a} = \frac{0 - 2.8^2}{2 \times -9.8} = 0.4$ m

So particle A moves 0.4 m from the instant the string breaks until it comes to rest.

[5 marks available in total]:
* *1 mark for correct value for speed*
* *1 mark for using '$F = ma$'*
* *1 mark for correct value for acceleration*
* *1 mark for using '$v^2 = u^2 + 2as$' or equivalent*
* *1 mark for correct answer*

That was one beast of a question. But you made it. And honestly, this is the best kind of practice you can get. There's balancing forces, resolving forces and Newton's 2nd law. All in one big question. It might feel like you've gone through the mill a bit, but if you got that question all right, I reckon you've got a pretty good understanding of mechanics.

M1 — Practice Exam Two

1 a) Resolve along *x*-axis:

$P\sin40° - 20\cos(105-90)° = 0$

so, $P = \frac{20\cos15°}{\sin40°} = 30.054... = 30.1$ N (3 s.f.)

[2 marks available in total]:
* *1 mark for correct workings*
* *1 mark for correct value of P*

Something simple to get you started. I bet you'd never have guessed it would involve resolving forces.

b) Resolve along *y*-axis:

$R = 30.05\cos40° + 35 - 20\sin15°$

$= 52.8$ N (3 s.f.) up the *y*-axis

[3 marks available in total]:
* *1 mark for correct workings*
* *1 mark for correct value of R*
* *1 mark for correct direction*

2 a) Using $F_{net} = ma$ and resolving vertically:

$34\,000\,000 - (1\,400\,000 \times 9.8) = (1\,400\,000 \times a)$

So, $a = \frac{34\,000\,000 - 13\,720\,000}{1\,400\,000}$

$= 14.485... = 14.5$ ms^{-2} (3 s.f.)

[2 marks available in total]:
* *1 mark for resolving vertically*
* *1 mark for correct value of a*

b) Again, using $F_{net} = ma$ and resolving vertically:

$34\,000\,000 - 13\,720\,000 - R = 1\,400\,000 \times 12$

so, $R = 34\,000\,000 - 13\,720\,000 - 16\,800\,000$

$= 3\,480\,000$ N

[2 marks available in total]:
- *1 mark for resolving vertically*
- *1 mark for correct value of R*

c) $u = 0$; $a = 12$; $s = 20\,000$; $t = ?$
Using $s = ut + \frac{1}{2}at^2$:
$20\,000 = (0 \times t) + \frac{1}{2}(12 \times t^2)$
so, $t^2 = 20\,000 \div 6$ and $t = 58$ s (to the nearest second)

[2 marks available in total]:
- *1 mark for using 's = ut + $\frac{1}{2}$at²'*
- *1 mark for correct value of t*

d) e.g. g is constant/R is constant up to 20 km/the force from the engines is constant/the mass of the rocket is constant.

[1 mark for any valid assumption]

3 a) Here's the diagram again, with the forces shown:

The painting is in equilibrium, so, resolving horizontally:
$T_1\cos30° = T_2\cos30°$ *[1 mark]*
$\Rightarrow T_1 = T_2$ *[1 mark]*
So the tensions in the two strings are equal.

b) Resolving vertically:
$T_1\sin30° + T_2\sin30° = mg$ *[1 mark]*
$T_1 = T_2 = 49$, so:
$49\sin30° + 49\sin30° = 9.8m$
$\Rightarrow m = 98\sin30° \div 9.8$ *[1 mark]*
$m = 5$ kg. *[1 mark]*

These resolving questions really are marks in the bag once you've got the hang of them. So there's no excuse for not learning it.

4 a) Consider motion vertically, taking up as positive:
$u = 10\sin20°$, $a = -9.8$, $v = 0$.
Use $v^2 = u^2 + 2as$ *[1 mark]*:
$0 = (10\sin20°)^2 - 19.6s$ *[1 mark]*
$\Rightarrow s = (10\sin20°)^2 \div 19.6 = 0.597$ m.
The stone is thrown from 1 m above the ground, so the maximum height reached is $1 + 0.597 = 1.60$ m (3 s.f.)
[1 mark]

b) Again consider vertical motion:
$u = 10\sin20°$, $a = -9.8$, $s = -1$, $t = ?$.
Use $s = ut + \frac{1}{2}at^2$ *[1 mark]*:
$-1 = (10\sin20°)t - 4.9t^2$ *[1 mark]*
$\Rightarrow 4.9t^2 - (10\sin20°)t - 1 = 0$.
Use the quadratic formula to find t:
$t = \dfrac{10\sin20° + \sqrt{(-10\sin20°)^2 + (4 \times 4.9 \times 1)}}{9.8}$
[1 mark]

$= 0.91986... = 0.920$ s (3 s.f.) *[1 mark]*

You don't need to worry about the other value of t that the formula gives you as it will be negative, and you can't have a negative time.

5 a)

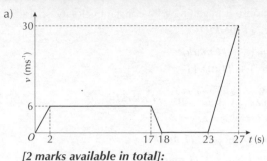

[2 marks available in total]:
- *1 mark for correct shape*
- *1 mark for correct numbers*

b) a = gradient of graph
$t = 0 - 2$ s: $a = 6 \div 2 = 3$ ms⁻²...

$t = 0 - 2$ s: $a = 6 \div 2 = 3$ ms^{-2}
$t = 17 - 18$ s: $a = -6 \div 1 = -6$ ms^{-2}
$t = 23 - 27$ s: $a = 30 \div 4 = 7.5$ ms^{-2}
Greatest acceleration is 7.5 ms^{-2}.

[3 marks available in total]:
- *1 mark for finding gradients or equivalent*
- *1 mark for correct workings*
- *1 mark for correct statement of greatest acceleration*

c) Distance = area under the graph
$t = 0 - 2$ s: $s = \frac{1}{2}(6)2 = 6$ m (triangle: area = $\frac{1}{2}bh$)
$t = 2 - 17$ s: $s = 6 \times 15 = 90$ m (rectangle)
$t = 17 - 18$ s: $s = \frac{1}{2}(6)1 = 3$ m (triangle)
$t = 18 - 23$ s: $s = 0 \times 5 = 0$ m (rectangle)
$t = 23 - 27$ s: $s = \frac{1}{2}(30)4 = 60$ m (triangle)
Total distance = $6 + 90 + 3 + 0 + 60 = 159$ m

[3 marks available in total]:
- *1 mark for using distance = area under graph*
- *1 mark for correct workings*
- *1 mark for correct value of total distance*

I don't really like roller coasters, but they do have some great maths involved. I'd give up writing books to go and design them, unless I had to test them. I feel sick thinking about that.

6 a)

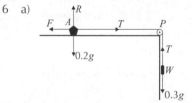

For W, $F_{net} = ma$:
$0.3g - T = 0.3(4)$
$T = 2.94 - 1.2 = 1.74$
For A, $F_{net} = ma$:
$T - F = 4(0.2) = 0.8$
So $F = T - 0.8$
$F = 1.74 - 0.8 = 0.94$ N.

[3 marks available in total]:
- *1 mark for using 'F = ma'*
- *1 mark for correct value of T*
- *1 mark for correct value of F*

b) 'The pulley is smooth' means that the tension in the string is equal on both sides of the pulley. *[1 mark]*

Answers

7 a) The mouse is travelling with constant velocity, so use
$\mathbf{s} = \mathbf{v}t.$ *[1 mark]*
$\binom{9}{12} = \binom{3}{4}t$ *[1 mark]*
$\Rightarrow t = 3$ s. *[1 mark]*

b) $\mathbf{s} = \binom{9}{12} - \binom{-3}{3} = \binom{12}{9}$ *[1 mark]*
$\mathbf{u} = \mathbf{0}, t = 3, \mathbf{a} = \mathbf{a}.$
Use $\mathbf{s} = \mathbf{u}t + \frac{1}{2}\mathbf{a}t^2$: *[1 mark]*
$\binom{12}{9} = \frac{1}{2} \times \mathbf{a} \times 9$ *[1 mark]*
$\Rightarrow \mathbf{a} = \frac{2}{9}\binom{12}{9} = \binom{8/3}{2}$ ms^{-2}. *[1 mark]*

c) Taking $\binom{1}{0}$ as the 'horizontal', the required angle can be found using trig:

$\tan\theta = \frac{2}{\left(\frac{8}{3}\right)} = \frac{3}{4}$ *[1 mark]*
$\Rightarrow \theta = \tan^{-1}\frac{3}{4} = 36.9°$ (3 s.f.). *[1 mark]*

d) Call the forward force $\mathbf{T}$ and the resistive force $\mathbf{R}$:
Using $\mathbf{F} = m\mathbf{a}$:
$\mathbf{T} - \mathbf{R} = m\mathbf{a}$ *[1 mark]*
$\binom{28}{12} - \mathbf{R} = 3\binom{8/3}{2}$ *[1 mark]*
$\Rightarrow \mathbf{R} = \binom{28}{12} - 3\binom{8/3}{2} = \binom{20}{6}$ N. *[1 mark]*
So $|\mathbf{R}| = \sqrt{20^2 + 6^2} = \sqrt{436} = 20.9$ N (3 s.f.). *[1 mark]*

e) For this part of the question, consider the time that the cat passes through O as the start of the motion. Then:
$\mathbf{u} = \binom{-5}{-4}, \mathbf{a} = \binom{-2}{1}, t = t, \mathbf{v} = \mathbf{v}, \mathbf{s} = \mathbf{s}.$
Use $\mathbf{v} = \mathbf{u} + \mathbf{a}t$ to find the time that the cat is moving parallel to $\binom{1}{0}$: *[1 mark]*
$\mathbf{v} = \binom{-5}{-4} + \binom{-2}{1}t$ *[1 mark]*
When the cat is moving parallel to $\binom{1}{0}$, the 'vertical' component of its motion is zero.
i.e. $-4 + t = 0 \Rightarrow t = 4$ s. *[1 mark]*

Now use $\mathbf{s} = \mathbf{u}t + \frac{1}{2}\mathbf{a}t^2$ to find the distance the cat has travelled by this time: *[1 mark]*
$\mathbf{s} = 4\binom{-5}{-4} + \frac{1}{2}(16)\binom{-2}{1}$ *[1 mark]*
$\mathbf{s} = \binom{-20}{-16} + \binom{-16}{8} = \binom{-36}{-8}$ m.
As the cat was at O at the start of the motion, the position vector of the cat relative to O when it is travelling parallel to $\binom{1}{0}$ is therefore $\binom{-36}{-8}$ m *[1 mark]*.

8 a) Sub $t = 2$ into the equation for displacement:
$x(2) = 2^4 - 4(2)^3 - 8(2)^2 + 1 = -47$ m. *[1 mark]*
'x(2)' just means 'the value of x when t = 2'.

b) Differentiate the equation for displacement to get an expression for the velocity: *[1 mark]*
$v = \frac{dx}{dt} = 4t^3 - 12t^2 - 16t$ *[1 mark]*
Now plug in $t = 1$:
$v(1) = 4 - 12 - 16 = -24$ ms^{-1}. *[1 mark]*

c) $v = 0 \Rightarrow 4t^3 - 12t^2 - 16t = 0$
$\Rightarrow t^3 - 3t^2 - 4t = 0$ *[1 mark]*
$t(t^2 - 3t - 4) = 0$
$t(t + 1)(t - 4) = 0$ *[1 mark]*
$\Rightarrow$ Particle is stationary at $t = 0$ *[1 mark]* and $t = 4$ *[1 mark]*
Notice that t = −1 is not included as time can't be negative.

d) The particle is stationary at $t = 4$ (which means the particle could change direction at this point), so you need to consider the motion for $0 < t < 4$ and the motion for $4 < t < 5$ separately. *[1 mark]*
The distance travelled from $t = 0$ to $t = 4$ is given by:
$|x(4) - x(0)| = |-127 - 1| = |-128| = 128.$ *[1 mark]*
The distance travelled from $t = 4$ to $t = 5$ is given by:
$|x(5) - x(4)| = |-74 + 127| = |53| = 53.$ *[1 mark]*
So the total distance travelled is:
$128 + 53 = 181$ m. *[1 mark]*
A bit tricky, that one. The modulus signs (| |) mean that you take the magnitude of whatever is inside (i.e. make it positive). You need to do this because the displacement may be negative, and you're asked for the total distance travelled.

e) Differentiate the equation for velocity to get an expression for the acceleration: *[1 mark]*
$a = \frac{dv}{dt} = 12t^2 - 24t - 16$ *[1 mark]*
$a = 0 \Rightarrow 12t^2 - 24t - 16 = 0$
$\Rightarrow 3t^2 - 6t - 4 = 0$ *[1 mark]*
Use the quadratic formula to solve for t:
$t = \frac{6 + \sqrt{36 - (4 \times 3 \times -4)}}{6}$ *[1 mark]*
$t = 2.53$ s (3 s.f.) *[1 mark]*

You don't need to worry about the other t-value that the formula gives you, as it is negative, and you can't have a negative time.
Well, that's M1 in the bag, so practise, practise and practise some more until the exam. If the next thing you have to do is the exam, then good luck — Mechanics loves you.

Answers

D1 Section 1 — Algorithms
Warm-up Questions

1) a) Input: raw ingredients (e.g. vegetables, water etc.)
      Output: vegetable soup.
   b) Input: starting point (Leicester Square)
      Output: final destination (the Albert Hall)
   c) Input: components (e.g. shelves, screws etc.)
      Output: finished TV cabinet *(in theory — I'm not much good at flat-pack)*

2)

x	y
17	56
~~8~~	~~112~~
~~4~~	~~224~~
~~2~~	~~448~~
1	896
Total	952

So $17 \times 56 = 952$.

3) Diamond-shaped boxes are used for decisions — they'll ask a question.

4) $a = 16$

n	b	Output	$n = a$?
1	16	1	No
2	8	2	No
3	$5\frac{1}{3}$		No
4	4	4	No
5	$3\frac{1}{5}$		No
6	$2\frac{2}{3}$		No
7	$2\frac{2}{7}$		No
8	2	8	No
9	$1\frac{7}{9}$		No
10	$1\frac{3}{5}$		No
11	$1\frac{5}{11}$		No
12	$1\frac{1}{3}$		No
13	$1\frac{3}{13}$		No
14	$1\frac{1}{7}$		No
15	$1\frac{1}{15}$		No
16	1	16	Yes

So the factors of 16 are 1, 2, 4, 8 and 16.

5)
<u>72, 57</u>, 64, 54, 68, 71	swap
57, <u>72, 64</u>, 54, 68, 71	swap
57, 64, <u>72, 54</u>, 68, 71	swap
57, 64, 54, <u>72, 68</u>, 71	swap
57, 64, 54, 68, <u>72, 71</u>	swap
57, 64, 54, 68, 71, 72	end of first pass.

At the end of the second pass, the list is:
57, 54, 64, 68, 71, 72.
At the end of the third pass, the list is:
54, 57, 64, 68, 71, 72.
There are no swaps on the fourth pass, so the list is in order. It took 3 passes to get the list in order.

6) The maximum number of comparisons is $9 + 8 + 7 + 6 + 5 + 4 + 3 + 2 + 1 = 45$ (or $\frac{1}{2} \times 9 \times 10 = 45$).

7) $60 = 20 \times 3$, and as the algorithm is quadratic, it'll take approx. $3^2 = 9$ times as long for 60 numbers. $0.4 \times 9 = 3.6$ s.

8)
First pass:	<u>21, 11</u>, 23, 19, 28, 26	swap
Second pass:	11, <u>21, 23</u>, 19, 28, 26	no swap
Third pass:	11, 21, <u>23, 19</u>, 28, 26	swap
	11, <u>21, 19</u>, 23, 28, 26	swap
	<u>11, 19</u>, 21, 23, 28, 26	no swap
Fourth pass:	11, 19, 21, <u>23, 28</u>, 26	no swap
Fifth pass:	11, 19, 21, 23, <u>28, 26</u>	swap
	11, 19, 21, <u>23, 26</u>, 28	no swap

9)
<u>101</u>
<u>98</u>, 101
<u>79</u>, 98, 101
79, 98, 101, <u>113</u>
79, <u>87</u>, 98, 101, 113
79, 87, 98, 101, <u>108</u>, 113
79, <u>84</u>, 87, 98, 101, 108, 113

Underlining the number you insert each time helps you keep track of what you're doing.

10) Use the first item (0.8) as the pivot. The list becomes:
0.7, 0.5, 0.4, 0.1, <u>0.8</u>, 1.2, 1.0.
Use 0.7 as the pivot for the first list, and 1.2 as the pivot for the second list. The list becomes:
0.5 0.4, 0.1, <u>0.7</u>, <u>0.8</u>, 1.0, <u>1.2</u>.
1.0 is in a list on its own, so it's in the right place. In the other list, use 0.5 as the pivot, so the list becomes:
0.4, 0.1, <u>0.5</u>, <u>0.7</u>, <u>0.8</u>, <u>1.0</u>, <u>1.2</u>.
Use 0.4 for the pivot in the remaining list, so the final (ordered) list is:
0.1, <u>0.4</u>, <u>0.5</u>, <u>0.7</u>, <u>0.8</u>, <u>1.0</u>, <u>1.2</u>.

11) a)
Box 1: 5, 8	space left: ~~10 kg~~ 2 kg
Box 2: 11	space left: 4 kg
Box 3: 9	space left: 6 kg
Box 4: 12	space left: 3 kg
Box 5: 7	space left: 8 kg.

So the items are packed in 5 boxes, with $2 + 4 + 6 + 3 + 8 = 23$ kg wasted space.

   b) First, reorder the numbers in descending order:
12, 11, 9, 8, 7, 5. Then,
Box 1: 12	space left: 3 kg
Box 2: 11	space left: 4 kg
Box 3: 9, 5	space left: ~~6 kg~~ 1 kg
Box 4: 8, 7	space left: ~~7 kg~~ 0 kg

So the items are packed in 4 boxes, with $3 + 4 + 1 + 0 = 8$ kg wasted space.

   c) By eye, $8 + 7 = 15$, so this fills one box.
Box 1: 8, 7	space left: 0 kg
Box 2: 5, 9	space left: ~~10 kg~~ 1 kg
Box 3: 11	space left: 4 kg
Box 4: 12	space left: 3 kg

So the items are packed in 4 boxes, with $0 + 1 + 4 + 3 = 8$ kg wasted space.

Answers

This is actually the same as the answer to part b), but in a slightly different order — sometimes different methods produce the same solution.

Exam Questions

1 a) Use the first item (77) as the pivot. The list becomes:
<u>77</u>, 83, 96, 105, 78, 89, 112, 80, 98, 94 *[1 mark]*
Use 83 as the next pivot. The list becomes:
<u>77</u>, 78, 80, <u>83</u>, 96, 105, 89, 112, 98, 94 *[1 mark]*
Use 78 as the pivot in the first list, and 96 as the pivot in the second list. The list becomes:
<u>77</u>, <u>78</u>, 80, <u>83</u>, 89, 94, <u>96</u>, 105, 112, 98 *[1 mark]*
80 is in a list on its own, so it's in the correct place.
Use 89 and 105 as the pivots. The list becomes:
<u>77</u>, <u>78</u>, <u>80</u>, <u>83</u>, <u>89</u>, 94, <u>96</u>, 98, <u>105</u>, 112 *[1 mark]*
94, 98 and 112 are in lists on their own, so they are in the correct places. The list is now in order.
[1 mark for stating all pivots used]

b) (i) After the first pass, the final / biggest / 6th number in the list will be in the correct position. *[1 mark]*

(ii) There are 6 items, so the maximum number of passes is 5 *[1 mark]*. The maximum number of swaps is 5 + 4 + 3 + 2 + 1 = 15 *[1 mark]*.

2 a)

N	C	D	Output	$N = A$?
1	8	12	1	No
2	4	6	2	No
3	$2\frac{2}{3}$	4		No
4	2	3	4	No
5	$1\frac{3}{5}$	$2\frac{2}{5}$		No
6	$1\frac{1}{3}$	2		No
7	$1\frac{1}{7}$	$1\frac{5}{7}$		No
8	1	$1\frac{1}{2}$		Yes

The results are 1, 2 and 4.
[3 marks available in total:
• 1 mark for correct values of C;
• 1 mark for correct values of D;
• 1 mark for correct outputs (there should be 3 outputs)]

b) (i) This algorithm produces the common factors of the inputs. *[1 mark]*

(ii) The output would be 1 *[1 mark]*, as 19 and 25 have no common factors. *[1 mark]*

3 <u>Mark</u>
<u>Adam</u>, Mark
Adam, <u>Dan</u>, Mark
Adam, Dan, <u>James</u>, Mark
Adam, Dan, James, Mark, <u>Stella</u>
Adam, Dan, <u>Helen</u>, James, Mark, Stella
Adam, Dan, Helen, James, Mark, <u>Robert</u>, Stella
[2 marks available — 1 mark for using correct sorting algorithm, 1 mark for completely correct implementation.]

4 a)

Plank 1: 1.2, 0.6, 0.8	space left: ~~1.8~~ ~~1.2~~ 0.4
Plank 2: 2.3	space left: 0.7
Plank 3: 1.5, 1.0	space left: ~~1.5~~ 0.5
Plank 4: 0.9	space left: 2.1
Plank 5: 2.5	space left: 0.5 *[1 mark]*

So 5 planks are used *[1 mark]* and there is 0.4 + 0.7 + 0.5 + 2.1 + 0.5 = 4.2 m wasted wood. *[1 mark]*

b) (i) By eye, 1.2 + 0.8 + 1.0 = 3 and 0.6 + 1.5 + 0.9 = 3 *[1 mark]*, so there are 2 full planks. The rest are placed using the first fit algorithm.
Plank 1: 1.2, 0.8, 1.0   space left: 0
Plank 2: 0.6, 1.5, 0.9   space left: 0
Plank 3: 2.3   space left: 0.7
Plank 4: 2.5   space left: 0.5 *[1 mark]*
So 4 planks are used and there is 0.7 + 0.5 = 1.2 m wasted wood *[1 mark]*.

(ii) The lengths of wood you need add up to 10.8 m. The planks are 3 m long. $10.8 \div 3 = 3.6$ *[1 mark]*, so a minimum of 4 planks are needed. Therefore, 4 is the optimal number of planks *[1 mark]*.

c) $120 = 30 \times 4$, and as the algorithm is quadratic, it will take approximately $4^2 = 16$ times as long *[1 mark]* when there are 4 times as many numbers. $16 \times 2.1 = 33.6$ s *[1 mark]*.

5 a) First pass: <u>1.3, 0.8</u>, 1.8, 0.5, 1.2, 0.2, 0.9   swap
Second pass: 0.8, <u>1.3, 1.8</u>, 0.5, 1.2, 0.2, 0.9   no swap
Third pass: 0.8, 1.3, <u>1.8, 0.5</u>, 1.2, 0.2, 0.9   swap
              0.8, <u>1.3, 0.5</u>, 1.8, 1.2, 0.2, 0.9   swap
              <u>0.8, 0.5</u>, 1.3, 1.8, 1.2, 0.2, 0.9   swap
[1 mark]
Fourth pass: 0.5, 0.8, 1.3, <u>1.8, 1.2</u>, 0.2, 0.9   swap
              0.5, 0.8, <u>1.3, 1.2</u>, 1.8, 0.2, 0.9   swap
              0.5, <u>0.8, 1.2</u>, 1.3, 1.8, 0.2, 0.9   no swap
[1 mark]
Fifth pass: 0.5, 0.8, 1.2, 1.3, <u>1.8, 0.2</u>, 0.9   swap
              0.5, 0.8, 1.2, <u>1.3, 0.2</u>, 1.8, 0.9   swap
              0.5, 0.8, <u>1.2, 0.2</u>, 1.3, 1.8, 0.9   swap
              0.5, <u>0.8, 0.2</u>, 1.2, 1.3, 1.8, 0.9   swap
              <u>0.5, 0.2</u>, 0.8, 1.2, 1.3, 1.8, 0.9   swap
[1 mark]
Sixth pass: 0.2, 0.5, 0.8, 1.2, 1.3, <u>1.8, 0.9</u>   swap
              0.2, 0.5, 0.8, 1.2, <u>1.3, 0.9</u>, 1.8   swap
              0.2, 0.5, 0.8, <u>1.2, 0.9</u>, 1.3, 1.8   swap
              0.2, 0.5, <u>0.8, 0.9</u>, 1.2, 1.3, 1.8   no swap
[1 mark]
There are 7 numbers, so there must be $7 - 1 = 6$ passes *[1 mark]*.

b) On the first pass, there was 1 comparison and 1 swap *[1 mark]*.

Answers

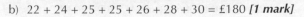

D1 Section 2 — Graphs and Networks
Warm-up Questions

1) a) A graph which has a number associated with each edge.

b) A graph in which one or more of the edges have a direction associated with them.

c) A connected graph with no cycles.

d) A subgraph which contains all the vertices of the original graph and is also a tree.

2) E.g.

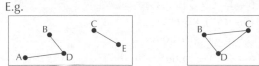

3) a) No loops or multiple arcs.

b) Arcs do not cross at all, so definitely planar.

Planar graphs can be drawn so that the arcs only cross at nodes.

4) Cycle: E.g. BCDB

5) Walk: E.g. ADCECB, trail: E.g. ADBCD

6) E.g.

7) A = 1, B = 2, C = 3, D = 3, E = 1
Sum of orders = double number of edges

8) a) ABDEF. Shortest route A to F is 9.

Trace back from F to A on the final diagram on page 220. The weight of each arc you go along must equal the difference in the final labels of the vertices at each end of the arc.

b)

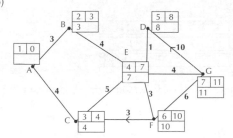

ABEG (11)

9)

Exam Questions

1 a) DG (22) – add; EF (24) – add; BE (25) – add; DE (25) – add; EG (26) – don't add; AB (26) – add; BD (27) – don't add; BF (28) – don't add; FH (28) – add; CF (30) – add; AC (32) – don't add; GH (33) – don't add. Vertices of equal length can be considered in either order. *[3 marks available — 1 mark for edges in correct order, 2 marks for all added edges correct. Lose 1 mark for each error.]*

b) 22 + 24 + 25 + 25 + 26 + 28 + 30 = £180 *[1 mark]*

c)

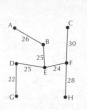

[2 marks for correct edges. Lose 1 mark for each error.]

d) FC / CF.
Order edges added: EF, EB, ED, DG (or ED, DG, EB), BA, FH, FC.

[2 marks available. 1 mark for correct edge, 1 mark for evidence that Prim's algorithm has been applied.]

e) E.g. Prim's algorithm can be applied to data in matrix form; you don't have to check for cycles using Prim's; the tree grows in a connected way using Prim's.
[2 marks — 1 mark for each.]

2 a) Bipartite graph *[1 mark]*

b) 3 (A2, B1, B3) *[1 mark]*

c) 1 (e.g. AD) *[1 mark]*

d) 8 (2 × number of edges) *[1 mark]*

e) The sum of the orders is double the number of edges, so is always even *[1 mark]*. There are 5 vertices, and the sum of 5 odd numbers is always odd *[1 mark]*.

f) A and D are the odd nodes, so the route must start from one of them and end at the other. E.g. AFEABEDCBD.
[2 marks — 1 mark for recognising that route must start/end from A or D, 1 mark for correct route.]

3 a)

	A	B	C	D	E
A	–	14	22	21	18
B	14	–	19	21	20
C	22	19	–	21	15
D	21	21	21	–	24
E	18	20	15	24	–

Order arcs added: AB, AE, EC, AD/BD/CD
(You only need one of AD, BD or CD — they're interchangeable.)

[3 marks available — 2 marks for arcs in correct order (1 mark if one error). 1 mark for correct use of matrix.]

Each time you circle a number, write down which arc it represents by reading the row and column labels. Don't leave it until the end, or you'll have forgotten the order you added them in. Doh.

b) E.g.

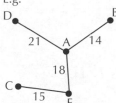

[1 mark]

D may be connected to B or C instead of A.

weight = 68 *[1 mark]*.

Answers

c) 2 (using any of the alternatives AD, BD and CD) *[1 mark]*.

4 a) 8 (no. of vertices – 1) *[1 mark]*

   b)

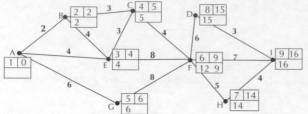

Fastest route = ABCFI, 16 minutes

[6 marks available — 1 mark for route, 1 mark for 16 minutes, 4 marks for all vertices correctly completed in diagram, lose 1 mark for each error.]

Find the fastest route by tracing back from the final destination. You know if a path is on the route because its weight is the difference between the final labels at either end of it.

   c) $6 + x + 4 < 16$, $x < 6$

   Fastest route from A to G is 6. Fastest route from H to I is 4. Total route AGHI must be less than 16 minutes.

   [2 marks available — 1 mark for $6 + x + 4$ as new route length, 1 mark for solving inequality for x.]

   d) Dijkstra's algorithm is quadratic ($O(n^2)$, where n is the number of vertices). Repeating it n times gives an order of $O(n^2 \times n) = O(n^3)$, or cubic.

   [2 marks available — 1 mark for implying that Dijkstra's algorithm is quadratic and 1 mark for identifying new order as cubic.]

D1 Section 3 — Critical Path Analysis

Warm-up Questions

1) a)

Activity	Immediate preceding activities
A	—
B	—
C	A
D	B
E	C, D

   b)

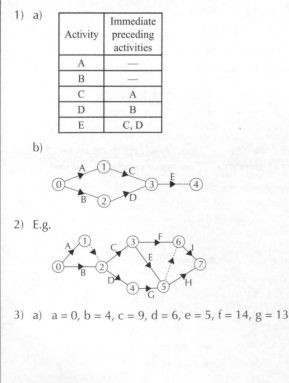

2) E.g.

3) a) a = 0, b = 4, c = 9, d = 6, e = 5, f = 14, g = 13

b) (i) A series of activities running from the start to the end of the project (source node to sink node). The activities have zero total float (they are all critical) and if their start is delayed, the entire project time will be extended.

   (ii) ACGH and ADJ

c) E's duration isn't equal to the difference between the time at the node before and the time at the node after ($10 - 4 \neq 3$).

d) 14 hours

e) B = 6 – 3 – 0 = 3 hours
   E = 10 – 3 – 4 = 3 hours
   I = 14 – 1 – 11 = 2 hours

f) B = 6 – 3 – 0 = 3 hours
   E = 10 – 3 – 4 = 3 hours
   I = 14 – 1 – 13 = 0 hours

g)

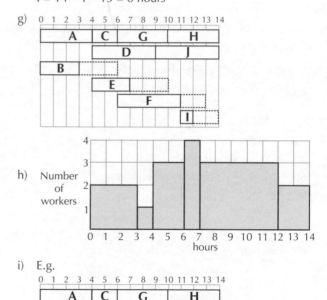

h) Number of workers

i) E.g.

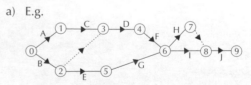

So, worker 1: A, C, G, H; worker 2: B, D, J; worker 3: E, F, I.

Exam Questions

1 a) E.g.

[5 marks available — 1 mark for 9 numbered nodes (not including 0), 1 mark for each correctly placed dummy (2 dummies), 2 marks for other correct precedences. Lose 1 mark for each error.]

b) The dummy between nodes 2 and 3 is needed to show dependency (that D depends on B and C, but E depends on B only). *[1 mark]*

The dummy between nodes 7 and 8 is needed so that all activities are uniquely represented in terms of their events. *[1 mark]*

Answers

2 a)

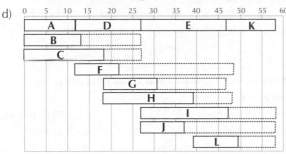

[4 marks available for all correct, lose 1 mark for each error]

b) Critical activities: ADEK *[2 marks for all 4 correct or 1 mark for 2 or 3 correct.]*
Minimum completion time = 58 days *[1 mark]*

c) Total float on F = 48 − 10 − 12 = 26 days
Total float on G = 47 − 13 − 18 = 16 days
[3 marks available — 1 mark for each total float and 1 mark for showing correct working.]

d)

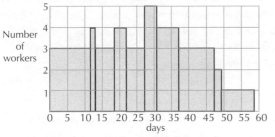

[4 marks available — 1 mark for every 3 correctly plotted activities.]

e)

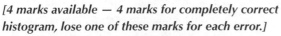

[4 marks available — 4 marks for completely correct histogram, lose one of these marks for each error.]

f) E.g.

Worker 1: A, D, E, K
Worker 2: B, F, G, I
Worker 3: C, H, J
Worker 4: L

[3 marks available — 1 mark for each 4 activities correctly scheduled.]

Your resource histogram showed that 5 workers are needed at one point if the activities all start at their earliest possible times. You need to do a little resource smoothing so that 4 workers can complete the project.

3 a)

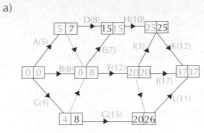

[3 marks available — 1 mark for every 2 correct numbers.]

b) BEHK *[1 mark]*, BFJ *[1 mark]*.

c) H (critical activity between day 15 and day 25) *[1 mark]*
J (critical activity between day 20 and day 37) *[1 mark]*

d) No *[1 mark]*. D won't be finished until day 22. Critical activity H must start after 15 days, and depends on D being completed *[1 mark]*.

e) Shorten B by 2 days *[1 mark]* and H and J by 1 day each *[1 mark]*.
Cost = (£100 × 2) + £75 + £50 = £325 *[1 mark]*
Just shortening B by 3 days doesn't work — if it's reduced to 5 days, the critical path becomes ADHK. This takes 35 days unless you shorten H too.

D1 Section 4 — Linear Programming
Warm-up Questions

1) a) Decision variables represent the quantities of the things being produced in a linear programming problem.

b) The objective function is the thing you're trying to optimise — a function in terms of the decision variables that you want to maximise or minimise.

c) The optimal solution is a feasible solution that optimises the objective function (i.e. maximises or minimises it).

2) A dotted line represents a strict (< or >) inequality.
You don't include this line in the feasible region.

3) An objective line is a line in the form $Z = ax + by$, which represents all solutions of the objective function that have the same value of Z.

4) E.g. A linear programming problem involving liquid doesn't need integer solutions — e.g. mixing vinegar and oil to make vinaigrette. You can have fractions of a litre.
E.g. A linear programming problem about making musical instruments needs integer solutions — you can't make half a trumpet.

5) a) The decision variables are the number of large posters and the number of small posters, so let x = number of large posters and y = number of small posters.
The constraints are the different amounts of time available.
Printing a large poster takes 10 minutes, so printing x large posters takes $10x$ minutes. Printing a small poster takes 5 minutes, so printing y small posters takes $5y$ minutes.
There are 250 minutes of printing time available, so the inequality is $10x + 5y \leq 250 \Rightarrow 2x + y \leq 50$. Using the same method for laminating time produces the inequality $6x + 4y \leq 200 \Rightarrow 3x + 2y \leq 100$. The company wants to

Answers

sell at least as many large posters as small posters, so $x \geq y$, and at least 10 small posters, so $y \geq 10$. Also, $x, y \geq 0$ (the non-negativity constraints).
The objective function is $P = 6x + 3.5y$ (profit) which needs to be maximised.

You could use x for the number of small posters and y for the number of large posters instead — so x and y in each inequality would just swap round.

b)

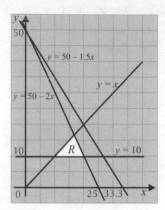

The line y = 50 − 1.5x isn't actually used to form the feasible region.

c) E.g. starting with the objective line for $P = 42$ (which goes through $(0, 12)$ and $(7, 0)$) and moving it towards R gives:

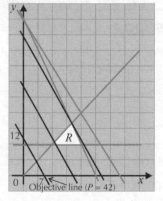

So the final point in the feasible region touched by the objective line is the point of intersection of the lines $y = x$ and $y = 50 - 2x$. Solving these simultaneous equations gives the point of intersection as $\left(\frac{50}{3}, \frac{50}{3}\right)$.
Putting these values into the objective function gives a maximum profit of £158.33.
You can choose any value of P as a starting value — 42 makes it easy to draw the line. This answer uses the objective line method, but you could have used the vertex method instead.

d) From part c) above, the maximum profit is found at $\left(\frac{50}{3}, \frac{50}{3}\right)$. However, you can't have fractions of a poster, so an integer solution is required. The points with integer coordinates nearby are $(16,16)$, $(16,17)$, $(17, 17)$ and $(17, 16)$. $(16, 17)$ doesn't satisfy the constraint $x \geq y$ and $(17, 17)$ doesn't satisfy the constraint $y \leq 50 - 2x$. The value of the objective function at $(16, 16)$ is £152 and at $(17, 16)$ it's £158, so $(17, 16)$ gives the maximum solution.

Exam Questions

1 The objective function is to minimise the cost *[1 mark]*, $C = 0.75x + 0.6y$ in £ (or $C = 75x + 60y$ in pence) *[1 mark]* (where x is the number of red roses and y is the number of white roses), subject to the constraints:
$x, y > 0$ *[1 mark]* (from the statement that she will sell both red and white roses — x and y can't be 0).
$x > y$ *[1 mark]* (from the statement that she will sell more red roses than white roses).
$x + y \geq 100$ *[1 mark]* (from the statement that she will sell a total of at least 100 flowers).
$x \leq 300$ *[1 mark]* and $y \leq 200$ *[1 mark]* (from the statement that the wholesaler has 300 red roses and 200 white roses).

Don't waste time trying to solve these inequalities — the question doesn't ask you to find a solution. Just write them down and run.

2 a) There are 6 sheets of foil in a gold pack, so in x gold packs there will be $6x$ sheets of foil. There are 2 sheets of foil in a silver pack, so in y silver packs there will be $2y$ sheets of foil. There is 1 sheet of foil in a bronze pack, so in z bronze packs there will be z sheets of foil. There are 30 sheets of foil available, so the inequality is $6x + 2y + z \leq 30$ *[2 marks — 1 mark for LHS, 1 mark for correct inequality sign and RHS]*. Using the same method for sugar paper produces the inequality $15x + 9y + 6z \leq 120$ *[1 mark]*, which simplifies to give $5x + 3y + 2z \leq 40$ *[1 mark]*. For tissue paper, the inequality is $15x + 4y + z \leq 60$ *[2 marks — 1 mark for LHS, 1 mark for correct inequality sign and RHS]*. Finally, the amount of foil used is $6x + 2y + z$, and the amount of sugar paper used is $15x + 9y + 6z$. The amount of sugar paper used needs to be at least three times the amount of foil, so the inequality for this constraint is $15x + 9y + 6z \geq 3(6x + 2y + z)$ *[1 mark]*
$15x + 9y + 6z \geq 18x + 6y + 3z$
$3y + 3z \geq 3x$
$y + z \geq x$ *[1 mark]*

b) (i) If the number of silver packs sold is equal to the number of bronze packs, then $y = z$. Substituting this into the inequalities from part (a) gives:
$6x + 2y + y \leq 30 \Rightarrow 6x + 3y \leq 30 \Rightarrow 2x + y \leq 10$
$5x + 3y + 2y \leq 40 \Rightarrow 5x + 5y \leq 40 \Rightarrow x + y \leq 8$
$15x + 4y + y \leq 60 \Rightarrow 15x + 5y \leq 60 \Rightarrow 3x + y \leq 12$
$y + y \geq x \Rightarrow 2y \geq x$. *[3 marks available — 1 mark for making the correct substitution, 1 mark for correctly forming the inequalities and 1 mark for simplifying the inequalities.]*

Answers

(ii)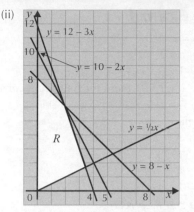

[5 marks available — 1 mark for each of the four inequality lines (with equations as shown on the graph) and 1 mark for correct feasible region]

(iii) Using the vertex method, the feasible region has vertices (0, 0) (the origin), (0, 8) (intersection of the y-axis and $y = 8 - x$), (2, 6) (intersection of $y = 8 - x$ and $y = 10 - 2x$) and $\left(\frac{24}{7}, \frac{12}{7}\right)$ (intersection of $y = \frac{1}{2}x$ and $y = 12 - 3x$) *[1 mark]*. The number of packs made on Monday is $x + y + z = x + 2y$, so the numbers made at each vertex are 0, 16, 14 and $\frac{48}{7} = 6\frac{6}{7}$, so the maximum number of packs made that day is 16 = 8 silver and 8 bronze *[1 mark]*.

You could have used the objective line method instead, using the line $Z = x + y + z = x + 2y$ to find the maximum.

(iv) The objective function is $P = 3.5x + 2y + z$ $= 3.5x + 2y + y = 3.5x + 3y$, which needs to be maximised. The value of P for each of the vertices found in part (iii) is £0, £24, £25 and £17.14 *[1 mark]*. The maximum value is £25 *[1 mark]*, which occurs at (2, 6), so the company needs to sell 2 gold packs, 6 silver packs and 6 bronze packs (as the number of bronze packs is equal to the number of silver packs) *[1 mark]*.

3 a) First, the non-negativity constraints are $x, y \geq 0$. The solid line that passes through (0, 6) and (3, 0) has equation $y = 6 - 2x$, and as the area below the line is shaded, the inequality is $2x + y \geq 6$. The dotted line that passes through (2, 0) has equation $y = x - 2$, and as the area below the line is shaded, the inequality is $x - y < 2$. The horizontal solid line that passes through (0, 4) has the equation $y = 4$, and as the area above the line is shaded, the inequality is $y \leq 4$.

[5 marks available — 1 mark for non-negativity constraints, 1 mark for each line equation and 1 mark for all inequality signs correct]

b) The coordinates of the vertices of R are (1, 4) (the intersection of the lines $y = 4$ and $y = 6 - 2x$) *[1 mark]*, (6, 4) (the intersection of the lines $y = 4$ and $y = x - 2$) *[1 mark]* and $\left(\frac{8}{3}, \frac{2}{3}\right)$ *[1 mark]* (the intersection of the lines $y = 6 - 2x$ and $y = x - 2$) *[1 mark for solving the simultaneous equations]*.

c) The value of C at (1, 4) is 8, the value of C at (6, 4) is 28 *[1 mark if both are correct]* and the value of C at $\left(\frac{8}{3}, \frac{2}{3}\right)$ is $\frac{34}{3} = 11\frac{1}{3}$ *[1 mark]*. Hence the minimum value of C is 8, which occurs at the point (1, 4) *[1 mark]*.

This answer uses the vertex method, but you could also have used the objective line method to answer this question — pick whichever method you prefer.

D1 Section 5 — Simulation
Warm-up Questions

1) a)

Result	Win	Lose	Draw
Probability	0.3	0.6	0.1
Random numbers	0, 1, 2	3, 4, 5, 6, 7, 8	9

This isn't the only solution — you could assign the numbers in any way you like, as long as there are 3 numbers for 'win', 6 for 'lose' and 1 for 'draw'.

b) For the rule above, 1 = win, 3 = lose, 7 = lose, 5 = lose, 7 = lose. So the cricket team will win their next match then lose the four after that.
Hmmm... with odds like that, I think I'd pick a different team to support.

2 a)

Time interval	0	2	4	6	8
Probability	$\frac{1}{4}$	$\frac{1}{6}$	$\frac{1}{3}$	$\frac{1}{6}$	$\frac{1}{12}$
Random numbers	00 - 23	24 - 39	40 - 71	72 - 87	88 - 95

ignore numbers 96, 97, 98 and 99.

You could assign the numbers differently — you'll get the marks as long as the proportions are right. The common denominator is 12, which isn't a factor of 100 so you'll have to ignore some numbers.

b) For the rule above, 64 = 4 mins, 40 = 4 mins, 36 = 2 mins, 97 = ignore, 26 = 2 mins, 66 = 4 mins. You don't need the last two random numbers as there are now 5 people in the group. The waiting time is 4 + 4 + 2 + 2 + 4 = 16 mins.

This depends on your rule from part a) — if you assigned the numbers differently, you'd get different results here.

c)

Simulation	Time intervals					Waiting time
1	4	4	6	0	4	18
2	2	4	6	6	0	18
3	2	0	4	8	6	20
4	2	4	2	0	4	12
5	4	4	2	2	4	16

Total waiting time: 18 + 18 + 20 + 12 + 16 = 84.
Average waiting time: 84 ÷ 5 = 16.8 mins.

This bit depends on your simulation from part b).

d) To improve the estimate, you should run more simulations.

Answers

Exam Question

1) a)

Time interval	5	10	15	20
Probability	0.25	0.375	0.125	0.25
Random numbers	00 - 23	24 - 59	60 - 71	72 - 95

ignore numbers 96 - 99.

[3 marks available — 2 marks for all 4 correct ranges of random numbers (1 mark for 3 correct), 1 mark for ignoring 4 numbers]

As fractions, these probabilities are 1/4, 3/8, 1/8 and 1/4. The common denominator is 8, which isn't a factor of 100 — this means that you'll have to ignore some numbers. 100 ÷ 8 = 12 r 4, so you need 96 numbers (00 - 95) and you ignore 4 numbers (96, 97, 98 and 99). Again, you could assign the numbers any way you like, as long as the proportions are right.

b) For the rule above, 19 = 5 mins, 08 = 5 mins, 63 = 15 mins, 70 = 15 mins, 04 = 5 mins, 29 = 10 mins, 44 = 10 mins, 10 = 5 mins, 19 = 5 mins, 01 = 5 mins.

[2 marks for all 10 correct, or 1 mark for 5-9 correct]

c)

Consultation time	5	10	15	20
Probability	0.1	0.55	0.3	0.05
Random numbers	00 - 09	10 - 64	65 - 94	95 - 99

[3 marks available — 2 marks for all 4 correct ranges of random numbers (1 mark for 3 correct), 1 mark for using all 100 numbers]

d) For the rule above, 12 = 10 mins, 38 = 10 mins, 36 = 10 mins, 83 = 15 mins, 30 = 10 mins, 63 = 10 mins, 69 = 15 mins, 53 = 10 mins, 92 = 15 mins, 53 = 10 mins.

[2 marks for all 10 correct, or 1 mark for 5-9 correct]

e) For the rule above,

Patient number	Time interval	Arrival time	Start of consul.	Consul. time	End of consul.	Waiting time
1	5	5	5	10	15	0
2	5	10	15	10	25	5
3	15	25	25	10	35	0
4	15	40	40	15	55	0
5	5	45	55	10	65	10
6	10	55	65	10	75	10
7	10	65	75	15	90	10
8	5	70	90	10	100	20
9	5	75	100	15	115	25
10	5	80	115	10	125	35

Average waiting time: 0 + 5 + 0 + 0 + 10 + 10 + 10 + 20 + 25 + 35 = 115. 115 ÷ 10 = 11.5 mins.

[5 marks available — 1 mark for correct arrival times, 1 mark for correct start times, 1 mark for correct end times, 1 mark for waiting times and 1 mark for calculating average waiting time

The start of consultation time is just the end of consultation time of the previous patient, except for Patient 4 (let's call him Max), who actually arrives after Patient 3's (Amy's) appointment has ended. This just means that Max can be seen as soon as he arrives, so his waiting time is 0.

D1 — Practice Exam 1

1 a) First iteration: A = 2, N = 1.
P = A ÷ N = 2 ÷ 1 = 2
Q = P + N = 2 + 1 = 3
R = Q ÷ 2 = 3 ÷ 2 = 1.5 *[1 mark for P, Q and R correct]*
|R − N| = |1.5 − 1| = 0.5 > 0.01, so go to Step 8.
N = R = 1.5 *[1 mark]*.
Second iteration: A = 2, N = 1.5.
P = 2 ÷ 1.5 = 1.33333...
Q = 1.33333... + 1.5 = 2.83333...
R = 2.83333... ÷ 2 = 1.41666...
[1 mark for P, Q and R correct]
|R − N| = |1.4166... − 1.5| = 0.0833... > 0.01, so go to Step 8.
N = R = 1.4166... *[1 mark for correct iteration]*.
Third iteration: A = 2, N = 1.4166...
P = 2 ÷ 1.4166... = 1.4117...
Q = 1.4117... + 1.4166... = 2.8284...
R = 2.8284... ÷ 2 = 1.4142...
[1 mark for P, Q and R correct]
|R − N| = |1.4142... − 1.4166...| = 0.0024... < 0.01
So R = 1.41 *[1 mark]*.
The square root of 2 to 2 d.p. is 1.41.

b) The algorithm calculates square roots to 2 decimal places, so for A = 9, the output would be 3.00 *[1 mark]*.

c) 2 d.p. = 20 seconds
4 d.p. = 80 seconds
So doubling d.p. means time is multiplied by 4 (2^2).

2 d.p. = 20 seconds
6 d.p. = 180 seconds
So tripling d.p. means time is multiplied by 9 (3^2).

Therefore, the order is quadratic *[1 mark]*.

2 a) Simple:

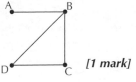

[1 mark]

Not simple, e.g.:

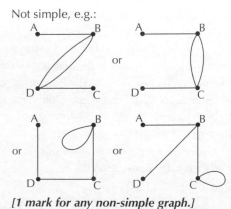

or

[1 mark for any non-simple graph.]

A loop counts as 1 arc but it adds 2 to the order of the vertex it's attached to. There are other possible 'not simple' graphs with a loop — just check you've drawn one with 4 nodes, 4 arcs, and that A has an order of 1 and B has an order of 3.

b) Cycle, e.g.: BDCB *[1 mark]*

Any closed path which doesn't repeat any vertices would do here.

Trail, e.g.: BDCBA *[1 mark]*

Any route which doesn't repeat any edges would do here (it can repeat vertices though).

c) 2 (AC and AD) *[1 mark]*

d) No *[1 mark]*. Trees have no cycles *[1 mark]*.

e) It can be redrawn so that the edges only cross at nodes *[1 mark]*.

E.g. moving nodes C and E out a bit, but keeping all of the connections the same makes the graph look like this:

3 a) (i) There are 100 numbers from 00 - 99, so 10 numbers for each tenth *[1 mark for this idea]*.
E.g. £0 - £9.99 = 00 - 29,
£10 - £19.99 = 30 - 69, £20 - £39.99 = 70 - 79,
over £40 = 80 - 99 *[1 mark]*.

(ii) There are 100 numbers from 00 - 99.
100 ÷ 15 = 6 r 10 numbers *[1 mark for this idea]*.
So reject 10 numbers, e.g. 90 to 99 *[1 mark]*.
E.g. £0 - £9.99 = 00 - 23 (4 × 6 = 24 numbers),
£10 - £19.99 = 24 - 41 (3 × 6 = 18 numbers),
£20 - £39.99 = 42 - 71 (5 × 6 = 30 numbers),
over £40 = 72 - 89 (3 × 6 = 18 numbers) *[1 mark]*.

b) E.g. £10 - £19.99; £20 - £39.99; £10 - £19.99;
over £40; £0 - £9.99 *[2 marks for all correct, or 1 mark for 3 or 4 correct.]*

c) Run more simulations / Use a larger set of random numbers *[1 mark]*.

4 a) and b)

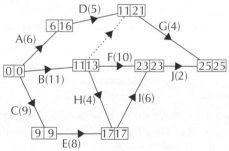

a): *[5 marks available for activity on arc network. 1 mark for each pair of activities shown with correct precedences.]*

b): *[4 marks available for early and late times. 2 marks for early times — lose 1 mark for each error (up to a maximum of 2). 2 marks for late times — lose 1 mark for each error (up to a maximum of 2).]*

c) 25 days *[1 mark]*. Critical activities: C, E, I, J *[1 mark]*.

d) 21 – 5 – 6 = 10 days *[1 mark]*

e) C and I are critical activities, so need to reduce one of these to reduce project duration. You can only reduce I by 3 days, which isn't enough to bring the project duration down to 21 days (and anyway, it's more expensive). So reduce C by 4 days.

However, this means that I must start after 13 days, and J after 19 days. This doesn't leave enough time for B and H, or for B and F to be done. Reducing B by 2 days solves this.

To summarise, B *[1 mark]* must be reduced by 2 days *[1 mark]* and C *[1 mark]* by 4 days *[1 mark]*.

The activity network now looks like this:

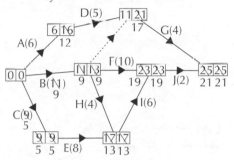

5 a) (i) Number of tickets: $5x + 10y \leq 300 \Rightarrow x + 2y \leq 60$ *[1 mark]*. Number of bottles of wine:
$2x + 8y \leq 160 \Rightarrow x + 4y \leq 80$ *[1 mark]*.

(ii) $x \geq 5$ *[1 mark]*, $y \geq 5$ *[1 mark]*.

There have to be at least 5 business class packages and at least 5 premier packages sold

$x + y \geq 20$ *[1 mark]*

The total number of packages sold has to be more than 20.

b) (i)

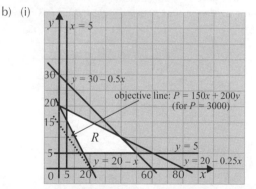

[7 marks available — 1 for each correct line (with equations as shown on graph — 5 in total), 1 for correct feasible region and 1 for objective line with correct gradient]

(ii) Using the objective line, the last point in the feasible region it touches is the point (50, 5), the intersection of the lines $y = 5$ and $y = 30 - 0.5x$. At this point, $P = £8500$ *[1 mark]*, so this is the maximum profit possible, achieved when 50 business class packages and 5 premier packages are sold *[1 mark]*.

Answers

(iii) Using the objective line, the first point in the feasible region it touches is the point (15, 5), the intersection of the lines $y = 5$ and $y = 20 - x$. At this point, $P = £3250$ *[1 mark]*, so this is the minimum profit possible, achieved when 15 business class packages and 5 premier packages are sold *[1 mark]*.

6 a) Order paths added:
GF, FB, BC, CA, GH/CH, HI, ID, IK, KL, KJ, IE

*[4 marks for answer fully correct.
Lose 1 mark for each mistake.]*

b)

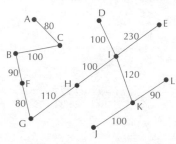

[1 mark] (CH is an alternative to GH.)
Length = 1200 metres *[1 mark]*

c) [AC – add; FG – add]; [BF – add; KL – add]; [BC – add; DI – add; HI – add; JK – add]; [AB – don't add; GH/CH – add; GH/CH – don't add]; IK – add; [HJ – don't add; HK – don't add; IL – don't add]; CD – don't add; EI – 230 – add; GJ – 250 – don't add; DE – 270 – don't add; EL – 280 – don't add; FJ – 300 – don't add. (The edges in square brackets can be considered in any order.)

The tenth and eleventh edges are IK and EI.

[3 marks available — 1 mark for each correct edge, 1 mark for evidence that Kruskal's algorithm has been applied.]

d)

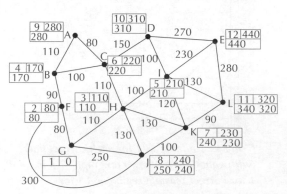

Route: GHIE, Length = 440 m

[7 marks available — 5 marks for correct application of Dijkstra's algorithm (lose 1 mark for each error up to a maximum of 5 marks), 1 mark for correct route and 1 mark for length of route.]

D1 — Practice Exam 2

1 a)
Box 1: 1.8, 3.5	space left: ~~4.2~~ 0.7
Box 2: 2.6, 1.2, 0.8	space left: ~~3.4~~ ~~2.2~~ 1.4
Box 3: 4.1	space left: 1.9
Box 4: 2.0, 2.4	space left: ~~4.0~~ 1.6
Box 5: 3.1	space left: 2.9 *[1 mark]*

5 boxes are used *[1 mark]* and there is:
$0.7 + 1.4 + 1.9 + 1.6 + 2.9 = 8.5$ kg wasted space *[1 mark]*.

b) In decreasing order, the weights of the items are:
4.1, 3.5, 3.1, 2.6, 2.4, 2.0, 1.8, 1.2, 0.8 *[1 mark]*.
Using the first fit method on this new list gives:
Box 1: 4.1, 1.8	space left: ~~1.9~~ 0.1
Box 2: 3.5, 2.4	space left: ~~2.5~~ 0.1
Box 3: 3.1, 2.6	space left: ~~2.9~~ 0.3
Box 4: 2.0, 1.2, 0.8	space left: ~~4.0~~ ~~2.8~~ 2.0

[1 mark] 4 boxes are used and there is:
$0.1 + 0.1 + 0.3 + 2.0 = 2.5$ kg wasted space *[1 mark]*.

c) The boxes in part a) are lighter so will be easier to carry *[1 mark]*.

d) It won't. The weights of all the items add up to 21.5 kg. Each box can hold 6 kg. $21.5 \div 6 = 3.6$ boxes, so you need at least 4 boxes, which is the solution found by the first fit decreasing method *[1 mark]*.

2

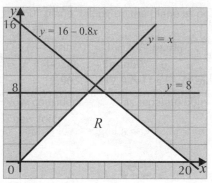

[4 marks available for graph — 1 for each correct line (with equations as shown on graph), 1 for correct feasible region.]

Using the vertex method, the vertices of the feasible region are (0,0), (8, 8) (the intersection of $y = x$ and $y = 8$), (10, 8) (the intersection of $y = 16 - 0.8x$ and $y = 8$) and (20, 0) *[1 mark]*. Putting these values into the objective function gives P values of 0, 18, 19.5 and 15, so the maximum P value is 19.5 *[1 mark]*, which occurs at (10, 8), so the optimal x value is 10 *[1 mark]*, and the optimal y value is 8 *[1 mark]*.

You could have used the objective line method instead, using the line $P = 0.75x + 1.5y$ to find the maximum.

Answers

3 a)

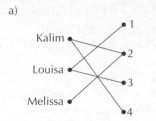

[2 marks available — 2 marks for completely correct graph or 1 mark for 3 or 4 arcs correct.]

b) 4 × 3 = 12 arcs would be needed for a complete graph. There are currently 5. So 7 would need to be added.
[1 mark]

c) Kalim – 2; Kalim – 2 – Melissa; Kalim – 4
[2 marks available — 2 marks for three correct paths or 1 mark for two correct paths.]

d) There is no path between some nodes, e.g between Kalim and 1 *[1 mark]*

e) 1 arc *[1 mark]* between Melissa and 4 *[1 mark]*.

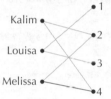

You have to keep the graph as two separate units. Unit 1 — Kalim and Melissa and jobs 2 and 4, and Unit 2 — Louisa and jobs 1 and 3.

4 a) Immediate predecessors for F: just B *[1 mark]*
Immediate predecessors for L: D, G and K *[1 mark]*
Watch out for the dotted line. It's a dummy activity showing that L depends on G being completed.

b) $w = 8$, $x = 8$, $y = 11$, $z = 12$
[2 marks available — 1 mark for each 2 values.]

For the early times, go from source to sink, taking the biggest number each time. For the late times, go from sink to source, taking the smallest number each time.

c) Independent float: $D = 11 - 6 - 7 = -2 = 0$ hours *[1 mark]*
Total float: $D = 13 - 6 - 4 = 3$ hours *[1 mark]*

If your independent float calculation results in a negative number, the float is 0 hours.

d)

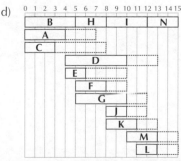

[4 marks available — 4 marks for all correctly plotted, 3 marks for 12 or 13 activities correctly plotted, 2 marks for 9, 10 or 11 correctly plotted, 1 mark for 6, 7 or 8 correctly plotted.]

e) Hour 4: A, B
Hour 10: D, G, I
[3 marks available — 1 mark for critical activities B and I. 2 marks for activities A, D and G, or 1 mark for any two of these activities. Lose 1 mark for each incorrect activity included in answer.]

f) Between hours 5 and 6 and between hours 8 and 10, five workers are required.

E.g. if activity D is started 2 hours later *[1 mark]*, this reduces the number of workers required between hours 5 and 6 to four.

If J is started as late as possible *[1 mark]*, only four workers are needed between 8 and 10 hours, but five are now needed between 10 and 12 hours. Starting M as late as possible *[1 mark]* solves this.

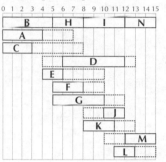

You might have come up with a different solution to this. Drawing a resource histogram under your cascade chart would help you see when too many workers are needed, and when there are spare workers.

5 a)

	Ⓐ	Ⓑ	C	Ⓓ	E	Ⓕ
A	–	140	240	–	150	170
B	⑭⓪	–	90	100	170	170
C	240	⑨⓪	–	210	–	–
D	–	⑩⓪	–	–	300	60
E	⑮⓪	170	–	300	–	–
F	170	170	–	⑥⓪	–	–

Order of arcs = AB, BC, BD, DF, AE
[3 marks available — 1 mark for first 3 vertices in correct order or 2 marks for all 5 vertices in correct order. 1 mark for correct crossing out and circling on matrix.]

Once you get into the swing of this — cross out, circle, cross out circle — it's easy. Check back to D1 Section 2 if you've forgotten what you're crossing out and circling.

b) 540 metres *[1 mark]*

c) Cycles can only be formed when joining vertices already in the tree *[1 mark]*. Prim's algorithm only considers connections to vertices not already in the tree, so a cycle can't form *[1 mark]*.

d) E.g.

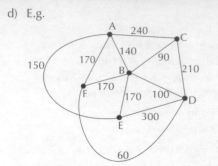

[3 marks available — 1 mark for 6 correct arcs, 2 marks for 9 correct arcs, 3 marks for all arcs correct.]

Your network might look a lot different to this one, depending how you arranged your nodes. As long as your connections between them are correct, then it'll be fine.

e) (i) Dijkstra's algorithm **[1 mark]**

(ii)

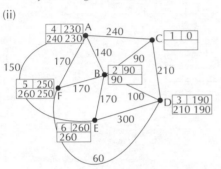

[4 marks — 2 marks for a correct final label at each node, or 1 mark for 4 correct final labels; 2 marks for correct working values, or 1 mark for correct working values at 4 nodes.]

E is furthest **[1 mark]**. Route CBE **[1 mark]**.

6 a) There are 100 numbers from 00 - 99, so 5 numbers for each twentieth **[1 mark for this idea]**.
E.g. 10 mins = 00-34 (7 × 5 = 35 numbers),
20 mins = 35-54 (1/5 = 4/20, so 4 × 5 = 20 numbers) **[1 mark]**,
30 mins = 55-84 (3/10 = 6/20, so 6 × 5 = 30 numbers),
40 mins = 85-99 (3 × 5 = 15 numbers) **[1 mark]**.

You can split your numbers up any way you choose. You could use a fancy, complicated way, but there's no point — you'll only confuse yourself. The answers for each part of this question depend on the rules you choose though.

b) There are 100 numbers from 00 - 99. 100 ÷ 12 = 8 r 4 **[1 mark for this idea]**. So reject 4 numbers, e.g. 96 to 99 **[1 mark]**.
E.g. 1 = 00-39 (5 × 8 = 40 numbers),
2 = 40-47 (1 × 8 = 8 numbers) **[1 mark]**,
3 = 48-79 (1/3 = 4/12, so 4 × 8 = 32 numbers),
4 = 80-95 (1/6 = 2/12, so 2 × 8 = 16 numbers) **[1 mark]**.

c) E.g. Customer 1: 46 = 20 mins, 15 = 1 lolly **[1 mark]**,
Customer 2: 54 = 20 mins, 66 = 3 lollies **[1 mark]**,
Customer 3: 81 = 30 mins, 98 reject, 67 = 3 lollies
[1 mark],
Customer 4: 71 = 30 mins, 5 = 1 lolly,
Customer 5: 12 = 10 mins, 46 = 2 lollies **[1 mark]**,
Ben will have sold 7 lollies after 70 minutes **[1 mark]**.

There are different ways you could have used the random numbers provided in the question. E.g. you could have used the first half for time intervals and the second half for the number of lollies. Just be consistent with your method.

d)

	Time until 7 lollies are sold (mins)
Simulation 2	130
Simulation 3	40
Simulation 4	90
Simulation 5	60
Simulation 6	60

[2 marks — 2 marks for all 5 correct, or 1 mark for 3 correct.]

E.g. mean = (70 + 130 + 40 + 90 + 60 + 60) ÷ 6 **[1 mark]**
= 75 mins **[1 mark]**

Your mean will be different if you got a different answer for part c).

Index

Index